Student Study Guide

to accompany

Biology

Eighth Edition

Jonathan B. Losos
Harvard University

Kenneth A. Mason
Purdue University

Susan R. Singer
Carleton College

based on the work of

Peter H. Raven
Director, Missouri Botanical Garden
Engelmann Professor of Botany
Washington University

George B. Johnson
Professor Emeritus of Biology
Washington University

Student Study Guide prepared by

Brian L. Olson
Saint Cloud State University
and
Erin N. Olson

McGraw-Hill
Higher Education

Boston   Burr Ridge, IL   Dubuque, IA   New York   San Francisco   St. Louis
Bangkok   Bogotá   Caracas   Kuala Lumpur   Lisbon   London   Madrid   Mexico City
Milan   Montreal   New Delhi   Santiago   Seoul   Singapore   Sydney   Taipei   Toronto

The McGraw-Hill Companies

McGraw-Hill
Higher Education

Student Study Guide to accompany
BIOLOGY, EIGHTH EDITION
RAVEN, JOHNSON, LOSOS, MASON, & SINGER

Published by McGraw-Hill Higher Education, an imprint of The McGraw-Hill Companies, Inc., 1221 Avenue of the Americas, New York, NY 10020. Copyright © 2008, 2005, 2002, 1999, and 1996 by The McGraw-Hill Companies, Inc. All rights reserved.

1 2 3 4 5 6 7 8 9 0 QPD\QPD 0 9 8 7

ISBN: 978-0-07-296585-8
MHID: 0-07-296585-1

www.mhhe.com

CONTENTS

PREFACE
Getting the Most Out of This Study Guide and Your Studying

Welcome to the world of introductory biology! It is a fascinating and exciting world, but one that can also seem overwhelming at times. This study guide is designed to help you appreciate the fascination and excitement without being overwhelmed. By reading this preface, you are taking a first and very important step toward helping yourself do as well as possible in your biology endeavors. In the next few pages we will explain the philosophy behind the way we have written this study guide, what is in the study guide, and the best way to use it. Our philosophies and suggestions come from over 60 combined years of helping students learn about biology and seeing what works well and what doesn't. We believe that working through this study guide will help you master and truly understand the material in each chapter of the text, rather than just memorizing seemingly random facts.

In addition to this study guide, the *Biology, Eighth Edition*, website, also can be used to test your knowledge and practice your skills. Related material for each chapter can be found by going to: www.ravenbiology.com.

This study guide was written specifically to accompany the eighth edition of *Biology* by Raven, Johnson, Losos, Mason, and Singer. Just as the textbook has changed between the seventh and eighth editions, so has the study guide. Each chapter in the textbook has an accompanying chapter in this study guide. To help you organize the material, each of our chapters follows a consistent format.

A section called **Mastering Key Concepts** sets the scene for you. It provides a brief overview of the chapter and then runs through the chapter's concept outline, summarizing key points and giving helpful hints on topics to notice or consider.

The concepts section is followed by the **Challenging Your Understanding** section, which is designed to help you recognize the relationships or connections between the major concepts in the chapter. This helps ensure that you don't compartmentalize your new knowledge as random, isolated bits of information.

Next, the **Key Terms** section focuses on the new vocabulary. Every specialized discipline has its own terminology and biology is no exception. Studying introductory biology is similar in many ways to studying a foreign language. You must know the vocabulary in order to communicate. To understand all the concepts and how they relate to each other, you must first know what the words mean. We have listed the key terms in the sequence in which they are presented in the textbook to maintain the coherency of the material and the flow of ideas. This should help you remember the development of the various concepts more easily than if the list of terms were alphabetized. We have included in our key terms every word in the chapter that is in boldface type. These words are taken from the figure captions as well as the text.
Web Component: Test your knowledge of key terms by using the flashcard vocabulary.

The remaining sections of each study guide chapter are designed to help you actively test yourself and make sure you have mastered the material in the chapter. Active rather than passive learning is one of the guiding philosophies behind the way we have written this study guide. The more actively you are involved with this study guide, the more likely you are to learn and retain the information. That is why we have you fill in charts, make drawings, label drawings, make lists, stage discussions, and answer questions rather than just passively reading text summaries to yourself. We want you to understand, apply, synthesize, and work with the material, not just memorize it.

The **Learning by Experience** section is intended to reinforce important concepts or topics in the chapter. The exact nature of each activity varies with the different chapters, but all are designed to have you actively *use* the knowledge you have acquired.

The other active section, **Exercising Your Knowledge**, is your chance to test yourself and practice for your class exams. Answering these questions not only will let you know if you have thoroughly learned the material, but also will help you overcome test anxiety by practicing at your own speed and as often as you wish. This section begins with 10 short-answer essay questions designed to help you articulate your understanding of the key concepts, as well as apply the understanding to new situations or make connections between concepts.

Next come 20 multiple choice questions; some of these test for understanding of concepts, while others test for knowledge of specific detail. Although you need to know the detail and the specific meanings of the words, just memorizing the new vocabulary is not enough. You must be able to put those words into meaningful sentences, and you must understand the concepts as well. For each multiple choice question, we have provided four or five answer choices; only one of them is correct. One of the most effective ways to study and take a multiple choice test is to read the question and all the choices carefully and make sure you know what each is saying. Then ask yourself not only which is the correct answer, but also *why* is it correct and why are the other choices wrong?

We do not provide true/false questions because we believe that the short-answer and multiple choice formats are better study tools for you. If you can answer them, you should not have trouble handling true/false questions if your biology instructor uses them. Remember, each multiple choice question is essentially four or five true/false questions; you have to decide if each choice is true or not.

Web Component: Test your knowledge further by using online multiple choice and animation quizzing.

Focusing Your Study

The answers for each of the questions in the Learning by Experience and Exercising Your Knowledge sections are listed in **Assessing Your Knowledge** at the end of each chapter. For Exercising Your Knowledge, we have listed the text chapter section number to help guide your review if necessary.

The answers also indicate whether each Exercising Your Knowledge question is either:

- a concept question (denoted by an asterisk) or
- a detail question.

By looking at which questions you get right and which ones you miss, you may see a pattern (e.g., do you tend to miss more detail questions or more concept questions?). This is valuable information for helping focus your studies.

1. If you consistently miss **detail questions**, you can use the electronic flashcards to help you master the vocabulary.
2. If you have more trouble with the **concept questions**, you need to know how to put all the details into a bigger, integrated picture. One of the best aids to really understanding is explaining. Try explaining the process or concept—it really doesn't matter to whom. Sometimes it's even better if your audience knows nothing about the material. It is the act of explaining that is important; if you can explain fully and easily, you understand. If you reach a point in the explanation where you feel uneasy or simply can't complete it, you have identified a problem in understanding. This is the point you need to study more. If rereading doesn't solve the problem, it is time to consult with the professor, a teaching assistant, or a classmate you have identified as one who usually gets it right.

In addition to using this study guide, there are many other ways you can help yourself do well in your biology course. First, *go to class*. Your instructor will help guide you and help you focus on the most important aspects of the material. If you could master everything on your own just by reading the textbook, colleges and universities wouldn't bother scheduling lectures and paying faculty!

Second, *keep up with your reading and studying*. Leaving it all until the weekend or the night before the exam is *not* a good strategy. It will prevent you from getting the most from the weekly lectures and from taking advantage of your instructors' office hours or help sessions. It will also put tremendous stress on you right before the exam, and will probably result in poor grades.

Third, *ask questions*. Ask your instructor, your graduate teaching assistant, or your classmates. It is better to clear up any confusion as you go along. Remember that you are trying to build a solid foundation from the very beginning. A point you don't understand early in the semester may come back to haunt you later. You may feel shy about asking, but many of your classmates probably have the same question and will be glad you asked. You may not want to interrupt the instructor in the middle of a lecture to ask your questions, but most instructors set aside some class time just for questions or have office hours or help sessions. And they are usually thrilled to help students who are trying to learn more.

Fourth, *study actively, not passively*. Don't just sit and read your textbook and lecture notes; do something active. Study with your classmates; make up and ask each other questions. Active participation makes learning easier.

We hope this preface has given you good ideas about how to enjoy biology and do well in your course. We also hope this study guide will prove to be a valuable aid in your learning. We cannot predict exactly how your instructor will give tests in your course, but by successfully working through each section in the study guide chapters, you will be well on your way toward mastering the material in *Biology* and doing well on tests. You should check with your instructor, however, to make sure you understand the format of the exams that will be given to you and the level of detail you are expected to know.

We wish you good luck, excitement, and appreciation of life as you explore the world of biology.

Brian L. Olson
Erin N. Olson

CHAPTER 1 THE SCIENCE OF BIOLOGY

MASTERING KEY CONCEPTS

Biology is the scientific study of life. This is a neat and simple definition, but it covers a fascinating and diverse world, including what living organisms are made of, how they function, and how they have evolved and continue to do so. All the information, hypotheses, and theories presented in your textbook have been derived by countless scientists asking questions; collecting data; making, testing, and refining hypotheses; and formulating and refining theories.

1.1 Biology is the science of life.

- **Overview**: There are seven **characteristics of living organisms--cellular organization, ordered complexity, sensitivity, growth/development/reproduction, energy utilization, homeostasis**, and **evolutionary adaptation**. Living systems display **hierarchical organization** at the **cellular, organismal, populational, ecosystem**, and **biosphere** levels. **Emergent properties** exist at each of these levels.
- **Details**: Know the definitions of each of the seven characteristics shared by living systems. Know the **building blocks** for each of **the levels of hierarchical organization**, and how **emergent properties** can affect each level.

1.2 Scientists form generalizations from observations.

- **Overview**: Scientists question the world by making objective observations, noting unexplained phenomena, and developing explanations called **hypotheses,** which are then tested by **experiments** that, when properly controlled, are designed to discriminate between alternative explanations.
- **Details**: Know the differences between **deductive** and **inductive reasoning**. Understand the concept of **reductionism** to study complex systems and when this approach is useful. Know the two definitions of a **scientific theory** and the difference between **basic** and **applied research**.

1.3 Darwin's theory of evolution illustrates how science works.

- **Overview**: **Darwin** proposed the idea of **natural selection** to describe how life on Earth **evolved**. Darwin noted that the characteristics of the descendants of a common ancestor varied from place to place. These variations represented **evolutionary adaptations** that improved an organism's ability to survive in a particular geographical location.
- **Details**: Be familiar with the observations that **Darwin** made that help to develop his **theory of natural selection**. Understand the concepts of **geometric and arithmetic progressions** described by **Thomas Malthus**. Know how the **age of the Earth, fossil records, comparative anatomy**, and **molecular evidence** support Darwin's idea that all living things evolved from a single ancestor.

1.4 Four themes unify biology as a science.

- **Overview**: The **cell theory** developed by **Schleiden and Schwann** concluded that all living organisms consist of **cells,** which process information, can sense their environments, and are the basis for reproduction and growth of all organisms. **DNA**, consisting of multiple genes, specifies a cell's makeup. **Evolutionary conservation** suggests that a specific gene plays a critical function in an organism.
- **Details**: Understand the concepts behind the **unifying themes of biology,** which state that **life is organized, life has a molecular basis of heredity, life changes over time**, and **life displays its evolutionary past**. Know how a similar structure, or function, of two or more molecules can imply relationships among different organisms. Recognize how the diversity of life is organized by first dividing organisms into three **domains** and then subdividing each domain into **kingdoms** consisting of organisms that all share similar characteristics.

CHALLENGING YOUR UNDERSTANDING

Draw a flowchart detailing the scientific method that is used to formulate and test a hypothesis. Your flowchart should begin with an observation, and end with the hypothesis becoming a scientific theory.

KEY TERMS

Match the numbered term with the definition that fits it best. Put the corresponding number in front of the appropriate definition.

1. molecules
2. organelles
3. cells
4. tissues
5. organs
6. organ systems
7. population
8. species
9. biological community

10. ecosystem
11. emergent properties
12. deductive reasoning
13. inductive reasoning
14. hypothesis
15. experiment
16. variables
17. control experiment
18. theory

19. evolution
20. artificial selection
21. natural selection
22. homologous
23. analogous
24. phylogenetic tree
25. cell theory
26. DNA (deoxyribonucleic acid)
27. gene

a. _____ The variable being altered in a specific scientific experiment is left unaltered in this parallel test.
b. _____ A biological community and the physical habitat within which it lives together.
c. _____ The evolutionary history of a gene tracing the origins of particular nucleotide changes in the sequence.
d. _____ Structures having the same evolutionary origin that now differ in their appearance and function.
e. _____ The application of general principles to predict specific results.
f. _____ A discrete unit of information made up of specific nucleotide sequences encoding one or more proteins.
g. _____ The process by which living things have changed during their history on Earth.
h. _____ A body of interconnected concepts, supported by scientific reasoning and experimental evidence.
i. _____ A molecule consisting of nucleotides linked together in a chain, which encodes the genetic plan for a cell.
j. _____ The test of a hypothesis that is designed to eliminate one or more possible explanations for an observation.
k. _____ All populations of one kind of organism whose members look similar and can interbreed.
l. _____ Structures with similar functions in different organisms, but with different evolutionary origins.
m._____ Tiny functional structures assembled from complex biological molecules that are contained in cells.
n. _____ A structure composed of groups of similar cells acting as a single functional unit in multicellular organisms.
o. _____ Darwin's theory that nature selects for organisms with traits that help them to survive in their environments.
p. _____ All of the populations of different species living together in one place.
q. _____ The conclusion reached by Schleiden and Schwann that all living organisms consist of cells.
r. _____ A group of organisms of the same species living in the same place.
s. _____ Multiple organs acting together within an organism to carry out a necessary function.
t. _____ Different factors that influence processes and can alter the outcomes of experiments if not controlled for.
u. _____ Membrane-bound functional units that carry out the basic activities of life.
v. _____ Clusters of atoms, the fundamental elements of matter, joined together by covalent bonds.
w._____ A suggested explanation that may or may not be true and is proposed to account for careful observations.
x. _____ The ability to foster variation and produce certain characteristics by selective breeding.
y. _____ Body structures composed of several different tissues that act as a structural and functional unit.
z. _____ Novel properties that result from the way in which components interact at each level in the living hierarchy.
aa._____ The use of specific observations to construct general scientific principles.

2

LEARNING BY EXPERIENCE

1. Arrange the following terms to show the proper hierarchical organization of life: *biological community, cell, ecosystem, molecule, organ, organelle, organism, organ system, population, species, tissue*. What does it mean to say that life is organized hierarchically?

2. Make a flowchart that diagrams the scientific method by using these terms: *experiments, hypotheses, observations, questions, theory*. Briefly explain how the method works. On the following graph, draw a line representing a geometric progression and a line representing an arithmetic progression. Then explain in the space below the implications of the two lines with regard to rates of increase.

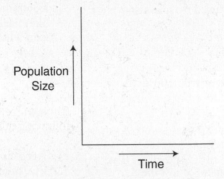

3. Color the homologous bones in these vertebrate forelimbs the same color. For example, color the upper arm bone (the humerus) green in all five limbs, use yellow for the two lower arm bones (the radius and ulna) in all five limbs, and use purple for all the bones of the wrist and hand in all five limbs. Note: Human anatomy is being used as the reference point here, but some fusion of bones has occurred in different species.

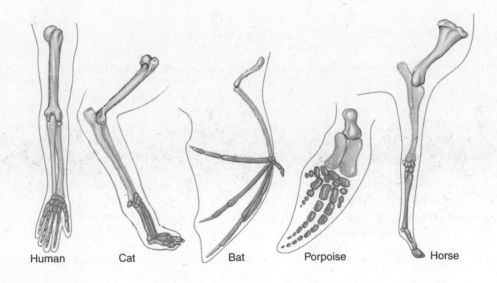

4. Why is biology important?

EXERCISING YOUR KNOWLEDGE

Briefly answer each of the following questions in the space provided.

1. We seem to know intuitively if something qualifies as living, but defining life precisely can be difficult. Is there any one characteristic that defines life? If not, what does?

2. What is the difference between deductive and inductive reasoning? Is either used by scientists?

3. Can a scientific theory ever be proven 100% true?

4. You are conducting an experiment to test the hypothesis that dairy cows give more milk if they listen to classical music while being milked. You have 20 cows listen to classical music during milking and then collect all their milk and measure how much there is. What would you do for your control experiment?

5. What is the difference between basic and applied research? Which do you think is more important?

6. It took Darwin many years to formulate his theory of evolution by natural selection, and he used many different pieces of evidence and ideas from different people in the process. Briefly describe the contribution made by each of the following to Darwin's thoughts: fossils, geographic distribution of species, oceanic islands, Lyell, Malthus.

7. How has molecular biology contributed to our current understanding of evolution?

8. Explain the statement "species evolve, but selection acts on individuals."

9. Explain Darwin's theory of evolution by natural selection in your own words.

10. Biologists often talk about the seemingly contradictory unity and diversity of life. What do they mean by that? What is uniform about life and what is diverse?

Circle the letter of the one best answer in each of the following questions.

11. According to the hierarchical organization of life, organelles are made up of
   a. organs.
   b. molecules.
   c. populations.
   d. tissues.
   e. organ systems.

12. Which of the following did not provide strong evidence for Darwin's theory of evolution?
   a. comparative anatomy
   b. mechanisms of heredity
   c. age of the Earth
   d. comparison of genomes
   e. microscopic fossils

13. If a scientist collects data and then formulates a general hypothesis that explains all of the observations, the scientist has engaged in
   a. inductive reasoning.
   b. deductive reasoning.
   c. natural selection.
   d. artificial selection.
   e. applied research.

14. To be of use in science, a hypothesis must be
   a. testable.
   b. able to yield predictions.
   c. proven true beyond a shadow of a doubt.
   d. a and b are correct.
   e. All of these are correct.

15. A control experiment has all of the conditions identical to the primary experiment except that it
    a. uses twice as many experimental subjects.
    b. runs for a longer period of time.
    c. does not have the variable being tested.
    d. has more of the variable being tested.
    e. None of these are correct; it is completely different.

16. When scientists talk about a scientific theory, they are talking about something that
    a. has been tested frequently and is supported by a lot of evidence.
    b. has been proven true.
    c. is wild speculation.
    d. is likely to never change.

17. Research designed to solve specific problems is called
    a. basic research.
    b. applied research.
    c. peer review.
    d. the scientific method.
    e. progression.

18. Which of the following represents a geometric progression?
    a. 4, 8, 12, 16
    b. 2, 4, 6, 8
    c. 2, 4, 16, 256
    d. 4, 16, 64, 256
    e. 1, 2, 3, 4

19. The hierarchical organization of life leads to which of the following?
    a. survival of the fittest
    b. emergent properties
    c. natural selection
    d. the cell theory
    e. evolution

20. Darwin explained his theory of evolution in a book called
    a. *The Principle of Population.*
    b. *Survival of the Fittest.*
    c. *The Descent of Man.*
    d. *On the Origin of Species.*
    e. *Around the World in Eighty Days.*

21. According to Darwin's theory of evolution,
    a. all individuals have an equal chance of surviving and reproducing.
    b. species are immutable.
    c. tortoises are the modern descendants of glyptodonts.
    d. All of these are correct.
    e. None of these are correct.

22. By finding molecules similar to the insulin receptor in different organisms, we may be able to discern which of the following about glucose uptake in humans and other organisms?
    a. population levels
    b. emergent properties
    c. comparative anatomy
    d. ordered complexity
    e. evolutionary relationship

23. The numbers 3, 6, 9, 12, and 15 represent
    a. emergent properties.
    b. a phylogenetic tree.
    c. a geometric progression.
    d. an arithmetic progression.
    e. a molecular clock.

24. Who else came up with the idea of evolution by natural selection at the same time as Darwin?
    a. Charles Lyell
    b. Alfred Russel Wallace
    c. Thomas Malthus
    d. Eratosthenes
    e. no one

25. Based on conservation of the hemoglobin polypeptide, which of the following vertebrates are most closely related?
    a. dogs and birds
    b. humans and frogs
    c. dogs and frogs
    d. humans and birds
    e. monkeys and frogs

26. Structures that have the same evolutionary origin even though they may now have different structures or functions are said to be
    a. phylogenetic.
    b. analogous.
    c. homologous.
    d. immutable.
    e. geometric.

27. Scientists currently classify life into three major groups called
    a. genomes.
    b. kingdoms.
    c. phylogenetic trees.
    d. domains.
    e. biological communities.

28. Which of the following are analogous structures?
    a. the front leg of a horse and a human arm
    b. the front leg of a frog and a bat wing
    c. the front flipper of a porpoise and a human arm
    d. the wing of a bird and a bat wing
    e. the wing of a bird and a butterfly wing

29. In the hierarchy of life, species are made up of
    a. populations.
    b. variables.
    c. ecosystems.
    d. biological communities.
    e. phylogenetic trees.

30. The more closely related two species are, the
    a. less similar their DNA is.
    b. more similar their DNA is.
    c. Neither of these is correct; no pattern is found.
    d. None of these are correct; we don't have the technology to analyze DNA.

ASSESSING YOUR KNOWLEDGE

Answers to the questions in the following sections test your ability to synthesize information gained from the chapter and to solve challenging problems on an exam or in everyday life.

Challenging Your Understanding—Answers

Observations → Formulation of questions → Hypotheses → Experiments (introducing variables one at a time with controls) → Support, reject, or refine hypotheses → Predictions → More experiments → Strongly supported hypotheses → Theories

Key Terms—Answers

a. 17, b. 10, c. 24, d. 22, e. 12, f. 27, g. 19, h. 18, i. 26, j. 15, k. 8, l. 23, m. 2, n. 4, o. 21, p. 9, q. 25, r. 7, s. 6, t. 16, u. 3, v. 1, w. 14, x. 20, y. 5, z. 11, aa. 13.

Learning by Experience—Answers

1. molecule, organelle, cell, tissue, organ, organ system, organism, population, species, community, ecosystem. Life is ordered or structured, going from the smallest unit to the largest. Each level is made up of the level immediately preceding it and makes up the next immediate one: for example, tissues are made up of cells, and tissues in turn make up organs.
2. observations → questions → hypotheses → experiments → theory. Scientists notice things about the world and ask questions. They then formulate possible explanations (hypotheses) to answer the questions and to explain what they have observed. Experiments are then performed to test the hypotheses, and hypotheses are supported, rejected, or refined. Predictions are made and further experiments done. When a hypothesis has been tested many times and all the evidence supports it, it is called a scientific theory.
3. 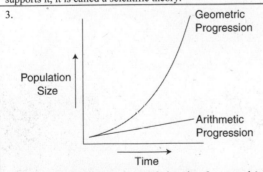Over time, the increase (as in population size, for example) will be much greater and faster in a geometric progression than in an arithmetic progression.
4. Compare your work to text figure 1.9.
5. Biology may be important to you for immediate and practical reasons, as when you need the course to graduate from college or you hope to have a career in some field of biology. On a more fundamental level, biology is important to everyone because we are organisms ourselves and biology is the study of life. Only by

studying and understanding life can we hope to maintain it and improve its quality.

Exercising Your Knowledge—Answers

As you check your answers, put a mark in the review (Rvw.) column for the answers you missed. If you didn't miss any, congratulations—you have mastered the chapter! If you missed some, review the section (Sect.) in the text where this concept is discussed. In order to develop an efficient review strategy, it is important that you understand what types of questions you missed. The questions with asterisks test more for understanding of the **concepts**, whereas the others test more for **detail**. *See the preface for learning strategies for concepts and for detail.*

	Sect.	Rvw.
*1. No single characteristic defines life; all living organisms share seven traits: cellular organization, order, sensitivity, growth/development/reproduction, energy utilization, evolutionary adaptation, and homeostasis.	1.1, 1.4	
*2. Deductive reasoning uses general principles to predict specific results, whereas inductive reasoning uses specific observations to formulate general principles; scientists use both types of reasoning.	1.2	
*3. No, there is no absolute truth in science; a theory can be rejected if data from a properly designed experiment does not support the theory, but it can never be proven since it is always possible that a future experiment will provide new information that will require the theory to be revised or rejected.	1.2	
*4. The control should also have 20 cows, and they should be as similar to the experimental cows as possible in terms of age, size, etc.; they should be given the same type and amount of food, water, bedding, same milking methods, etc. Essentially all conditions should be the same except that no music is played to them during milking. All conditions should be the same except the experimental variable.	1.2	
*5. Basic research extends the boundaries of what we know, increasing our overall body of knowledge. Applied research is designed to solve a particular problem. Both are important. You can't have applied research without the foundation of knowledge provided by basic research, but applied research has the most direct impact on improving the quality of life on Earth.	1.2	

*6. Fossils showed progressive changes in characteristics over time and resembled living species, suggesting that species were not immutable but gradually changed over time and that living species arose from fossil species. Geographical distribution suggested that species diversity is not determined solely by climate and that lineages change as species migrate from one area to another. Oceanic islands often have unique, endemic species closely related to each other but also resembling species on the nearest mainland, suggesting that individuals from the mainland colonized the islands, and the isolated populations gradually changed and evolved into new species over time. Lyell provided evidence that the Earth was much more ancient than 4,000 years, providing enough time for evolution to have occurred. Malthus pointed out that populations increase geometrically, outstripping resources, resulting in competition and survival of the most well adapted, and setting up the mechanism of natural selection for evolution.	1.3	
*7. Using molecular biology, scientists can compare the actual genetic information (the DNA) of different species to determine how closely related two or more organisms are and how long ago they diverged from a common ancestor; this helps establish rates at which evolution occurs.	1.3	
*8. A single individual does not evolve—that is, it does not change its genetic characteristics during the course of its life. However, a single individual is acted upon by natural selection—its traits either make it well adapted and likely to survive and reproduce or not. Since some individuals reproduce more than others, some traits get passed on more than others, and the genetic makeup of the population or species changes to some extent with each generation (for example, evolves or changes over time).	1.3	

*9. Evolution is the process by which species or populations change over time, and natural selection is the mechanism that causes the changes; see answer #8.	1.3	
*10. There is a unity to all life since it shares the five characteristics of order, sensitivity, growth/development/reproduction, regulation, and homeostasis, as well as undergoing and resulting from evolution. The diversity of environments and natural selection have led to the evolution of an amazing diversity of species over the course of life on earth.	1.4	

*11. b	1.1	
12. b	1.3	
*13. a	1.2	
*14. d	1.2	
*15. c	1.2	
16. a	1.2	
17. b	1.2	
18. d	1.3	
*19. b	1.1	
20. d	1.3	
*21. e	1.3	
*22. e	1.4	
23. d	1.3	
24. b	1.3	
25. a	1.3	
26. c	1.3	
27. d	1.4	
28. e	1.3	
29. a	1.1	
*30. b	1.3	

CHAPTER 2 THE NATURE OF MOLECULES

MASTERING KEY CONCEPTS

Living things are composed of chemicals, and life processes follow chemical rules. All matter, living and nonliving, is made up of atoms. Atoms can interact by transferring electrons and forming ions or by sharing electrons and forming molecules. The single most important molecule for life as we know it is water, whose unique and vital properties are a direct consequence of its chemistry.

2.1 Atoms are nature's building material.

- **Overview**: The basic structure of an **atom** is a **nucleus** consisting of **positively charged protons**, **neutrons** with no charge, and **negatively charged electrons** located in **orbitals** that surround the nucleus. The number of electrons and their orbital arrangement determine the chemical behavior of an atom. Each **element** is defined by its **atomic number**, which is the number of protons found in the nucleus.
- **Details**: Understand the relationship between **atomic number**, the number of **protons**, **neutrons**, **electrons**, and **atomic mass**. Understand how these numbers are affected in different **isotopes** and in **ions**. Know the contributions of Niels **Bohr**. Understand how the number of electrons in the outermost energy level determines the behavior of an atom and how electrons are transferred between atoms in **oxidation/reduction** reactions.

2.2 The atoms of living things are among the smallest.

- **Overview**: The **periodic table** organizes **elements** based on **atomic number** and orders them such that the elements in each column belong to the same family having similar **chemical properties** determined by the **number of valence electrons** that the atom has.
- **Details**: Know the contribution of Dmitri **Mendeleev** and the concept behind the observation of **eight-element periodicity**. Understand how electrons are assigned to orbitals and how the number of **valence electrons** determines an atom's reactivity.

2.3 Chemical bonds hold molecules together.

- **Overview**: **Chemical bonds** form when two atoms interact based on an electrical interaction that stabilizes valence electrons by satisfying the **octet rule** either by transfer of an electron, sharing of electron pairs, or sharing a hydrogen atom. Chemical reactions form or break bonds and are influenced by temperature, concentration of the reactants and products, and catalysts.
- **Details**: Know the basis and strength of **covalent**, **ionic**, and **hydrogen bonds**; **hydrophobic interactions**; and **van der Waals attractions**. Understand how many bonds an atom must form to satisfy the **octet rule**. Understand how **electronegativity** of an atom establishes its **polarity**.

2.4 Water is the cradle of life.

- **Overview**: Life depends on **water**, a molecule consisting of **two hydrogen atoms** bound to **one oxygen atom** by two single **covalent bonds**. Water is highly **polar** allowing it to be **cohesive** and establishing many of its physical properties. Water can form **hydrogen bonds** with other molecules of water or with other polar substances.
- **Details**: Know the **properties of water**, the **molecular structure**, and the **forms** that water can take at different temperatures. Know why the properties of water are so beneficial and are essential to life.

2.5 Properties of Water

- **Overview**: A number of the properties of water are a result of its polar nature and are critical to life. Water can **moderate temperature** because it has a **high specific heat** allowing organisms to maintain constant natural temperature. Water has a **high heat of vaporization** allowing organisms to get rid of excess body heat. Water acts as a **solvent** for polar molecules and can cause hydrophobic molecules to **aggregate**. The dissociation of water results in one H^+ ion and one OH^- ion.
- **Details**: Know the nature of **hydrophobic** and **hydrophilic** molecules and what happens to each in water. Know the chemical reaction for the **dissociation of water**. Understand why salt dissolves in water.

2.6 Acids and Bases

- **Overview**: A solution with a balance between H^+ ions and OH^- ions, such as that which exists in water, is neutral and has a pH value of 7. Solutions with a pH value < 7 are acidic and have a high $[H^+]$ concentration relative to the concentration of OH^- ions, and solutions with a pH value > 7 are basic and have a low $[H^+]$ concentration relative to the concentration of OH^- ions. Buffers are used to stabilize the pH of a solution. A difference of 1 pH unit is equal to a 10-fold change in $[H^+]$.
- **Details**: Know how pH correlates with the $[H^+]$ concentration of a solution. Know an example of an acid and a base. Understand how buffers can resist changes in pH, and how organisms resist pH changes in the blood.

CHALLENGING YOUR UNDERSTANDING

1. Identify the number of protons, neutrons, electrons, and valence electrons for potassium, chlorine, nitrogen, and argon. Explain the reactivity of these atoms.

2. List five properties of water and describe why these properties are beneficial to living organisms.

3. Fill in the missing values in the following chart, indicate in the last column whether each is acidic, basic, or neutral.

Solution	pH	$[H^+]$ mol/L	$[OH^-]$ mol/L	Category
1. human blood	7	a._____	b._____	neutral
2. stomach acid	c.____	10^{-2}	d._____	e.____
3. saliva	f.____	g._____	10^{-8}	h.____
4. sodium hydroxide	14	i._____	j._____	k.____

4. Fill in the blanks in the following statements.

a. A solution with a pH of 4 has 10 times the $[H^+]$ of a solution with a pH of _____.

b. A _____ solution has a pH value above _____.

c. An acidic substance _____ in water to _____ the concentration of H^+ ions.

d. The _____ of hydrogen ions in pure water is _____ to the _____ of hydroxide ions making it a _____ solution.

e. A buffer _____ changes in pH by either accepting or donating H^+ ions.

f. The $[H^+]$ concentration of a solution can be _____ by adding an acid or _____ by adding a base.

KEY TERMS

Match the numbered term with the definition that fits it best. Put the corresponding number in front of the appropriate definition.

1. matter	19. organic	37. water
2. atoms	20. valence electrons	38. electronegativity
3. electrons	21. inert	39. polar molecules
4. protons	22. octet rule	40. hydrogen bonds
5. neutrons	23. molecule	41. cohesion
6. atomic number	24. compound	42. adhesion
7. atomic mass	25. chemical bonds	43. surface tension
8. element	26. ionic bonds	44. specific heat
9. isotopes	27. ionic compound	45. heat of vaporization
10. radioactive isotopes	28. covalent bond	46. buffer
11. half-life	29. double bonds	47. hydrophobic
12. neutral atoms	30. single bonds	48. hydrophilic
13. ions	31. triple bonds	49. acid
14. cation	32. structural formula	50. base
15. anion	33. molecular formula	51. ionization
16. orbital	34. chemical reaction	52. mole
17. oxidation	35. reactants	53. molar concentration
18. reduction	36. products	54. pH scale

a. _____ A group of atoms held together by energy in a stable association.

b. _____ Tiny, subatomic particles with neutral charge that are involved in forming the nucleus of an atom.

c. _____ An atom that has more protons than electrons and as a result has a net positive charge.

d. _____ The time it takes for one-half of the atoms in a sample to decay.

e. _____ Carbon compounds that make up the majority of the molecules in living organisms.

f. _____ Atoms tend to establish completely full outer energy levels.

g. _____ The loss of an electron that occurs as a result of a chemical reaction between two atoms.

h. _____ When a molecule contains atoms of more than one element.

i. _____ An atom that has more electrons than protons and carries a net negative charge.

j. _____ Tiny, positively charged, subatomic particles involved in forming the nucleus of an atom.

k. _____ An isotope of an element whose nucleus tends to break up into elements with lower atomic numbers.

l. _____ The gain of an electron that occurs as a result of chemical reaction between two atoms.

m. _____ Joining together the atoms of a molecule as a result of opposite charge or sharing electrons.

n. _____ Atoms of a single element that possess different numbers of neutrons.

o. _____ Any substance that cannot be broken down to any other substance by ordinary chemical means.

p. _____ Ions in a crystal matrix held together by forces between any one ion and surrounding ions of opposite charge.

q. _____ Any substance in the universe that has mass and occupies space.

r. _____ Atoms with the same number of protons and electrons that have no net charge.

s. _____ A bond formed when atoms with opposite electrical charges attract.

t. _____ Tiny, negatively charged, subatomic particles located in a series of orbitals surrounding the nucleus of all atoms.

u. _____ A number equal to the sum of the masses of an atom's protons and neutrons.

v. _____ Elements that are nonreactive because they possess all eight electrons in their outermost energy level.

w. _____ Regions occupied by electrons that lie at varying distances around the nucleus of an atom.

x. _____ The number of protons found in different atoms that designates its location in the periodic table.

y. _____ Particles located in the outermost energy level that are responsible for the chemical properties of an element.

z. _____ Extremely small particles of which all matter is composed.

aa. _____ Atoms that are charged because the number of electrons is not equal to the number of protons.

bb. _____ Any substance that dissociates in water to increase the concentration of H^+ ions and lower the pH.

cc. _____ The attraction of water for other polar substances with which it can form hydrogen bonds.

dd. _____ Spontaneous ion formation, such as the dissociation of water into one hydroxide and one hydrogen ion.

ee. _____ A property of atoms that defines their affinity for electrons.

ff. _____ Two atoms satisfying the octet rule by sharing one electron pair.

gg. _____ Formed at air-water interface as a result of surface molecules hydrogen bonding with those below them.

hh. ____ Weak chemical associations formed between partially negative and partially positive charged atoms.

ii. ____ The weight of a substance in grams corresponding to the atomic masses of all of the atoms in a molecule.

jj. ____ The molecules that are formed as the result of a chemical reaction.

kk. ____ The amount of energy required to change 1 gram of substance from a liquid to a gas.

ll. ____ Nonpolar molecules that are forced into association with one another when placed in a solution of water.

mm. ____ Indicates the identity and the number of atoms present in any particular molecule.

nn. ____ The polarity of water is a property that allows water molecules to be attracted to one another.

oo. ____ An oxygen atom bound to two hydrogen atoms by two single covalent bonds.

pp. ____ A substance that combines with H^+ ions when dissolved in water and lowers the $[H^+]$ of a solution.

qq. ____ The concentration of a given element in a solution that is expressed as the number of moles per liter.

rr. ____ A bond formed when two atoms share one or more pairs of valence electrons.

ss. ____ Lines drawn between atoms of a compound to indicate how many electron pairs are shared.

tt. ____ Polar molecules that readily form hydrogen bonds with water.

uu. ____ A bond that satisfies the octet rule by two atoms sharing two electron pairs.

vv. ____ The original molecules present before a chemical reaction takes place.

ww. ____ The negative logarithm of the hydrogen ion concentration of a solution.

xx. ____ Shifting atoms from one molecule or ionic compound to another without change in number or identity of atoms.

yy. ____ Molecules that contain regions of partial positive charge and regions of partial negative charge.

zz. ____ The amount of heat that must be absorbed or lost by 1 gram of a substance to change its temperature by 1°C.

aaa. ____ Any substance that can resist changes in pH by releasing or absorbing hydrogen ions.

bbb. ____ The strongest covalent bond in which the octet rule is satisfied by sharing three electron pairs.

LEARNING BY EXPERIENCE

1. Draw and label a picture of a carbon-12 atom and a carbon-14 atom. Your diagram should show energy levels, electrons, the nucleus, protons, and neutrons. List the atomic number and atomic mass of each atom.

2. Use atomic diagrams to illustrate what happens when an ionic bond is formed and when a single covalent bond is formed.

3. Write the structural formulas and molecular formulas for hydrogen gas, oxygen gas, and nitrogen gas. What type of bond forms each of these molecules? Which is the strongest of these bonds?

4. Draw a drop of water containing five (5) water molecules. Show the hydrogen and oxygen atoms within each water molecule, and use a (+) or (−) to indicate the electronegativity of each atom. Use solid lines to indicate covalent bonds and dotted lines to indicate hydrogen bonds.

EXERCISING YOUR KNOWLEDGE

Briefly answer each of the following questions in the space provided.

1. Why is the chemical behavior of an atom determined more by the electrons than by the protons or neutrons?

2. For any particular element, which of the three subatomic particles (protons, neutrons, electrons) never varies in number? Explain.

3. Carbon-14 has a half-life of about 5,600 years. Archaeologists analyze a piece of wood found at an ancient village site and determine that, of the initial 100 grams of C-14 in the wood, only 3.125 grams are left. How old is the wood?

4. In a periodic table of elements, the elements in any given vertical column tend to behave chemically the same way. Why?

5. What three major tendencies guide the interactions of all atoms?

6. Explain the differences in the types of substances or compounds formed by ionic bonds versus covalent bonds.

7. Why do crystals such as table salt (NaCl) dissolve in water?

8. Why do you think so many of the molecules that make up organisms (for example, proteins, carbohydrates, lipids) are large molecules with covalent bonds rather than ionic bonds?

9. If you dip a corner of a paper towel into a drop of water, why does the water spread along the paper towel?

10. Why does sweating cool us off?

Circle the letter of the one best answer in each of the following questions.

11. The atomic mass of an atom is determined by its total number of
    a. nuclei.
    b. orbitals.
    c. electrons and protons.
    d. electrons and neutrons.
    e. protons and neutrons.

12. The greater the energy of an electron,
    a. the larger it is.
    b. the closer it orbits to the nucleus.
    c. the farther it orbits from the nucleus.
    d. the more likely it is to be transferred rather than shared.
    e. the greater the number of other electrons that can share its orbital.

13. Most of the volume of an atom is taken up by
    a. empty space.
    b. electrons.
    c. protons.
    d. neutrons.
    e. none of the above; atoms have no volume.

14. Which of the following atoms would you expect to behave similarly to oxygen (atomic number = 8)?
    a. carbon (atomic number = 12)
    b. sulfur (atomic number = 16)
    c. argon (atomic number = 18)
    d. all of these
    e. none of these

15. During oxidation, molecules
    a. disintegrate.
    b. lose carbon.
    c. gain electrons.
    d. lose electrons.
    e. are converted to oxygen atoms.

16. Isotopes of the same element differ in their number of
    a. protons.
    b. neutrons.
    c. electrons.
    d. energy levels.
    e. bonds.

17. Which of the following elements is *least* common in living organisms?
    a. carbon
    b. hydrogen
    c. nitrogen
    d. oxygen
    e. sodium

18. Dmitri Mendeleev
    a. created the periodic table of elements.
    b. discovered the first known isotopes.
    c. developed the pH scale.
    d. discovered the structure of atoms.
    e. discovered that water is a polar molecule.

19. Consider atoms with the atomic numbers listed below. Assuming the atoms were neutral, which of them would be inert?
    a. 1
    b. 4
    c. 8
    d. 10
    e. 16

20. In general, electronegativities among the elements in the periodic table
    a. increase as the number of electrons decreases.
    b. increase down the columns.
    c. increase from left to right.
    d. increase as the number of protons decreases.
    e. increase with increasing atomic number.

21. Regions of partial negative charge in polar covalent bonds are found near
    a. the more electronegative atom.
    b. the atom with more protons.
    c. the atom with a larger atomic mass.
    d. the atom with electrons in higher energy levels.
    e. the atom that loses more electrons.

22. In ionic bonds,
    a. electrons are shared unequally between atoms.
    b. electrons are shared equally between atoms.
    c. electrons are transferred between atoms.
    d. protons are transferred between atoms.
    e. neutrons are transferred between atoms.

23. In a crystal of table salt (NaCl), each sodium ion is surrounded by
    a. other sodium ions.
    b. chlorine ions.
    c. water molecules.
    d. buffers.

24. Which of the following will increase the rate of chemical reactions?
    a. lowering the temperature of the reactants
    b. decreasing the number of reactants present
    c. making sure no catalyst gets into the reaction
    d. all of these
    e. none of these

25. Ammonia has a higher specific heat than water because it is _____ than water.
    a. a larger molecule
    b. more acidic
    c. more basic
    d. more polar
    e. more likely to ionize

26. Which of the following pH values represents the greatest concentration of H^+?
    a. 2
    b. 4
    c. 7
    d. 10
    e. 12

27. Hydrophobic interactions are exhibited by
    a. ions.
    b. hydration shells.
    c. polar molecules.
    d. nonpolar molecules.
    e. all of these.

28. In a single water molecule, the oxygen and hydrogen atoms
    a. are held together by ionic bonds.
    b. are held together by hydrogen bonds.
    c. have the same electronegativity.
    d. have no electrons.
    e. share electrons unequally.

29. Which property of water is responsible for the surface tension that enables some insects to walk on water?
    a. adhesion
    b. cohesion
    c. high specific heat
    d. high heat of vaporization
    e. capillary action

30. Which of the following pH values would require the most buffering to reach a neutral pH?
    a. 2
    b. 4
    c. 7
    d. 9
    e. 11

ASSESSING YOUR KNOWLEDGE

Answers to the questions in this section test your ability to synthesize information gained from the chapter and to solve challenging problems on an exam or in everyday life.

Map of Understanding—Answers

1. Potassium (K): 19 protons, 19 neutrons, 19 electrons, 1 valence electron. This is a highly reactive element because to satisfy the octet rule it needs to lose a single valence electron.

Chlorine (Cl): 17 protons, 17 neutrons, 17 electrons, 7 valence electrons. This is a highly reactive element because to satisfy the octet rule it needs to gain only one extra valence electron.

Nitrogen (N): 7 protons, 7 neutrons, 7 electrons, 5 valence electrons. This is a reactive element because of the five valence electrons in its outer shell, 3 of them are unpaired.

Argon (Ar): 18 protons, 18 neutrons, 18 electrons, 8 valence electrons. This is inert or nonreactive because it has eight electrons in its outer energy level.

2. Water is cohesive-- leaves pull water upward from the roots.

Water has a high specific heat-- it can stabilize the temperature of organisms and the environment.

Water has a high heat of vaporization-- evaporation of water cools body surfaces.

Water has a lower density than ice-- lakes do not freeze solid, allowing life to survive in lakes during the winter.

Water is polar making ions and polar molecules soluble in it-- molecules can move freely in cells permitting chemical reactions to take place.

3. a. 10^{-7}

b. 10^{7}

c. 2

d. 10^{-12}

e. acidic

f. 6

g. 10^{-6}

h. acidic

i. 10^{-14}

j. 10^{0}

k. basic

4. a. 5

b. basic; 7

c. dissociates; increase

d. molar concentration; equal; molar concentration; neutral

e. resists

f. increased; decreased

Key Terms—Answers

a. 23, b. 5, c. 14, d. 11, e.19, f. 22, g. 17, h. 24, i. 15, j. 4, k. 10, l. 18, m. 25, n. 9, o. 8, p. 27, q. 1, r. 12, s. 26, t. 3, u. 7, v. 21, w. 16, x. 6, y. 20, z. 2, aa. 13, bb. 49, cc. 42, dd. 51, ee. 38, ff. 30, gg. 43, hh. 40, ii. 52, jj. 36, kk. 45, ll. 47, mm. 33, nn. 41, oo. 37, pp. 50, qq. 53, rr. 28, ss. 32, tt. 48, uu. 29, vv. 35, ww. 54, xx. 34, yy. 39, zz. 44, aaa. 46, bbb. 31.

Learning by Experience—Answers

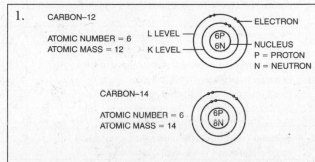

2. Compare your work to text figures 2.10a and 2.11a.

3.

Gas	Structural formula	Molecular formula	Bond
Hydrogen	H–H	H_2	Single covalent
Oxygen	O=O	O_2	Double covalent
Nitrogen	N≡N	N_2	Triple covalent

4.

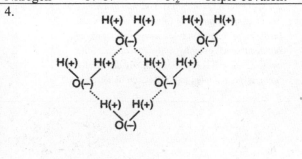

Exercising Your Knowledge—Answers

As you check your answers, put a mark in the review (Rvw.) column for the answers you missed. If you didn't miss any, congratulations—you have mastered the chapter! If you missed some, review the section (Sect.) in the text where this concept is discussed. In order to develop an efficient review strategy, it is important that you understand what types of questions you missed. The questions with asterisks test more for understanding of the **concepts**, whereas the others test more for **detail**. *See the preface for learning strategies for concepts and for detail.*

	Sect.	Rvw.
*1. The nuclei never come close enough to interact; electrons orbit so far from the nucleus that electrons from two atoms run into each other and interact long before the nuclei of the atoms can meet and interact.	2.1	
*2. Protons never vary in number. Different atoms of the same element can differ in their number of neutrons (as with isotopes) or in the number of electrons (as with ions), but if you change the number of protons, you have a different element with a different atomic number.	2.1	
*3. 28,000 years old; 3.125 g remaining of 100 g originally is 5 half-lives (100 g → 50 g → 25 g → 12.5 g → 6.25 g → 3.125 g), and 5,600 years (carbon-14's half-life) multiplied by 5 = 28,000 years.	2.1	
*4. According to the octet rule (rule of eight), most energy levels are completely full when they contain eight electrons, and atoms behave in ways to obtain a completely filled outermost energy level. If it is already full, the atom is inert and does not interact with others. The elements in the same columns have the same number of valence electrons (electrons in the outermost energy level) and therefore tend to behave the same way.	2.2	
*5. Atoms interact in ways that allow them to (a) completely fill their outermost energy level, (b) have paired electrons, and (c) balance positive and negative charges; they do this by transferring or sharing electrons (unless they are inert).	2.1-2.3	
*6. Ionic bonds result in ionic compounds or crystals where negative and positive ions surround each other and are attracted (bonded) to each other, but no discrete molecule forms. Covalent bonds result in discrete molecules where two atoms are bonded to each other by sharing electrons. Since many atoms can form more than one covalent bond, large, complex molecules can be built this way.	2.3	

	Sect.	Rvw.
*7. Water is very polar, and when NaCl is put into water, the individual Na^+ and Cl^- ions are attracted to the polar water molecules, dissociate from each other (breaking apart the crystal lattice), and become surrounded by a hydration shell of water molecules.	2.3-2.4	
*8. Covalent bonds allow large, discrete molecules to form; ionic bonds don't (see question #6). Covalent bonds are much stronger than ionic bonds, and therefore molecules made with covalent bonds are more stable and do not spontaneously ionize or fall apart, important features for maintaining life.	2.3	
*9. Because of adhesion, polar water molecules are attracted to and adhere to the polar paper towel molecules. As the water molecules are pulled along the paper towel, they bring other water molecules along with them because of the cohesion between water molecules caused by hydrogen bonds.	2.4	
*10. When we sweat, water evaporates from our bodies; it takes energy to make water evaporate (go from liquid to gas), so sweating is a way of using up or getting rid of excess heat energy.	2.5	
11. e	2.1	
*12. c	2.1	
13. a	2.1	
*14. b	2.1	
15. d	2.1	
16. b	2.1	
17. e	2.2	
18. a	2.2	
*19. d	2.2	
20. c	2.3	
21. a	2.3	
22. c	2.3	
23. b	2.3	
*24. e	2.3	
*25. d	2.5	
26. a	2.6	
27. d	2.4	
28. e	2.4	
29. b	2.4	
30. a	2.6	

CHAPTER 3 THE CHEMICAL BUILDING BLOCKS OF LIFE

MASTERING KEY CONCEPTS

Life is built upon the macromolecules of proteins, nucleic acids, lipids, and carbohydrates. These macromolecules help control chemical reactions within the organism, store the hereditary information that directs every aspect of the organism's life, and are passed on to the next generation, form membranes, store energy for later use, and provide structural support.

3.1 Carbon: The framework of biological molecules.

- **Overview**: **Biological macromolecules**, such as **carbohydrates**, **proteins**, **lipids**, and **nucleic acids**, are **polymers** made up of similar **monomeric subunits** that provide the basis of all living systems. **Carbon** is the common element found in all of the monomeric subunits of these four biological polymers. **Dehydration** can link monomeric subunits into polymers, while polymers can be broken down by **hydrolysis**.

- **Details**: Know the **primary functional groups** and the biological molecules that they occur in. Know the cellular functions of the four major biological macromolecules and the **building blocks** from which these macromolecules are made. Know how a dehydration reaction can form polymers, and how hydrolysis can break the bond between two monomers.

3.2 Carbohydrates: Energy storage and structural molecules.

- **Overview**: **Carbohydrates** are energy-storage molecules with the empirical formula $(CH_2O)_n$. **Sugars** are the most important energy-storage molecules in biological systems. In their simplest form, sugars are **monosaccharides** containing three-, to six-carbon atoms. **Glucose** is a common, biologically important six-carbon sugar. **Fructose** is a **structural isomer** of glucose, and **galactose** is a **stereoisomer**. By dehydration synthesis, more complex **disaccharides**, such as **lactose**, and **polysaccharides**, such as **starch**, **glycogen**, **cellulose**, and **chitin**, are formed. Polysaccharides are used both for energy storage and for **structural purposes** by cells.

- **Details**: Know ring-structures of **ribose** and **glucose**. Know the structural differences between glucose and its two **isomers** with the empirical formula $C_6H_{12}O_6$. Understand the difference between a **structural isomer** and a **stereoisomer**, and the difference between α-, and β-**glucose**. Know how monosaccharides form di-, and polysaccharides and the biological functions of the three forms of sugars. Understand how **branching** affects the

glycosidic linkage, solubility, and function of polysaccharides.

3.3 Nucleic acids store and transfer genetic information.

- **Overview**: **Nucleic acids**, such as **DNA** and **RNA**, are composed of a chain of **nucleotides** linked by a series of **phosphodiester bonds**. Each nucleotide consists of a five-carbon sugar, a phosphate group, and 1 of 5 nitrogenous bases, **adenine**, **cytosine**, **guanine**, **thymine**, or **uracil**. Nucleic acids are vital biological macromolecules because they **store hereditary information** of a cell, which directs the synthesis of proteins.

- **Details**: Know the **structure of a nucleotide**, the difference between DNA and RNA, and the biological significance of each. Know the five different nitrogenous bases, whether they are **purines** or **pyrimidines**, whether each is found in DNA or RNA, what bases are **complementary**, and what this means. Be familiar with **other nucleotide-containing molecules** and their biological functions.

3.4 Proteins are molecules with diverse structures and functions.

- **Overview**: **Proteins** are the most functionally diverse biological macromolecules. They are made up of **amino acids** linked by **peptide bonds**. Amino acids have the general structure:

$$\begin{array}{c} R \\ | \\ H2N—C—COOH \\ | \\ H \end{array}$$

where R is a side group that determines the chemical properties of the amino acid. The function of a protein is determined in part by its structure, which is determined by its amino acid sequence (**primary structure**), regions of α-helices and β-sheets (**secondary structure**), how regions of secondary structure are arranged in space (**tertiary structure**), and how multiple subunits are arranged in space in proteins containing more than one polypeptide (**quaternary structure**). Different proteins contain identifiable **motifs** and **domains** that are suggestive of their structure or function. Most proteins need to be properly folded to carry out their cellular functions, highlighting the importance of **chaperone proteins**. Changes in local conditions, such as pH, temperature, or salinity, can cause a protein to **denature**, or unfold and lose its ability to function.

- **Details**: Know the **seven functional categories** into which proteins can be divided. Know the **five chemical classes of amino acids** and why each of the 20 is assigned to each of these classes. Know how a peptide bond is formed. Know the **four levels of structure** of a protein. Understand how a common motif or domain among different proteins can be identified and what type of information it can provide about a protein. Understand **how a chaperone protein functions** and the importance of protein folding and unfolding.

3.5 Lipids are hydrophobic molecules.
- **Overview**: **Lipids**, such as **fats** and **oils**, are made up of **fatty acids**, long chains of nonpolar hydrocarbons, and **glycerol**, and are **insoluble** in water. This property makes lipids vital energy-

storing molecules and essential components of cellular **membranes**. Biological membranes consist of **phospholipids** that have a **polar head group** and **two hydrophilic tails**. The hydrophobic tails of different lipid molecules interact to form **micelles**, or **lipid bilayers,** with the polar head groups oriented to the outside.
- **Details**: Know the difference between **saturated**, **unsaturated**, and **polyunsaturated** fatty acids. Know the basic structure of fats and phospholipids. Understand how lipids form micelles, or lipid bilayers, in water and the biological importance.

CHALLENGING YOUR UNDERSTANDING

1. Indicate the building blocks of the following macromolecules and then indicate the basic composition of each of the building blocks.

Proteins

Nucleic acids

Lipids

Carbohydrates

2. List the seven functional classifications of proteins. Give an example of each category.

3. Classify each amino acid side chain as nonpolar, polar uncharged, charged, aromatic, or special function. Indicate which amino acid the side chain belongs to from the list at the bottom.

Methionine, Lysine, Valine, Serine, Phenylalanine

KEY TERMS

Match the numbered term with the definition that fits it best. Put the corresponding number in front of the appropriate definition.

1. hydrocarbons	10. polypeptide	19. carbohydrates
2. functional groups	11. domains	20. phospholipids
3. isomers	12. chaperone proteins	21. triglyceride
4. chiral	13. denaturation	22. saturated
5. polymers	14. dissociation	23. unsaturated
6. dehydration synthesis	15. deoxyribonucleic acid (DNA)	24. monosaccharides
7. hydrolysis	16. ribonucleic acid (RNA)	25. alpha (α)-glucose
8. amino acid	17. nucleotides	26. beta (β)-glucose
9. peptide bond	18. complementary	27. polysaccharides

a. _____ The covalent bond that links together two amino acids in a polypeptide.

b. _____ Functional units within a larger structure that perform different aspects of a protein's function.

c. _____ Synthesized from the DNA and directs the synthesis of proteins.

d. _____ Molecular chaperones that assist other proteins in folding correctly.

e. _____ Starch is composed of hundreds of these molecules linked together in long, unbranched chains.

f. _____ Consisting of a five-carbon sugar, a phosphate group, a nitrogenous base, it is the building block of DNA.

g. _____ The simplest form of carbohydrates with a name meaning simple sugars.

h. _____ The reversible separation of the subunits of a protein with quaternary structure, where subunits stay folded.

i. _____ Composed of three fatty acids that need not be identical and can vary in length.

j. _____ The change in a protein's shape that occurs when there is a change in pH, temperature, or salinity.

k. _____ Specific molecular groups that act as units during chemical reactions and confer special properties.

l. _____ Complex molecules with a polar head, and two nonpolar tails that form biological membranes.

m. _____ Long polymers made up of monosaccharides that have been joined through dehydration synthesis.

n. _____ If all of the internal carbon atoms in the fatty acid chains are bonded to at least two hydrogen atoms.

o. _____ Disassembles macromolecules into their constituent subunits by addition of a water molecule.

p. _____ Each chain of a protein that will fold and associate with other chains to form a functional protein.

q. _____ A long molecule built by linking together a large number of small, similar chemical subunits.

r. _____ Cellulose is composed of hundreds of these molecules linked together in long, unbranched chains.

s. _____ Different forms of organic molecules having the same structural formula.

t. _____ One of the 20 building blocks used for protein synthesis, each one consisting of a specific side chain.

u. _____ A fatty acid that has double bonds between one or more pairs of successive carbon atoms.

v. _____ Molecules consisting only of carbon and hydrogen that store considerable energy.

w. _____ A group of molecules that contains carbon, hydrogen, and oxygen in a molar ratio of 1:2:1.

x. _____ Adenine base-pairing with thymine and guanine base-pairing with cytosine.

y. _____ Long chains of nucleotides linked by a phosphodiester bond that contain an organism's genetic code.

z. _____ Forms a covalent bond between two monomers by removing a OH group from one and a H from the other.

aa. _____ A molecule that has mirror-image versions of itself, such as D-, and L-amino acids.

LEARNING BY EXPERIENCE

1. Complete the following chart pertaining to macromolecules.

Molecule	Subunits	Function	Examples
Disaccharide	a.	b.	Lactose, sucrose
c.	d.	Energy storage	Starch, glycogen
e.	f.	Structural	Cellulose
Fat	g.	h.	Cooking oils
i.	Amino acids	j.	Enzymes
k.	Amino acids	Movement	Muscles
l.	m.	Store hereditary Information	DNA

2. Draw a colored circle around the three atoms that would be removed if these two monosaccharides were linked to form a disaccharide.

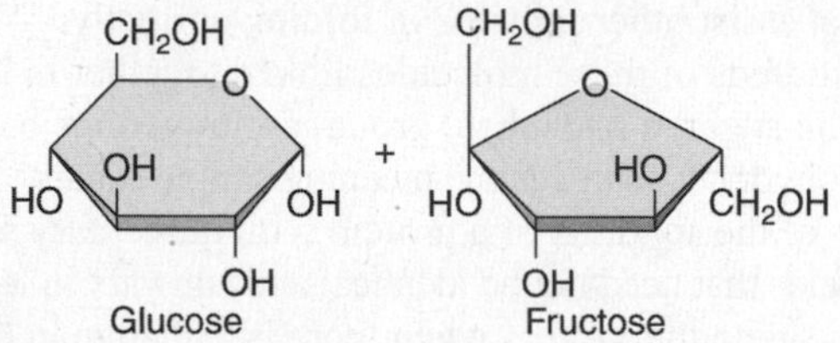

CH₂OH ... Glucose + Fructose (structures)

3. Match the following numbers with the appropriate statements. A number may be used more than once.

Numbers: 0, 1, 2, 3, 4, 5, 6, 12, 20
Statements:
_____ a. Number of different nitrogenous bases in DNA
_____ b. Number of carbon atoms in a glucose molecule
_____ c. Number of fatty acids in a molecule of fat
_____ d. Number of different chemical classes of amino acids
_____ e. Number of chains of nucleotides in a DNA molecule
_____ f. Number of glycerol subunits in a molecule of fat
_____ g. Number of hydrogen atoms in a glucose molecule
_____ h. Number of different nitrogenous bases in RNA
_____ i. Number of simple sugars in a disaccharide
_____ j. Number of carbon–carbon double bonds in a saturated fatty acid
_____ k. Number of oxygen atoms in a glucose molecule
_____ l. Number of different amino acids in proteins
_____ m. Number of chains of nucleotides in most RNA molecules

4. Label the subunits in this symbolic fat molecule.

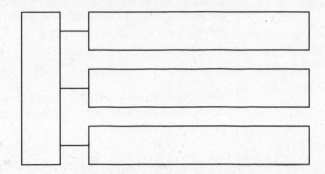

5. Arrange the following terms to form a symbolic amino acid, and then draw a colored circle around the part that is unique to each type of amino acid. Terms: *amino group, C, carboxyl group, H, R side group.*

6. Indicate whether each of the following nitrogenous bases is found only in DNA, only in RNA, or in both DNA and RNA. Then indicate their proper complementary base pairings. Bases: adenine (A), cytosine (C), guanine (G), thymine (T), uracil (U).

EXERCISING YOUR KNOWLEDGE

Briefly answer each of the following questions in the space provided.

1. All biological molecules contain carbon. What properties of carbon make it such a fundamental building block?

2. Explain the statement, "The large polymers important to living organisms are all built the same basic way."

3. How do the side groups of amino acids determine the structure of proteins?

4. Based on what you know about the chemistry of biological molecules, why do you think high fevers are so dangerous for humans and other animals?

5. The double helix structure of DNA has been compared to a spiral staircase. What components make up the sides of the staircase, and what component makes up the steps? What types of bonds hold the sides together and the steps together?

6. Why do scientists think DNA evolved from RNA, rather than vice versa?

7. Fats are referred to as saturated or unsaturated. In a saturated fat, what exactly is saturated with what?

8. Which is a better source of energy, carbohydrates or fats? Why?

9. What do the sugar isomers glucose, fructose, and galactose tell us about the relationship between the empirical formula, structure, and function of molecules?

10. What does cellulose tell us about the three-dimensional shape of molecules with regard to their ease of digestibility?

Circle the letter of the one best answer in each of the following questions.

11. Polypeptides are polymers of _____, while starch is a polymer of _____.
    a. amino acids, monosaccharides
    b. triglyceride, fatty acids
    c. filaments, adipose
    d. nucleotides, triglyceride
    e. fatty acids, lipids

12. What happens during a hydrolysis reaction?
    a. Water breaks ionic bonds.
    b. Saturated fats become unsaturated.
    c. Protein coils into its secondary structure.
    d. A bond is formed between two subunits of a molecule.
    e. A bond is broken between two subunits of a molecule.

13. Dehydration synthesis and hydrolysis reactions involve removing or adding _____ to molecules.
    a. carbon
    b. water
    c. side groups
    d. functional groups
    e. macromolecules

14. Which of the following is *not* a function of proteins?
    a. transport
    b. movement
    c. catalysis
    d. storage of genetic information
    e. structural support

15. What are the three components of a nucleotide?
    a. fatty acid, phosphate group, glycerol
    b. triglyceride, lipid, alcohol
    c. carbon, phosphate group, carboxyl
    d. amino group, carboxyl, group, hydrogen
    e. sugar, phosphate group, nitrogenous base

16. The complex folding that forms the tertiary structure of a protein is caused by
    a. hydrophobic interactions between side groups and water.
    b. the length of the polypeptide chain.
    c. van der Waal's forces between the different polypeptide chains.
    d. the ring structure of the glucose subunits
    e. denaturation.

17. Chaperone proteins help other proteins
    a. denature.
    b. dissociate.
    c. fold properly.
    d. acquire their primary structure.
    e. make copies of themselves.

18. What is the name of the bond formed between two nucleotides in the backbone of DNA?
    a. peptide
    b. glycosidic linkage
    c. hydrogen
    d. phosphodiester
    e. ionic

19. If a person has a mutation in the hemoglobin gene that changes one amino acid to a different amino acid, the _____ structure was altered.
    a. secondary
    b. primary
    c. tertiary
    d. quaternary

20. Which of the following statements is true?
    a. Adenine and guanine are pyrimidines.
    b. By definition, a nucleotide contains a five-carbon sugar, a phosphate group, and a nitrogenous base.
    c. Hereditary information is stored in RNA and then used by DNA to make proteins.
    d. DNA molecules are so large that it is possible to see them with a good optical microscope.
    e. In the complementary pairing of nitrogenous bases, cytosine always pairs with adenine.

Assuming they all had the same number of carbon atoms, which of the following types of molecules would have the most C–H bonds?
    a. a polysaccharide
    b. a polyunsaturated fat
    c. an unsaturated fat
    d. a saturated fat

21. Triacylglycerols contain glycerol and
    a. amino acids.
    b. fatty acids.
    c. nucleic acids.
    d. side groups.
    e. glucose.

22. Which of the following are soluble in water?
    a. terpenes
    b. steroids
    c. prostaglandins
    d. all of these
    e. none of these

23. Phospholipids always orient so their tails face
    a. toward water.
    b. away from water.

24. The empirical formula for carbohydrates is
    a. $2(CHO)_n$
    b. $(CHO)_2$
    c. $(CH_2O)_n$
    d. $(C_2HO)_n$
    e. $(C_nHO_n)_2$

25. Which of the following is a disaccharide?
    a. lactose
    b. glucose
    c. cellulose
    d. all of these
    e. none of these

26. Why is cellulose so difficult for most organisms to digest?
    a. It has a large number of hydrogen bonds.
    b. The bonds holding the subunits together are stronger than those in most other molecules.
    c. It is such a large molecule.
    d. Lack of the proper enzyme to break the bond between cellulose subunits.
    e. Cellulose is made up of chitin, which is indigestible.

27. Animals store glucose in the form of
    a. starch.
    b. fructose.
    c. galactose.
    d. glycerol.
    e. glycogen.

28. Isomers have the same
    a. structures.
    b. functions.
    c. empirical formulas.
    d. all of these.
    e. none of these.

29. When proteins fold into a 3-D structure, _____ amino acids tend to be buried within the protein and _____ amino acids are exposed on the surface.
    a. hydrophilic, hydrophobic
    b. charged, nonpolar
    c. hydrophobic, polar
    d. special function, nonpolar
    e. charged, special function

ASSESSING YOUR KNOWLEDGE

Answers to the questions in this section test your ability to synthesize information gained from the chapter and to solve challenging problems on an exam or in everyday life.

Challenging Your Understanding—Answers

1. **Proteins**: amino acids: An amino and carboxyl group bonded to a central carbon atom with an additional hydrogen and a functional side group.

Nucleic acids: nucleotides: a five-carbon sugar, ribose or deoxyribose, a phosphate group, and an organic nitrogenous base.

Lipids: glycerol and fatty acids: long hydrocarbon chains and a three-carbon alcohol with each carbon bearing a hydroxyl group.

Carbohydrates: monosaccharides: three-, five-, six-carbon sugars.

2. Functional Protein Classifications: **Enzyme catalysis** – kinases phosphorylate proteins, **Defense**- antibodies mark foreign proteins for elimination, **Transport**- hemoglobin carries O_2 and CO_2 in the blood, **Support**- fibrin forms blood clots, **Motion**- actin contracts muscle fibers, **Regulation** – insulin controls blood glucose levels, **Storage** – Calmodulin binds calcium ions.

3. polar uncharged – serine; charged - lysine; aromatic- phenylalanine; special function- methionine; nonpolar- valine.

Key Terms—Answers

a. 9, b. 11, c. 16, d. 12, e. 25, f. 17, g. 24, h. 14, i. 21, j. 13, k. 2, l. 20, m. 27, n. 22, o. 7, p. 10, q. 5, r. 26, s. 3, t. 8, u. 23, v. 1, w. 19, x. 18, y. 15, z. 6, aa. 4.

Learning by Experience—Answers

1.		
	a.	Monosaccharides
	b.	Transport
	c.	Polysaccharides
	d.	Monosaccharides
	e.	Polysaccharides
	f.	Monosaccharides
	g.	Glycerol and 3 fatty acids
	h.	Energy storage
	i.	Protein
	j.	Catalysis
	k.	Proteins
	l.	Nucleic acids
	m.	Nucleotides

2.

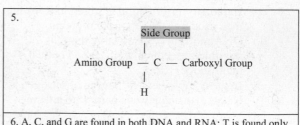

Glucose + Fructose

3.		
	a.	4
	b.	6
	c.	3
	d.	5
	e.	2
	f.	1
	g.	12
	h.	4
	i.	2
	j.	0
	k.	6
	l.	20
	m.	1

4.

Glycerol
- Fatty Acid
- Fatty Acid
- Fatty Acid

5.

Side Group
|
Amino Group — C — Carboxyl Group
|
H

6. A, C, and G are found in both DNA and RNA; T is found only in DNA; U is found only in RNA. Pairings: A-T, A-U, C-G

Exercising Your Knowledge—Answers

As you check your answers, put a mark in the review (Rvw.) column for the answers you missed. If you didn't miss any, congratulations—you have mastered the chapter! If you missed some, review the section (Sect.) in the text where this concept is discussed. In order to develop an efficient review strategy, it is important that you understand what types of questions you missed. The questions with asterisks test more for understanding of the **concepts**, whereas the others test more for **detail**. *See the preface for learning strategies for concepts and for detail.*

	Sect.	Rvw.
*1. Carbon has unique atomic and chemical properties: 4 valence electrons in outermost shell; can form 4 covalent bonds (single, double, or triple) with other carbons or with other elements; can form chain by bonding with other carbon atoms.	3.1	
*2. Polysaccharides, fats, proteins, and nucleic acids are all polymers made up of subunits. The same dehydration reaction process links together the subunits to make the polymer.	3.1	
*3. Each amino acid has a side group with its own particular chemical properties (e.g., nonpolar, polar, aromatic). The side group makes each amino acid unique; the sequence of amino acids (with their side groups) determines the primary structure of the polypeptide, and this in turn determines the secondary and tertiary structure as nearby side groups interact with each other and with the environment (e.g., forming hydrogen bonds or interacting hydrophobically with water).	3.2	
*4. The ability of a protein to function properly is dependent on its complex, three-dimensional structure. Higher-than-normal temperatures can cause proteins to denature or lose their proper three-dimensional shape and thus limit or prevent their ability to function. This would be harmful, even lethal, depending on the degree and duration of the denaturation, since enzymes, structural proteins, and other proteins would not be functioning properly.	3.2	
*5. The sides of the staircase are composed of alternating phosphate groups and five-carbon deoxyribose sugars. The steps are made of two complementary paired nitrogenous bases (A and T, or C and G). The bases are held together by hydrogen bonds. The phosphate group of one nucleotide is linked to the sugar of the next nucleotide by a phosphodiester bond.	3.3	

	Sect.	Rvw.
*6. DNA appears to be a way of protecting the genetic information. The hereditary information is stored more safely in the double helix of DNA and then passed to the single-stranded RNA, which is exposed to more damage because it is out in the cell actively involved in making proteins. Scientists feel the ability to synthesize proteins came first, followed by the safety improvement.	3.3	
*7. The carbon atoms in the fatty acid subunits of the fat are bonded to the maximum number of H atoms possible (i.e., are saturated with H) because there are no double or triple C—C bonds in the fatty acid chains.	3.4	
*8. Fats have more C—H bonds, which store energy. Fats have about 9 kcal of energy per gram of fat; carbohydrates have less than 4 kcal/g.	3.4	
*9. Even though molecules have the same type and numbers of atoms (i.e., same empirical formula), they don't have the same function. The structural arrangement of the atoms is important in determining function; glucose, fructose, and galactose all have 6 carbon atoms, 12 hydrogen atoms, and 6 oxygen atoms (empirical formula = $C_6H_{12}O_6$), but different structural arrangements of those atoms and different functions, such as taste and the types of polymers they build.	3.5	
*10. A molecule must have the proper shape to be digested by an enzyme; very few organisms have enzymes that can break down the beta form of glucose found in cellulose.	3.5	
*11. a	3.1	
*12. e	3.1	
13. b	3.1	
14. d	3.2	
*15. e	3.3	
*16. a	3.2	
17. c	3.2	
18. d	3.3	
*19. b	3.4	
20. b	3.3	
*21. d	3.4	
22. b	3.4	
23. e	3.4	
*24. b	3.4	
25. c	3.5	
26. a	3.5	
27. d	3.5	
28. e	3.5	
*29. c	3.5	
*30. c	3.4	

CHAPTER 4 CELL STRUCTURE

MASTERING KEY CONCEPTS

The first sentence in this chapter is short but profound. One would expect the study of a structure basic to all of the diverse organisms to be complex, and it is. It is best to focus first on the commonality of cells and then consider the unique features.

4.1 All organisms are composed of cells.

- **Overview**: **Cells** are the smallest basic units of life. All organisms are composed of one or more cells, which arise only by division of a preexisting cell. Common characteristics of all cells include a **nucleiod, cytoplasm, ribosomes**, and a **plasma membrane**. Most cells are so small they can be visualized only by using **microscopic techniques**.
- **Details**: Know the **definition of a cell** and why small cell size is advantageous. Know the **four major features** that all cells have and the basic biological function of each. Know the **different types of microscopes** and the general strength of each relative to the others.

4.2 Prokaryotic cells are small and simple.

- **Overview**: **Prokaryotes** are the simplest organisms and are divided into two domains, **archea** and **bacteria**. Archea appear to be more closely related to eukaryotes. A prokaryotic cell is small, consisting of a **single circular molecule of DNA** surrounded by **cytoplasm,** which is enclosed by a **plasma membrane** and a **cell wall** composed of **peptidoglycan** in bacteria, and made from polysaccharides and protein in archea. Prokaryotic cells have **no membrane-bound organelles**, and they lack an internal support structure like the cytoskeleton in eukaryotes. Some prokaryotes are motile because they have rotating structures on the outside called **flagella**.
- **Details**: Know the structure and contents of a prokaryotic cell. Know the function of the rigid cell wall and the difference between the cell walls of bacteria and those of archea. Know the difference between **gram-positive** and **gram-negative bacteria**.

4.3 Take a tour of a eukaryotic cell.

- **Overview**: **Eukaryotic** cells are more complex than prokaryotic cells due to the **compartmentalization** of internal biochemical reactions within numerous **membrane-bound organelles**, and the presence of the **cytoskeleton**. Eukaryotic DNA is divided into multiple linear chromosomes and is packaged into **nucleosomes** and contained in a **nucleus** that is surrounded by a **nuclear envelope**. Cytoplasmic proteins necessary for nuclear structures, or activities, and RNA, or RNA-

protein complexes formed in the nucleus can pass through **nuclear pores** in the nuclear envelope to or from the cytoplasm. **Ribosomes** are essential, universal organelles because they are the **protein-synthesis factories** of the cell.

- **Details**: Know the composition and the function of the nucleus and the nuclear envelope in eukaryotic cells. Know how DNA is packaged. Understand how ribosomes are assembled and the difference in the functions of membrane-associated ribosomes and free cytoplasmic ribosomes. Know the basic functions of the different forms of RNA (**tRNA, mRNA, rRNA**).

4.4 Endomembrane system

- **Overview**: The **endoplasmic reticulum** consisting of the rough and the smooth sections (**RER** and **SER**) are part of the **endomembrane system**. **Ribosomes** synthesize proteins on the surface of the RER that are transported to the **Golgi apparatus** in **transport vesicles**. There the proteins are modified, collected in **cisternae**, packaged into **secretory vesicles,** and travel to the plasma membrane or other cellular locations. The **SER** stores Ca^{2+}, control toxicity of foreign substances, synthesize lipids, and contain embedded enzymes. **Lysosomes** that contain digestive enzymes to breakdown organelles or cells also arise from the Golgi. Plants and some fungi contain **vacuoles** that have multiple functions ranging from water balance to storage.
- **Details**: Know the composition of the endoplasmic reticulum and the difference in the cellular functions of the smooth and the rough ER. Know how proteins are transported through the endomembrane system and the roles of the *cis* and the *trans* Golgi. Know the functions of the lysosomes, vacuoles, and **microbodies**, such as the **peroxisomes**.

4.5 Mitochondria and chloroplasts: Cellular generators

- **Overview**: **Mitochondria** and **chloroplasts** are structurally similar, each containing its own DNA and protein synthesis machinery, and both surrounded by a double membrane. There is evidence that both structures likely arose by the process of **endosymbiosis**. Mitochondria function in oxidative metabolism, generate ATP, and replicate each time a cell divides relying on genes in the nucleus and some cytoplasmic proteins to do so. Chloroplasts contain **chlorophyll** and synthesize their own food and ATP, but many chloroplast components are also located in the nucleus.
- **Details**: Know the common characteristics of the mitochondria and chloroplasts and the functions of each. Know the evidence that supports the

idea that both mitochondria and chloroplasts arose via endosymbiosis.

4.6 The cytoskeleton
- **Overview**: The **cytoskeleton** consists of protein fibers, such as **actin**, **microtubules,** and **intermediate filaments** that support the shape of the cell and anchor organelles to specific locations. Actin and microtubules are also involved in moving materials within cells and moving cells themselves.
- **Details**: Know the characteristics, differences between, and the functions of the three cytoskeletal fibers.

4.7 Extracellular structures and cell movement
- **Overview**: Actin, microfilaments, or both are responsible for essentially all internal cell movement. Cells change shape by actin filaments' forming and disassembling. Cells crawl by the action of actin filaments and myosin motors. Eukaryotic **flagellum** and **cilia** are external structures involved in a cell's movement. These structures consist of microtubules with a **9 + 2 structural** organization. Cilia have a variety of motility functions in the body, removed from the original function of flagella. **Cell walls** in plants and the **extracellular matrix (ECM)** in animal cells give cells support and protection.
- **Details**: Know the basic structure of flagellum and cilia, how they work, and the cellular functions they provide. Know the importance of the cell wall (plants) and the ECM (animal cells).

CHALLENGING YOUR UNDERSTANDING
1. List the major differences between a prokaryotic and a eukaryotic cell.

2. List the major differences between an animal cell and a plant cell. For structures present in one but not the other, list the function of each.

KEY TERMS

Match the numbered term with the definition that fits it best. Put the corresponding number in front of the appropriate definition.

1. prokaryotes
2. nucleoid
3. eukaryotes
4. nucleus
5. nuclear envelope
6. cytoplasm
7. organelles
8. plasma membrane
9. surface area: volume ratio
10. resolution
11. compound microscope
12. transmission electron microscope
13. scanning electron microscope
14. cell wall
15. gram-positive
16. gram-negative
17. flagellum

18. endomembrane system
19. central vacuole
20. chromosomes
21. cytoskeleton
22. nucleolus
23. nuclear pores
24. histones
25. Golgi apparatus
26. cisternae
27. ribosomes
28. rough ER
29. smooth ER
30. lysosome
31. glyoxysome
32. peroxisome
33. mitochondria
34. cristae
35. matrix
36. intermembrane space

37. chloroplasts
38. grana
39. thylakoids
40. amyloplast
41. endosymbiotic theory
42. actin
43. centrosome
44. kinesin
45. dynein
46. 9 + 2 structure
47. basal body
48. cilia
49. myosin
50. middle lamella
51. extracellular matrix
52. fibronectin
53. integrins
54. microtubules

a. _____ Bacteria with a complex, multilayered cell wall that appears red after a Gram stain.
b. _____ Used to magnify specimens in stages using several lenses.
c. _____ Cellular machines that carry out protein synthesis that are found in all known cells.
d. _____ Long, threadlike structures that protrude from the surface of a cell and are used in locomotion.
e. _____ Proteins that wrap up the DNA and package it into nucleosomes.
f. _____ A prokaryotic structure that protects the cell, maintains its shape, and prevents excess water loss.
g. _____ Organisms containing one or more cells that have a well-defined, enclosed nucleus.
h. _____ An internal protein scaffold found in all eukaryotic cells.
i. _____ Structures in the nuclear envelope that allow small molecules to diffuse from the nucleus to the cytoplasm.
j. _____ An area near the center of the cell in prokaryotes where the molecule of DNA typically resides.
k. _____ The minimum distance two points can be apart and still be distinguished as two separated points.
l. _____ Weaves through the cell interior and by organelles to achieve compartmentalization in eukaryotes.
m. _____ A structure in the nucleus where intensive ribosomal RNA synthesis takes place.
n. _____ A semifluid matrix that fills the interior of cells and contains the sugars, amino acids, and proteins a cell uses.
o. _____ The simplest organisms, including bacteria and archea, lacking a nucleus and having a single DNA molecule.
p. _____ Compact units into which histone-bound DNA is packaged in eukaryotic organisms.
q. _____ The organelle in eukaryotic cells that contains the DNA and is separated from the cytoplasm by an envelope.
r. _____ An organelle that functions in the collection, packaging, and distribution of molecules throughout the cell.
s. _____ Capable of resolving objects only .2nm apart. A sample is visualized by transmitting electrons through it.
t. _____ Flattened, stacked membrane folds where newly formed or altered glycoproteins collect in the Golgi.
u. _____ Two phospholipid bilayer membranes bound to the surface of the nucleus, one is continuous with the ER.
v. _____ Bacteria with a thick, single-layer peptidoglycan cell wall that retains a violet dye from a Gram stain.
w. _____ As a cell's size increases, its volume increases much more rapidly than its surface area.
x. _____ Structure responsible for enclosing a cell and separating its contents from its surroundings.
y. _____ Specialized membrane-bound compartments found in the cytoplasm of eukaryotic cells.
z. _____ Specimens visualized by beaming electrons onto its surface, yielding 3-D images that can be photographed.
aa. _____ A large, membrane-bound sac found in plants, which stores proteins, pigments, and waste materials.
bb. _____ Closed compartments of stacked membranes, which lie inside the inner membrane of a chloroplast.
cc. _____ The region surrounding the centrioles that acts as a cell's microtubule-organizing center.
dd. _____ A structure situated just below the point where the flagellum protrudes from the surface of a cell.
ee. _____ A protein that acts with actin to pull a cell forward allowing it to crawl.
ff. _____ A cytoskeletal fiber consisting of α-, and β-tubulin subunits arranged side by side to form a hollow tube.
gg. _____ A DNA-containing organelle in plants that stores starch.

hh. _____ A special type of microbody in plant cells that contains enzymes to convert fats into carbohydrates.

ii. _____ A network of tubules whose membranes contain embedded enzymes, and is involved in Ca^{2+} storage.

jj. _____ A sticky substance that is located between the walls of adjacent plant cells and glues the cells together.

kk. _____ The idea that some eukaryotic organelles arose by symbiosis of two free-living cells.

ll. _____ An arrangement of microtubules found in eukaryotic flagellum and cilia.

mm. _____ A motor protein that uses ATP to power its movement toward the periphery of a cell.

nn. _____ Proteins that link the ECM to the cytoskeleton and allow the ECM to influence cell behavior.

oo. _____ Membrane-bound vesicles containing digestive enzymes that arise from the Golgi apparatus.

pp. _____ The region of the mitochondria, created by the cristae, that is located inside the inner membrane.

qq. _____ Short, external cellular projections with a 9 + 2 structure that carry out functions like water or cell movement.

rr. _____ A type of microbody that contains enzymes that catalyze the removal of electrons and hydrogen atoms.

ss. _____ A glycoprotein that attaches the ECM to the plasma membrane.

tt. _____ Numerous contiguous layers found in the inner folded membrane of the mitochondria.

uu. _____ An organelle that can synthesize its own food by the process of photosynthesis.

vv. _____ Tubular organelle found in all eukaryotes involved in energy metabolism that contains its own DNA.

ww. _____ An elaborate mixture of glycoproteins secreted into the space surrounding animal cells.

xx. _____ An outer compartment lying between the two mitochondrial membranes.

yy. _____ Ribosomes synthesize proteins on its surface that are transported in vesicles to the Golgi.

zz. _____ A globular protein that forms microfilaments and is responsible for cellular movements, such as crawling.

aaa. _____ Disk-shaped structures in chloroplasts that contain light-capturing photosynthetic pigments.

bbb. _____ A motor protein that directs the movement of vesicles toward a cell's interior.

LEARNING BY EXPERIENCE

Color coding the following illustrations should help reinforce your understanding of the identity and location of cell structures. Fill in the circle at the end of each title with the color you will use for that structure or substance, and color accordingly. Colored pencils are recommended because they can be sharpened for details. Use figure 4.6 as a guide for the first diagram and figure 4.7 for the second.

Plasma membrane ◯   Nuclear envelope ◯
Microvilli ◯   Nucleolus ◯
Cytoplasm ◯   RER ◯
Cytoskeleton ◯   SER ◯
Lysosome ◯   Ribosome ◯
Mitochondrion ◯   Centriole ◯
Golgi apparatus ◯

Cell wall ◯   Lysosome ◯
Plasma membrane ◯   Golgi apparatus ◯
Cytoplasm ◯   Nuclear envelope ◯
Central vacuole ◯   Nucleus ◯
Chloroplast ◯   Nucleolus ◯
Mitochondrion ◯   RER ◯
Ribosome ◯   SER ◯

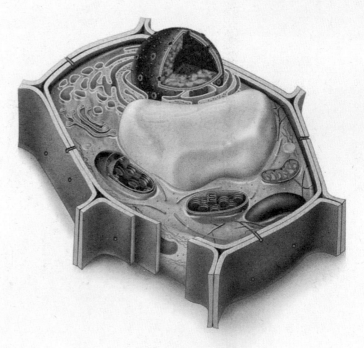

EXERCISING YOUR KNOWLEDGE

Briefly answer each of the following questions in the space provided.

1. Compare the location of DNA in bacteria to that in eukaryotes.

2. A cell with ten times the diameter of another cell will have one hundred times the smaller cell's surface area and one thousand times its volume. Explain why that is a problem for the larger cell.

3. Compare the cell wall structure of gram-positive bacteria to those of gram-negative bacteria.

4. Compare the movement of eukaryotic flagella to that of prokaryotes.

5. What are two ways that lysosomes and microbodies differ?

6. Explain how proteins are transported through the endomembrane system.

7. How are ribosomes of the RER and those in the cytoplasm similar in function but different in role?

8. Explain how a cell crawls.

9. Compare eukaryotic flagella to cilia.

10. Briefly state the endosymbiotic theory.

Circle the letter of the one best answer in each of the following questions.

11. While there are other differences between prokaryotes and eukaryotes, the most defining difference is the absence of _____ in prokaryotes.
    a. a plasma membrane
    b. mitochondria
    c. DNA
    d. cytoplasm
    e. a membrane-bound nucleus

12. Which of the following is *not* a part of the cell theory in its modern form?
    a. Cells are the smallest living things.
    b. Cells develop through endosymbiosis.
    c. All organisms are composed of one or more cells.
    d. Cells arise only by division of previously existing cells.
    e. None of these are correct.

13. Plants differ from most animals in that plants have
    a. an endoplasmic reticulum.
    b. a central vacuole.
    c. a Golgi apparatus.
    d. vesicles.
    e. organelles.

14. The cell walls of prokaryotes are composed of
    a. glycolipids.
    b. keratin.
    c. peptidoglycans.
    d. chitin.
    e. phospholipids.

15. A gram-positive bacterium is enclosed by
    a. a single thick wall.
    b. a single thin wall.
    c. a double thick wall.
    d. a double thin wall.
    e. no wall, just a plasma membrane.

16. The cytoplasm of a bacterium
    a. is supported by the cytoskeleton.
    b. is supported by microtubules.
    c. is supported by keratin.
    d. has no internal support structure.
    e. is supported by folds in the interstitial membrane.

33

17. Passage through pores in the nuclear envelope is restricted to
    a. proteins, RNA, and protein-RNA complexes.
    b. lipids and glycolipids.
    c. DNA and RNA.
    d. RNA and protein-carbohydrate complexes.
    e. marker proteins for the plasma membrane.

18. Cells that secrete a large amount of lipids have more _____ than cells that do not secrete lipids.
    a. smooth endoplasmic reticulum
    b. glyoxysomes
    c. plastids
    d. rough endoplasmic reticulum
    e. liposomes

19. Enzymes embedded in the membrane of the smooth ER
    a. synthesize lipids.
    b. may be used for detoxification.
    c. synthesize carbohydrates.
    d. may act as a catalyst.
    e. All of these are correct.

20. A transport vesicle containing proteins from the rough endoplasmic reticulum will travel to the
    a. cell membrane.
    b. *cis* face of the Golgi apparatus.
    c. smooth endoplasmic reticulum.
    d. nucleus.
    e. *trans* face of the Golgi apparatus.

21. A lysosome's hydrolytic enzymes are activated by
    a. activating enzymes.
    b. low pH.
    c. the presence of food.
    d. high pH.
    e. contact with a membrane.

22. Which of the following is not an organelle?
    a. chloroplast
    b. mitochondrion
    c. ribosome
    d. leucoplast
    e. amyloplast

23. The RNA used to make proteins within the mitochondria comes from
    a. the nucleus.
    b. the RER.
    c. the mitochondrion.
    d. ribosomes in the cytoplasm.
    e. the nucleus.

24. Areas where ribosomes are assembled in the nucleus are called
    a. nuclei.
    b. cisternae.
    c. nucleoli.
    d. Golgi complexes.
    e. centrioles.

25. Mitochondrial enzymes for oxidative metabolism are
    a. on or within the surfaces of cristae.
    b. located on the outer membrane.
    c. in the matrix.
    d. floating freely in intermembrane space.
    e. in mitochondrial lysosomes.

26. High-speed transport over long distances in a cell requires
    a. microtubules along which to transport the material.
    b. a motor molecule such as dynein.
    c. a connector molecule.
    d. a vesicle or organelle to be transported.
    e. all of these.

27. Organelles are moved toward the center of a cell by
    a. dyneins.
    b. tubulin.
    c. actin.
    d. kinesin.
    e. vimentin.

28. If an organelle needs to be moved toward the plasma membrane of a cell, it should connect to the motor protein by
    a. kinectin.
    b. kinesin.
    c. keratin.
    d. actin.
    e. dynein.

29. Cells can change their shape by rapidly polymerizing and depolymerizing
    a. neurofilaments.
    b. intermediate filaments.
    c. vimentin fibers.
    d. actin filaments.
    e. guanosine triphosphate.

30. Eukaryotic flagella undulate by
    a. microtubules moving past each other.
    b. rotation of the basal body.
    c. contraction of actin fibers.
    d. the action of kinesin.
    e. changes in the gel-sol state.

ASSESSING YOUR KNOWLEDGE

Answers to the questions in the following sections test your ability to synthesize information gained from the chapter and to solve challenging problems on an exam or in everyday life.

Challenging Your Understanding—Answers

1. Eukaryotes have a nucleus and a nuclear envelope. They also have an endomembrane system for intracellular compartmentalization. Eukaryotes have organelles that are specialized membrane-bound compartments, a cytoskeleton to provide an internal protein scaffold, and vesicles that are small sacs that store and transport molecules throughout the cell. Eukaryotes also have lysosomes, which are vesicles containing digestive enzymes to rid the cell of particles, phagocytosized cells, or old organelles. Prokaryotes have a cell wall, which is absent in animal cells but present in plant cells. This structure protects the cell, maintains its shape, and prevents excess water loss or uptake.

2. Plant cells have a vacuole for storage and water balance. They also have chloroplasts for food synthesis and ATP production. Plants also have a cell wall for protection and preventing water loss and excess take up. Plant cells also have plasmodesmata for communication between adjacent cells. Animal cells contain a centriole, which is an organelle composed of microtubules that assist in organizing microtubules.

Key Terms—Answers

a. 16, b. 11, c. 27, d. 17, e. 24, f. 14, g. 3, h. 21, i. 23, j. 2, k. 10, l. 18, m. 22, n. 6, o. 1, p. 20, q. 4, r. 25, s. 12, t. 26, u. 5, v. 15, w. 9, x. 8, y. 7, z. 13, aa. 19, bb. 38, cc. 43, dd. 47, ee. 49, ff. 54, gg. 40, hh. 31, ii. 29, jj. 50, kk. 41, ll. 46, mm. 44, nn. 53, oo. 30, pp. 35, qq. 48, rr. 32, ss. 52, tt. 34, uu. 37, vv. 33, ww. 51, xx. 36, yy. 28, zz. 42, aaa. 39, bbb. 45.

Learning by Experience—Answers

| For the animal cell, compare your work to figure 4.6. |
| For the plant cell, compare your work to figure 4.7. |

Exercising Your Knowledge—Answers

As you check your answers, put a mark in the review (Rvw.) column for the answers you missed. If you didn't miss any, congratulations—you have mastered the chapter! If you missed some, review the section (Sect.) in the text where this concept is discussed. In order to develop an efficient review strategy, it is important that you understand what types of questions you missed. The questions with asterisks test more for understanding of the **concepts**, whereas the others test more for **detail**. *See the preface for learning strategies for concepts and for details.*

	Sect.	Rvw.
1. The DNA of prokaryotes is in a central area of the cell called the nucleoid, whereas the DNA of eukaryotes is in a membrane-bound nucleus.	4.1 --	--
*2. The internal components of the larger cell are more remote from the membrane, which is the place where substances are transferred into and out of the cell.	4.1	
3. The cell wall of a gram-positive bacterium is composed of a single thick wall, whereas the cell wall of a gram-negative bacterium is multilayered.	4.2	
4. Eukaryotic flagella undulate, whereas prokaryotic flagella rotate.	4.7	
*5. Lysosomes bud from the endomembrane system, while microbodies grow by incorporating chemicals such as proteins and lipids and dividing. Lysosomes contain a variety of enzymes for digesting food or organelles. Microbodies contain enzymes for converting a variety of chemicals to other forms.	4.4	
*6. See figure 4.13. Proteins are synthesized by ribosmes on the RER, and translocated to the internal compartment of the endoplasmic reticulum. Vesicles containing the proteins bud off the RER and travel to the *cis* face of the Golgi apparatus. The proteins packaged into vesicles that bud off the *trans* Golgi. Vesicles leaving the *trans* Golgi transport proteins to other cellular locations, or fuse with the plasma membrane.	4.4	
*7. Ribosomes in both locations synthesize proteins from amino acids. The proteins synthesized by ribosomes of the RER are to be exported from the cell, whereas those produced by the cytoplasmic ribosomes are for use within the cell.	4.4	
*8. To crawl, actin filaments rapidly polymerize, forcing the edge of the cell forward; the new region stabilizes, and contracted myosin motors along the actin filaments pull the cell contents toward the new region.	4.7	
9. Flagella and cilia have the same internal structure and are sheathed by the plasma membrane. Flagella are longer and less numerous than cilia.	4.7	
10. Mitochondria and chloroplasts arose from prokaryotes engulfed by other prokaryotes.	4.5	

*11. e	4.1		*21. b	4.4	
*12. b	4.1		*22. c	4.5	
13. b	4.3		*23. c	4.5	
14. c	4.2		24. c	4.3	
15. a	4.2		25. a	4.5	
16. d	4.2		26. e	4.6	
17. a	4.3		27. a	4.6	
*18. a	4.4		*28. b	4.6	
19. e	4.4		*29. d	4.7	
*20. b	4.4		*30. a	4.7	

CHAPTER 5 MEMBRANES

MASTERING KEY CONCEPTS

Along with chapter 4, this chapter is key to understanding many of the processes discussed in later chapters. Cells do most of their work with membranes and their inclusions.

5.1 Biological membranes are fluid layers of lipid.

- **Overview**: **Cell membranes** consist of **phospholipid bilayers**, **integral membrane proteins**, **peripheral membrane proteins,** and **cell surface markers**, such as glycoproteins and glycolipids. **Singer and Nicolson** proposed the **fluid mosaic model** for membranes, which suggests that globular proteins are inserted into the lipid bilayers with their nonpolar segments facing toward the interior of the bilayer and the polar segments facing out. Proteins that are inserted into the membrane are known as integral membrane proteins. Peripheral membrane proteins are associated with the surface of the membrane and act to reinforce its shape. Microscopic techniques have been used to study membrane structures. Accumulating evidence suggests that membranes are not homogeneous.
- **Details**: Know the identity, composition, and function of the four basic components of cell membranes.

5.2 Phospholipids: The membrane's foundation

- **Overview**: Phospholipid bilayers form spontaneously in water with the **nonpolar hydrophobic tails** aggregating toward one another, and the **polar head groups** hydrogen bonded with water on the outside to hold the membrane together. The nonpolar interior is a key component of the membrane because it prevents water-soluble substances from passing through it. **Membrane fluidity** is determined by its composition. In fluid membranes, phospholipids and unanchored proteins are free to move about in the bilayer, but always maintain the same orientation.
- **Details**: Understand the structure of a phospholipid, the polar and nonpolar components, and what happens when a phospholipid is place in water. Know the effect of increasing the concentrations of **saturated** or **unsaturated fats** in the membrane, and how **temperature** can affect membrane fluidity in single-celled organisms. Know how bacterial **fatty acid desaturates** prevent changes in fluidity.

5.3 Proteins: Multifunctional components

- **Overview**: Membrane proteins either are docked to the surface (peripheral proteins) by molecules that associate with phospholipids, or are anchored in the membrane (integral membrane proteins) with one or more **hydrophobic transmembrane domains** spanning the lipid bilayer. Transmembrane domains consist of hydrophobic amino acids typically arranged into α-helices (bacteriorhodopsin) or β-sheets (porins) and can allow either the passage of protons (bacteriorhodopsin) or molecules (porins). Other transmembrane proteins act as receptors that can activate a series of intracellular events.
- **Details**: Know the six key functions of membrane proteins, and the basic composition of transmembrane and peripheral proteins.

5.4 Passive transport across membranes moves down the concentration gradient.

- **Overview**: **Passive transport** across a membrane occurs by **diffusion,** which moves molecules or ions from one side to another depending on the **concentration gradient**. **Facilitated diffusion** requires a **carrier protein** to move ions, sugar, and amino acids down a concentration gradient across a membrane. Ions diffuse across membranes through **ion channels**. Cell membranes are **selectively permeable**, allowing specific molecules to diffuse from one side to the other by way of **channel proteins**, or **carrier proteins**. Water moves across membranes through water channels, **aquaporins**, toward the side with a higher concentration of **solutes** by **osmosis**. All forms of passive diffusion do not require or use energy.
- **Details**: Understand the difference between **simple diffusion** and **facilitated diffusion**. Know how channel and carrier proteins function. Know the three conditions that determine the direction of ion movement across membranes. Understand how water can pass through a hydrophobic membrane, and the direction of water flow when a cell is placed in a **hypertonic**, **hypotonic**, and **isotonic** solution. Know how different organisms maintain **osmotic balance**.

5.5 Active transport across membranes requires energy.

- **Overview**: Movement of substances across a membrane against the concentration gradient requires **active transport**. Active transport, such as that of the sodium-potassium pump, requires **carrier proteins** and the direct use of **ATP**. Transport of a molecule against its concentration gradient can also occur indirectly by capturing the energy released as another molecule moves down its concentration gradient in **coupled transport**.
- **Details**: Know how active transport uses ATP

directly or indirectly to move molecules or ions across membranes. Know the difference between **uniporters**, **symporters**, and **antiporters**.

5.6 Bulk transport utilizes endocytosis.

- <u>Overview</u>: Cells take up large molecules by **endocytosis** and release them by **exocytosis**, two energy-requiring processes. Endocytosis, such as **phagocytosis**, and **pinocytosis** occur by the plasma membrane enveloping particles and ingesting them in vesicles. Other materials are taken up by **receptor-mediated endocytosis**. **Exocytosis** removes materials from cells in secretory vesicles.

- <u>Details</u>: Know the details of how cells take up and release bulk material.

CHALLENGING YOUR UNDERSTANDING

1. List the four different functions of membranes. Briefly explain how membranes accomplish these functions and the cellular importance of each.

2. Distinguish between passive and active transport.

3. Detail the steps involved in the sodium-potassium pump. Indicate how this system directly uses ATP.

KEY TERMS

Match the numbered term with the definition that fits it best. Put the corresponding number in front of the appropriate definition.

1. phospholipid bilayer
2. fluid mosaic model
3. transmembrane proteins
4. diffusion
5. selectively permeable
6. ion channels
7. carrier proteins
8. channel proteins
9. facilitated diffusion

10. countertransport
11. osmotic concentration
12. aquaporins
13. osmosis
14. passive transport
15. hypertonic
16. hypotonic
17. isotonic
18. hydrostatic pressure

19. osmotic pressure
20. turgor pressure
21. endocytosis
22. phagocytosis
23. pinocytosis
24. active transport
25. coupled transport
26. antiporter
27. symporter

a. _____ The pressure of the cytoplasm pushing out against the cell membrane.
b. _____ If two solutions have unequal osmotic concentrations, the solution with the higher concentration of solutes.
c. _____ Carrier proteins that transport two molecules in the same direction.
d. _____ The net diffusion of water across a membrane toward a higher solute concentration.
e. _____ Movement of a molecule against its conc. gradient with energy created by moving a different molecule.
f. _____ A process requiring energy in which the plasma membrane envelops food particles and fluids.
g. _____ The force to stop osmotic flow that depends on the solute concentration in the cell and extracellular fluid.
h. _____ A collection of proteins that float in the lipid bilayer and provide channels for substances to cross.
i. _____ If two solutions have unequal osmotic concentrations, the solution with the lower concentration of solutes.
j. _____ The proposal that globular proteins are inserted in the lipid bilayer and are free to move around in, or on it.
k. _____ The movement of substances across a cell membrane up their concentration gradients requiring ATP.
l. _____ A characteristic of membranes, which allow only certain molecules or ions to pass across them.
m. _____ Internal hydrostatic pressure in plant cells caused by a high concentration of solutes in the central vacuole.
n. _____ Carrier proteins that transport two molecules in the opposite direction.
o. _____ The process by which a cell takes in a particulate material, or an organic fragment.
p. _____ A net movement of substances from regions of high concentration to regions of lower concentration.
q. _____ Proteins that bind to molecules to assist certain molecules across membranes.
r. _____ A process in which a carrier protein can help transport ions or molecules across the membrane.
s. _____ If two solutions have the same osmotic concentration and water diffuses in and out at the same rate.
t. _____ The concentration of all solutes in a solvent that determines the direction in which water will diffuse.
u. _____ Channels that possess a hydrated interior that spans the membrane allowing ions to pass in either direction.
v. _____ Use of energy released as one substance moves down its conc. gradient to eject another against its conc. gradient.
w. _____ Specialized channels that facilitate water flow across membranes in living cells.
x. _____ Proteins with a hydrophilic interior that provide an aqueous channel through which polar molecules pass.
y. _____ Movement of substances in and out of a cell without the cell having to expend energy.
z. _____ Sheets, two molecules thick, that form the foundation of a cell's membranes.
aa. _____ The process by which a cell takes in a liquid material from its surroundings.

LEARNING BY EXPERIENCE

Color coding the following illustration should help reinforce your understanding of the identity and location of membrane structures. Fill in the circle at the end of each title with the color you will use for that structure or substance, and color accordingly. Use figure 5.2 in your text as a guide.

Hydrophilic heads ○
Hydrophobic tail region ○
Peripheral protein ○

Glycoprotein ○
Glycolipid ○

Transmembrane protein ○
Filaments of cytoskeleton ○

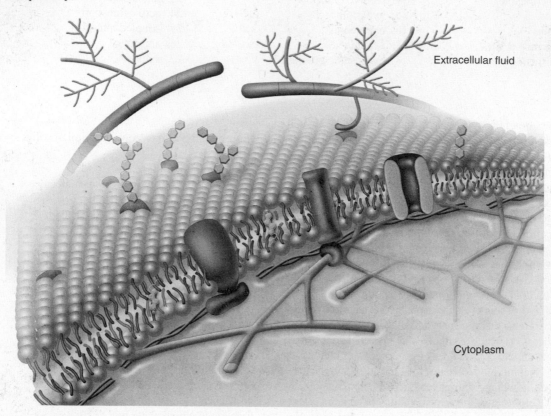

Extracellular fluid

Cytoplasm

EXERCISING YOUR KNOWLEDGE

Briefly answer each of the following questions in the space provided.

1. (a) How do double bonds in phospholipid tails affect the fluidity of the phospholipid layers? (b) Why do they have this effect?

2. What is the role of aquaporins in a cell membrane?

3. How do nonpolar regions of membrane proteins cause the proteins to be held in the membrane?

4. An algal cell with a hard cell wall is in a birdbath filled with hard water rich in calcium ions. As the water evaporates, the calcium concentration increases. (a) What passive transport mechanism would help the cell cope with the increased calcium outside the cell? (b) How would the microscopic appearance of the cell change as water is lost? (c) Why would the change in appearance occur?

5. A unicellular freshwater organism is carried into the ocean. (a) What term would you use to describe the osmotic concentration within the organism compared to the seawater? (b) How could the organism increase its osmotic pressure to reach equilibrium with the seawater if it has no pores for sodium ions? (Note that sea salt is more than sodium chloride.)

6. A free-living one-celled organism, lacking a cell wall, is collected from a stream containing mineral-rich water. The organism is placed on a microscope slide in distilled water. (a) What microscopic changes in the cell would be observed? (b) What are the causes of these changes?

7. Both cotransport of sugar molecules and countertransport of potassium ions utilize membrane transport proteins. (a) How do the binding locations differ between the two processes? (b) How is the sodium-potassium pump important to each?

8. What are the three characteristics of facilitated diffusion?

9. What two conditions determine the direction of movement through ion channels?

10. (a) What is the scientific term for "drinking" by a cell? (b) What is an example?

Circle the letter of the one best answer in each of the following questions.

11. A phospholipid has a phosphate group in place of
    a. one fatty acid.
    b. each of two fatty acids.
    c each of three fatty acids.
    d. a carbon in glycerol.
    e. none of these.

12. A lipid bilayer is held together by
    a. surface tension.
    b. double bonds in their fatty acids.
    c. the attraction of the phospholipid heads to each other.
    d. hydrogen bonding with water.
    e. the electrostatic attraction of phosphate groups for each other.

13. Red blood cells have a characteristic concave shape because of
    a. spectrin.
    b. dextrin.
    c. hemoglobin.
    d. hemocyanin.
    e. iron.

14. Equilibrium is reached in an aqueous solution when
    a. random motion stops.
    b. water molecules and dissolved molecules are moving at the same rate.
    c. the dissolved molecules or ions are equally distributed throughout the solution.
    d. molecular motion stops.
    e. there are the same number of water molecules as dissolved molecules.

15. _____ are transported across a semipermeable membrane by a particular carrier or pass through a particular channel.
    a. All water-soluble molecules or ions
    b. Certain water-soluble molecules or ions
    c. All insoluble molecules or ions
    d. Certain insoluble molecules or ions
    e. Only the smallest molecules or ions

16. Substances transported by facilitated diffusion
    a. move passively through specific channels from an area of greater concentration to one of lower concentration.
    b. are limited to solvents.
    c. must have movements coupled to those of other substances.
    d. may flow to a region of higher concentration by expenditure of energy.
    e. are restricted to only one direction through the membrane.

17. Carrier-mediated processes saturate because
    a. the carriers are too specific.
    b. the number of carriers in a membrane is limited.
    c. the concentration gradient is too strong.
    d. they run out of ATP.
    e. the concentration gradient is too weak.

18. To flow freely across a lipid membrane, water needs
    a. aquaporins.
    b. no special mechanism.
    c. active transport.
    d. coupled transport.
    e. polarity.

19. A net gain of water tends to occur in
    a. a hypoosmotic solution from an isosmotic solution.
    b. an isosmotic solution from a hyperosmotic solution.
    c. a hyperosmotic solution from a hypoosmotic solution.
    d. a hypoosmotic solution from a hyperosmotic solution.
    e. an isosmotic solution from another isosmotic solution of the same composition.

20. A cell engulfs an organism, enclosing it in a vesicle. The organism is partially digested in that vesicle. The cell then expels the indigestible waste through the membrane. The cell is using
    a. endocytosis followed by pinocytosis.
    b. pinocytosis followed by exocytosis.
    c. endocytosis followed by phagocytosis.
    d. phagocytosis followed by exocytosis.
    e. exocytosis followed by phagocytosis.

21. In receptor-mediated endocytosis,
    a. clathrin-coated pits indiscriminately engulf substances from the extracellular fluid.
    b. clathrin senses desirable molecules and traps them.
    c. clathrin transfers trapped substances to the cytoplasm.
    d. the clathrin lining acts as a pore, allowing molecules to flow into the cell.
    e. clathrin-coated pits close when an embedded protein receptor detects a target molecule.

22. Exocytosis is a process by which a cell
    a. passes substances out of the cell from vesicles.
    b. passes substances out of the cell through the membrane by osmosis.
    c. releases substances directly into the extracellular fluid through a pore.
    d. releases substances directly into the extracellular fluid through a pit.
    e. identifies substances in the environment.

23. Imagine a cell at equilibrium with its environment and without any transport mechanisms other than the sodium-potassium pump. If the pump functioned continuously, the cell would
    a. remain at equilibrium.
    b. experience increased hydrostatic pressure.
    c. become hyperosmotic.
    d. shrink.
    e. None of these are correct.

24. By a mechanism called cotransport,
    a. sugar moves inward down its concentration gradient while sodium moves inward up its concentration gradient.
    b. sodium moves outward against its concentration gradient while sugar moves inward down its concentration gradient.
    c. sugar and sodium both move inward down their concentration gradients.
    d. sodium moves inward down its concentration gradient while sugar moves inward up its concentration gradient.
    e. both sodium and sugar move outward up their concentration gradients.

25. The pressure that must be applied to stop the osmotic movement of water across a membrane is called _____ pressure.
    a. osmotic
    b. hydrostatic
    c. turgor
    d. isosmotic
    e. negative

26. Newer, softer portions of plants hold their shape largely by
    a. cell wall thickness.
    b. root pressure.
    c. turgor pressure.
    d. wood fibers.
    e. intermediate fibers.

27. Contractile vacuoles are important in maintaining water balance in some single-celled eukaryotes. These organelles remove water through
    a. exocytosis.
    b. endocytosis.
    c. isocytosis.
    d. extrusion.
    e. intrusion.

28. In coupled transport, needed ATP is often created by the movement of
    a. K^+.
    b. Na^+.
    c. glucose.
    d. both K^+ and Na^+.
    e. none of these.

29. A polar solute added to one side of a semipermeable membrane will cause water to
    a. flow to that side of the membrane.
    b. be repelled.
    c. dissolve the solute.
    d. flow to the other side of the membrane.
    e. become isosmotic.

30. Most healthy plant cells are turgid because they are _____ to their environment.
    a. isosmotic
    b. hyperosmotic
    c. hypoosmotic
    d. responsive
    e. immune

ASSESSING YOUR KNOWLEDGE

Answers to the questions in the following sections test your ability to synthesize information gained from the chapter and to solve challenging problems on an exam or in everyday life.

Challenging Your Understanding—Answers

1. Four functions of membranes: support, transport, recognition, reactions. Cells require membranes for support. Since the polar head groups in the phospholipid bilayer of membrane's hydrogen bond with surrounding water, the structure of the membrane is held together. This function of membranes is necessary in order to keep the contents of a cell together and intact. Cells require membranes for transport. While the phospholipid bilayer prevents most water-soluble substances from moving into cells, membranes contain protein passageways that permit the movement of certain substances across the membrane. This ability to transport and prevent transport is critical to the maintenance of a cell and to its communication with its environment. Cells require membranes for recognition. A number of cell surface receptors are located on the external side of the plasma membrane, providing for recognition of certain molecules that when bound either initiate a cascade of intracellular events (G protein-coupled receptors), or are allowed to pass through the plasma membrane by way of transmembrane proteins. Establishing recognition before substances are allowed to enter cells is important to maintain the proper internal composition and to receive the appropriate signals or molecules at the appropriate time. Cells require membranes for reactions. Membranes compartmentalize the cell and allow biochemical reactions in the cell to take place in different compartments at different times without being disturbed. This allows for regulation and control.

2. Passive transport includes the processes of diffusion, facilitated diffusion, and osmosis. All of these processes do not require the cell to expend any energy and involve the movement of ions, molecules, or water across a membrane from a region of high concentration to a region of lower concentration. Passive transport can require a channel protein, a carrier protein (facilitated diffusion), or specialized proteins like aquaporins (osmosis), but these processes always move a substance down its concentration gradient. Active transport includes the direct use of ATP (Na^+-K^+ pump), coupled transport, which indirectly uses ATP, or bulk transport such as endocytosis or exocytosis. All of these processes require energy because they involve the transport of ions, molecules, or other substances against their concentration gradients. Endocytosis (phagocytosis, and pinocytosis) and receptor-mediated endocytosis move large molecules into cells in vesicles. Exocytosis removes materials from vesicles after they fuse with the plasma membrane, releasing them into the extracellular space.

3. Steps involved in the sodium-potassium pump: a. The carrier protein in the membrane binds intracellular Na^+. b. ATP phosphorylates the carrier protein with Na^+ bound. c. Phosphorylation causes a conformational change in the protein, reducing its affinity for Na^+. Na^+ diffuses out of the cell. d. The phosphorylated carrier protein has a higher affinity to bind K^+. Extracellular K^+ binds to exposed sites. e. Binding of potassium causes dephosphorylation of the carrier protein. f. Dephosphorylation changes the protein back to its original conformation with a low affinity for K^+. K^+ diffuses into the cell and the cycle repeats. ATP is used directly by the carrier protein to move these two ions across the membrane. The energy stored in ATP is used to change the conformation of the carrier protein, which changes its affinity for either Na^+ ions or K^+ ions.

Key Terms—Answers

a. 18, b.15, c. 27, d. 13, e. 25, f. 21, g. 19, h. 3, i. 16, j. 2, k. 24, l. 5, m. 20, n. 26, o. 22, p. 4, q. 7, r. 9, s. 17, t. 11, u. 6, v. 10, w. 12, x. 8, y. 14, z. 1, aa. 23.

Learning by Experience—Answers

Refer to figure 5.2 of the text.

Exercising Your Knowledge—Answers

As you check your answers, put a mark in the review (Rvw.) column for the answers you missed. If you didn't miss any, congratulations—you have mastered the chapter! If you missed some, review the section (Sect.) in the text where this concept is discussed. In order to develop an efficient review strategy, it is important that you understand what types of questions you missed. The questions with asterisks test more for understanding of the **concepts**, whereas the others test more for **detail**. *See the preface for learning strategies for concepts and for detail.*

	Sect.	Rvw.
*1. (a) Double bonds in phospholipid tails increase fluidity. (b) Fluidity is increased because double bonds cause bends in the tails that interfere with the alignment of those tails.	5.1	
2. Aquaporins are specialized channels for water.	5.4	
*3. The protein cannot move in or out because such movement would drag nonpolar segments into contact with water.	5.3	

*4. (a) If the cell had a channel for calcium ions, they could diffuse into the cell and improve the balance across the membrane. (b) As water is lost, the cell membrane would shrink away from the cell wall. (See fig. 5.13). (c) The shrinkage would result from loss of turgor pressure by the cell.	5.4	
*5. (a) The concentration within the organism would be hypoosmotic to the seawater. (b) Since the sum of all ions constitutes the osmotic pressure, diffusion of any ions into the cell would increase its osmotic pressure.	5.4	
*6. (a) An observer would see the cell swell and, perhaps, burst. (b) A cell adjusted to a high mineral environment would be hyperosmotic to the distilled water. Therefore, water would flow into the cell by osmosis.	5.4	
*7. (a) In the cotransport of sugar, both the sugar and the sodium bind to the transport protein on the same side of the membrane. In the countertransport of potassium, the potassium and sodium bind to the transport protein on opposite sides of the membrane. (b) Both mechanisms depend upon a sodium-rich environment outside the cell.	5.5	
8. Facilitated diffusion is specific and passive, and can be saturated.	5.4	
9. The direction of movement through ion channels is determined by the concentrations on either side of the membrane and the voltage across the membrane.	5.4	
10. (a) Pinocytosis is cell "drinking." (b) An example is mammalian egg cells "nursing" from the surrounding cells.	5.6	
11. a	5.2	
12. d	5.2	
*13. a	5.1	
*14. c	5.4	
*15. b	5.4	
*16. a	5.4	
*17. b	5.4	
*18. a	5.4	
*19. c	5.4	
*20. d	5.6	
*21. e	5.6	
22. c	5.6	
23. d	5.5	
24. a	5.5	
25. d	5.4	
26. c	5.4	
27. d	5.6	
28. b	5.5	
29. d	5.4	
30. b	5.4	

CHAPTER 6 ENERGY AND METABOLISM

MASTERING KEY CONCEPTS

Living is hard work; energy must be expended to perform all the processes that occur in organisms. Chemical reactions, cellular functioning, running, growing, and reproducing all require energy. In obtaining and processing energy, the cells of organisms follow the laws of thermodynamics, use catalysts to speed up chemical reactions, and employ regulated, multistep pathways that have evolved over time.

6.1 The flow of energy in living systems

- **Overview**: **Energy**, or the capacity to do work, can take many forms in biological systems, and it is typically measured in terms of **heat**, or **calories**. The Sun provides energy for living organisms. **Oxidation-reduction (redox)** reactions play a key role in the transfer of energy between biological molecules.
- **Details**: Know the different forms in which energy can exist. Understand the difference between **kinetic energy** and **potential energy**. Know the result of a redox reaction in terms of which atom is oxidized and which is reduced.

6.2 The laws of thermodynamics describe how energy changes.

- **Overview**: The laws of thermodynamics govern changes in energy states. **The First Law of Thermodynamics** states that energy cannot be created or destroyed, so the total amount of energy in the universe remains constant. **The Second Law of Thermodynamics** states that **entropy**, or disorder, is constantly increasing. **Chemical bonds** are the primary location of energy storage and release in cells. The direction in which a reaction proceeds is determined solely by the **difference in free energy (ΔG)** between reactants and products. An **exergonic** reaction **($-\Delta G$)** has an equilibrium favoring the products and releases free energy as heat. Such reactions proceed spontaneously but require **activation energy**. An **endergonic** reaction **($+\Delta G$)** has an equilibrium favoring the reactants and requires an input of energy. **Catalysts** accelerate reactions by lowering the activation energy required to initiate a reaction.
- **Details**: Know the characteristics of endergonic and exergonic reactions in terms of the change in free energy (ΔG), and the spontaneity of the reactions. Understand how the components in the reaction: $\Delta G = \Delta H - T\Delta S$ are affected in exergonic and endergonic reactions. Know two ways in which the rate of a reaction can be increased. Understand how catalysts affect chemical reactions.

6.3 ATP is the energy currency of life.

- **Overview**: ATP, **adenosine triphosphate**, is a key molecule for short-term energy storage in cells. The terminal two phosphate bonds of ATP are high-energy bonds. **Hydrolysis** of these two bonds can be used by cells to drive endergonic reactions. Synthesis and hydrolysis of ATP are in a constant, cyclic process in cells. While ATP hydrolysis releases energy, ATP synthesis requires energy.
- **Details**: Know the structures of **AMP, ADP,** and **ATP**. Understand how ATP stores energy.

6.4 Enzymes are biological catalysts.

- **Overview**: **Enzymes** increase the rate of a reaction by lowering the **activation energy**, without being consumed or altered themselves. An enzyme binds specifically to its **substrate** through its **active site**. Substrate binding can alter the shape of an enzyme (**induced fit**), or can facilitate the binding of other substrates. Proteins and RNAs (**ribozymes**) can act as enzymes, and some enzymes require **cofactors**, or **coenzymes**. Many reactions occur within **multienzyme complexes**, which increases catalytic efficiency. Optimum temperature and pH can also increase enzymatic efficiency. **Inhibitors** and **activators** can affect the activity of some enzymes.
- **Details**: Know the benefits of reactions occurring in multienzyme complexes. Know the difference between how **competitive** and **noncompetitive inhibitors** affect an enzyme. Know how temperature and pH affect enzymes.

6.5 Metabolism is the chemical life of the cell.

- **Overview**: The **metabolism** of an organism is determined by all of the chemical reactions that occur within it. Many of these reactions occur in a stepwise manner in defined **biochemical pathways**. Some of these pathways are regulated. One mechanism of regulation is **feedback inhibition**, where the end product of a pathway can inhibit the enzyme that catalyzes the first reaction in the same pathway.
- **Details**: Understand how biochemical pathways may have evolved backward.

CHALLENGING YOUR UNDERSTANDING

1. Describe the importance of the following in biological systems: Enzymes, ATP, coenzymes in oxidation-reduction reactions.

2. Describe how an enzyme binds its substrate and carries out the catalytic process. Use the following words in your answer: active site, enzyme-substrate complex, induced fit, stress, activation energy, rate of reaction, not altered.

3. Briefly describe two different ways that an enzyme can be inhibited.

KEY TERMS

Match the numbered term with the definition that fits it best. Put the corresponding number in front of the appropriate definition.

1. kinetic energy
2. potential energy
3. thermodynamics
4. calorie
5. oxidation-reduction reaction
6. First Law of Thermodynamics
7. heat
8. Second Law of Thermodynamics
9. oxidation
10. free energy

11. endergonic
12. exergonic
13. activation energy
14. catalysis
15. substrates
16. enzyme
17. active site
18. competitive inhibitor
19. noncompetitive inhibitor
20. allosteric inhibitor

21. activators
22. coenzyme
23. anabolism
24. adenosine triphosphate (ATP)
25. metabolism
26. biochemical pathways
27. feedback inhibition

a. _____ A reaction that expends energy to make or transform chemical bonds.
b. _____ Regulation in which the end-product of a pathway inhibits the enzyme that catalyzes the initial reaction.
c. _____ A pocket or cleft on the surface of an enzyme to which its substrate binds.
d. _____ Binds to a specific site on an enzyme and keeps it in its active configuration thereby increasing its activity.
e. _____ The process by which an atom or a molecule loses an electron.
f. _____ The process of stressing chemical bonds to lower the activation energy needed to initiate a reaction.
g. _____ A protein or RNA that increases the rate of a specific reaction, and is not consumed or altered in the reaction.
h. _____ A substance that binds to an enzyme changing its shape and preventing it from binding to its substrate.
i. _____ Objects that are not actively moving but have the capacity to do so have this stored energy.
j. _____ The total of all chemical reactions carried out by an organism.
k. _____ Energy cannot be created or destroyed; it can only change from one form to another.
l. _____ Any reaction that requires an input of energy and therefore does not occur spontaneously.
m. _____ The nucleotide that powers almost every energy-requiring process in cells.
n. _____ Nonprotein organic molecule that assists an enzyme in its function.
o. _____ The laws of this branch of chemistry govern the changes in energy state.
p. _____ A substance that binds to a specific region on an enzyme and reduces its enzyme activity.
q. _____ A measure of the random motion of molecules. During each conversion, some energy dissipates as this.
r. _____ A sequence of enzyme-catalyzed reactions where the product of one reaction is the substrate for the next.
s. _____ The disorder, or entropy, of the universe is constantly increasing.
t. _____ Molecules that bind to enzymes and undergo chemical reactions.
u. _____ The amount of energy actually available to break and subsequently form other chemical bonds in a system.
v. _____ This is the energy of motion. Moving objects perform work by causing other matter to move.
w. _____ A substance that competes with the substrate of an enzyme for binding to the same active site.
x. _____ The transfer of electrons from one atom to another while bonds are being made or broken.
y. _____ The extra energy required to destabilize existing chemical bonds and initiate a chemical reaction.
z. _____ A reaction that releases excess free energy as heat and can occur spontaneously if activation energy is supplied.
aa. _____ The heat required to raise the temperature of one gram of water one degree Celsius.

LEARNING BY EXPERIENCE

1. Complete the following graphs to illustrate an endergonic reaction and an exergonic reaction. Be sure to label the reactants, products, and activation energy. Indicate for each reaction whether the products or reactants have more energy.

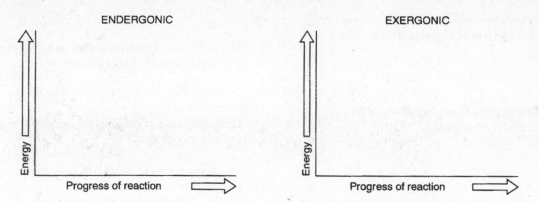

2. If an enzyme has the shape shown below, draw what its substrate would look like. Use these caricatures to show how enzymes function and then how drastic changes in temperature or pH affect the enzyme.

Enzyme	Substrate	Function	Temperature or pH change

3. As the energy currency of life, ATP uses its high-energy bonds to drive endergonic reactions. In the following symbolic diagram of ATP, use a squiggly line to indicate where the high-energy bonds are, and use a straight line to show where the regular covalent bonds are.

| Phosphate Group |

| Phosphate Group |

| Phosphate Group |

| Adenine |

| Ribose |

EXERCISING YOUR KNOWLEDGE

Briefly answer each of the following questions in the space provided.

1. Why is there a reduction reaction every time there is an oxidation reaction?

2. Briefly explain how biochemical pathways may have evolved backwards.

3. The literal translations of endergonic and exergonic are "inward energy" and "outward energy," respectively. Explain what this means.

4. Why do organisms or cells need to have only very small quantities of a particular enzyme?

5. Are all enzymes proteins?

6. How do enzymes speed up chemical reactions?

7. Many vitamins are parts of coenzymes. How does this help explain why it's important to have vitamins in our diets if we wish to stay healthy?

8. Acid rain is a serious environmental problem in many parts of the world. Using your knowledge of enzyme activity, explain why acid rain harms and even kills organisms.

9. Why do organisms use fats and carbohydrates, rather than ATP, as long-term energy storage molecules?

10. Why is feedback inhibition an efficient way to regulate biochemical pathways?

Circle the letter of the one best answer in each of the following questions.

11. In the reaction, $\Delta G = \Delta H - T\Delta S$, H is equal to the
    a. electron potential.
    b. activation energy.
    c. enthalpy.
    d. free energy.
    e. entropy.

12. Which of the following has more potential energy?
    a. a reduced molecule
    b. the same molecule when it is oxidized
    c. the same molecule when it is neither oxidized nor reduced
    d. There is no way of telling.

13. The energy of random molecular motion is called
    a. activation energy.
    b. potential energy.
    c. free energy.
    d. enthalpy.
    e. heat.

14. Cells primarily use energy from which of the following to do work?
    a. catalysts
    b. chemical reactions
    c. heat
    d. entropy
    e. cofactors

15. Which of the following is true of an endergonic reaction?
    a. $T\Delta S$ is greater than ΔH between reactants and products.
    b. The products contain less free energy than the reactants.
    c. It has an equilibrium favoring the products.
    d. ΔG is positive and the reaction is not spontaneous.
    e. More than one of the above are correct.

16. Competitive inhibition can be overcome by which of the following?
    a. increasing the substrate concentration
    b. lowering the activation energy
    c. binding of an activator
    d. modifying an enzyme's active site
    e. binding of an allosteric inhibitor

17. The loss of an electron by a molecule is called
    a. oxidation.
    b. reduction.
    c. induced fit.
    d. enthalpy.
    e. allosteric inhibition.

18. Useful energy decreases because much energy is lost from systems in the form of
    a. sunlight.
    b. ATP.
    c. heat.
    d. enzymes.
    e. inhibitors.

19. Enzymes
    a. make endergonic reactions proceed spontaneously.
    b. lower the activation energy of a reaction.
    c. are needed in large quantity because they are used up so quickly during catalysis.
    d. are usually carbohydrates.
    e. can interact with a wide range of substrate molecules.

20. The conversion of carbon dioxide and water to carbonic acid occurs much faster in cells because of the presence of the enzyme carbonic anhydrase. How much does the enzyme speed up the conversion?
    a. 10 times
    b. 100 times
    c. 1,000 times
    d. 1,000,000 times
    e. 10,000,000 times

21. Which of the following statements about enzymes is true?
    a. Different types of cells contain different sets of enzymes.
    b. Substrates can induce a better fit with their enzyme.
    c. Different enzymes have different optimal temperature and pH requirements.
    d. All of these are true.
    e. None of these are true.

22. Noncompetitive inhibitors
    a. bind to a product to prevent its activity.
    b. increase the activation energy.
    c. bind to the active site.
    d. alter the shape of an enzyme.
    e. disrupt the function of cofactors.

23. The names of most enzymes end in the suffix
    a. –ose.
    b. –ase.
    c. –ate.
    d. –yst.
    e. –cid.

24. Which of the following is NOT true regarding substrate-enzyme interactions?
    a. Substrate binding induces enzymes to change shape.
    b. The rate of an enzymatic reaction is limited by substrate binding.
    c. Enzymes can bring together more than one substrate.
    d. Enzymes stress the chemical bonds of a substrate.
    e. One enzyme can utilize multiple substrates.

25. How many high energy bonds does ATP have?
    a. 0
    b. 1
    c. 2
    d. 3
    e. 4

26. Which of the following is NOT an advantage of reactions that occur in multienzyme complexes?
    a. All reactions are regulated as a unit.
    b. Products are not able to diffuse away.
    c. Enzymes more readily bind their substrates.
    d. Enzymes are not subject to inhibition.
    e. Unwanted side reactions are eliminated.

27. Consider the hypothetical biochemical pathway Q → R → S → T → U. Which step in this pathway most likely evolved last (most recently)?
    a. Q → R
    b. R → S
    c. S → T
    d. T → U
    e. Q → U

28. The high-energy bonds of ATP
    a. are extremely stable.
    b. have a high activation energy.
    c. are found within the adenine subunit.
    d. All of these are true.
    e. None of these are true.

29. Which of the following is most likely to serve as an allosteric inhibitor providing feedback inhibition to a biochemical pathway?
    a. the initial substrate in the pathway
    b. the first intermediate product of the pathway
    c. the second intermediate product of the pathway
    d. the end (final) product of the pathway
    e. Any of these would work effectively

30. Metabolic reactions that expend energy to make or transform chemical bonds are called
    a. allosteric reactions.
    b. induced-fit reactions.
    c. anabolic reactions.
    d. catabolic reactions.
    e. cofactor reactions.

ASSESSING YOUR KNOWLEDGE

Answers to the questions in the following sections test your ability to synthesize information gained from the chapter and to solve challenging problems on an exam or in everyday life.

Challenging Your Understanding—Answers

1. Enzymes: Enzymes carry out most of the catalysis in living organisms. These catalysts lower the activation energy of reactions required for new bonds to form, allowing cellular reactions to take place much more quickly. Enzymes bind a specific substrate, or bring together two substrates, and stress some of the internal bonds of these substrates, allowing reactions to take place more rapidly. Enzymes are not altered or consumed in these reactions, so only very small amounts are required within the cell. Different cells contain different sets of enzymes.

ATP: In cells, ATP powers almost every energy-requiring process. It is required for making sugars, driving endergonic reactions, and supplying activation energy, actively transporting substances across membranes, cell movement, and growing. ATP has two high-energy bonds that are easily broken by hydrolysis. Breaking these bonds can transfer a significant amount of energy. Therefore, the synthesis and the hydrolysis of ATP are critical cellular processes.

Coenzymes in oxidation-reduction reactions: Nonprotein organic molecules and modified nucleotides serve as coenzymes to help enzymes function. In oxidation-reduction reactions, coenzymes serve as electron acceptors of electrons that are passed from the active site of enzymes. The coenzyme passes the electrons to a different enzyme, which releases them to the substrates in another reaction. When electrons combine with protons to form hydrogen atoms, coenzymes shuttle hydrogen atoms, and thus energy, from one enzyme to another within the cell. Acting as electron/proton shuttlers, coenzymes play a critical role in cellular oxidation-reduction reactions.

2. A specific substrate binds to an enzyme's active site, forming an enzyme-substrate complex. Substrate binding to its enzyme slightly changes the shape of the enzyme, leading to a better induced fit between the enzyme and its substrate. Binding allows proper alignment of the substrate molecule to stress or distort some of its internal bonds. This stress makes it easier to break these bonds and lowers the activation energy that is required for the reaction. The rate of the reaction increases because of the lower activation energy. The products of the reaction are released from the enzyme and the enzyme which is not altered, or consumed by the reaction, starts over by binding more substrate.

3. An enzyme can be inhibited by competitive inhibition, noncompetitive inhibition, or allosteric inhibition. In competitive inhibition, a molecule binds to an enzyme's active site and prevents the regular substrate from binding. In noncompetitive inhibition, a molecule binds to an enzyme in a place other than its active site. This binding changes the conformation of the enzyme and in doing so alters the shape of the active site. This change prevents the regular substrate from being able to bind to the enzyme's active site.

Key Terms—Answers

a. 23, b. 27, c. 17, d. 21, e. 9, f. 14, g. 16, h. 19, i. 2, j. 25, k. 6, l. 11, m. 24, n. 22, o. 3, p. 20, q. 7, r. 26, s. 8, t. 15, u. 10, v. 1, w. 18, x. 5, y. 13, z. 12, aa. 4.

Learning by Experience—Answers

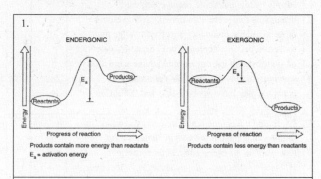

1.

2. A substrate must fit into the active site of the enzyme. Drastic changes in temperature or pH change the shape of the active site as the enzyme denatures, making it impossible for the substrate to bind properly and therefore impossible for the enzyme to function.

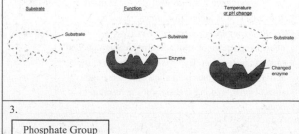

3.

Exercising Your Knowledge—Answers

As you check your answers, put a mark in the review (Rvw.) column for the answers you missed. If you didn't miss any, congratulations—you have mastered the chapter! If you missed some, review the section (Sect.) in the text where this concept is discussed. In order to develop an efficient review strategy, it is important that you understand what types of questions you missed. The questions with asterisks test more for understanding of the **concepts**, whereas the others test more for **detail**. *See the preface for learning strategies for concepts and for detail.*

	Sect.	Rvw.
*1. The electron has to go someplace. The molecule being oxidized is losing an electron; another molecule picks up that electron and is therefore reduced.	6.1	
*2. The first catalyzed reactions were likely simple, one-step reactions that brought two molecules together in various combinations. Eventually, the supply of the two molecules ran out and only organisms capable of making those molecules by some other means could survive. A new reaction was then added in which the depleted molecule was made from another molecule which was also present in the environment. When the supply of this molecule became depleted, organisms that were able to make it from some other available precursor, survived. When that molecule became depleted, only organisms capable of synthesizing it from another source were able to survive. In this way the final reactions in a pathway may have evolved first and the earlier reactions evolved later.	6.5	
*3. In an endergonic reaction, energy is added in—the products have more energy than do the reactants. In an exergonic reaction, energy is released or sent out—the products have less energy than the reactants.	6.2	
*4. Enzymes are not changed or consumed when they catalyze reactions. At the end of the process, they are exactly the way they were at the start, so they can be used over and over again.	6.4	
*5. No; evidence indicates that RNA can also act as an enzyme at times (ribozymes).	6.4	
*6. Enzymes speed chemical reactions by decreasing the amount of activation energy needed to start the reaction. By binding substrates at their active sites, enzymes help align substrates and stress bonds, making it easier for the reaction to occur.	6.4	
*7. Coenzymes help enzymes function, and enzymes control the chemistry of life. Without their necessary vitamins, coenzymes couldn't function properly, and thus their enzymes couldn't function properly, resulting in improper metabolism.	6.4	
*8. Acid rain alters the pH of soil and water. Organisms living in or using the soil and water will be exposed to different pH levels than normal. If the change in pH is too great, the organism's enzymes may denature. When enzymes lose their proper shape, they cannot function properly, and biochemical pathways slow down or stop. Organisms cannot live if their metabolism is disrupted too severely.	6.4	
*9. The high-energy phosphate bonds of ATP, while a good source of immediate energy, are not stable and are easily broken so would not be good for long-term storage of energy. Fats and carbohydrates, on the other hand, have much more stable covalent bonds in which energy can be stored efficiently for long periods.	6.3	
*10. Feedback inhibition prevents energy and materials from being wasted on unnecessary reactions. As the final product of a pathway builds up, it inhibits the first step in the pathway from occurring. This shuts down the pathway (which takes energy to run) and prevents more product from being produced when there is already product present.	6.5	
11. c	6.2	
*12. a	6.1	
13. e	6.2	
*14. b	6.2	
15. d	6.2	
16. a	6.4	
17. a	6.1	
18. c	6.2	
*19. b	6.4	
20. d	6.4	
*21. d	6.1	
22. d	6.4	
23. b	6.4	
24. e	6.4	
25. c	6.3	
26. d	6.4	
*27. a	6.5	
28. e	6.3	
*29. d	6.5	
30. e	6.5	

CHAPTER 7 HOW CELLS HARVEST ENERGY

MASTERING KEY CONCEPTS

Work must be done if an organism or cell is to stay alive, and energy must be expended for work to be done. All organisms—from prokaryotes and protists to fungi, plants, and animals—obtain energy by carrying out cellular respiration. They break down energy-rich food molecules and then use the released energy to synthesize ATP, the universal energy currency for organisms. The food molecules are oxidized, and ADP is reduced to ATP.

7.1 Cellular respiration oxidizes food molecules.

- **Overview**: **Energy metabolism** in cells involves enzyme-facilitated **redox reactions** that take energy from the digestion food and convert it to **ATP**. This is done in a series of redox reactions that transfer electrons and the energy associated with them to **electron acceptors**. During **respiration**, glucose is oxidized to CO_2 and electrons are transferred through a number of electron carriers, including NAD^+ and the **electron transport chain**. The ultimate goal of respiration is the production of ATP, which can be used to drive endergonic reactions or perform a number of cellular processes.

- **Details**: Know the difference between **aerobic respiration, anaerobic respiration**, and **fermentation**. Know the two molecules that make up NAD^+ and the function of each. Know the reactants and the products of respiration and the role of NAD^+.

7.2 A summary of the oxidation of glucose

- **Overview**: The oxidation (catabolism) of glucose occurs in four stages, **glycolysis, pyruvate oxidation, the Krebs cycle, electron transport chain** followed by **chemiosmosis**. In the process of glycolysis, glucose is converted to two energy-rich pyruvate molecules through a series of 10 reactions. The net yield is two molecules of ATP, produced by **substrate-level phosphorylation**, and two molecules of NADH for **oxidative phosphorylation**. Pyruvate oxidation converts two pyruvate molecules into CO_2 and two molecules of acetyl-CoA. For each molecule of pyruvate oxidized, one NAD^+ is reduced to NADH. Each molecule of acetyl-CoA combines with oxaloacetate and is converted to citric acid to initiate the Krebs cycle. The Krebs cycle produces one molecule of ATP by substrate-level phosphorylation and several electrons. These electrons are transferred from NADH into the electron transport chain, which uses the energy to pump protons across a membrane. This proton gradient is used by **ATP synthase** to produce ATP by chemiosmosis.

- **Details**: Know the four basic stages of glucose oxidation and the reactants and end products of each. Know how ATP is synthesized by substrate-level phosphorylation and by ATP synthase in oxidative phosphorylation. Know how much ATP is produced and by which method for each of the four stages of glucose oxidation.

7.3 Glycolysis: Splitting glucose

- **Overview**: **Glycolysis** occurs in the cytoplasm and the net reaction is: **glucose + 2ADP + 2P$_i$ + 2NAD$^+$ → 2 pyruvate + 2ATP + 2NADH + 2H$^+$ + 2H$_2$O**. Glycolysis begins with the addition of two high-energy phosphates from two ATP molecules to convert glucose to a six-carbon sugar diphosphate. This molecule is cleaved into two three-carbon sugar phosphates. Five subsequent reactions convert the two three-carbon sugar phosphates to two molecules of pyruvate through a series of intermediates that produces two NADH molecules and transfers phosphate to ADP in two different reactions to form two molecules of ATP. **Pyruvate** is oxidized to **acetyl-CoA** and **NADH is recycled** to NAD^+ by either **aerobic respiration** in the presence of O_2, or pyruvate is reduced or partially reduced to oxidize NADH back to NAD^+ by **fermentation** in the absence of O_2.

- **Details**: Know the three changes that occur in glycolysis and the two problems that result from it. Understand the two ways that NADH can be recycled into NAD^+ and how these two methods differ.

7.4 The oxidation of pyruvate produces acetyl-CoA.

- **Overview**: **Pyruvate** is oxidized to produce **acetyl-CoA** and CO_2, in the **mitochondria** by a **multienzyme complex**. This reaction reduces one molecule of NAD^+ to NADH. The net reaction is: **pyruvate + NAD$^+$ + CoA → acetyl-CoA + NADH + CO2 + H$^+$** for each molecule of pyruvate.

- **Details**: Know the reactants and the products of pyruvate oxidation.

7.5 The Krebs cycle

- **Overview**: The **Krebs cycle** shuttles acetyl-CoA into a cycle that is a series of **nine reactions,** which occur in the matrix of the mitochondria to extract electrons, produce ATP, and complete the oxidation of glucose. A two-carbon group from each molecule of acetyl-CoA enters the cycle and **two CO$_2$ molecules, one ATP, and four pairs of electrons are produced**

- **Details**: Know the three segments of the Krebs cycle. Know the purpose of the Krebs cycle and the products generated from one turn of the cycle. Know what types of reactions are involved in the cycle. Understand the conversion from the reactants to products in each reaction and be able to follow the flow of electrons.

7.6 The electron transport chain and chemiosmosis

- **Overview**: **NADH** molecules carry electrons to the inner mitochondrial membrane where they are transferred by **mobile electron carriers** to three different membrane protein complexes, **NADH dehydrogenase**, **bc_1 complex**, and **cytochrome oxidase complex**. **$FADH_2$** is located in the inner mitochondrial membrane and transfers its electrons to **ubiquinone**, which carries them to the bc_1 complex. Each of the membrane complexes uses a portion of the electrons' energy to pump protons out of the matrix into the intermembrane space, creating an **electrochemical gradient** across the membrane. **ATP synthase** uses the energy released as the protons move down their concentration gradient across the membrane to synthesize ATP.
- **Details**: Know the components of the electron transport chain and how electrons from NADH and $FADH_2$ feed their electrons into this chain. Understand how and where the **proton gradient** is formed, and how it is used to synthesize ATP. Know the structure of ATP synthase and how this enzyme functions.

7.7 Energy yield of aerobic respiration

- **Overview**: Aerobic respiration yields **38 ATP in bacteria**, and yields a predicted 36 ATP in eukaryotes (2 less than prokaryotes because transport of NADH produced in glycolysis from the cytoplasm to the mitochondria costs 1 ATP per NADH). The **actual yield for eukaryotes (30 ATP)** is even lower because the inner mitochondrial membrane leaks some protons and the proton gradient generated by chemiosmosis is often used for purposes other than ATP synthesis.
- **Details**: Know how the energy yield from aerobic respiration is calculated (**how much ATP each molecule of NADH and $FADH_2$ produces**). Understand why the high-energy yield from aerobic respiration led to the evolution of heterotrophs.

7.8 Regulation of aerobic respiration

- **Overview**: The key reactions of glycolysis, the Krebs cycle, and fatty acid breakdown are controlled by the **relative levels of ATP and ADP**. When ATP levels are high, an enzyme in the glycolytic pathway, one in the pyruvate oxidation pathway, and one in the Krebs cycle are inhibited. All of these enzymes catalyze irreversible reactions and, therefore, act at

critical steps in their respective pathways when the substrates that they act on will be committed to the pathway.
- **Details**: Know the **key enzymes** in glycolysis, pyruvate oxidation, and the Krebs cycle that high levels of ATP inhibit.

7.9 Oxidation without O_2

- **Overview**: When oxygen is not present, some organisms can still respire **anaerobically** using **inorganic molecules** as final **electron acceptors** for an electron transport chain. Less free energy is released from anaerobic respiration than aerobic respiration. Cells that cannot use inorganic molecules for respiration must rely solely on glycolysis for ATP production. In these cells, electrons are donated to organic molecules in **fermentation**, recycling NAD^+, and converting pyruvate to **ethanol** or **lactate**, allowing only a partial oxidation of glucose.
- **Details**: Know examples of **inorganic and organic molecules** that are used as final electron acceptors. Understand why **aerobic respiration is more advantageous** to organisms than both anaerobic respiration and fermentation. Know how an oxidation-reduction reaction is used to convert pyruvate to ethanol or lactate, and recycle NAD^+ in the process of fermentation.

7.10 Catabolism of proteins and fats

- **Overview**: Major metabolic pathways are linked by **common intermediates**. Proteins are broken down into amino acids, which are **deaminated** and converted into carbon chains that can enter glycolysis or the Krebs cycle. Fats are broken down into fatty acids and glycerol. Fatty acids are oxidized in the matrix of the mitochondria converting them to acetyl groups that are then combined with coenzyme A to form acetyl-CoA by **β-oxidation**. Polysaccharides are broken down into sugars, which are used in the glycolytic pathway, and nucleic acids are broken down into nucleotides, which are used in the Krebs cycle.
- **Details**: Know the **key intermediates** that link the major metabolic pathways. Understand how **nucleotides**, **amino acids**, **sugars**, and **fatty acids** can feed into the glycolytic pathway or the Krebs cycle.

7.11 Evolution of metabolism

- **Overview**: Major events in the history of metabolism include the ability of organisms to harness chemical bond energy, to carry out glycolysis, to carry out anaerobic photosynthesis, to substitute H_2O for H_2S in photosynthesis, to carry out nitrogen fixation, and to carry out aerobic respiration.

CHALLENGING YOUR UNDERSTANDING

Fill in the blanks in the pathway of cellular respiration and then answer the questions below.

CELLULAR RESPIRATION

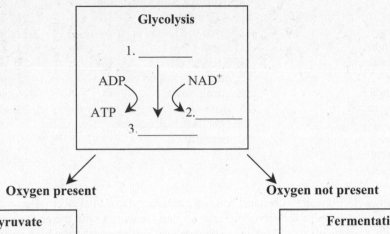

Glycolysis

1. _____

ADP NAD$^+$

ATP 2._____

3._____

Oxygen present   Oxygen not present

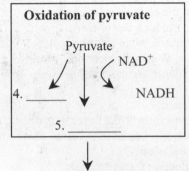

Oxidation of pyruvate

Pyruvate

NAD$^+$

4. _____

NADH

5. _____

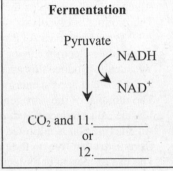

Fermentation

Pyruvate

NADH

NAD$^+$

CO$_2$ and 11._____

or

12._____

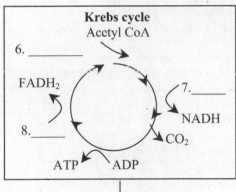

Krebs cycle

Acetyl CoA

6. _____

FADH$_2$

7._____

NADH

8._____

CO$_2$

ATP ADP

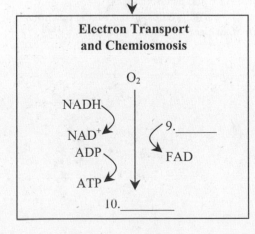

Electron Transport and Chemiosmosis

O$_2$

NADH

NAD$^+$

ADP

ATP

9._____

FAD

10._____

13. How many molecules of ATP are required for glycolysis? _____
14. What is the net yield of ATP from glycolysis? _____
15. How many molecules of NAD$^+$ are reduced in glycolysis per six-carbon glucose molecule? _____
16. How many molecules of pyruvate are produced from one glucose molecule? _____
17. How many molecules of NAD$^+$ are reduced per molecule of glucose in the oxidation of pyruvate? _____
18. How many molecules of the product formed by the oxidation of pyruvate are produced per glucose? _____
19. How many turns does the Krebs cycle make to break down one molecule of glucose? _____
20. How many molecules of NADH are generated by the Krebs cycle per molecule of glucose? _____
21. How many molecules of FADH$_2$ are produced by the Krebs cycle per molecule of glucose? _____
22. How many molecules of ATP are produced by the Krebs cycle per molecule of glucose? _____
23. How many theoretical molecules of ATP are produced per glucose molecule by the electron transport chain? ___
24. How many total NADH molecules are produced per molecule of glucose by respiration? _____
25. How many total FADH$_2$ molecules are produced per molecule of glucose by respiration? _____

KEY TERMS

Match the numbered term with the definition that fits it best. Put the corresponding number in front of the appropriate definition.

1. autotrophs
2. heterotrophs
3. digestion
4. dehydrogenations
5. nicotinamide adenine dinucleotide (NAD^+)
6. aerobic respiration
7. anaerobic respiration
8. fermentation
9. substrate-level phosphorylation

10. oxidative phosphorylation
11. ATP synthase
12. glycolysis
13. acetyl-CoA
14. Krebs cycle
15. electron transport chain
16. chemiosmosis
17. pyruvate
18. NADH dehydrogenase
19. deamination

20. β-oxidation
21. ethanol
22. lactate
23. catabolic
24. phosphofructokinase
25. pyruvate dehydrogenase
26. citrate synthase
27. ubiquinone

a. _____ High-energy electrons from chemical bonds are transferred to a final electron acceptor, which is oxygen.
b. _____ An enzyme that couples the reentry of protons into the matrix with the phosphorylation of ADP to ATP.
c. _____ The product of glycolysis, which is oxidized when O_2 is present to produce acetyl-CoA.
d. _____ ATP synthase makes ATP with energy from a proton gradient generated by an electron transport chain.
e. _____ The mobile electron carrier that passes electrons to the bc_1 complex, or accepts electrons from $FADH_2$.
f. _____ Yeast cells produce this as a by-product of fermentation following decarboxylation of pyruvate.
g. _____ Reactions that harvest energy when chemical bonds are broken.
h. _____ The removal of the nitrogen-containing side group from an amino acid.
i. _____ Muscle cells produce this during fermentation in the transfer of electrons from NADH back to pyruvate.
j. _____ An enzyme that is inhibited by high levels of ATP and is the main control point in pyruvate oxidation.
k. _____ Organisms that live on the organic compounds produced by other organisms.
l. _____ The use of inorganic molecules as final electron acceptors for an electron transport chain.
m. _____ Conversion of fatty acids into acetyl groups that are combined with coenzyme A to form acetyl-CoA.
n. _____ A series of 10 reactions used to catabolize glucose and produce ATP by substrate-level phosphorylation.
o. _____ Reactions in which electrons lost are accompanied by protons.
p. _____ NADH passes electrons to this membrane-embedded enzyme in the electron transport chain.
q. _____ ATP is formed by transfer of a phosphate group directly to ADP from a phosphate-bearing intermediate.
r. _____ An enzyme in the glycolytic pathway that catalyzes the first reaction of glycolysis that is not readily reversible.
s. _____ The utilization of an electrochemical gradient to drive the synthesis of ATP.
t. _____ Oxidation of pyruvate in the mitochondria produces this substrate of the Krebs cycle and CO_2.
u. _____ The enzymatic breakdown of large molecules into smaller ones.
v. _____ The electrons generated by glycolysis are donated to organic molecules, and NAD^+ is recycled.
w. _____ An enzyme in the Krebs cycle that is inhibited by high levels of ATP.
x. _____ Organisms that harvest energy from the Sun and convert it into chemical energy by photosynthesis.
y. _____ Nine reactions that oxidize the acetyl group from pyruvate, produce ATP and electrons.
z. _____ A cofactor of oxidation-reduction reactions that accepts electrons, along with protons, in enzymatic reactions.
aa. _____ A set of electron carriers that produce potential energy in the form of an electrochemical gradient.

LEARNING BY EXPERIENCE

1. Complete the following chart outlining the various carbon compounds involved in cellular respiration.

Stage	Beginning carbon compound(s)	Carbon end product
Glycolysis	Glucose	a. _____
Oxidation of pyruvate	Pyruvate	b., c. _____
Krebs cycle	d., e. _____	f., g. _____
h. _____	i. _____	Various (for example, lactate, CO_2, ethanol)

2. For each of the listed stages of cellular respiration, indicate which of the following substances are produced in that stage. Substances: ATP, FAD, $FADH_2$, NAD^+, NADH. A substance may be listed more than once.

Stage	Substance(s) produced
Glycolysis	a., b. _____
Oxidation of pyruvate	c. _____
Krebs cycle	d., e., f. _____
Electron transport and chemiosmosis	g., h., i. _____
Fermentation	j. _____

3. Fill in the blanks to complete the story of what happens in the electron transport chain of aerobic respiration. Each blank should be filled with the name of one substance.

   a. Electrons are taken from _____ and _____, which

   b. then revert to _____ and _____. The electrons are passed along the transport chain, a series of

   carrier molecules (electron acceptors) such as cytochrome c.

   c. The final electron acceptor is _____, which

   d. combines with the electrons and H^+ to form _____.

   e. As the electrons travel the transport chain, they provide energy to drive proton pumps, which causes

   _____ to be produced by chemiosmosis.

4. The stages of cellular respiration occur in specific places in a cell. Indicate where each of the following stages takes place by writing its name in the appropriate location on the following diagram. Stages: glycolysis, oxidation of pyruvate, Krebs cycle, electron transport and chemiosmosis, fermentation.

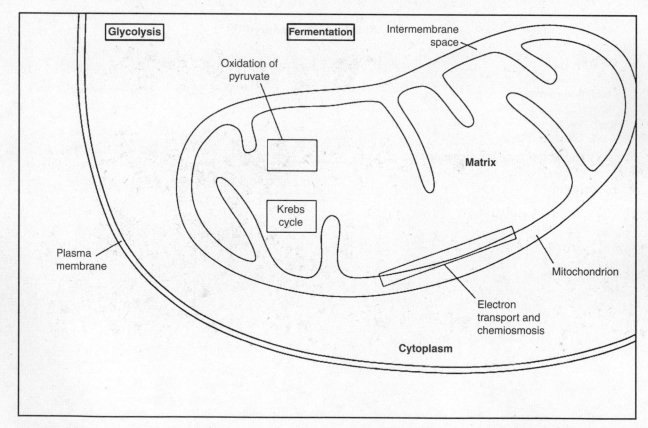

EXERCISING YOUR KNOWLEDGE

Briefly answer each of the following questions in the space provided.

1. Why are the terms "autotroph" (self-feeder) and "heterotroph" (fed by others) accurate descriptors?

2. Glycolysis is inefficient compared to aerobic respiration in terms of the amount of ATP produced per molecule of glucose. What are the yields of ATP from just glycolysis versus from aerobic respiration? If glycolysis is so inefficient, why do virtually all organisms still carry it out?

3. Why is acetyl-CoA so important in catabolic metabolism?

4. Why is energy released when glucose is oxidized during aerobic respiration?

5. Theoretically, 36 molecules can be produced from every molecule of glucose that goes through aerobic respiration, but the actual yield is closer to 30. Why?

6. Drowning, suffocation, and carbon monoxide poisoning all kill a person by preventing sufficient oxygen from reaching his or her cells. Using what you know about aerobic respiration, explain why lack of oxygen kills a person.

7. Some animals that live in deserts and other very dry places can survive without having to drink water. They obtain some water from the food they eat, but many also rely on "metabolic water." What do you suppose metabolic water is? (Hint: Think about what happens at the end of the electron transport chain.)

8. Briefly describe the breakdown of each of the cellular macromolecules. How do the monomeric subunits of each enter glycolysis or the Krebs cycle? What are the key intermediates that connect the major metabolic pathways?

9. Why do wines contain alcohol, but not more than about 12%?

10. If fermentation is so inefficient compared with aerobic respiration, why does it still exist?

Circle the letter of the one best answer in each of the following questions.

11. Glycolysis produces ATP by which of the following?
    a. electrochemical gradient
    b. substrate-level phosphorylation
    c. oxidative phosphorylation
    d. ATP synthase
    e. reduction of cofactors

12. Which of the following organisms carries out cellular respiration?
    a. corn plant
    b. goat
    c. yeast
    d. bacterium
    e. all of these

13. The vast majority of ATP produced in a cell is made by the action of
    a. a rotary motor.
    b. a proton gradient.
    c. ATP synthase.
    d. all of these.
    e. none of these.

14. Which enzyme is the key point of control in glycolysis?
    a. isomerase
    b. phosphoglycerate kinase
    c. hexokinase
    d. phosphofructokinase
    e. pyruvate kinase

15. The Krebs cycle includes how many oxidation reactions?
    a. 0
    b. 1
    c. 2
    d. 3
    e. 4

16. $FADH_2$ is located in the _____
    a. intermembrane space.
    b. inner mitochondrial membrane.
    c. mitochondrial matrix.
    d. bc_1 complex.
    e. NADH dehydrogenase complex.

17. The proper sequence of stages in glycolysis is
    a. ATP generation, oxidation, glucose priming, cleavage and rearrangement.
    b. cleavage and rearrangement, glucose priming, ATP generation, oxidation.
    c. glucose priming, cleavage and rearrangement, oxidation, ATP generation.
    d. oxidation, cleavage and rearrangement, ATP generation, glucose priming.
    e. glucose priming, ATP generation, oxidation, cleavage and rearrangement.

18. At the end of glycolysis, energy is located in
    a. pyruvate.
    b. ATP.
    c. NADH.
    d. all of these.
    e. none of these.

19. What substance is produced at the end of the oxidation of pyruvate and feeds into the Krebs cycle?
    a. glucose
    b. acetyl-CoA
    c. carbon dioxide
    d. FAD
    e. NADH

20. The Krebs cycle starts and ends with the four-carbon molecule
    a. citrate.
    b. pyruvate.
    c. ethanol.
    d. lactate.
    e. oxaloacetate.

21. NADH is produced during
    a. glycolysis.
    b. the oxidation of pyruvate.
    c. the Krebs cycle.
    d. all of these.
    e. none of these.

22. Which of the following is NOT part of the electron transport chain?
    a. NADH dehydrogenase
    b. ubiquinone
    c. pyruvate dehydrogenase
    d. bc_1 complex
    e. cytochrome c

23. In a chemical reaction, the larger the amount of energy released in a single step, the greater the amount of _____ that is likely to be produced.
    a. heat
    b. ATP
    c. CO_2
    d. water
    e. O_2

24. During what stage of cellular respiration is the most ATP synthesized?
    a. Krebs cycle
    b. electron transport and chemiosmosis
    c. glycolysis
    d. fermentation
    e. oxidation of pyruvate

25. What role does O_2 play in aerobic respiration?
    a. It plays no role.
    b. It combines with acetyl-CoA at the start of the Krebs cycle.
    c. It is given off as a by-product during the oxidation of pyruvate.
    d. It combines with water to help drive the formation of ATP.
    e. It is the final electron acceptor at the end of the electron transport chain.

26. During chemiosmosis in aerobic respiration, protons are pumped
    a. out of the cell.
    b. out of the mitochondria into the cell cytoplasm.
    c. out of the cell cytoplasm into the outer compartment (intermembrane space) of the mitochondria.
    d. out of the cell cytoplasm into the matrix of the mitochondria.
    e. out of the matrix into the outer compartment of the mitochondria.

27. What happens when there are high levels of ATP in a cell?
    a. Feedback inhibition shuts down aerobic respiration.
    b. Aerobic respiration is speeded up.

c. The synthesis of fat stops.
d. Aerobic respiration becomes more efficient.
e. Multienzyme complexes denature.

28. Oxidizing which of the following substances yields the most energy?
    a. proteins
    b. glucose
    c. fatty acids
    d. alcohol
    e. water

29. What substance is regenerated by fermentation?
    a. O_2
    b. acetyl-CoA
    c. ATP
    d. NAD^+
    e. glucose

30. Which of the following metabolic processes is believed to have evolved most recently?
    a. nitrogen fixation
    b. aerobic respiration
    c. glycolysis
    d. oxygen-forming photosynthesis
    e. anaerobic photosynthesis

ASSESSING YOUR KNOWLEDGE

Answers to the questions in the following sections test your ability to synthesize information gained from the chapter and to solve challenging problems on an exam or in everyday life.

Challenging Your Understanding—Answers

1. glucose, 2. NADH, 3. pyruvate, 4. CO_2,

5. Acetyl-CoA, 6. oxaloacetate, 7. NAD^+, 8. FAD,

9. $FADH_2$, 10. H_2O, 11. and 12. ethanol, lactate,

13. 2, 14. 2, 15. 2, 16. 2, 17. 2, 18. 2, 19. 2,

20. 6, 21. 2, 22. 2, 23. 32, 24. 10, 25. 2.

Key Terms—Answers

a. 6, b. 11, c. 17, d. 10, e. 27, f. 21, g. 23, h. 19, i. 22, j. 25, k. 2, l. 7, m. 20, n. 12, o. 4, p. 18, q. 9, r. 24, s. 16, t. 13, u. 3, v. 8, w. 26, x. 1, y. 14, z. 5, aa. 15.

Learning by Experience—Answers

1.	a. pyruvate
	b., c. acetyl-CoA, CO_2
	d., e. acetyl-CoA, oxaloacetate
	f., g. oxaloacetate, CO_2
	h. fermentation
	i. pyruvate
2.	a., b. ATP, NADH
	c. NADH
	d., e., f. ATP, NADH, $FADH_2$
	g., h., i. ATP, NAD^+, FAD
	j. NAD^+
3.	a. NADH, $FADH_2$
	b. NAD^+, FAD
	c. O_2
	d. H_2O
	e. ATP

4. Glycolysis and fermentation occur in the cell cytoplasm; oxidation of pyruvate and the Krebs cycle occur in the mitochondrion matrix; electron transport and chemiosmosis occur in and across the mitochondrion inner membrane.

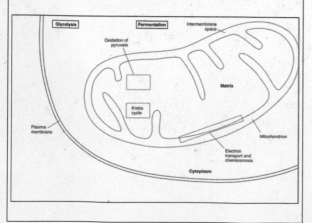

Exercising Your Knowledge—Answers

As you check your answers, put a mark in the review (Rvw.) column for the answers you missed. If you didn't miss any, congratulations—you have mastered the chapter! If you missed some, review the section (Sect.) in the text where this concept is discussed. In order to develop an efficient review strategy, it is important that you understand what types of questions you missed. The questions with asterisks test more for understanding of the **concepts**, whereas the others test more for **detail**. *See the preface for learning strategies for concepts and for detail.*

	Sect.	Rvw.
*1. Autotrophs photosynthesize and make their own food (energy-rich organic molecules such as glucose) from inorganic molecules and solar energy; they feed themselves. Heterotrophs cannot make their own food (for example, glucose); they must obtain it from others, already made.	7.1	
*2. 2 ATP from glycolysis and theoretically 36 ATP from glycolysis plus aerobic respiration, but closer to 30 in actuality. The retention of glycolysis is a good example that evolution is an incremental process and builds on the past. Glycolysis evolved before aerobic respiration; the slate was not wiped clean and started anew with aerobic respiration, but rather aerobic respiration was added onto the biochemical pathway.	7.7, 7.3	
*3. Almost all molecules that are catabolized for energy are converted into acetyl-CoA; the acetyl-CoA then gets channeled into fat synthesis or ATP synthesis depending on the available energy supplies and needs of the cell.	7.1	
*4. The positions of the valence electrons shift; as the glucose is oxidized, they are drawn closer to the oxygen atoms than they were to the carbon atoms in glucose. The closer an electron is to the nucleus of an atom, the lower its energy; energy is "lost" (released) as the electron moves closer to the nucleus.	7.1	
*5. The inner membrane of the mitochondrion is leaky, allowing some protons to cross back over without going through the special channels that generate ATP. Also, the proton gradient is used for other purposes than just making ATP.	7.7	

*6. Oxygen is the final electron acceptor at the end of the electron transport chain in aerobic respiration. If no oxygen is present, the preceding carrier molecules in the chain cannot pass on their electrons, and the chain becomes backlogged or jammed and stops functioning. Without the electron transport chain, there is no chemiosmotic synthesis of ATP, and chemiosmosis is responsible for producing 32 of the 36 ATP gained from a molecule of glucose. Without chemiosmosis, ATP cannot be produced rapidly enough to do all the work that has to be done to keep a person alive (for example, nerves firing, heart pumping, biochemical pathways operating). The body has only a few seconds' supply of ATP available at any one time; it must constantly make more. | 7.6 |

*7. Metabolic water is the water formed at the end of the electron transport chain of aerobic respiration. Oxygen, the final electron acceptor, combines with electrons and hydrogen ions to make water; it is called metabolic water because it is produced internally by the organism's metabolism rather than being taken in through drinking or in food. Metabolic water can be used to help meet the water needs of cells and organisms. | 7.6 |

*8. Fats are broken down into fatty acids plus glycerol. Fatty acids are oxidized in the mitochondrial matrix by β-oxidation. The entire fatty acid is converted into acetyl groups and combined with coenzyme A to form acetyl-CoA, which is a key intermediate in the breakdown of glucose. This acetyl-CoA can be fed into the Krebs cycle. Proteins are broken down into individual amino acids that then undergo deamination. The carbon chain is converted into a molecule that can enter glycolysis or the Krebs cycle. Polysaccharides are broken down into monosaccharides that can then enter glycolysis and the Krebs cycle. Nucleic acids are broken down into individual nucleotides that can be used in the Krebs cycle. The key intermediates that link all of theses metabolic pathways are pyruvate and acetyl-CoA. By using a small number of common intermediates, oxidation of food molecules can be linked allowing interconversion of different types of molecules. Thus, the forward and reverse reactions to either breakdown molecules or to synthesize molecules can share common enzymes. | 7.10 |

*9. The yeast that live on the grapes and in the grape juice carry out fermentation in the anaerobic conditions in the vats or bottles where the wine is being made. Ethanol is an end product of their fermentation and is added to the wine. However, the ethanol is toxic to the yeast, and when it reaches levels of about 12% in the confined system (i.e., vat or bottle), it kills the yeast, stopping the fermentation and any further production of ethanol. | 7.9 |

*10. Fermentation may be less efficient than aerobic respiration, but it is better than nothing, and is the only option under anaerobic conditions. Fermentation allows organisms to live in otherwise uninhabitable anaerobic environments and also allows normally aerobic cells and organisms to keep functioning (albeit at a reduced level) under temporarily anaerobic conditions (for example, muscle cells during strenuous exercise). | 7.9 |

11. b	7.2
*12. e	7.3
13. d	7.6
14. d	7.8
15. e	7.5
16. b	7.6
17. c	7.3
*18. d	7.3
19. b	7.4
20. e	7.5
21. d	7.2
22. c	7.6
*23. a	7.1
*24. b	7.7
*25. e	7.6
26. e	7.6
27. a	7.8
28. c	7.10
29. d	7.9
30. b	7.11

CHAPTER 8 PHOTOSYNTHESIS

MASTERING KEY CONCEPTS

Life as we know it depends on photosynthesis. Photosynthetic organisms capture solar energy and convert it to chemical energy. This chemical energy is then utilized by the photosynthesizers and by all other organisms to fuel their life processes. Photosynthesizers use the energy in light to make energy-rich ATP and NADPH, which in turn supply the energy necessary to reduce carbon dioxide to glucose. Along the way, oxygen (O_2) is produced as a by-product. Photosynthesis is the source of all the oxygen that we and all other aerobic organisms depend on for life.

8.1 What is photosynthesis?

- **Overview**: **Photosynthesis** uses light energy to synthesize glucose from CO_2 and H_2O. Photosynthesis primarily takes place in the leaves of plants, which contain specialized organelles called **chloroplasts**. Algae and some prokaryotes carry out photosynthesis as well. Photosynthesis occurs in three stages. The first two, capturing energy from sunlight and using the energy to make ATP and reduce NADP+, are **light-dependent** reactions occurring in the **thylakoid membrane**. The third stage, **carbon fixation**, which forms organic molecules from CO_2, is a **light-independent** reaction occurring in the **stroma**. The overall process of photosynthesis is summarized by the equation: $6CO_2 + 12H_2O + light \rightarrow C_6H_{12}O_6 + 6H_2O + 6O_2$, the **reverse of respiration**.
- **Details**: Understand the **structure of a plant leaf**, the **organelles in a plant cell**, and the **arrangement of the chloroplast**. Know the similarities and the differences between **oxygenic** and **anoxygenic** photosynthesis. Understand the **function of photosystems** and the pigments within.

8.2 The discovery of the photosynthetic process

- **Overview**: The process by which plants increase their mass has been studied for many years. Scientific experiments demonstrated that water and soil alone could not account for the increase in the mass of a plant, and that plants could split carbon dioxide into carbon and oxygen, releasing O_2 gas into the air, and at the same time forming carbohydrates from CO_2 and H_2O. The fact that photosynthesis requires light-dependent and light-independent reactions came from the observation that at low levels of light intensity, photosynthesis could be accelerated by increasing the light, but not the temperature or the CO_2, while at high light intensities, increasing temperature, or the CO_2 concentration, but not the light intensity

accelerated photosynthesis. Later, **ATP** and **NADPH** were found to reduce CO_2 to make glucose.

- **Details**: Understand the experiments that elucidated the details of photosynthesis and the origin of the O_2 in the balanced equation. Know the three conclusions that could be reached from Hill's experiments on isolated chloroplasts.

8.3 Pigments capture energy from sunlight.

- **Overview**: A **photon** is a particle of light with an energy content inversely proportional to the wavelength of light. **Pigments** found in the membrane of **thylakoids** absorb light energy (photons) in the visible range. **Chlorophylls** (green plants), **carotenoids** (green plants, other organisms), and **phycobiloproteins** (cyanobacteria, algae) are pigments that absorb photons within narrow energy ranges. Used together they efficiently absorb photons over a larger range of **absorption spectrum**.
- **Details**: Understand the role of **chlorophyll *a***, **chlorophyll *b***, carotenoids, and phycobiloproteins. Understand the relationship between **wavelength** and **energy**. Know the general structure of chlorophyll.

8.4 Photosystem organization

- **Overview**: Clusters of chlorophyll *a*, accessory pigment molecules, and associated proteins are arranged into **photosystems** on the surface of the photosynthetic membrane. These clusters of chlorophyll molecules, not just one pigment molecule, absorb light. Light is captured by the **antenna complex** and its excitation energy is channeled from one pigment molecule to the next to the **reaction center** chlorophylls, which pass an excited electron to an electron acceptor.
- **Details**: Know the roles of the antenna complex and the reaction center. Understand why photosystems saturate at O_2 levels lower than expected for the number of individual chlorophyll molecules.

8.5 Cells use the energy and reducing power captured by the light-dependent reactions to make organic molecules.

- **Overview**: The **light-dependent reactions** take place in the internal **thylakoid membrane** and are organized into four stages: **primary photoevent**, **charge separation**, **electron transport**, and **chemiosmosis**. Some bacteria use only a single photosystem and **cyclic photophosphorylation** that produces ATP, but not NADPH. Plants use two photosystems that work sequentially (**noncyclic photophosphorylation**). Two electrons are excited by the absorption of one photon of light by **photosystem II**. These two electrons are passed to **photosystem I** through a series of cytochromes and the **b_6-f complex**. This complex uses energy released to pump protons across the thylakoid membrane, creating an electrochemical gradient that is used by **ATP synthase** to make ATP. Electrons lost from photosystem II are replaced by **oxidizing water**. The absorption of light by **photosystem I** excites two electrons also. The two electrons excited in photosystem I are passed to **$NADP^+$**, reducing it to **NADPH**. Electrons lost from photosystem I are replaced by electrons transported from photosystem II. Plants can **short-circuit photosystem I** to **produce additional ATP** by passing electrons back to the b_6-f complex, rather than to $NADP^+$.

- **Details**: Know the general arrangement of the **photosystems**, **b_6-f complex**, **NADP reductase**, and **ATP synthase** in the thylakoid membrane. Understand the transfer of electrons between these complexes, how and where the proton gradient is formed, and how ATP is synthesized. Know how noncyclic photophosphorylation differs from cyclic photophosphorylation.

8.6 Carbon fixation: The Calvin cycle

- **Overview**: Carbon is fixed in the **Calvin cycle** using the energy and the reducing potential of NADPH produced from the light-dependent reactions. The Calvin cycle occurs in three stages, **carbon fixation**, **reduction**, and **regeneration of RuBP**. Carbon is fixed by combining inorganic CO_2 with the organic molecule, **RuBP,** in a reaction catalyzed by **rubisco**, forming a six-carbon intermediate that splits into two three-carbon molecules, **3-phosphoglycerate** (PGA). Using ATP and NADPH from the light-dependent reactions, PGA is reduced to **glyceraldehyde 3-phosphate** (G3P) and RuBP is recycled. Two molecules of G3P are used to make one molecule of glucose by running reactions in the glycolytic pathway in reverse. For every six molecules of CO_2 fixed, a molecule of glucose can be synthesized. The net equation is:
  $6CO_2$ + 18ATP + 12NADPH + water → 2 G3P + 16P_i + 18ADP + 12$NADP^+$.
- **Details**: Understand how the products of the light reactions are used to power the Calvin cycle to fix CO_2 and make glucose in the **light-independent reactions**. Know the key components of the Calvin cycle. Know what parts of the light-independent reactions indirectly require light. Understand the **connection between photosynthesis and respiration**.

8.7 Photorespiration

- **Overview**: Besides carbon fixation, the enzyme **rubisco** catalyzes the **oxidation of RuBP,** which releases CO_2 by **photorespiration** and reduces the yield of photosynthesis. **C_3 plants** use only the Calvin cycle to fix carbon in **mesophyll cells**. **C_4 plants** initially fix carbon using **PEP carboxylase** in mesophyll cells to produce **malate,** which is then transported to the **bundle sheath cells** where malate is decarboxylated to form pyruvate and CO_2. In bundle sheath cells, the level of CO_2 is high and the Calvin cycle is efficient, minimizing photorespiration. Thus, C_4 plants use both the C_3 and C_4 pathways in different cells. **CAM plants** use both the C_3 and the C_4 pathways in the same cell, but at different times to minimize photorespiration and water loss. At night, the C_4 pathway fixes carbon when the stomata are open. During the day, organic acids are decarboxylated to yield high levels of CO_2 to drive the C_3 pathway when the stomata are closed.

Details: Know how **rubisco** catalyzes both carboxylation and oxidation of **RuBP**. Know what conditions favor **photorespiration**. Understand why **PEP carboxylase** is advantageous to rubisco in carbon fixation. Understand the difference between the **C_3 and C_4 pathways** of carbon fixation.

CHALLENGING YOUR UNDERSTANDING

Study the diagram below and figures 8.13-8.16 in the text and then answer the questions below.

PHOTOSYNTHESIS

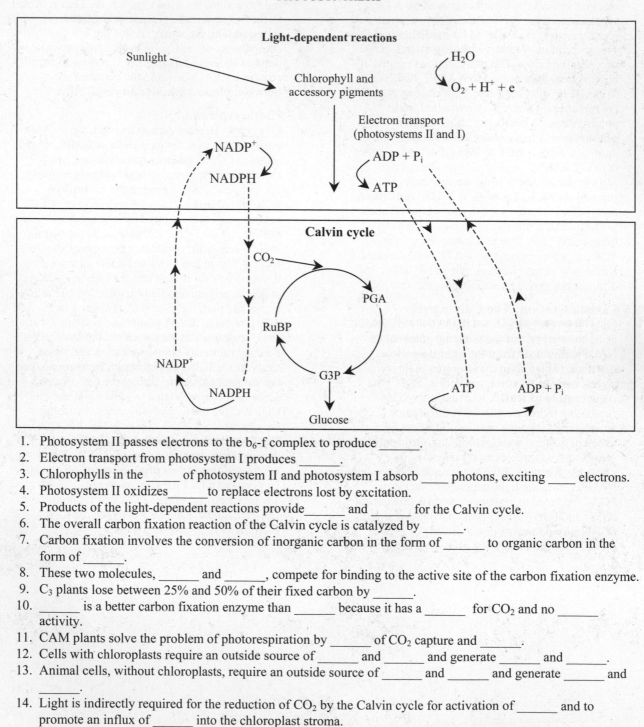

1. Photosystem II passes electrons to the b_6-f complex to produce _____.
2. Electron transport from photosystem I produces _____.
3. Chlorophylls in the _____ of photosystem II and photosystem I absorb ____ photons, exciting ____ electrons.
4. Photosystem II oxidizes_____to replace electrons lost by excitation.
5. Products of the light-dependent reactions provide_____ and _____ for the Calvin cycle.
6. The overall carbon fixation reaction of the Calvin cycle is catalyzed by _____.
7. Carbon fixation involves the conversion of inorganic carbon in the form of _____ to organic carbon in the form of _____.
8. These two molecules, _____ and _____, compete for binding to the active site of the carbon fixation enzyme.
9. C_3 plants lose between 25% and 50% of their fixed carbon by _____.
10. _____ is a better carbon fixation enzyme than _____ because it has a _____ for CO_2 and no _____ activity.
11. CAM plants solve the problem of photorespiration by _____ of CO_2 capture and _____.
12. Cells with chloroplasts require an outside source of _____ and _____ and generate _____ and _____.
13. Animal cells, without chloroplasts, require an outside source of _____ and _____ and generate _____ and _____.
14. Light is indirectly required for the reduction of CO_2 by the Calvin cycle for activation of _____ and to promote an influx of _____ into the chloroplast stroma.
15. The production of glucose from glyceraldehyde 3-phosphate uses part of the _____ pathway run in reverse.

KEY TERMS

Match the numbered term with the definition that fits it best. Put the corresponding number in front of the appropriate definition.

1. light-dependent reactions
2. stomata
3. light-independent reactions
4. chloroplast
5. photosystem I
6. carbon fixation
7. absorption spectrum
8. photon
9. pigments
10. chlorophylls
11. action spectrum
12. carotenoids
13. phycobiliproteins
14. photosystem II
15. cyclic photophosphorylation
16. photoelectric effect
17. noncyclic photophosphorylation
18. C_3 pathway
19. enhancement effect
20. photorespiration
21. C_4 pathway
22. crassulacean acid metabolism
23. thylakoid membrane
24. stroma
25. antenna complex
26. reaction center
27. cytochrome/b_6-f complex

a. _____ A semiliquid substance surrounding the thylakoid membrane.

b. _____ Carbon fixation occurs only through the Calvin cycle and the enzyme rubisco.

c. _____ Accessory pigments in cyanobacteria composed of proteins attached to a tetrapyrrole group.

d. _____ A particle of light that acts as a discrete bundle of energy.

e. _____ The incorporation of O_2 into RuBP that undergoes additional reactions to release CO_2.

f. _____ Perform a valuable role in capturing light energy and also in scavenging free radicals.

g. _____ Occurs when a photon transfers energy to electrons and its strength depends on the wavelength of light.

h. _____ It uses the energy from the passage of electrons to move protons across the thylakoid membrane.

i. _____ Specialized opening in the leaf that closes to conserve water.

j. _____ This complex uses energetic electons to reduce $NADP^+$ to NADPH during photosynthesis.

k. _____ The capture of CO_2 occurs in one cell and the decarboxylation occurs in an adjacent cell.

l. _____ The series of reactions used in photosynthesis to convert inorganic carbon in CO_2 into carbohydrates.

m. _____ A light-harvesting complex that captures photons and channels them to the reaction center in a photosystem.

n. _____ A continuous phospholipid bilayer organized into flattened sacs that contains photosynthetic pigments.

o. _____ Two photosystems acting in series where electrons ejected from one photosystem do not return.

p. _____ The range and efficiency of photons a pigment is capable of absorbing.

q. _____ Processes in photosynthesis involving the capture of energy from light to make ATP and reduce $NADP^+$.

r. _____ The main photosynthetic pigment in plants and cyanobacteria containing a porphyrin ring.

s. _____ The third, light-independent stage of photosynthesis that takes place via a cyclic series of reactions.

t. _____ A transmembrane protein-pigment complex where the photochemical reactions occur in a photosystem.

u. _____ A light-energized electron ejected from a photosystem reaction center returns, producing ATP but no NADPH.

v. _____ Molecules that absorb light energy in the visible range and have a characteristic absorption spectrum.

w. _____ A specialized organelle in plants and algae that carries out the photosynthetic process.

x. _____ A complex that absorbs two photons, exciting electrons that are passed to plastoquinone and the b_6-f complex.

y. _____ The rate of photosynthesis when red and far-red light are together is greater than the sum of individual rates.

z. _____ Perform both the C_3 and the C_4 pathways in the same cell at different times.

aa. _____ The relative effectiveness of different wavelengths of light in promoting photosynthesis.

LEARNING BY EXPERIENCE

1. Name the two parts of the chloroplast indicated here, and state what stage of photosynthesis takes place in each.

	Name	**Stage**
a.		
b.		

2. Each of the following people carried out experiments that helped advance our understanding of photosynthesis. Match each person with the discovery.

_____ a. Jan Baptista van Helmont (early 1600s)

_____ b. Joseph Priestly (1771)

_____ c. Jan Ingenhousz (1796)

_____ d. T. W. Englemann (1882)

_____ e. Heinrich Hertz (1887)

_____ f. F. F. Blackman (1905)

_____ g. C. B. van Niel (1930s)

_____ h. Melvin Calvin (1940s)

i. Characterized the action spectrum of photosynthesis using filamentous algae and aerobic bacteria

ii. Demonstrated that the green parts of plants release O_2 into the air

iii. Discovered the photoelectric effect while demonstrating the existence of electromagnetic waves

iv. Demonstrated that the substance or mass of a plant does not come primarily from the soil

v. Determined the cycle of reactions that occur during carbon fixation

vi. Discovered that photosynthesis splits water molecules

vii. Demonstrated that living plants add something to the air that "restores" the air

viii. Determined that photosynthesis is a two-stage process, consisting of the "light" reactions and the "dark" reactions

3. Certain substances are present either at the beginning or the end of the light-dependent reactions of photosynthesis. Fill in the following chart by listing which substance is present at the start and what it has been converted to at the end; connect the two with an arrow. Substances: $ADP + P_i$, $H^+ + e + O_2$, H_2O, $NADP^+$, NADPH (Note: e = electrons)

Start   **End**

a.

b.

c.

4. Use the following terms to complete the diagram of the Calvin cycle. A term may be used more than once.

Terms
ATP → $ADP + P_i$
CO_2
glucose and other sugars
NADPH → $NADP^+$
PGA
RuBP

Calvin Cycle

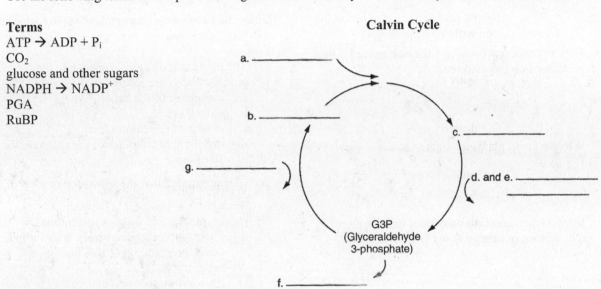

EXERCISING YOUR KNOWLEDGE

Briefly answer each of the following questions in the space provided.

1. A bumper sticker asks, "Have you thanked a green plant today?" Why should we thank green plants—what do they do for us?

2. Does most of the biomass of a plant come from the air, soil, or water? How do we know this?

3. Why is "dark reactions" not the best name for the process of carbon fixation?

4. Why do green plants look green to us?

5. Why do the leaves of many trees turn shades of red, yellow, or orange in the fall?

6. Briefly describe the structure and function of a photosystem.

7. What roles do electron transport and water play in aerobic respiration versus aerobic photosynthesis?

8. Briefly describe the interdependence between the light-dependent reactions and the Calvin cycle of a green plant.

9. Of all the organelles found inside eukaryotic cells, which two are the powerhouses of metabolism?

10. If C_4 photosynthesis and CAM help plants avoid the problems of photorespiration, why don't all plants use these types of metabolism instead of C_3 photosynthesis?

Circle the letter of the one best answer in each of the following questions.

11. The pigment molecules responsible for photosynthesis are located in the
    a. cytoplasm of the cell.
    b. mitochondria.
    c. stroma of the chloroplasts.
    d. thylakoid membranes of the chloroplasts.
    e. all of these.

12. Which of the following statements accurately describes the relationship between photosynthesis and cellular respiration?
    a. Photosynthesis occurs only in autotrophs; cellular respiration occurs only in heterotrophs.
    b. Photosynthesis uses solar energy to convert inorganics to energy-rich organics; respiration breaks down energy-rich organics to synthesize ATP.
    c. Photosynthesis involves the oxidation of glucose; respiration involves the reduction of carbon dioxide.
    d. The primary function of photosynthesis is to use solar energy to synthesize ATP; the primary function of cellular respiration is to break down ATP and release energy.
    e. Photosynthesis and cellular respiration are mutually exclusive and cannot occur in the same cell at the same time.

13. In C_4 plants, the Calvin cycle occurs
    a. during the day.
    b. in bundle-sheath cells.
    c. at night.
    d. in mesophyll cells.
    e. in the stomata.

14. In the overall equation for photosynthesis, water is
    a. just a reactant.
    b. just a product.
    c. both a reactant and a product.
    d. neither a reactant nor a product.

15. In photosystem I, light-energized electrons are replaced by
    a. oxygen.
    b. oxidation of NADPH.
    c. water.
    d. reduction of NADPH.
    e. photosystem II.

16. Many plant species are capable of short-circuiting photosystem I to produce additional ATP by passing electrons back to
    a. ATP synthase.
    b. $NADP^+$.
    c. photosystem II.
    d. b_6-f complex.
    e. NADP reductase.

17. High-energy photons
    a. have long wavelengths.
    b. have short wavelengths.
    c. have the same wavelength as every other type of photon.
    d. have no wavelengths.
    e. cannot be absorbed.

18. Light that is visible to humans occupies what part of the electromagnetic spectrum?
    a. the entire upper half
    b. the entire lower half
    c. a small portion in the middle
    d. the entire spectrum
    e. Visible light is not part of the electromagnetic spectrum.

19. Which of the following molecules have their electrons excited by solar energy and raised to higher energy levels?
    a. ATP
    b. NADPH
    c. glucose
    d. chlorophyll
    e. carbon dioxide

20. Compared to retinal, chlorophyll can be described as a pigment that has a
    a. narrow absorption range and high efficiency.
    b. narrow absorption range and low efficiency.
    c. wide absorption range and high efficiency.
    d. wide absorption range and low efficiency.

21. What type of atom is at the center of the chlorophyll porphyrin ring?
    a. oxygen
    b. carbon
    c. iron
    d. sulfur
    e. magnesium

22. The primary photosynthetic pigment of all plants, algae, and cyanobacteria is
    a. retinal.
    b. β-carotene.
    c. chlorophyll a.
    d. chlorophyll b.
    e. chlorophyll c.

23. Which of the following occurs during the light-dependent reactions of photosynthesis?
    a. electron transport
    b. chemiosmosis
    c. splitting of water molecules
    d. all of these
    e. none of these

24. The protein matrix of a photosystem's antenna complex is analogous to the
    a. first break by a cue stick in a game of pool.
    b. rack used to position the pool balls before the break.
    c. light used over the pool table.
    d. corner pockets that catch the most balls.
    e. side bumpers on the pool table.

25. The reaction center pigment in plant photosystem II is
    a. P_2.
    b. P_{120}.
    c. P_{680}.
    d. P_{700}.
    e. P_{870}.

26. The energy and reducing power needed to run the Calvin cycle are supplied by
    a. oxygen and water.
    b. RuBP and PGA.
    c. carbon dioxide and glucose.
    d. chlorophylls and carotenoids.
    e. ATP and NADPH.

27. How many carbon atoms are in a molecule of RuBP?
    a. 0
    b. 3
    c. 4
    d. 5
    e. 6

28. What energy-rich organic compound is produced at the end of the Calvin cycle?
    a. glucose
    b. ATP
    c. NADPH
    d. all of these
    e. none of these

29. Photorespiration is most likely to occur under conditions of
    a. cold temperatures.
    b. high temperatures.
    c. high CO_2 concentration.
    d. low O_2 concentration.
    e. heavy rainfall.

30. Photorespiration
    a. short-circuits photosynthesis.
    b. enhances photosynthesis.
    c. short-circuits cellular respiration.
    d. enhances cellular respiration.
    e. seems to have no impact on plants.

ASSESSING YOUR KNOWLEDGE

Answers to the questions in the following sections test your ability to synthesize information gained from the chapter and to solve challenging problems on an exam or in everyday life.

Challenging Your Understanding—Answers

1. ATP, 2. NADPH, 3. reaction centers, 2, 2,

4. H_2O, 5. energy, reducing power, 6. rubisco,

7. CO_2, carbohydrates, 8. CO_2, O_2,

9. photorespiration, 10. PEP carboxylase, rubisco, higher affinity, oxidase, 11. temporal separation, decarboxylation, 12. CO_2, H_2O, glucose, O_2,

13. glucose, O_2, CO_2, H_2O, 14. enzymes, Mg^{2+},

15. glycolytic.

Key Terms—Answers

a. 24, b. 18, c. 13, d. 8, e. 20, f. 12, g. 16, h. 27, i. 2, j. 5, k. 21, l. 3, m. 25, n. 23, o. 17, p. 7, q. 1, r. 10, s. 6, t. 26, u. 15, v. 9, w. 4, x. 14, y. 19, z. 22, aa. 11.

Learning by Experience—Answers

1.	a. stroma, Calvin cycle
	b. thylakoid, light-dependent reactions
2.	a. iv d. i g. vi
	b. vii c. iii h. v
	c. ii f. viii
3.	a. ADP + P_i → ATP
	b. H_2O → H^+ + e + O_2
	c. $NADP^+$ → NADPH
4.	a. CO_2
	b. RuBP
	c. PGA
	d. and e. ATP → ADP + P_i, NADPH → $NADP^+$
	f. glucose and other sugars
	g. ATP → ADP + P_i

Exercising Your Knowledge—Answers

As you check your answers, put a mark in the review (Rvw.) column for the answers you missed. If you didn't miss any, congratulations—you have mastered the chapter! If you missed some, review the Section (Sect.) in the text where this concept is discussed. In order to develop an efficient review strategy, it is important that you understand what types of questions you missed. The questions with asterisks test more for understanding of the **concepts**, whereas the others test more for **detail**. *See the preface for learning strategies for concepts and for detail.*

	Sect.	Rvw.
*1. Without green plants, we wouldn't be here. They produce O_2 as a by-product of the light reactions of photosynthesis; this oxygen is released and becomes part of the atmosphere, and we are dependent upon it for aerobic respiration. As heterotrophs, we also depend on autotrophic plants as the ultimate source of the energy-rich organics that we utilize as food but cannot synthesize ourselves.	8.1	
*2. Most of a plant's biomass comes from the air. We know this because experiments dating back to the 1600s and continuing into this century have revealed the details of photosynthesis. During carbon fixation (the Calvin cycle), carbon dioxide from the air is converted (reduced) to organic molecules, which are the building blocks of plants and other organisms.	8.2	
*3. The reactions of carbon fixation do not require darkness in order to occur. They can occur in the light or dark; they are light-independent. ATP and NADPH, made during the light reactions, are required.	8.6	
*4. Green plants contain chlorophyll, which appears green because it reflects light of certain wavelengths that our brains perceive as green; other wavelengths (for example, red) are absorbed by the plant.	8.3	
*5. In the fall, chlorophyll is no longer produced, and you are able to see the carotenoid and other accessory pigments that are also present in the leaves.	8.3	
*6. A photosystem is a cluster or network of pigment molecules (chlorophyll and accessory pigments) and proteins on the thylakoid membrane of chloroplasts (on the plasma membrane of bacteria). Each pigment molecule that is excited by light energy passes the energy to the reaction center molecule, which donates excited electrons to electron transport, resulting in the production of ATP and NADPH.	8.4	
*7. In both respiration and photosynthesis, electron transport produces ATP by chemiosmosis. In respiration, water is formed as an end product when oxygen acts as the final electron acceptor at the end of the electron transport chain. In photosynthesis, water molecules are split and provide the electrons to replace those that are excited and leave chlorophyll during noncyclic photophosphorylation.	8.5 7.6	
*8. The light-dependent reactions produce the ATP and NADPH that provide the energy and reducing power to run the Calvin cycle. The Calvin cycle in turn converts the ATP and NADPH back into ADP + P_i and $NADP^+$ that can be reused to keep the light-dependent reactions running when light and water are available.	8.5 8.6	
*9. Chloroplasts and mitochondria are the powerhouses of metabolism.	8.6	

*10. C$_4$ photosynthesis and CAM are energetically costly and only make energetic sense under conditions most likely to promote photorespiration (e.g., high temperatures, as in the tropics). Under conditions that do not promote photorespiration, C$_3$ photosynthesis is much more efficient.	8.7	
11. d	8.1	
*12. b	8.1	
13. b	8.7	
14. c	8.1	
15. e	8.5	
*16. d	8.5	
17. b	8.3	
18. c	8.3	

19. d	8.3	
*20. a	8.3	
21. e	8.3	
22. c	8.3	
23. d	8.5	
*24. b	8.4	
25. c	8.5	
26. e	8.6	
27. d	8.6	
28. a	8.6	
29. b	8.7	
*30. a	8.7	

CHAPTER 9 CELL COMMUNICATION

MASTERING KEY CONCEPTS

There are no real recluses in the communities we call tissues and organs. They all must interact with each other and the environment they share. Some do it very actively, while others do it more sedately.

9.1 Extracellular signaling pathways lead to cellular responses.

- **Overview**: Cells respond to their environments when **ligands**, or signaling molecules, bind to their **receptors**, initiating a particular intracellular signal transduction pathway. Peptides, large proteins, gases, amino acids, nucleotides, steroids, or other lipids can all act as ligands. Cells use these molecules to communicate by four mechanisms: **direct contact**, **paracrine signaling**, **endocrine signaling** and **synaptic signaling**, depending upon the distance between the signaling and the responding cells. Different cells can have either the same or different responses to the same signal. The **phosphorylation state** of a protein can determine whether a protein is active or inactive, allowing proteins to transmit information from an extracellular signal through a signal transduction pathway. Proteins are phosphorylated on serine, threonine, or tyrosine residues by **protein kinases** and dephosphorylated by **protein phosphatases**.
- **Details**: Know the mechanisms by which cells can signal, how far the signal travels, how the signal is transmitted through the cell, and the signaling molecules involved. Know how protein phosphorylation and dephosphorylation occurs and how a change in phosphorylation state can affect cell signaling.

9.2 Proteins in the cell and on its surface receive signals from other cells.

- **Overview**: Ligands specifically bind to their receptors based on their complementary shapes. Ligand-receptor binding causes a structural change in the receptor that activates it, initiating a signal transduction pathway. There are four different types of receptors based on structure and function. These include **intracellular receptors**, and **cell surface receptors**, such as **chemically gated ion channels, enzymatic receptors**, and **G protein-coupled receptors**. Some enzymatic receptors and G protein-coupled receptors utilize **second messengers**, such as **cAMP**, or **calcium ions,** by binding to cellular proteins and altering their structure and function.
- **Details**: Know the structure of different types of receptors involved in cell signaling, how they are activated, and the result of activation.

9.3 Intracellular receptors

- **Overview**: Receptors for hydrophobic ligands, or for small molecules that can readily pass through the plasma membrane, can be located in the cytoplasm, or within the nucleus. **Nonpolar steroid hormones** bind to their receptors and cause the receptor to be **translocated** from the cytoplasm to the nucleus where they can regulate gene expression. All of the steroid hormones bind to receptors that are evolutionarily related and are part of the **nuclear receptor superfamily**. These receptors act with **coactivators** allowing different responses in different cells based on the presence of the receptor and the coactivator. Besides nuclear hormone receptors, other intracellular receptors act as **enzymes**.
- **Details**: Know the **three functional domains** of nuclear receptors, and how they act to regulate gene expression. Understand the importance of coactivators. Know an example of an intracellular receptor that acts as an enzyme.

9.4 Signal transduction through receptor kinases

- **Overview**: **Receptor tyrosine kinases** and **plant receptor kinases** are **transmembrane receptors** that bind to hydrophilic molecules that cannot readily cross the plasma membrane. Ligands, such as hormones or growth factors, bind to the **extracellular domain** of the receptor causing two receptors to **dimerize** and phosphorylate each other (**autophosphorylation**) on the **intracellular kinase domain**. This allows either intracellular **response proteins** or **adapter proteins** to bind to the phosphorylated receptor at **"docking" sites**, or other intracellular targets to become phosphorylated by the receptor, initiating a cellular response. Receptor tyrosine kinases can activate a **signaling cascade**, such as the **MAP kinase cascade** by **Ras**, a GTP-binding protein that exchanges GDP for GTP, activating it and causing an activation of the first MAP kinase in a cascade. Receptor tyrosine kinases are **inactivated by dephosphorylation**, or **internalization** leading to termination of the response.
- **Details**: Know the structure of the receptor tyrosine kinases, how they bind to ligands and initiate a cellular response. Know how the **insulin receptor** leads to the conversion of glucose to glycogen. Know how the **MAP kinase cascade** is activated, the result of the activation, and how this cascade can cause **signal amplification**. Understand the role of **scaffold proteins** and Ras in kinase cascades. Understand why transient activation of signaling pathways is critical to cell signaling.

9.5 Signal transduction through G protein-coupled receptors

- **Overview**: **G protein receptors** are coupled to **G proteins** that bind **guanosine nucleotides** (GDP or GTP). G proteins are **heterotrimeric proteins** consisting of three subunits, α, β, and γ, and function as a switch, exchanging **GDP** in its **inactive state** for **GTP** in its **active state**, when ligand binds to the receptor. The G protein then **dissociates**, with the G_α subunit bound to GTP, and the G_β and G_γ subunits bound to each other. One of these subunit complexes propagates the signal to activate effector proteins that produce a specific cellular response. Hydrolysis of GTP to GDP by G_α, causes G_α to reassociate with G_β and G_γ, and shuts the signal off. **Effector proteins** are usually enzymes, but can also be protein kinases, or can produce a second messenger, **cAMP** (adenylyl cyclase), or **DAG and IP3** (phospholipase C). Different receptors of the same type or different receptor types can activate the same pathway by different ligands binding to their receptors. In other cases, the same ligand-receptor complexes can have different effects in different cells due to **receptor isoforms**.

- **Details**: Understand the structure of G protein-coupled receptors and how these receptors function. Know the cAMP signaling pathway and the inositol phospholipid/Ca^{2+} signaling pathway. Understand why Ca^{2+} is a good second messenger.

9.6 Cell surface proteins and cell connections mediate cell–cell interactions.

- **Overview**: **Surface markers**, such as glycolipids and integral proteins give a cell its identity. **Tight junctions**, **anchoring junctions**, and **communicating junctions** are three ways in which cells form connections with each other. Tight junctions connect the plasma membranes of adjacent cells into sheets. Anchoring junctions, such as **desmosomes** and **adherens junctions**, mechanically attach the cytoskeleton of a cell to the cytoskeletons of other cells or to the extracellular matrix, providing strength and flexibility. Communicating junctions, such as **gap junctions** in animals or **plasmodesmata** in plants, allow the passage of chemical or electric signals from one cell to an adjacent cell.

- **Details**: Know the structures and functions of different cell junction types. Understand the importance of cell surface markers.

CHALLENGING YOUR UNDERSTANDING

Specifically describe the ligand and the receptor used for each signaling event, indicating critical domains on the receptor. Then describe the series of steps involved in the signal transduction pathway that is activated. What is the result, or the potential result of the pathway?

1. Insulin binding to its receptor

2. Ras activating a MAP kinase cascade

3. Steroid hormone binding to its receptor

4. A G protein activates Phospholipase C

5. Relaxation of smooth muscles

KEY TERMS

Match the numbered term with the definition that fits it best. Put the corresponding number in front of the appropriate definition.

1. ligand
2. paracrine signaling
3. hormones
4. neurotransmitters
5. chemical synapse
6. intracellular receptors
7. cell surface receptors
8. autocrine signaling
9. endocrine signaling
10. ion channel

11. protein kinases
12. G protein
13. second messengers
14. cyclic AMP (cAMP)
15. adenylyl cyclase
16. cell junctions
17. desmosomes
18. tight junctions
19. adherens junctions
20. communicating junctions

21. gap junctions
22. plasmodesmata
23. coactivators
24. scaffold proteins
25. adapter proteins
26. mitogen-activated protein kinases (MAPK)
27. signal transduction

a. _____ The events that occur within a cell upon receipt of a signal.
b. _____ Single-pass, or multi-pass transmembrane protein whose extracellular domain binds to a ligand.
c. _____ A protein inserted between the receptor and the effector that activates the effector when ligand binds.
d. _____ An anchoring junction that connects the cytoskeletons of adjacent cells.
e. _____ An enzyme that acts as an effector to produce cyclic AMP from ATP.
f. _____ A junction in which a chemical or electrical signal passes directly from one cell to an adjacent cell.
g. _____ A second messenger produced within the cell that is used to bind and activate protein kinase A.
h. _____ A signaling molecule that binds to a receptor to initiate a cellular response.
i. _____ Proteins that are not involved in signal transduction but link the receptors and proteins that initiate a response.
j. _____ A junction in animal cells made of connexons to allow the passage of small molecules between cells.
k. _____ The association between a neuron and its target cell that is necessary for intercellular communication.
l. _____ Proteins that organize the components of a kinase cascade into a single protein complex.
m. _____ When cells send signals to themselves by secreting signaling molecules that bind to their own receptors.
n. _____ Connects the plasma membranes of adjacent cells into a sheet to prevent small molecules from leaking between.
o. _____ Molecules that act in concert with receptors to determine the cell's response to signaling molecules.
p. _____ A class of cytoplasmic kinases that are activated by a phosphorylation cascade.
q. _____ A process by which hormones are used for intercellular communication.
r. _____ Cytoplasmic connections in plants that occur where the plasma membranes of adjacent cells contact each other.
s. _____ A process by which short-lived signals are used to send messages to other cells in the immediate vicinity.
t. _____ Receives signals from lipid-soluble or noncharged, nonpolar small molecules.
u. _____ Signaling molecules that have relatively long lives, which can affect cells far away from the signaling cell.
v. _____ An enzyme that adds a phosphate group to a protein when it is activated by a ligand binding to its receptor.
w. _____ Small molecules or ions that alter the behavior of proteins by binding to them, changing their shape.
x. _____ Signaling molecules released from fiberlike extensions of nerve cells close to their target cells.
y. _____ A long-lasting or permanent connection between a cell and the cluster of cells around it.
z. _____ Anchoring junctions that connect the actin filaments of one cell with those of neighboring cells.
aa. _____ A pore in the center of a protein that connects the extracellular fluid with the cytoplasm.

LEARNING BY EXPERIENCE

Color coding the following illustration should help reinforce your understanding of the identity and location of cell structures. Fill in the circle at the end of each title with the color you will use for that structure or substance, and color accordingly. Colored pencils are recommended because they can be sharpened for details. Use figure 9.17 as a guide, but see how many structures you can recognize first.

Tight junction ○
Anchoring junction ○
Intermediate filament ○
Cadherin ○
Communicating junction ○
Connexons ○
Basal lamina ○
Microvilli ○

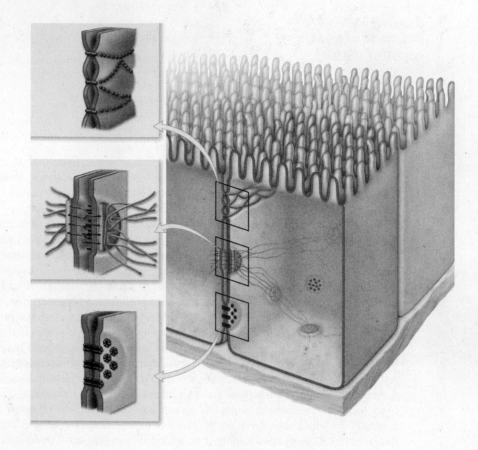

EXERCISING YOUR KNOWLEDGE

Briefly answer the following questions in the space provided.

1. How is a cell's response limited to appropriate stimuli when exposed to a bloodstream teeming with many signal molecules?

2. What property of hormones makes them useful in signaling distant cells?

3. Describe how the MAP kinase cascade can lead to signal amplification.

4. Many proteins are controlled by their phosphorylation state. Which amino acids are phosphorylated by protein kinases? Why are these the only amino acids phosphorylated?

5. What is meant when an ion channel is said to be chemically gated?

6. Describe how scaffold proteins work. What are the advantages and disadvantages of this kind of organization?

7. Describe the inactive and active state of a G protein. Once activated, how is a G protein-coupled receptor shut "off"?

8. Describe the action of adenylyl cyclase as an effector protein in a signal transduction pathway.

9. Describe a situation where different receptors activate the same signaling pathway.

10. Describe how our immune system utilizes MHC proteins.

Circle the letter of the one best answer in each of the following questions.

11. The receptor proteins that bind neurotransmitters
    a. have multiple transmembrane domains.
    b. are intracellular.
    c. are translocated to the nucleus.
    d. are autophosphorylated on the intracellular domain.
    e. are protein kinases.

12. With respect to the plasma membrane, most enzyme receptors are
    a. entirely internal.
    b. seven pass.
    c. entirely on the surface.
    d. multipass.
    e. single pass.

13. Which of the following is NOT a domain on nuclear hormone receptors?
    a. inhibitor-binding domain
    b. hormone-binding domain
    c. intracellular kinase domain
    d. DNA-binding domain
    e. coactivator-interacting domain

14. Synaptic signaling involves the release of
    a. neurotransmitters.
    b. enzymes.
    c. G proteins.
    d. hormones.
    e. ions.

15. Steroid hormones are more suitable for endocrine signaling than neurotransmitters and water-soluble hormones because of their
    a. size.
    b. polarity.
    c. configuration.
    d. reactivity.
    e. longevity.

16. If you were to inject a substance into a person's bloodstream to bind to an intracellular receptor, you should choose a
    a. water-soluble hormone.
    b. neurotransmitter.
    c. water-soluble protein.
    d. nonsteroid hormone.
    e. lipid-soluble substance.

17. If a cell is to pass a molecule to an adjacent cell by way of a gap junction, that molecule must be
    a. small.
    b. a protein.
    c. a gas.
    d. a hormone.
    e. lipid-soluble.

18. The signal molecule, nitric oxide (NO),
    a. is used primarily in autocrine signaling.
    b. binds with guanylyl cyclase in a neighboring cell, causing the production of GMP.
    c. binds with a gene-regulating intracellular receptor, resulting in the transcription of a protein.
    d. binds with an intracellular receptor that converts GMP to cGMP.
    e. dissolves in blood, where it acts as a signal molecule in endocrine signaling.

19. Receptor tyrosine kinases are inactivated by
    a. dephosphorylation or internalization.
    b. dissociation or exchange of GTP for GDP.
    c. proteins binding to docking sites or internalization.
    d. dissociation or dephosphorylation.
    e. desensitization or dephosphorylation.

20. In the calcium pathway, the G protein
    a. catalyzes the production of inositol triphosphate.
    b. binds to calmodulin.
    c. opens a calcium channel in the endoplasmic reticulum.
    d. activates phospholipase C.
    e. stimulates adenylyl cyclase.

21. When four calcium ions bind to calmodulin,
    a. the calcium ions are transferred to the endoplasmic reticulum.
    b. the calmodulin opens a gated channel in the plasma membrane.
    c. the calmodulin activates adenylyl cyclase.
    d. an inhibiting molecule is released, and the calmodulin is activated.
    e. the calmodulin changes conformation and binds with a cytoplasmic protein.

22. Which of the following is activated by autophosphorylation?
    a. epinephrine receptor
    b. β-adrenergic receptor
    c. chemically-gated ion channel
    d. insulin receptor
    e. nuclear hormone receptor

23. Which of the following is a protein that is critical to link adjacent cells to each other and to the basement membrane?
    a. integrins
    b. cadherins
    c. connexons
    d. channel proteins
    e. tubulin

24. A single-pass protein that acts as a "self" marker is
    a. GTP.
    b. MHC.
    c. GMP.
    d. MCA.
    e. ADP.

25. Partitioning in a sheet of cells is achieved by
    a. hemidesmosomes.
    b. adherens junctions.
    c. tight junctions.
    d. desmosomes.
    e. plasmodesmata.

26. _____ junctions may protect a damaged cell through chemical gating.
    a. Tight
    b. Gap
    c. Adherens
    d. Occluding
    e. Macular

27. In desmosomes,
    a. cadherin proteins attach to integrins and the cytoplasmic skeleton.
    b. intermediate fibers extend from one cell to another.
    c. cadherin proteins attach to other cadherin molecules and to intermediate filaments.
    d. integrin molecules extend into both cells, connecting to matrix proteins.
    e. two cells are glued together by cytoplasmic plaque.

28. Ca^{2+} is a good second messenger because
    a. proteins on the ER are extremely sensitive to it.
    b. cytoplasmic levels are low.
    c. most intracellular enzymes require it for activation.
    d. it activates effector proteins.
    e. It keeps G protein-coupled receptors "on."

29. Plasmodesmata differ from gap junctions of animals by
    a. using connexons of six identical proteins.
    b. allowing only smaller molecules to pass between cells.
    c. separating the two cells by a membrane.
    d. having a central tubule connecting the endoplasmic reticulum of the two cells.
    e. joining the two cell walls.

30. Which of the following is NOT a true statement about the Ras protein?
    a. It is a G protein.
    b. It activates a MAP kinase cascade.
    c. It has intrinsic GTPase activity.
    d. It links growth factor receptors to their cellular response.
    e. It dissociates into α and βγ subunits when activated.

ASSESSING YOUR KNOWLEDGE

Answers to the questions in the following sections test your ability to synthesize information gained from the chapter and to solve challenging problems on an exam or in everyday life.

Challenging Your Understanding—Answers

1. The insulin receptor is a receptor tyrosine kinase that has a single transmembrane domain with an extracellular ligand-binding domain and an intracellular kinase domain. When insulin binds to the extracellular domain of two receptors, the receptors dimerize and the β-subunit of one phosphorylates the other, activating insulin response proteins. These phosphorylated response proteins activate glycogen synthase, which converts glucose to glycogen.

2. A specific growth factor acts as the ligand and binds to a growth factor receptor, which is a receptor tyrosine kinase that has a single transmembrane domain with an extracellular ligand-binding domain and intracellular kinase domain. Ligand binding causes receptors to dimerize and autophosphorylate each other. This activates Ras, which exchanges GDP (inactive) for GTP (active). Ras activates the first kinase, which is Raf. Raf activates the second kinase, which is MEK. MEK activates the MAP kinase, ERK. This MAP kinase phosphorylates response proteins including transcription factors that can lead to an alteration in gene expression.

3. Steroid hormones, which are hydrophobic molecules, cross the plasma membrane and bind to cytoplasmic receptors. These receptors have three functional domains, a hormone-binding domain, a DNA-binding domain, and transcription-activating domains. Ligand binding to the receptor, changes the conformation of the receptor, which leads to the release of an inhibitor that binds to the DNA-binding site. The hormone-receptor complex translocates to the nucleus and binds to DNA to turn on or off transcription of specific target genes with the DNA-binding sequence in their promoters. This leads to a change in gene expression.

4. Ligand binds to a G protein-coupled receptor, a seven-pass transmembrane protein with a cytoplasmic binding site for the associated G protein. When ligand binds to the receptor, it activates the G protein, which exchanges GDP for GTP and dissociates into G_α and $G_{\beta\gamma}$. The G_α-GTP complex activates the effector protein, Phospholipase C, which converts PIP_2 to DAG and IP_3. IP_3 binds to a channel-linked receptor on the ER membrane causing the ER to release Ca^{2+} into the cytoplasm. This Ca^{2+} can bind to calmodulin or PKC to cause a cellular response. One potential result of Ca^{2+} release is muscle contraction in skeletal muscle cells, or the secretion of hormones in endocrine cells.

5. Nitric oxide is a small molecule that readily diffuses out of the cells in which it is produced to neighboring cells. Acting as a ligand, nitric oxide binds to an intracellular receptor, which is an enzyme, guanylyl cyclase. The enzyme is activated and catalyzes the synthesis of cyclic guanosine monophosphate, an intracellular messenger that produces cell-specific responses. In muscle cells, the increase in cGMP levels leads to relaxation.

Key Terms—Answers

a. 27, b. 7, c. 12, d. 17, e. 15, f. 20, g. 14, h. 1, i. 25, j. 21, k. 5, l. 24, m. 8, n. 18, o. 23, p. 26, q. 9, r. 22, s. 2, t. 6, u. 3, v. 11, w. 13, x. 4, y. 16, z. 19, aa. 10.

Learning by Experience—Answers

Compare your work to figure 9.17.

Exercising Your Knowledge—Answers

As you check your answers, put a mark in the review (Rvw) column for the answers you missed. If you didn't miss any, congratulations—you have mastered the chapter! If you missed some, review the section (Sect.) in the text where this concept is discussed. In order to develop an efficient review strategy, it is important that you understand what types of questions you missed. The questions with asterisks test more for understanding of the **concepts**, whereas the others test more for **detail**. *See the preface for learning strategies for concepts and for details.*

	Sect.	Rvw.
*1. A cell responds to signals that fit its receptor proteins.	9.1	--
2. Hormones tend to survive in the bloodstream long enough to reach the target receptor.	9.1	
*3. Each step in the MAP kinase cascade involves activation of an enzyme. Each enzyme can act on many substrates producing a large amount of final product, allowing a small number of initial signaling molecules to produce a large response.	9.4	
*4. Serine, threonine, and tyrosine residues are phosphorylated by protein kinases. These three amino acids are the only amino acids that have an OH functional group as part of their R group.	9.1	
5. The ion channel is said to be chemically gated because it is opened when a chemical binds with it.	9.2	

6. Scaffold proteins organize the components of a kinase cascade into a single protein complex. The scaffold protein binds to each individual kinase such that they are spatially organized for optimal function. This system is advantageous because it organizes them so each substrate is next to its enzyme and it does not depend on diffusion to produce the appropriate order of events. It also allows the segregation of signaling modules in different cytoplasmic locations. The disadvantage of this organization is that it reduces the amplification effect of the kinase cascade since enzymes held in one place are not free to find new substrate molecules.	9.4	
*7. G proteins are activated by exchanging GDP for GTP when a ligand binds to a G protein-coupled receptor. The heterotrimeric G protein dissociates into Gα and Gβγ. The hydrolysis of bound GTP to GDP by Gα causes reassociation of the heterotrimer and restores the "off" state of the system.	9.5	
*8. When a signaling molecule binds to a G protein-coupled receptor that uses adenylyl cyclase as an effector, this enzyme synthesizes a large amount of cAMP that binds to and activates PKA, which adds phosphate groups to target proteins.	9.5	
*9. The hormones glucagon and epinephrine both act through G protein-coupled receptors. Each of these receptors acts via a G protein that activates adenylyl cyclase, producing cAMP. The activation of PKA begins a kinase cascade that leads to the breakdown of glycogen.	9.5	

*10. All cells of a given individual have "self" markers called major histocompatibility complex (MHC) proteins. The immune system inspects cells it encounters and causes the destruction of those with foreign MHCs.	9.6	

11. a	9.2	
12. e	9.2	
13. c	9.3	
14. a	9.1	
*15. e	9.1	
*16. e	9.3	
*17. a	9.6	
*18. b	9.3	
19. a	9.4	
*20. d	9.5	
*21. e	9.5	
*22. d	9.4	
23. b	9.6	
24. b	9.6	
*25. c	9.6	
26. b	9.6	
*27. c	9.6	
28. b	9.5	
*29. d	9.6	
30. e	9.4	

CHAPTER 10 HOW CELLS DIVIDE

MASTERING KEY CONCEPTS

Students usually memorize the names and order of mitotic phases and learn to recognize their appearance through a microscope or in a textbook. You should do that too, but that is not enough. It is imperative that you also learn the events that occur in each phase. Only then can you understand mitotic division, genetics, and cancer.

10.1 Prokaryotes divide far more simply than do eukaryotes.
- **Overview**: Bacterial cells divide by **binary fission** in which DNA replication of the bacterial chromosome and partitioning of the chromosome occur as a concerted process. After partitioning of the chromosome, the other cellular components are partitioned by **septation** beginning with the assembly of the **FtsZ protein** at the septum. After the accumulation of other proteins, the septum contracts inward and pinches off into two cells.
- **Details**: Understand the steps of **binary fission**. Know the function of the **FtsZ protein**.

10.2 The chromosomes of eukaryotes are highly ordered structures.
- **Overview**: Eukaryotic chromosomes are composed of **chromatin** consisting of DNA wrapped around **histone proteins** into structures called **nucleosomes**. Nucleosomes are further packaged into **solenoids**, or **30-nm fibers**. This packaging is essential in order for a large amount of DNA to fit into a eukaryotic nucleus, and also seems to be related to gene expression, with genes found in **euchromatin** being actively expressed, while genes found in **heterochromatic** regions are not expressed. The products of replication (**sister chromatids**) are held together by **cohesion** proteins at the **centromeres** until chromosome segregation ensures that one chromatid goes to each daughter cell. During mitosis, solenoids are arranged around a scaffold of proteins, and are assisted by **condensin** proteins to allow maximum compaction.
- **Details**: Understand how histone proteins interact with DNA. Know the different **levels of chromatin organization**. Understand the difference between **haploid** and **diploid** number of chromosomes and the difference between **homologous chromosomes** and **sister chromatids**.

10.3 The eukaryotic cell cycle is divided into five phases.
- **Overview**: The **cell cycle** is divided into **five distinct phases**. The first gap phase (G_1) involves growth and preparation for DNA synthesis. The second phase (S) is when the DNA is replicated. The third phase (G_2) prepares the cell to divide. In the fourth phase, **mitosis (M)**, the replicated chromosomes separate. The final phase, **cytokinesis**, involves the division of the cytoplasm to create two daughter cells. The length of the cell cycle is different in different organisms. Most of the variation is due to the length of G_1 in which some organisms enter a resting state known as G_0 before they replicate their DNA.
- **Details**: Know the different phases of the cell cycle and what cellular events occur in each.

10.4 Interphase: Preparation for mitosis.
- **Overview**: **Interphase** is the portion of the cell cycle between cell divisions (G_1, S, G_2), when cells grow, DNA is replicated, chromosomes condense and begin to assemble the cellular materials necessary for mitosis. After DNA replication, **kinetochore proteins** are assembled on the **centromere** of two **sister chromatids**. These proteins play an essential role in cell division.
- **Details**: Know the structures that hold together sister chromatids after DNA replication and how these structures allow sister chromatids to be separated during mitosis.

10.5 Mitosis: Chromosome segregation
- **Overview**: The first stage of mitosis is **prophase** when chromosome condensation initiated in G_2 continues and the **spindle apparatus**, made up of **microtubule fibers,** is assembled. During the formation of the spindle, the nuclear envelope breaks down and the orientation of the spindle fibers determines where the cell will divide. Following the breakdown of the nuclear envelope, the cell enters **prometaphase** in which the condensed chromosomes become attached to the spindle by their kinetochores. A second set of microtubules grows from the poles of a cell toward the centromeres and is captured by the kinetochores on each pair of sister chromatids, anchoring each chromatid to the opposite pole. The chromosomes begin to move to the center of the cell. The stage of **metaphase** is marked by the chromosomes lining up at the **metaphase plate** to properly separate sister chromatids. **Anaphase** begins when the **centromeres** of the sister chromatids split, and each is pulled toward the poles where their kinetochores are attached as the microtubules shorten (**anaphase A**), and the spindle poles move apart (**anaphase B**). The final phase of mitosis is **telophase**, when the spindle apparatus disassembles, a nuclear envelope forms around each set of sister chromatids, and the chromosomes begin to uncoil.

- **Details**: Understand the **stages of mitosis** and what occurs during each stage. Know the two possible mechanisms proposed to explain the movement of chromosomes in prometaphase.

10.6 Cytokinesis: The division of the cytoplasmic contents of a cell.

- **Overview**: The cell actually divides after telophase is complete during **cytokinesis** when the cytoplasm and organelles separate into two daughter cells. In animal cells, **actin filaments** constrict, pinching the cell and creating a **cleavage furrow** where the cell divides into two. In plant cells, a **cell plate** grows outward until it fuses with the plasma membrane to divide the cell in two and overcome the problem of squeezing the rigid cell wall into two. In some organisms (fungi and protists), all the events of mitosis occur within the nucleus and the nucleus actually divides into two before cytokinesis.
- **Details**: Understand how the cytoplasmic contents of a cell are divided into two daughter cells and how it can differ in different organisms.

10.7 The cell cycle is carefully controlled.

- **Overview**: **Cyclin-dependent kinases (Cdks)** are active when they are properly phosphorylated and complexed with **cyclins**, proteins with no intrinsic enzymatic activity, whose production occurs at critical times in a cell to promote cell-cycle progression and cell division. Active Cdk-cyclin complexes can phosphorylate critical target substrates. There are three main points, called **cell cycle checkpoints**, where the cell cycle can be delayed if an internal or an external signal indicates that the conditions are not correct for the cell to continue to divide. The **G1/S checkpoint**, called START (yeast), or the restriction point (animals), is the primary time when a cell commits to replicating its genome and therefore commits to divide. The **G2/M checkpoint** commits a cell to mitosis. If DNA replication has not been successfully accomplished, the cell cycle will stall at this checkpoint. The **spindle checkpoint** ensures that chromosomes are properly attached to the spindle. This checkpoint functions through the **APC,** which normally triggers anaphase. **Cancer** is a loss of cell cycle control that results from the inactivation of **tumor-suppressor genes**, the overexpression of **oncogenes**, or the mutation of **proto-oncogenes**.
- **Details**: Know the two mechanisms that control cell cycle progression. Know what two components **maturation promoting factor** (mitosis promoting factor) consists of, the role of each, and the regulation of its activity. Understand the timing of the three cell cycle checkpoints and the necessity for each. Understand the differences between cell cycle control in animals and that of single-celled organisms. Understand how **growth factors** function and how mutations in growth factor receptors can lead to cancer. Know how **p53** functions and the importance of its action in preventing the loss of cell cycle control. Understand the difference between how **mutations in tumor suppressor genes** and **proto-oncogenes** can lead to **cancer**.

CHALLENGING YOUR UNDERSTANDING

Draw an outline of the phases of the yeast cell cycle and the critical checkpoints. Indicate the critical cellular requirements at each checkpoint that determines whether the cell cycle is stalled. Indicate the state of Cdk2, Cdk1, and APC before and after the relevant checkpoints in a normal cell when the checkpoint is not activated.

KEY TERMS

Match the numbered term with the definition that fits it best. Put the corresponding number in front of the appropriate definition.

1. binary fission	14. G_1	27. telophase
2. tubulin	15. G_2	28. cell plate
3. histones	16. S	29. middle lamella
4. nucleosome	17. interphase	30. cyclin-dependent kinases
5. heterochromatin	18. mitosis (M)	31. growth factors
6. euchromatin	19. cytokinesis (C)	32. proto-oncogenes
7. karyotype	20. G_0	33. tumor suppressor
8. haploid (n)	21. kinetochore	34. septum
9. diploid (2n)	22. centrioles	35. M phase-promoting factor
10. homologues	23. prophase	36. oncogenes
11. centromere	24. aster	37. cyclins
12. chromatids	25. metaphase	38. anaphase-promoting complex
13. cell cycle	26. anaphase	

a. _____ The phase in which the cell synthesizes a replica of its genome.

b. _____ The normal number of chromosomes in a cell reflecting the equal contribution from both parents.

c. _____ The overall process of genome duplication, segregation, and division of cellular contents.

d. _____ A disklike structure that functions as an attachment site for microtubules to separate chromatids.

e. _____ The two replicas of a single chromosome held together at their centromeres by cohesin proteins.

f. _____ The protein that forms microtubules, which cells extensively synthesize in G_2.

g. _____ The region on the chromosome where two sister chromatids are held together and the kinetochore forms.

h. _____ The phase in the cell cycle during which mitochondria and other organelles replicate.

i. _____ The phase in mitosis when chromosomes are clustered at opposite poles and the spindle apparatus disappears.

j. _____ A resting state that cells often enter before resuming cell division.

k. _____ The first stage of mitosis in which the chromosomes condense and the spindle apparatus is assembled.

l. _____ A domain of chromatin in which the genes are being actively expressed.

m. _____ The phase in the cell cycle when the cytoplasm divides creating two daughter cells.

n. _____ The mitotic phase in which chromosomes are pulled to opposite poles and the spindle poles move apart.

o. _____ A radial array of microtubules extended from the centrioles toward the nearby plasma membrane.

p. _____ The complex of DNA wrapped around histone proteins that looks like beads on a string.

q. _____ A pair of microtubule-organizing centers replicated in G_2 to produce one for each pole of the cell.

r. _____ The particular array of chromosomes an individual organism possesses.

s. _____ The mitotic phase in which all of the chromosomes are aligned at the equator of the cell.

t. _____ The phase in the cell cycle in which the spindle apparatus assembles and sister chromatids move apart.

u. _____ The process used by bacteria to duplicate genetic information and segregate it into two daughter cells.

v. _____ A domain of chromatin in which the genes are not actively expressed.

w. _____ One complete set of chromosomes necessary to define an organism.

x. _____ The portion of the cell cycle between cell divisions consisting of G_1, S, and G_2 together.

y. _____ The primary growth phase of the cell encompassing the major portion of the cell cycle.

z. _____ Proteins that have an overall positive charge that promote and guide the coiling of the DNA.

aa. _____ Each of the maternal and paternal copies of the same chromosome in a pair.

bb. _____ Composed of both a cyclin and a kinase and acts as a positive regulator of cell cycle progression in frogs.

cc. _____ Regulatory proteins that are required to activate Cdks.

dd. _____ A division formed at the midpoint of a bacterial cell facilitated by the FtsZ protein assembling there.

ee. _____ Marks the securin protein for degradation by the proteosome.

ff. _____ An expanding membrane partition in plants that grows outward and fuses with the plasma membrane.

gg. _____ Genes that can, when introduced into a cell, cause it to become a cancer cell.

hh. _____ Trigger intracellular signaling systems and can override cellular controls that inhibit cell division.

ii. _____ When both copies of this type of gene lose function, there is a loss of control of cell proliferation.

jj. _____ The space between the daughter cells in plants that is filled with pectins.

kk. _____ Mutations in these genes have dominant, gain-of-function effects leading to cancer.

ll. _____ Protein kinases that are regulated by cyclin binding and its phosphorylation state.

LEARNING BY EXPERIENCE

Procure at least six 4in. x 6in. note cards. You will need more than a dozen more for the next chapter. The cards need to be at least this size so that the print can be large enough for you to read quickly. The cards may be ruled on one side and blank on the other, but it doesn't matter. Label them INTERPHASE, MITOSIS PROPHASE, MITOSIS METAPHASE, MITOSIS ANAPHASE, MITOSIS TELOPHASE, and MITOSIS CYTOKINESIS. The reason for including mitosis in each title is to later compare them with meiosis in the next chapter. Draw the appropriate mitotic figures on the blank side if you wish. Figure 10.11 will be helpful. Note that cytokinesis is not diagrammed. Both G_1 and G_2 are shown. Now for the important part: on the ruled side of each labeled card, print clearly the events of that part of the cell cycle. Be thorough! Just filling out the cards starts you on the study process. Study each card by looking at the title on the front of the card and then reading the back of the card. Soon you should be able to anticipate what you will see on the back side. When you have reached that point, it is time to avoid a common problem. Sometimes students can describe a process from beginning to end, but cannot deal with components taken out of sequence. If you really understand the process, you should know the events of any phase in any order. Practice this by shuffling the cards until you can cite the events of all phases in any order. Save the cards to compare with those for meiosis in the next chapter.

EXERCISING YOUR KNOWLEDGE
Briefly answer the following questions in the space provided.

1. Describe genome replication, segregation, and cytokinesis in prokaryotes.

2. Describe how sister chromatids become connected to the spindle and to opposite poles of the cell. What will happen if this attachment does not occur properly?

3. Explain the two processes that complete the coiling of a chromosome.

4. How do chromosomes vary in appearance?

5. What happens to the nuclear envelope when it disappears in prophase?

6. Describe how cytokinesis differs in animal cells, plant cells, and fungi.

7. Describe how mutations in tumor-suppressor genes or proto-oncogenes can lead to cancer. Distinguish between these two mechanisms.

8. What is the role of cyclins in regulating the cell cycle?

9. At the G_2 checkpoint, (a) how is MPF formed, and, (b) what happens to the MPF thereafter to trigger mitosis?

10. What behavior of the p53 protein causes it to be referred to as a tumor-suppressing gene?

Circle the letter of the one best answer in each of the following questions.

11. Just before a prokaryotic cell divides, the two daughter genomes move away from the
    a. cell membrane.
    b. replication origin.
    c. centromeres.
    d. equatorial plate.
    e. kinetochore.

12. Immediately following the S phase, human cells have _____ chromatids.
    a. 23
    b. 46
    c. 69
    d. 92
    e. 122

13. Each chromosome replicates to produce two sister chromatids in
    a. anaphase.
    b. interphase.
    c. metaphase.
    d. prophase.
    e. telophase.

14. Preparations for genome separation are made in the ___ phase.
    a. C
    b. G_1
    c. G_2
    d. M
    e. S

15. In the life cycle of a human cell, each chromosome contains two chromatids by the end of the ___ phase.
    a. C
    b. G_1
    c. G_2
    d. M
    e. S

16. The G_0 phase is actually a pause in the ___ phase.
    a. C
    b. G_1
    c. G_2
    d. M
    e. S

17. The most variation in the length of the cell cycle from one organism or tissue to another occurs in the ___ phase.
    a. C
    b. G_1
    c. G_2
    d. M
    e. S

18. The primary growth phase of a cell is the ___ phase.
    a. G_0
    b. G_1
    c. G_2
    d. M
    e. S

19. A cleavage furrow forms in animal cells during the ___ phase.
    a. C
    b. G_1
    c. G_2
    d. M
    e. S

20. During mitosis, the point on the chromatids where microtubules are attached is the
    a. aster.
    b. kinetochores.
    c. centrioles.
    d. septum.
    e. spindle.

21. Histone proteins are positively charged because of an abundance of what type of amino acids?
    a. alanine and leucine
    b. serine and threonine
    c. methionine and cysteine
    d. lysine and arginine
    e. glutamic acid and aspartic acid

22. Which of the following is not part of a human chromosome in any phase?
    a. centriole
    b. histone
    c. nucleosome
    d. euchromatin
    e. centromere

23. Which of the following proteins hold sister chromatids together?
    a. histones
    b. condensins
    c. cohesins
    d. kinetochores
    e. microtubules

24. Which of the following is NOT completed during interphase?
    a. Cytoskeleton disassembles.
    b. Organelles are replicated.
    c. Microtubule-organizing centers are replicated.
    d. Chromosomes begin condensing.
    e. DNA is replicated.

25. In plant cytokinesis, cellulose is laid down, forming a
    a. middle lamella.
    b. cell plate.
    c. cell wall.
    d. plasma membrane.
    e. cleavage furrow.

26. Assessment of the success of DNA replication occurs at the _____ checkpoint.
    a. spindle
    b. G_1/S
    c. G_0/M
    d. G_2/M
    e. G_1/M

27. DNA damage-inducing agents will arrest the cell cycle
    a. at the end of G_2 phase.
    b. at the beginning of the G_2 phase.
    c. just before entering the S phase.
    d. Both b and c are correct.
    e. Both a and c are correct.

28. The APC is responsible for doing which of the following in mitosis?
    a. initiating a kinase cascade to stimulate cell division
    b. activate a signal transduction pathway to phosphorylate Cdk
    c. monitor the integrity of the DNA
    d. destroy mitotic cyclins
    e. prevent the expression of cyclins and Cdks

29. The third checkpoint in the cell cycle occurs at
    a. late prophase.
    b. interphase.
    c. metaphase.
    d. late telophase.
    e. late anaphase.

30. A growth factor released by clotting blood is
    a. EGF.
    b. FGF.
    c. NGF.
    d. TGF-ß
    e. PDGF.

ASSESSING YOUR KNOWLEDGE

Answers to the questions in the following sections test your ability to synthesize information gained from the chapter and to solve challenging problems on an exam or in everyday life.

Challenging Your Understanding—Answers

$G_1 \to S \to G_2 \to M \to C$

Critical checkpoints exist at the G_1/S transition, the G_2/M transition, and in the middle of M phase at the spindle checkpoint. For the G_1/S checkpoint, the cell cycle will be stalled and the checkpoint activated if the cell is too large or too small, if the cell is starved, or if the cell lacks growth factors. The G_2/M checkpoint will be activated if replication is not complete or if the integrity of the DNA is compromised. The spindle checkpoint (mid M) will be activated if all of the chromosomes are not properly arrayed at the metaphase plate. If the G_1/S checkpoint is not activated, inactive Cdk2 is activated and the cell progresses to S phase. If the G_2/M checkpoint is not activated, inactive Cdk1 is activated and the cell progresses to mitosis. If the spindle checkpoint is not activated, APC is activated and the cell progresses to anaphase.

Key Terms—Answers

a. 16, b. 9, c. 13, d. 21, e. 12, f. 2, g. 11, h. 15, i. 27, j. 20, k. 23, l. 6, m. 19, n. 26, o. 24, p. 4, q. 22, r. 7, s. 25, t. 18, u. 1, v. 5, w. 8, x. 17, y. 14, z. 3, aa. 10, bb. 35, cc. 37, dd. 34, ee. 38, ff. 28, gg. 36, hh. 31, ii. 33, jj. 29, kk. 32, ll. 30.

Learning by Experience—Answers

INTERPHASE EVENTS. Organisms do most of their growing. Chromosomes replicate. Sister chromatids attached at centromere. New organelles formed. Condensation of chromosomes begins. Centrioles replicate in animals. Tubulin is synthesized.

PROPHASE EVENTS. Chromosomes become visible. rRNA synthesis ends—nucleoli disappear. Centrioles in animals migrate to opposite poles. Poles established in plant cells. Spindle apparatus forms between poles. Asters form in some cells. Microtubules attach to kinetochores. Chromatids migrate toward the metaphase plate.

METAPHASE EVENTS. Chromosomes align on the metaphase plate. Centromeres split.

ANAPHASE EVENTS. Poles move apart. Centromeres move toward poles. Sister chromatids move toward opposite poles.

TELOPHASE EVENTS. Spindle apparatus disassembles. New nuclear envelope forms around each set of chromosomes. Chromosomes uncoil. rRNA synthesis resumes so nucleoli reappear.

CYTOKINESIS EVENTS. In animals, cleavage furrow forms and constricts, completely dividing the two cells. In plants, cell plate grows from the center to the sides, dividing the two cells. Cellulose is laid down to form cell walls. A middle lamella forms between the two new walls.

Exercising Your Knowledge—Answers

As you check your answers, put a mark in the review (Rvw) column for the answers you missed. If you didn't miss any, congratulations—you have mastered the chapter! If you missed some, review the Section (Sect.) in the text where this concept is discussed. In order to develop an efficient review strategy, it is important that you understand what types of questions you missed. The questions with asterisks test more for understanding of the **concepts**, whereas the others test more for **detail**. *See the preface for learning strategies for concepts and for details.*

	Sect.	Rvw.
1. Beginning at the replication origin, a battery of enzymes copies the DNA of each strand until the entire circle is copied. After the genome has been replicated, the two daughter genomes are attached, side by side, to the plasma membrane. The cell approximately doubles its size, inducing cell division. A new plasma membrane and cell wall are laid down, dividing the cell into two.	10.1	
2. During prometaphase, condensed chromosomes become attached to the spindle by their kinetochores, which is attached to the centromere region of each sister chromatid. A second group of microtubules grow from the poles of the cell toward the centromeres and are captured by the kinetochores on each pair of sister chromatids, connecting each to an opposite pole of the spindle. Any mistakes in this process will lead to a failure in sister chromatid separation, which could produce one daughter cell with both sister chromatids and one cell with none.	10.5	
3. The first coiling process is nucleosome formation. This is the wrapping of DNA around histones at every two hundred nucleotides. The second process is the coiling of nucleosomes into high-order coils called solenoids.	10.2	
4. Chromosomes differ in size, staining characteristics, centromere location, length of arms, and location of constrictions.	10.2	
5. The components of the nuclear envelope are reabsorbed by the ER.	10.5	

6. In animal cells, cytokinesis occurs by a constricting belt of actin filaments sliding past one another. As the diameter of the belt decreases, the cell is pinched creating a cleavage furrow. This furrow deepens as constriction proceeds, eventually slicing all of the way into the center of the cell, dividing it in two. In plant cells, membrane components are assembled in their interior at right angles to the spindle apparatus creating a cell plate that continues to grow outward until it fuses with the interior surface of the plasma membrane, dividing the cell in two. Cellulose laid down on the new membranes creates two new cell walls. Mitosis occurs within the fungal nucleus without the nuclear membrane breaking down. When mitosis is complete, the nucleus divides into two daughter nuclei. During cytokinesis, one nucleus goes to each daughter cell.	10.6	
7. Mutations in tumor-suppressor genes are recessive and can lead to cancer if both copies of the gene have inactivating mutations that lead to a loss of function of the tumor suppressor protein, or if one copy is mutated and the gene is haploinsufficient. Mutations in proto-oncogenes can lead to cancer if the mutation has a dominant, gain-of-function effect leading to loss of regulation of the normal cellular function of the protein and resulting therefore in loss of regulation of cell proliferation, or division.	10.7	
8. Cyclins bind to Cdks, enabling them to function as enzymes.	10.7	

9. (a) MPF is formed by the binding of cyclin to Cdk. (b) Enzymes phosphorylate MPF, increasing its activity. Active MPF increases the action of phosphorylating enzymes, thus increasing the number of active MPF molecules, etc. Mitosis is triggered when a threshold is exceeded.	10.7	
10. The *p53* checks DNA for damage. Damaged DNA is repaired or destroyed, reducing the number of mutations able to cause tumors.	10.7	
11. b	10.1	
12. d	10.2	
13. b	10.3	
14. c	10.3	
15. e	10.3	
16. b	10.3	
17. b	10.3	
18. b	10.3	
19. a	10.6	
20. b	10.5	
21. d	10.2	
22. a	10.4	
23. c	10.3	
24. a	10.4	
25. c	10.6	
26. d	10.7	
27. c	10.7	
28. d	10.7	
29. c	10.7	
30. e	10.7	

CHAPTER 11 SEXUAL REPRODUCTION AND MEIOSIS

MASTERING KEY CONCEPTS
Understanding this chapter is key to understanding genetics. As you study this chapter, compare it to chapter 10. Study the similarities, the differences, and the consequences of mitosis and meiosis.

11.1 Meiosis produces haploid cells from diploid cells.
- **Overview**: During **gamete** formation, cells with half the normal number of chromosomes (eggs and sperm) are produced by **meiosis**. These two cells with a **haploid** number of chromosomes fuse during **fertilization** to form a **zygote** with two copies of each chromosome (**diploid**), one **homologue** of each chromosome from the mother, and one homologue of each from the father. This cycle of producing cells with a haploid number of chromosomes by meiosis, followed by fertilization is common to organisms that undergo **sexual reproduction**. **Germ-line cells** are diploid cells set aside from other diploid **somatic cells** early in development. While somatic cells undergo mitosis to produce two daughter cells with a diploid number of chromosomes, germ-line cells undergo meiosis to form cells with a haploid number of chromosomes.
- **Details**: Understand the sexual life cycle in animals, and how it differs in algae and fungi, and in some plants.

11.2 Meiosis has unique features.
- **Overview**: Meiosis involves two successive divisions with no replication between them. These two divisions, **meiosis I** and **meiosis II**, each contain four stages, **prophase**, **metaphase**, **anaphase**, and **telophase**. Following DNA replication, homologous chromosomes are paired along their length in a **synaptonemal complex** during prophase I. Within this complex, homologues can exchange genetic material by **recombination** between nonsister chromatids. During metaphase I, the homologues of each pair are attached to opposite poles of the spindle, and move to opposite poles in anaphase I. This **reduction division** results in two daughter cells with one homologue from each chromosome pair. Meiosis I is immediately followed by meiosis II in which the sister chromatids from each pair of homologues are segregated to different cells forming four cells, each with a haploid number of chromosomes.
- **Details**: Understand the chromosomal structures important for meiotic division. Understand the differences between meiosis I and mitosis. Know what structures and what processes are unique to meiosis.

11.3 The sequence of events during meiosis involves two nuclear divisions.
- **Overview**: Homologous chromosomes become closely associated by **synapsis**. Each pair of homologous chromosomes undergoes one or more **crossovers** per arm forming **chiasmata**, which physically connect the homologues. In metaphase I, the chiasmata move to the ends of the paired chromosomes, the kinetochores of the sister chromatids fuse, and together they become attached to the microtubules extending from opposite poles as they align at the **metaphase plate**. The random orientation of chromosomes at the metaphase plate produces gametes with different combinations of parental chromosomes (**independent assortment**). In anaphase I, microtubules of the spindle fibers shorten, and homologues are pulled to opposite poles, while sister chromatids remain attached. The nuclear membrane reforms around each daughter nucleus in telophase I. Interphase between meiosis I and II varies in length and does not include replication of the genome. In every other regard, meiosis II resembles a mitotic division. In prophase II, the nuclear envelope breaks down and the spindle forms. In metaphase II, the spindle fibers bind to the kinetochores of the sister chromatids attaching each to an opposite pole. In anaphase II, the spindle fibers contract and the sister chromatids are pulled apart. In telophase II, the nuclear membranes re-form and cytokinesis occurs producing four cells with a haploid number of chromosomes.
- **Details**: Know how sister chromatids and homologous chromosomes are held together. Understand how alignment at the metaphase plate can produce gametes with different combinations of the parental chromosomes. Know the consequence of **nondisjunction** of the chromosomes in either meiotic division.

11.4 Summing up: Meiosis vs. mitosis
- **Overview**: The behavior of the chromosomes in the first meiotic division is distinctly different from how they behave in a mitotic division. In the first phase of meiosis I, homologous chromosomes find each other and pair allowing **recombination**, a process critical for proper disjunction, to occur. During metaphase I, the kinetochores of sister chromatids fuse and function together, allowing them to move to the same pole of the cell, while in meiosis II and in mitosis, the kinetochores of each sister chromatid become attached to opposite poles. In anaphase I, homologues separate, but sister chromatids do not because of a meiosis-specific cohesion at the centromeres. Both mitosis and

meiosis I begin with DNA replication, but replication is suppressed between the two meiotic divisions. Mitosis produces cells that are identical, while it is rare that meiosis produces identical cells.

- **Details**: Know the **four distinct features of meiosis**, and why these features are essential for a meiotic division to occur. Understand the two reasons why it is rare for meiosis to produce identical cells.

CHALLENGING YOUR UNDERSTANDING

Outline the sexual life cycles of animals, fungi, and some plants, starting with a diploid organism and ending with the generation of a second diploid individual. Indicate fertilization, meiosis and mitosis, and the chromosome number at each stage.

animals   fungi   some plants

KEY TERMS

Match the numbered term with the definition that fits it best. Put the corresponding number in front of the appropriate definition.

1. gamete
2. sister chromatids
3. zygote
4. homologous chromosomes
5. syngamy
6. meiosis
7. diploid
8. haploid
9. sexual reproduction

10. meiosis I
11. meiosis II
12. synapsis
13. crossing over
14. chiasmata
15. independent assortment
16. germ-line cells
17. synaptonemal complex
18. achiasmate segregation

19. aneuploid gametes
20. metaphase plate
21. recombination nodules
22. nondisjunction
23. somatic cells
24. prophase I
25. metaphase I
26. anaphase I
27. telophase I

a. _____ The cells that will eventually undergo meiosis to produce gametes.
b. _____ Sites of contact between homologous chromosomes that are produced as a result of crossing over.
c. _____ The number of chromosomes found in gametes (eggs or sperm).
d. _____ Gametes that contain an improper number of chromosomes and can lead to spontaneous abortion.
e. _____ The failure of chromosomes to move to opposite poles in either meiotic division.
f. _____ The different possible combinations of maternal and paternal chromosomes in gametes.
g. _____ An elaborate structure consisting of homologues closely paired with a lattice of proteins between them.
h. _____ Structures thought to contain the enzymatic machinery necessary to break and rejoin chromatids.
i. _____ The process by which two haploid gametes fuse to form a new diploid cell.
j. _____ Phase of meiosis in which homologous chromosomes align and kinetochore microtubules attach to each.
k. _____ Segregate to opposite poles during the meiosis II to produce four haploid cells.
l. _____ A specialized reduction divison that produces cells with half the normal number of chromosomes.
m. _____ Division, beginning without DNA replication, that resembles mitosis and produces four haploid cells.
n. _____ Phase of meiosis when chiasmata are broken as spindle fibers shorten and homologous pairs are pulled apart.
o. _____ One of two copies of a chromosome, each derived from one parent, found in diploid cell.
p. _____ Meiosis in which there is no recombination, but the homologous chromosomes still divide accurately.
q. _____ Two sets of chromosomes present in the somatic cells of adult individuals.
r. _____ Phase of meiosis in which the chromosomes begin to condense and the microtubule spindle begins to form.
s. _____ The process whereby homologous chromosomes find each other and become closely associated.
t. _____ Reproductive life cycle that involves an alternation between haploid and diploid cells, or organisms.
u. _____ A single cell with a diploid number of chromosomes resulting from the fusion of an egg and a sperm.
v. _____ The initial reduction division in which homologous chromosomes are segregated to two daughter cells.
w. _____ Phase of meiosis in which homologues cluster at the poles of the cells and the nuclear envelope reforms.
x. _____ Cells (egg or sperm) resulting from a meiotic division of germ-line cells, specialized for sexual reproduction.
y. _____ The imaginary plane along which homologous chromosomes align in metaphase I.
z. _____ The nonreproductive cells found in embryos and mature individuals.
aa. _____ A process unique to meiosis in which homologues exchange chromosomal material.

LEARNING BY EXPERIENCE

Set up note cards in much the same manner as for chapter 10. Start with premeiotic interphase since meiosis follows a mitotic division. That card would be identical to the one in your mitosis set. Refer to figure 11.8 in the text. Be sure to label the cards accordingly for meiosis I and meiosis II. When you are familiar with the contents of the cards in sequence, add the mitosis cards and compare them phase for phase, such as mitotic prophase with prophases I and II, etc. Notice any differences such as chromosome numbers and composition in the various phases. When you have mastered this process, you really understand mitosis and meiosis.

EXERCISING YOUR KNOWLEDGE

Briefly answer the following questions in the space provided.

1. Why is reduction division important in a sexual life cycle?

2. How is synapsis different from the manner of homologue pairing in mitosis?

3. Explain homologous recombination.

4. What in the meiotic process results in the reduction of chromosome numbers?

5. (a) When does the synaptonemal complex form? (b) What is it? (c) What results from it?

6. How do anaphase I and mitotic anaphase differ?

7. How do terminal chiasmata affect chromosome movement?

8. How is sexual reproduction disadvantageous to successful, well-adapted organisms?

9. Briefly describe the differences between meiosis and mitosis.

10. Meiosis is the basis of heredity. Explain this statement and why sexual reproduction is advantageous for genetic variation.

Circle the letter of the one best answer in each of the following questions.

11. In a hypothetical cell with six chromosome pairs, how many possible orientations of the chromosomes at the metaphase plate are there?
   a. 6
   b. 12
   c. 32
   d. 64
   e. 256

12. In plants, haploid cells
   a. divide by meiosis.
   b. must immediately undergo syngamy.
   c. will cross over.
   d. differentiate into somatic cclls.
   e. divide by mitosis.

13. In multicellular organisms, the zygote
   a. always divides by mitosis.
   b. may immediately engage in syngamy.
   c. always divides by meiosis.
   d. may divide by meiosis.
   e. can only divide by binary fission.

14. An organism with eight pairs of chromosomes in somatic tissue will have ___ chromosomes in germ-line tissue.
   a. 2
   b. 4
   c. 8
   d. 16
   e. 32

15. _____ distinguishes prophase I from mitotic prophase.
   a. The number of chromatids per chromosome
   b. Synapsis
   c. The number of homologues
   d. Terminal chiasmata
   e. The synergistic complex

16. The synaptonemal complex forms during
   a. prophase II.
   b. metaphase II.
   c. anaphase I.
   d. metaphase I.
   e. prophase I.

17. Crossing over occurs in
   a. prophase II.
   b. metaphase II.
   c. anaphase II.
   d. prophase I.
   e. metaphasc I.

18. Chromosomes condense tightly in
    a. prophase II.
    b. metaphase II.
    c. prophase I.
    d. metaphase I.
    e. telophase I.

19. When crossing over is complete in prophase I, sister chromatids
    a. are fused together by the synaptonemal complex.
    b. are attached by their ends to the nuclear envelope.
    c. are held together near their common centromeres.
    d. drift away from each other.
    e. are pulled toward the poles.

20. The presence of chiasmata indicates that two chromatids
    a. are about to form a synapse.
    b. are haploid.
    c. are identical.
    d. have exchanged parts.
    e. are in a synaptonemal complex.

21. Recombination nodules are found in
    a. prophase II.
    b. metaphase II.
    c. interphase.
    d. metaphase I.
    e. prophase I.

22. Homologues with exchanged parts separate in
    a. prophase II.
    b. metaphase II.
    c. telophase I.
    d. metaphase I.
    e. anaphase I.

23. The synaptonemal complex disassembles in
    a. prophase II.
    b. metaphase II.
    c. telophase I.
    d. metaphase I.
    e. prophase I.

24. Terminal chiasmata are most likely to be seen in
    a. prophase I.
    b. metaphase I.
    c. anaphase I.
    d. telophase I.
    e. interphase.

25. In telophase I,
    a. unaltered chromosomes cluster at the poles.
    b. identical chromatids cluster at the poles.
    c. nonidentical chromatids cluster at the poles.
    d. separate but identical chromatids cluster at the poles.
    e. chiasmata cluster at the poles.

26. In anaphase I, the _____ are pulled apart.
    a. homologous pairs
    b. centromeres
    c. kinetochores
    d. sister chromatids
    e. centrioles

27. Unique to meiosis is the omission of chromosome replication between
    a. telophase I and prophase II.
    b. prophase I and metaphase I.
    c. prophase II and telophase II.
    d. telophase II and interphase.
    e. metaphase I and anaphase I.

28. _____ may or may not occur between telophase I and prophase II.
    a. Synapsis
    b. Syngamy
    c. Diakinesis
    d. Chiasma
    e. Cytokinesis

29. In anaphase I,
    a. sister chromatids move toward opposite poles.
    b. homologous chromosomes move toward opposite poles.
    c. terminal chiasmata move toward opposite poles.
    d. homologues move toward the same poles.
    e. homologous chromosomes move randomly toward either pole.

30. Sexual reproduction favors
    a. genetic stability.
    b. retention of key genes.
    c. stable populations.
    d. beneficial recombination.
    e. genetic diversity.

ASSESSING YOUR KNOWLEDGE

Answers to the questions in the following sections test your ability to synthesize information gained from the chapter and to solve challenging problems on an exam or in everyday life.

Challenging Your Understanding—Answers

(Refer to figure 11.2 in the text.)

<u>Animal</u>
Diploid (2n)
   ↓ Meiosis
Gametes (n)
   ↓Fertilization
Zygote (2n)
   ↓Mitosis
Diploid individual (2n)

<u>Fungi</u>
Zygote (2n)
   ↓Meiosis
4 haploid cells (n)
   ↓Mitosis
8 haploid cells (n)
   ↓
Gametes (n)
   ↓Fertilization
Zygote (2n)

<u>Some plants</u>
Diploid (2n)
   ↓Meiosis
Haploid cells (n)
   ↓Mitosis
Haploid individual (n)
   ↓
Gametes (n)
   ↓Fertilization
Zygote (2n)
   ↓Mitosis
Diploid individual (2n)

Key Terms—Answers

a. 16, b. 14, c. 8, d. 19, e. 22, f. 15, g. 17, h. 21, i. 5, j. 25, k. 2, l. 6, m. 11, n. 26, o. 4, p. 18, q. 7, r. 24, s. 12, t. 9, u. 3, v. 10, w. 27, x. 1, y. 20, z. 23, aa. 13.

Learning by Experience—Answers

Premeiotic telophase   The same as for mitosis
Prophase I: Chromosomes condense tightly. Synaptonemal complex forms. Genes cross over between homologues. Synaptonemal complex disassembles. Chromosomes decondense, and transcription occurs, causing rapid growth. Transcription ceases, and chromosomes recondense. Chiasmata become terminal. Nuclear membrane disperses. Spindle forms.
Metaphase I: Homologues align on metaphase plate.

Microtubules attach to one side of each centromere.
Anaphase I: Centromeres remain together as both sister chromatids are drawn to the same pole. Distribution of maternal and paternal homologues occurs randomly.
Telophase I: Nuclear membrane forms around each daughter nucleus containing nonidentical sister chromatids. (Cytokinesis may or may not follow.)
Prophase II: Nuclear envelope breaks down, and a new spindle forms.
Metaphase II: Chromosomes align on the metaphase plate. Spindle fibers bind to both sides of centromeres.
Anaphase II: Centromeres split. Sister chromatids move to opposite poles.
Telophase II: Nuclear envelope forms around four nonidentical sets of daughter chromosomes.

Exercising Your Knowledge—Answers

As you check your answers, put a mark in the review (Rvw) column for the answers you missed. If you didn't miss any, congratulations—you have mastered the chapter! If you missed some, review the section (Sect.) in the text where this concept is discussed. In order to develop an efficient review strategy, it is important that you understand what types of questions you missed. The questions with asterisks test more for understanding of the **concepts**, whereas the others test more for **detail**. *See the preface for learning strategies for concepts and for details.*

	Sect.	Rvw.
*1. Reduction division is necessary to prevent the chromosome number from increasing with each generation.	11.1	
*2. In synapsis, homologous chromosomes pair along their length. In mitosis, the chromosomes pair only at their centromeres.	11.2	
*3. In homologous recombination, genes are exchanged between homologues as they are aligned, gene for gene, in the synaptonemal complex.	11.2	
*4. Chromosome reduction results from the omission of chromosome replication between telophase I and prophase II.	11.3	
*5. (a) The synaptonemal complex forms during prophase I. (b) The synaptonemal complex is a lattice of protein laid down between homologues. (c) Genes are matched between the homologues, allowing crossing over.	11.2 11.3	
*6. In anaphase I, homologous chromosomes are drawn toward opposite poles. In mitotic anaphase, sister chromatids are drawn to opposite poles.	11.3	
*7. Chiasmata hold the homologues in such a position that microtubules can only attach to one side. The result is that the sister chromatids travel together to the same pole.	11.3	
*8. Because of the recombination that occurs in meiosis, advantageous combinations are disrupted.	11.4	

*9. Mitosis is preceded by DNA replication, but the second meiotic division, which resembles mitosis, is not preceded by DNA replication. During metaphase I of the first meiotic division, the kinetochores of sister chromatids fuse and function together allowing chromatids to migrate to the same pole in anaphase I, but in mitosis, the sister chromatids migrate to opposite poles in anaphase. Sister chromatid cohesion is maintained through the first meiotic division, but not in the second meiotic division. The sister chromatids segregate to opposite poles in mitosis, similar to the second meiotic division, but distinctly different from the first. Homologous chromosomes are paired in meiosis I and undergo recombination to form chiasmata that physically connect the homologues, while recombination between sister chromatids is suppressed. Chromosomes are not paired with homologues in mitosis.	11.2 11.3	
*10. Meiosis produces gametes in males or females, which contain one set of chromosomes as a result of independent assortment of the maternal and paternal chromosomes. When two gametes fuse during fertilization, a zygote, or a single, diploid cell containing two sets of chromosomes, one from its mother and the second from its father, is formed. This zygote will undergo numerous mitotic divisions to become a multicellular organism. Each mitotic division will produce cells that are identical in chromosomal content as the original cell. Germ-line cells of this second individual will undergo meiosis to produce haploid gametes containing one set of chromosomes that represents a combination of his/her maternal and paternal chromosomes. In this way, chromosomes, and therefore genes, and heritable mutations are passed from one generation to the next, supporting the statement that meiosis is the basis of heredity. The haploid cells resulting from meiosis are not identical and therefore allow variation in the offspring because orientation of the chromosomes in meiosis I is random allowing for independent assortment of the genes. This variation is further increased by genetic recombination, which shuffles the arrangements of genes on chromosomes.	11.1 11.4	
11. d	11.3	
12. e	11.1	
13. a	11.1	
14. c	11.1	
15. b	11.2	
16. e	11.2	
17. d	11.2	
18. c	11.3	
*19. c	11.3	
*20. d	11.3	
21. e	11.3	
22. e	11.3	
23. e	11.3	
24. b	11.3	

*25. c	11.3	
26. a	11.3	
*27. a	11.3	
28. e	11.3	
*29. b	11.3	
30. e	11.4	

CHAPTER 12 PATTERNS OF INHERITANCE

MASTERING KEY CONCEPTS
Understanding this chapter is key to understanding genetics.

12.1 Mystery of heredity
- **Overview**: **Mendel's** experiments on the **inheritance of traits** in pea plants and the mathematical analysis of his results led to the present model that parental traits are transmitted to offspring and segregate among the progeny, and refuted the idea of blended inheritance.
- **Details**: Know the experiments of **Kolreuter** and **Knight** and the observations that supported Mendel's model of inheritance. Know the three stages of Mendel's experimental design.

12.2 Monohybrid crosses: The Principle of Segregation
- **Overview**: Using **monohybrid crosses**, Mendel observed that the **F_1 generation** exhibited only one of two possible traits and did not exhibit a blending of traits. The expressed trait is **dominant**, while the alternate, unexpressed trait is **recessive**. In the **F_2 generation**, Mendel found that both traits were again expressed in a **phenotypic ratio of 3 dominant: 1 recessive**. From these experiments, Mendel was able to devise the first law of heredity based on the physical behavior of chromosomes in meiosis. **The Principle of Segregation** states that two **alleles** of a gene **segregate** during gamete formation and will rejoin at random, one from each parent, at fertilization. Human **pedigrees** indicate that human traits exhibit both dominant and recessive inheritance.
- **Details**: Know the four results that Mendel learned from his experiments using monohybrid crosses. Understand the difference between **genotype** and **phenotype**, and **dominant** and **recessive** alleles. Know the five elements of Mendel's model of inheritance. Know how to use a **Punnett square** to analyze Mendelian crosses, and how to interpret the genotypic and phenotypic ratios of the offspring.

12.3 Dihybrid crosses: The Principle of Independent Assortment
- **Overview**: Mendel observed that in a **dihybrid cross**, the F_1 generation exhibits two of four possible traits and the F_2 generation exhibits four types of progeny in a **9:3:3:1 phenotypic ratio**. This result is the basis for Mendel's second law of heredity, the **Principle of Independent Assortment**, which states that when individuals with two different traits are crossed, the alleles of each gene **assort independently**.
- **Details**: Know how to use a Punnett square to analyze a dihybrid cross.

12.4 Probability can be used to predict the results of crosses.
- **Overview**: Two rules govern the probability of an outcome in a monohybrid cross, the **rule of addition**, and the **rule of multiplication**. For **two mutually exclusive events**, the probability of either event occurring is the **sum** of the individual probabilities. **For two independent events**, the probability of both events occurring is the **product** of their individual probabilities. Probabilities from monohybrid crosses can be used with the product rule to predict the outcome of a dihybrid cross.
- **Details**: Know how these two rules can be applied to monohybrid and dihybrid crosses to predict the outcomes of genetic crosses.

12.5 A testcross can be used to determine an unknown genotype.
- **Overview**: A **testcross** to a **homozygous recessive** individual can be used to determine whether the genotype of an unknown individual, exhibiting the dominant phenotype is **homozygous dominant** or **heterozygous** for a specific trait. A testcross can also be used when two traits are involved by determining whether either of the traits breed true among the progeny obtained when the individual is crossed with one that is homozygous recessive for both traits.
- **Details**: Know how to perform a monohybrid and a dihybrid testcross, the possible outcomes, and how to interpret the results.

12.6 Extensions to Mendel's laws of inheritance
- **Overview**: There are several **exceptions to Mendel's laws** that exist and make predicting a trait more complex. When the action of more than one gene affects one trait (**polygenic inheritance**), **continuous variation**, or a contribution of different combinations of alleles to one trait can occur. A single gene can also affect more than one trait (**pleiotropy**) and pleiotropic effects have been found to contribute to many inherited disorders. Other exceptions are the facts that **more than two alleles typically exist for any gene** in a given population, and some genes display **incomplete dominance**, or **codominance** of alleles. Genes can also be **affected by the environment** and gene products can affect the expression of other genes due to **epistatic relationships**. All of these factors can affect the traits of an individual.
- **Details**: Know the exceptions to Mendel's laws and examples of these exceptions. Understand why these exceptions occur.

CHALLENGING YOUR UNDERSTANDING

1. Draw a flowchart that demonstrates the steps that should be taken to perform a monohybrid cross.

2. Draw the gametes that result from TtYy x TtYy and a Punnett square that results from this dihybrid cross.

KEY TERMS

Match the numbered term with the definition that fits it best. Put the corresponding number in front of the appropriate definition.

1. monohybrid cross
2. true-breeding
3. segregation
4. cpistasis
5. self-fertilization
6. cross-fertilization
7. reciprocal crosses
8. alleles
9. homozygous
10. heterozygous

11. genotype
12. phenotype
13. Principle of Segregation
14. Punnett square
15. pedigree
16. dihybrid cross
17. Principle of Independent
   Assortment
18. testcross
19. polygenic inheritance

20. pleoitropic
21. continuous variation
22. incomplete dominance
23. first filial generation (F_1)
24. dominant
25. recessive
26. second filial generation (F_2)
27. codominant

a. _____ The second law of heredity that states that in a dihybrid cross, the alleles of each gene assort independently.

b. _____ The physical appearance and other observable features that result from the expression of an allele.

c. _____ Pollen from a white plant fertilizes a purple-colored plant; pollen from a purple plant fertilizes a white one.

d. _____ The form of each trait that is expressed in the F_1 generation.

e. _____ The heterozygote is intermediate in appearance between the two homozygotes.

f. _____ To follow the behavior of two different traits in a single cross.

g. _____ Offspring obtained by allowing the F_1 generation to self-fertilize.

h. _____ A gradation that results from a contribution of different combinations of alleles to a single trait.

i. _____ The first generation of offspring produced as a result of crossing two parental lines.

j. _____ Gametes produced by the male and female parts of two different flowers fuse to form viable offspring.

k. _____ The form of each trait that is present but not expressed in the F_1 generation.

l. _____ An allele that has more than one effect on the phenotype of an individual.

m. _____ Each allele has its own effect and some aspect of both alleles is seen in the heterozygote.

n. _____ A method in which an individual of unknown genotype is crossed to a homozygous recessive individual.

o. _____ The offspring produced when two haploid gametes containing the same allele fuse during fertilization.

p. _____ To follow the behavior of two variations of a single trait in a cross.

q. _____ Alternative forms of observed characters being distributed among the progeny of a mating.

r. _____ A graphical representation of matings and offspring over multiple generations for a particular trait.

s. _____ Gametes produced by the male and female parts of the same flower fuse to form viable offspring.

t. _____ The total set of alleles that an individual contains, which provides the blueprint for an individual's traits.

u. _____ A situation in which the expression of one gene can interfere with the phenotypic effects of a second gene.

v. _____ The first law of heredity states that two alleles for a gene segregate during gamete formation and rejoin randomly.

w. _____ The action of more than one gene can affect a single trait.

x. _____ The offspring produced from self-fertilization remain uniform from one generation to the next.

y. _____ The offspring produced when two haploid gametes containing different alleles fuse during fertilization.

z. _____ A simple diagram predicting the possible genotypes of a progeny based on the identity of the parental gametes.

aa. _____ The alternative forms of a single gene that exist in a population.

LEARNING BY EXPERIENCE

To better visualize Mendel's experiments and findings, construct Punnett squares. First, some advice about setting up the Punnett squares: The name *Punnett square* is always used even if the figure turns out to be oblong instead of square. The Punnett square consists of intersecting columns—vertical columns for the gametes of one parent and horizontal columns for the gametes of the other parent. It makes no difference which direction is assigned to which parent.

1. In the space below, try constructing a Punnett square to predict the offspring of a cross between one parent whose genotype is *WW* and one whose genotype is *ww* ($WW \times ww$). Draw one vertical column for each different gamete that can be produced by parent number one (*WW*) and one horizontal row for each different gamete that can be produced by parent number two (*ww*). In this case, there can only be one gamete produced (*W*) by parent number one and one gamete (w) produced by parent number two so you need to draw only one column consisting of one row. There are no other possible gametes; therefore, no other columns or rows are needed. Though you *could* draw two columns or two rows for each parent, both would be identical and predict the same progeny. Therefore, it is only necessary to draw a new column for different gamete types. Now fill in the resulting square by combining the two gametes, as in fertilization. The Punnett square is now complete. Next, using this Punnett square, determine the genotypic and phenotypic ratios for this F_1 generation.

2. Assume that the individuals are not human and it will be alright to mate members of this F_1 generation. Complete a Punnett square for the F_2 generation, and determine its genotypic and phenotypic ratios.

3. A more complex problem involves the simultaneous consideration of two traits. Remember that yellow seeds are dominant over green, and purple flowers are dominant over white. To keep this problem relatively simple, we will consider one parent to be heterozygous for one trait and the other parent to be heterozygous for the other trait. Each is homozygous for the second trait. Thus, the parental genotypes would be *Ppgg* and *ppYy*. Remember that one gene for each trait will appear in each gamete. Remember also that homologues are segregated in anaphase I. Observing some conventions reduces the probability of errors. Always keep capital letters first among alleles. However, when dealing with two traits at the same time, either in gametes or genotypes, always keep the same letter first, regardless of capital. Remember that gametes are haploid and offspring are diploid. In the genotypes, always group the same letters together (*PpYy* not *PGpy*). Complete a Punnett square for the parents described, and determine the genotypic and phenotypic ratios.

EXERCISING YOUR KNOWLEDGE
Briefly answer the following questions in the space provided.

1. Explain how to make a hybrid plant.

2. Explain where the recessive trait is hiding in the F_1 generation of Mendel's crosses.

3. What important information was Mendel able to interpret from the monohybrid crosses?

4. What important information was Mendel able to interpret from the dihybrid crosses?

5. Explain when to use the rule of addition vs. the rule of multiplication.

6. (a) How is a testcross performed? (b) How is it interpreted?

7. Explain polygenic inheritance.

8. Explain how codominance is different from incomplete dominance.

9. Why is one genotype possible for a person with type AB blood, while two are possible for a person with type A blood?

10. Explain epistasis.

Circle the letter of the one best answer in each of the following questions.

11. What are variations of a gene called?
    a. dominant genes
    b. progeny
    c. alleles
    d. homologues
    e. sisters

12. One of the early ideas about heredity that was refuted by Mendel was
    a. traits can be masked in some generations.
    b. traits are segregated among progeny.
    c. alleles do not influence each other.
    d. traits are transmitted directly.
    e. not all copies of a factor are identical.

13. Compared to the work of previous geneticists, the unique characteristic of Mendel's work was
    a. keeping quantitative records of numbers of different progeny.
    b. choosing the garden pea for his experiment.
    c. producing hybrids.
    d. studying more than one generation.
    e. crossing true-breeding plants.

14. If you cross a true-breeding dominant plant with a true-breeding recessive plant, what will be the phenotype of the resulting progeny?
    a. all dominant
    b. all recessive
    c. 50% dominant / 50% recessive
    d. 75% dominant / 25% recessive
    e. 25% dominant / 75% recessive

15. If you self-fertilize the progeny from above, what will be the dominant to recessive phenotypic ratio of the progeny?
    a. 4:1
    b. 3:1
    c. 2:1
    d. 1:2:1
    f. 1:3:1

16. An individual who has two of the same allele is said to be
    a. homozygous.
    b. heteromologous.
    c. homologous.
    d. heterozygous.
    e. diplozygous.

17. The appearance resulting from a given gene combination is referred to as the
    a. genotype.
    b. phenotype.
    c. phototype.
    d. allelotype.
    e. stereotype.

18. Where two alternatives for a trait are broad and narrow and broad is dominant, the phenotype of a homozygous dominant individual would be expressed as
    a. *BB*.
    b. *nn*.
    c. *Bn*.
    d. *NN*.
    e. broad.

19. If two alternatives for a trait are red and white and red is dominant, the genotype of a homozygous dominant individual would be expressed as
    a. *RR*.
    b. *rr*.
    c. *WW*.
    d. *ww*.
    e. red.

20. Where two alternatives for a trait are tall and short and tall is dominant, the genotype of a heterozygous individual would be expressed as
    a. *sS*.
    b. *ss*.
    c. *SS*.
    d. *Ss*.
    e. tall.

21. In Mendel's F_2 generation of purple and white flower crossing, the dominant to recessive phenotypic ratio was
    a. 1:3:1.
    b. 3:1.
    c. 1:1.
    d. 9:7.
    e. 9:3:3:1.

22. Which of the following represents a dihybrid?
    a. *WWSs*
    b. *WwSS*
    c. *WwSs*
    d. *WWss*
    e. WwSs

23. How many different phenotypes appear in the F_2 generation of a dihybrid cross?
    a. 1
    b. 2
    c. 3
    d. 4
    e. 5

24. The principle of independent assortment predicts that
    a. genes are malleable factors.
    b. genes are discrete factors.
    c. alleles segregate during meiosis.
    d. alleles of one gene assort independently of alleles of other genes.
    e. genes can be mutated.

25. If there is 25% chance that a child will inherit a recessive disease from it parents, what is the probability that one of a couple's first three children will have the disease?
    a. 10%
    b. 25%
    c. 50%
    d. 75%
    e. 100%

26. If there is an equal chance that a child will be male or female, what is the probability that both of a couple's first two children will be female?
    a. 0%
    b. 10%
    c. 25%
    d. 50%
    e. 100%

27. Which of the following represents a testcross?
    a. *Ww* × *WW*
    b. *ww* × *WW*
    c. *Ww* × *Ww*
    d. *WW* × *WW*
    e. none of these

28. Which of the following is the main reason to perform a testcross?
    a. determine the genotype of a plant
    b. determine the phenotype of a plant
    c. determine which allele is dominant
    d. make a mutation
    e. determine the age of a plant

29. An allele having more than one effect on an individual's phenotype is called
    a. a polygene.
    b. synteny.
    c. codominance.
    d. polysony.
    e. pleiotropy.

30. The darkness of the ears of Siamese cats is an example of
    a. a mutation.
    b. a pleiotropic effect.
    c. a polygene.
    d. epistasis.
    e. an environmental effect.

ASSESSING YOUR KNOWLEDGE

Answers to the questions in the following sections test your ability to synthesize information gained from the chapter and to solve challenging problems on an exam or in everyday life.

Challenging Your Understanding—Answers

1.

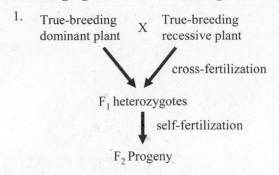

True-breeding dominant plant X True-breeding recessive plant

cross-fertilization

F$_1$ heterozygotes

self-fertilization

F$_2$ Progeny

2. **Gametes**: TY, Ty, tY, ty; TY, Ty, tY, ty

	TY	Ty	tY	ty
TY	TTYY	TTYy	TtYY	TtYy
Ty	TTYy	TTyy	TtYy	Ttyy
tY	TyYY	TtYy	ttYY	ttYy
ty	TtYy	Ttyy	ttYy	ttyy

Key Terms—Answers

a. 17, b. 12, c. 7, d. 24, e. 22, f. 16, g. 26, h. 21, i. 23, j. 6, k. 25, l. 20, m. 27, n. 18, o. 9, p. 1, q. 3, r. 15, s. 5, t. 11, u. 4, v. 13, w. 19, x. 2, y. 10, z. 14, aa. 8.

Learning by Experience—Answers

1.

	W
w	Ww

Genotypic ratio 1:0

Phenotypic ratio 1:0

2.

	W	w
W	WW	Ww
w	Ww	ww

Genotypic ratio 1:2:1

Phenotypic ratio 3:1

3.

	Py	py
pY	PpYy	ppYy
py	Ppyy	ppyy

Genotypic ratio 1:1:1:1

Phenotypic ratio 1:1:1:1

Exercising Your Knowledge—Answers

As you check your answers, put a mark in the review (Rvw) column for the answers you missed. If you missed some, review the section (Sect.) in the text where this concept is discussed. In order to develop an efficient review strategy, it is important that you understand what types of questions you missed. The questions with asterisks test more for understanding of the **concepts**, whereas the others test more for **detail**. *See the preface for learning strategies for concepts and for details.*

	Sect.	Rvw.
*1. A true-breeding plant displaying one trait is cross-fertilized with a true-breeding plant displaying a different trait. The progeny will be hybrids.	12.2	
*2. One allele of the recessive trait is present in the F$_1$ progeny but its expression is not observed because the expression of the dominant allele masks it.	12.2	
*3. Monohybrid crosses demonstrated that alleles segregate during reproduction.	12.2	
*4. Dihybrid crosses demonstrated that alleles of one trait segregate independently of the alleles of other traits.	12.3	
*5. The rule of addition is used when only one of several possibilities is sought while the rule of multiplication is used when more than one outcome is sought. Use the rule of addition when A OR B is required, use rule of multiplication when A AND B are required.	12.4	
*6. (a) A testcross is performed by mating a homozygous recessive individual with an individual displaying the dominant trait. (b) If any of the offspring display the recessive trait, the parent showing the dominant trait is heterozygous. If not, the parent is homozygous dominant.	12.5	
*7. Many traits result from the additive expression of more than one gene.	12.6	
*8. In codominance, both alleles are expressed and provide independent phenotypes. In incomplete dominance, both alleles expressed blend together to form an intermediate phenotype.	12.6	
*9. Three alleles of the I gene exist and produce the different ABO blood types. The AB type represents an A gene on one chromosome and a B gene on the other. The type A must have an A allele on one chromosome but the other could be either an A or an i (allele for type O).	12.6	
*10. Epistasis involves the inheritance of two or more enzymes that act sequentially. Any disruption of enzymes acting early in the sequence will prevent the action of those later in the sequence.	12.6	
11. c	12.2	
*12. d	12.2	
13. a	12.1	
*14. a	12.2	

*15. b	12.2	
16. a	12.2	
17. b	12.2	
18. e	12.2	
19. a	12.2	
20. d	12.2	
21. b	12.2	
*22. c	12.3	
*23. d	12.3	
*24. d	12.3	
*25. d	12.4	
*26. c	12.4	
27. b	12.5	
*28. a	12.5	
29. e	12.6	
30. e	12.6	

CHAPTER 13 CHROMOSOMES, MAPPING, AND THE MEIOSIS-INHERITANCE CONNECTION

MASTERING KEY CONCEPTS

Much of the information in this chapter is dealt with historically. Do not discount it as just a history lesson. As you see how scientists acquired their knowledge of genetics, you can gain from that knowledge. Follow closely.

13.1 Sex linkage and the chromosomal theory of inheritance

- **Overview**: **Genes** determining **Mendelian traits** are on **chromosomes**. These traits **segregate** in genetic crosses because homologues separate during gamete formation in **meiosis**. **Mutations** are heritable alterations in genetic material.
- **Details**: Know the experimental details of the genetic crosses in *Drosophila* performed by **Thomas Hunt Morgan**. Understand the results of the **parental cross**, the cross of the F_1 **progeny**, and the **testcross** performed by Morgan. Understand how his work supported **Walter Sutton's hypothesis** of the **chromosomal theory of inheritance** and how Morgan reached the conclusion that eye color is a **sex-linked** trait, determined by a gene on the **X chromosome**.

13.2 Sex chromosomes and sex determination

- **Overview**: While the structure and number of the **sex chromosomes** varies among species, there is always a difference between the chromosomes of the two sexes. For humans, maleness is typically determined by the presence of a **Y chromosome**, while females have **two X chromosomes**. One of these is inactivated (**Barr body**) to prevent the overproduction of proteins produced by genes located on the X chromosome. This inactivation can lead to **genetic mosaics**, where individual cells express different alleles.
- **Details**: Know the difference between **autosomes** and **sex chromosomes**. Know the function of the *SRY* gene on the Y chromosome. Understand why **color blindness** and **hemophilia** are more common in males. Analyze the Royal Hemophilia Pedigree and try to understand why some of the progeny of a genetic cross are afflicted, while their brothers or sisters are not. Understand in the example of the calico cat (a genetic mosaic), how the cat can have areas of orange, black, and white fur as a result of two different genetic effects, **X chromosome inactivation** and **epistasis**.

13.3 There are exceptions to the chromosomal theory of inheritance.

- **Overview**: Any trait determined by the action of genes in the **mitochondria** or in **chloroplasts** will not show Mendelian inheritance because these organelles contain their own genomes and are not partitioned with the nuclear genome in meiosis. Organelles, such as the mitochondria and chloroplasts, unlike nuclear material, are generally inherited from only one parent, the mother (**maternal inheritance**) because the egg cell contains a great deal more cytoplasm.
- **Details**: Understand why not all inheritance is determined by chromosomes. Know why **mitochondria and chloroplasts** are two organelles that exhibit **non-Mendelian inheritance**. Know the conclusions reached from **Ruth Sager's** work on *Chlamydomonas*.

13.4 Genetic mapping

- **Overview**: **Independent assortment** is not due solely to the alignment of chromosomes in meiosis, but is due also to the exchange of alleles by **crossing over of homologues** during meiosis. As the physical distance between two linked genes on a chromosome increases, so does the probability of crossover (**recombination**) occurring between the two genetic loci. Therefore, the frequency of recombination due to crossing over is a measure of genetic distance and the basis for the construction of **genetic maps**.
- **Details**: Understand the experimental details and the conclusions reached by **Morgan, McClintock, and Creighton**, and **Morgan and Sturtevant**. Know how to use the two-point testcross to map genes, how to determine the **recombinaton frequency** and the **distance between genetic loci** in **centimorgans**. Know how to use the **three-point cross** to put genes in order. Understand how **anonymous markers** and the characterization of **single-nucleotide polymorphisms** have contributed to the construction of human genetic maps.

13.5 Human genetic disorders

- **Overview:** Genetic disorders can result from a single base pair change in one critical protein, or from **aneuploidy,** which results from the **nondisjunction of autosomes** and leads to the gain or the loss of a chromosome. Genetic problems also arise from the **nondisjunction of the sex chromosomes,** but do not typically produce the severe developmental defects associated with the gain or loss of an autosome. Today, **genetic counseling** can be used to assess the genetic state of an embryo.
- **Details:** Understand how **sickle cell anemia, Down syndrome, Klinefelter syndrome,** and

Jacob syndrome arise. Understand the concept of **genomic imprinting**. Know how **pedigree analysis, amniocentesis,** and **chorionic villi sampling** can help to detect genetic defects in unborn embryos.

CHALLENGING YOUR UNDERSTANDING

1. Write these genes in order from the most tightly linked to gene A to the least tightly linked to gene A.

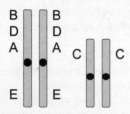

2. Draw the progression of the following pair of homologous, parental chromosomes as a crossover occurs between gene G and gene H.

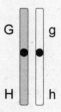

KEY TERMS

Match the numbered term with the definition that fits it best. Put the corresponding number in front of the appropriate definition.

1. chromosomal theory of inheritance
2. mutation
3. X chromosome
4. Y chromosome
5. sex-linked
6. autosomes
7. crossing over
8. hemophilia
9. genetic map
10. centimorgan
11. three-point cross
12. wild-type
13. sex chromosomes
14. Barr body
15. nondisjunction
16. aneuploidy
17. monosomics
18. trisomics
19. Down syndrome
20. amniocentesis
21. dosage compensation
22. genetic mosaic
23. chorionic villi sampling
24. maternal inheritance
25. anonymous markers
26. single-nucleotide polymorphisms
27. genomic imprinting

a. ____ Females whose individual cells may express different alleles depending on which chromosome is inactivated.
b. ____ The normal nucleotide sequence of a chromosome that is found in the wild.
c. ____ The failure of homologues or sister chromatids to separate properly during meiosis.
d. ____ Genetic markers detectable by molecular techniques that do not cause a detectable phenotype.
e. ____ The condition that occurs when a small portion of chromosome 21 is present in three copies instead of two.
f. ____ A map unit consisting of 1% of recombination determined from a two-point testcross.
g. ____ A difference between an individual of a population that affects a single base of a genetic locus.
h. ____ A procedure used in the prenatal diagnosis of genetic disorders by analysis of the fluid that bathes a fetus.
i. ____ Uniparental inheritance from the mother typical of cellular organelles such as the mitochondria.
j. ____ Humans that have gained an extra copy of an autosome and generally do not survive.
k. ____ Maleness is typically determined by the presence of this chromosome.
l. ____ An inactivated, highly condensed X chromosome attached to the nuclear membrane.
m. ____ A condition in which a chromosome is gained or lost as a result of nondisjunction.
n. ____ A trait determined by a gene located on the X chromosome.
o. ____ A procedure used in genetic screening where cells are removed from a membranous part of the placenta.
p. ____ Twenty-two chromosomal pairs perfectly matched in both males and females.
q. ____ Ensures an equal level of expression from the sex chromosomes in males and females.
r. ____ The physical exchange of genetic material between homologues during meiosis.
s. ____ An unnatural, heritable change in the nucleotide sequence of a chromosome.
t. ____ Allows the detection of double crossovers such that genes can be put into order.
u. ____ An individual with two of these chromosomes produces only one type of gametes.
v. ____ Humans that have lost even one copy of an autosome and generally do not survive embryonic development.
w. ____ The phenotype caused by a specific allele is exhibited when the allele comes from one parent, not the other.
x. ____ One pair of 23 pairs of chromosomes found in humans that distinguishes the gender of an individual.
y. ____ Genes determining Mendelian traits are located on chromosomes that play a central role in heredity.
z. ____ Positioning of genes on a chromosome based on genetic distance being proportional to recombination frequency.
aa. ____ A disease that is more common in males because the gene affected is on the X chromosome.

LEARNING BY EXPERIENCE

A crossover is the exchange of the ends of homologous chromosomes during meiosis I. These crossovers produce recombinant chromosomes and hence recombinant progeny when the homologues contain different alleles.

1. Draw the chromosomes of the two recombinant progeny that can result from cross of the following parents.

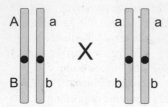

2. Draw the recombinant homologous pairs of chromosomes that can be produced from this homologous chromosome. Hint: remember that double crossovers can occur.

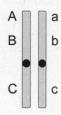

3. Thomas Hunt Morgan studied fruit flies and discovered that a mutation of a gene on the X chromosome caused the normal red eyes of flies to become white. Because this gene is located on the X chromosome, we say that the white-eye gene is sex-linked. You have learned that sex-linkage will cause this gene to follow a nontraditional pattern of inheritance. Draw a Punnett square for the cross of a heterozygous red-eyed female (Rr) with a red-eyed male (RY) to determine the genotypic and phenotypic ratios that would result.

EXERCISING YOUR KNOWLEDGE

Briefly answer the following questions in the space provided.

1. Why do sex-linked, recessive traits occur more often in males than in females?

2. Why did Thomas Morgan need to perform a testcross with his red-eyed females?

3. In Morgan's experiment, he found that female fruit flies could have white eyes. How could that happen if the trait is sex-linked?

4. (a) How can genes located on the same chromosome assort during meiosis as if they were on different chromosomes? (b) How far apart must they be for this to be true?

5. How are recombinant chromosomes distinguished from parental ones?

6. Why is the number of recombinant progeny an underestimate of the distance between two very distant genes?

7. All male individuals inheriting the gene for "Royal hemophilia" had the disease. Why is this not true of other forms of hemophilia?

8. How can nondisjunction lead to trisomy 21?

9. How are genes modified in genomic imprinting?

10. What is amniocentesis used for?

Circle the letter of the one best answer in each of the following questions.

11. What conclusion(s) is/are suggested if a normal and a mutant fly are crossed and the only mutant progeny observed are male?
    a. Mutation is located on the X chromosome.
    b. Mutation is located on the Y chromosome.
    c. Mutation is lethal to females.
    d. Mutation is lethal to males.
    e. Both a and c are possible explanations.

12. On which of the sex chromosomes is a sex-linked gene usually carried?
    a. 13
    b. 15
    c. 18
    d. Y
    e. X

13. If a red-eyed male fly is mated to a homozygous red-eyed female fly, what percentage of the male offspring will have red eyes?
    a. 100%
    b. 75%
    c. 50%
    d. 25%
    e. 0%

14. Morgan discovered that the white eye mutation in fruit flies is:
    a. autosomal.
    b. lethal in females.
    c. sex-linked.
    d. on the Y chromosome.
    e. dominant.

15. What important contribution did Thomas Morgan's experiments with the white eye mutation provide for the field of genetics?
    a. the importance of the eye color in flies
    b. genes reside on chromosomes
    c. flies have sex chromosomes
    d. independent assortment of genes
    e. segregation of alleles

16. What determines the sex of a human?
    a. presence or absence of an X chromosome
    b. presence of absence of a Y chromosome
    c. presence of two X chromosomes
    d. absence of a Y chromosome
    e. environmental conditions

17. Which of the following is an example of a sex-linked human disease?
    a. Tay-Sachs disease
    b. cystic fibrosis
    c. Huntington disease
    d. hemophilia
    e. sickle cell anemia

18. Of the two X chromosomes inherited by human females, one becomes
    a. a mutant.
    b. an allele.
    c. inactivated.
    d. an autosome.
    e. an O chromosome.

19. What molecular structure is responsible for the mosaic coloring of calico cats?
    a. Y chromosome
    b. Barr body
    c. nuclear envelope
    d. cell membrane
    e. mitochondria

20. The inheritance of mitochondrial genes is an example of which of the following?
    a. paternal inheritance
    b. biparental inheritance
    c. uniparental inheritance
    d. chromosomal inheritance
    e. Mendelian inheritance

21. Generation of a genetic map is dependent on which normal cellular process?
    a. mitosis
    b. asexual reproduction
    c. independent assortment
    d. mutation
    e. recombination

22. A centimorgan is a unit of measure that corresponds to:
    a. the length of a chromosome.
    b. the length of a gene.
    c. the length of DNA, which yields a recombination event in 1% of meioses.
    d. the distance between two alleles.
    e. the distance between two genes.

23. Which of the following is an example of a recombinant chromosome that can result from the parental homologous chromosomes Ab & aB?
    a. AB
    b. aB
    c. Ab
    d. Aa
    e. Bb

24. If an individual has homologous chromosomes (ABC & abc), which is a double recombinant chromosome that could result?
    a. ABc
    b. aBC
    c. AbC
    d. aBc
    e. Both C and D are correct.

25. When can double crossovers be observed in a two-point cross?
    a. always
    b. never
    c. only when the crossovers are close together
    d. only when the crossovers are far apart
    e. only on X chromosomes

26. In a three-point cross, the middle gene is the one
   a.   that never recombines.
   b.   that always recombines.
   c.   that recombines the most often.
   d.   that recombines the least often.
   e.   that is not observed.

27. Which of the following occurs most frequently?
   a.   recombination between two genes 0.1cM apart.
   b.   recombination between two genes 5cM apart.
   c.   recombination between two genes 10cM apart.
   d.   recombination between two genes 50cM apart.
   e.   recombination that occurs 20% of the time.

28. Why is trisomy 1 never observed in humans?
   a.   Trisomy 1 does exist.
   b.   Chr. 1 never undergoes nondisjunction.
   c.   Chr. 1 is very stable.
   d.   Chr. 1 has so many genes it causes lethality.
   e.   Chr. 1 is too small to cause an effect.

29. Genetic counselors look for which of the following in samples taken during pregnancy?
   a.   aneuploidy
   b.   chromosomal alterations
   c.   lack of normal enzymatic activities
   d.   gene mutations
   e.   all of the above

30. The genotype of an individual with Turner syndrome is
   a.   YO.
   b.   XXY.
   c.   XYY.
   d.   XO.
   e.   XXX.

ASSESSING YOUR KNOWLEDGE

Answers to the questions in the following sections test your ability to synthesize information gained from the chapter and to solve challenging problems on an exam or in everyday life.

Challenging Your Understanding—Answers

1. D→B→E→C

2.

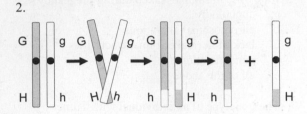

Key Terms----Answers

a. 22, b. 12, c. 15, d. 25, e. 19, f. 10, g. 26, h. 20, i. 24, j. 18, k. 4, l. 14, m. 16, n. 5, o. 23, p. 6, q. 21, r. 7, s. 2, t. 11, u. 3, v. 17, w. 27, x. 13, y. 1, z. 9, aa. 8.

Learning by Experience—Answers

1.   2.

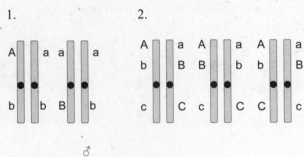

3.

	R	**Y**
R	Rr ♀	RY ♂
r	RR ♀	rY ♂

Genotypic ratio 1:1:1:1
Phenotypic ratio 2:1:1

2 red-eyed ♀: 1 red-eyed ♂: 1 white-eyed ♂

Exercising Your Knowledge—Answers

As you check your answers, put a mark in the review (Rvw) column for the answers you missed. If you didn't miss any, congratulations—you have mastered the chapter! If you missed some, review the section (Sect.) in the text where this concept is discussed. In order to develop an efficient review strategy, it is important that you understand what types of questions you missed. The questions with asterisks test more for understanding of the **concepts**, whereas the others test more for **detail**. *See the preface for learning strategies for concepts and for details.*

	Sect.	Rvw.
*1. Females have a second X chromosome that can have a dominant allele that will mask the recessive allele. Males display whatever allele is on the one X chromosome they have.	13.1	
*2. Morgan needed to demonstrate that the absence of red-eyed females in his previous experiment was not because they were not viable. The testcross proved that they were viable.	13.1	
*3. Females may acquire sex-linked characteristics if they receive recessive genes on both X chromosomes (for example, they are homozygous recessive)	13.1	
*4. (a) If the genes are located far enough apart, then recombination will occur between them more than 50% of the time; (b) greater than 50 cM.	13.4	
*5. Recombinant chromosomes contain some alleles from one parental chromosome and some alleles from the other parental chromosome.	13.4	
*6. When observing recombination events between two genes, double crossover events yield parental chromosomes and thus cannot be observed. The actual number of crossovers between two distant genes includes some double crossovers that are never scored, yielding an underestimate.	13.4	
*7. Other forms of hemophilia are caused by genes on somatic chromosomes where they may be paired with the opposing gene.	13.1	
*8. If sister chromatids of chromosome 21 fail to separate in meiosis, both will be passed to the same gamete. When this gamete fuses to a gamete with 1 chromosome 21, the resulting progeny zygote will contain 3 copies of chromosome 21.	13.5	
*9. The DNA can be modified by the addition of methyl groups.	13.5	
*10. Amniocentesis allows the collection of cells from a human fetus during pregnancy so that genetic tests may be performed to determine if any genetic disorders exist.	13.5	
*11. e	13.1	
12. e	13.1	
*13. a	13.1	
14. c	13.1	
*15. b	13.1	
*16. b	13.2	
17. d	13.2	
18. c	13.2	
*19. b	13.2	
20. c	13.3	
21. e	13.4	
*22. c	13.4	
*23. a	13.4	
*24. e	13.4	
*25. b	13.4	
*26. d	13.4	
*27. d	13.4	
*28. c	13.5	
29. e	13.5	
30. d	13.5	

CHAPTER 14 DNA: THE GENETIC MATERIAL

MASTERING KEY CONCEPTS

Once the role of chromosomes in heredity had been established and their behavior documented, scientists still didn't know what chromosomal substance carried the hereditary information. As you will see in this chapter, bit-by-bit, that identity was established.

14.1 What is the genetic material?

- **Overview**: A series of experiments by **Griffith**; **Avery, MacLeod, McCarty**; and **Hershey, Chase** identify DNA, not protein, as the genetic material in cells.
- **Details**: Know the details and the conclusions of the experiments performed by the above listed scientists.
  Griffith: Genetic information could be transferred from dead, virulent cells to live, nonvirulent cell's **transforming** them into virulent cells.
  Avery, MacLeod, McCarty: The genetic material responsible for transforming the cells in Griffith's experiments from nonvirulent to virulent is **DNA**, not protein.
  Hershey and Chase: Using **bacteriophages** containing only DNA and protein, the genetic material was identified by infecting bacterial cells with phages containing either **radiolabeled protein (^{35}S)**, or **radiolabeled DNA (^{32}P)**. After the infecting viral particles were removed from the bacterial surfaces, the cell pellet was found to contain ^{32}P, not ^{35}S, confirming the genetic material is DNA, not protein.

14.2 What is the structure of DNA?

- **Overview**: DNA is made up of **nucleotides** consisting of a five-carbon sugar, a phosphate group, and one of four nitrogenous bases (**purines: adenine, guanine; pyrimidines: cytosine, thymine**).
- **Details**: Know the conclusions reached by **Chargaff**, **Franklin**, and **Watson and Crick** regarding the structure of DNA.
  Chargaff: In the DNA, the percentages of A and T are always equal (**A=T**), and the percentages of G and C are always equal (**G=C**).
  Franklin: X-ray diffraction patterns of DNA suggested a **helical** structure.
  Watson and Crick: DNA is an **antiparallel** double-helix with a **phosphodiester** backbone composed of alternating sugar and phosphate groups. The nitrogenous bases protrude into the interior of the helix and **complementary** bases (**A with T; G with C**) on the opposing strands form hydrogen bonds with each other , which hold the helix together.

14.3 How does DNA replicate?

- **Overview**: DNA is replicated in a **semiconservative** fashion meaning that both strands of the double helix are used as templates to produce two new daughter strands. DNA replication originates at **origins of replication**, is **elongated in a 5' to 3' direction** by **DNA polymerase**, and terminates at specified sites.
- **Details**: Know the details of **Meselson-Stahl's** experiment. Understand why their results are not consistent with the conservative, or the dispersive models for replication. Know the three requirements for DNA replication and the three steps involved in the process.
  Meselson-Stahl: Bacteria grown in ^{15}N medium, is switched to ^{14}N medium and DNA is collected at time intervals. At 0 rounds of replication after the switch, all DNA contains ^{15}N and is of the same density; after one round of replication, all DNA has one density that is less than the density of the DNA after 0 rounds. After two rounds, the DNA has two densities because half of the molecules have two light strands, and the other half have a light and a heavy strand, confirming the **semiconservative model of replication**.

14.4 Prokaryotic replication

- **Overview**: DNA replication occurs **semidiscontinuously** because DNA polymerase can synthesize only in the 5' to 3' direction. The **leading strand** is synthesized continuously after the synthesis of a RNA primer. Synthesis of the **lagging strand** involves the synthesis and ligation of **Okazaki fragments** and is thus discontinuous. Replication begins at the *oriC*, proceeds **bidirectionally**, and ends at a **termination site**. A **replisome** containing all of the proteins necessary for replication is formed at the **replication fork** where the two DNA strands come apart.
- **Details**: Be familiar with the three DNA polymerases and their functions. Understand the requirement for the other proteins involved in DNA replication, including **DNA helicase, DNA gyrase, DNA primase, DNA ligase**, and the **single-stranded binding protein (SSB)**. Understand the difference between leading and lagging strand synthesis. Know the structure and the function of the β **subunit** of DNA pol. III.

14.5 Eukaryotic replication

- **Overview:** Similar to prokaryotes, eukaryotic replication also occurs in large, multiprotein complexes, but the situation is more complex because eukaryotes have multiple, linear chromosomes that are larger than the bacterial chromosome. To handle these complexities, eukaryotes use multiple origins of replication and a specialized enzyme, known as telomerase, to replicate the ends of linear chromosomes.

- **Details:** Know the two reasons why eukaryotic replication is more complex then prokaryotic replication and how eukaryotes deal with this situation. Understand how the ends of the chromosomes are replicated by telomerase in eukaryotic organisms.

14.6 DNA repair

- **Overview**: In addition to the "proofreading" activity of DNA polymerase, cells use multiple repair systems, **specific** and **nonspecific**, to ensure that errors in the DNA replication and errors introduced by **mutagens** are corrected before they are passed on.
- **Details**: Understand the difference between specific and nonspecific repair mechanisms and know examples of each.

CHALLENGING YOUR UNDERSTANDING

1. List the detailed steps necessary for both leading and lagging strand replication in a prokaryotic organism.

2. Draw the structure of a DNA molecule. Include at least a four-nucleotide chain containing each of the nitrogenous bases and show the linkage of the sugar-phosphate backbone between these four nucleotides. Then draw the complementary strand and try to draw the hydrogen bonds between the complementary bases on the two strands.

KEY TERMS

Match the numbered term with the definition that fits it best. Put the corresponding number in front of the appropriate definition.

1. genes
2. transformation
3. bacteriophages
4. purine
5. pyrimidine
6. nucleic acid
7. nucleotide
8. phosphodiester bond
9. Chargaff's rules

10. complementary
11. semiconservative
12. primer
13. endonuclease
14. exonuclease
15. leading strand
16. lagging strand
17. Okazaki fragments
18. replication fork

19. replisome
20. replicon
21. supercoiling
22. excision repair
23. thymine dimer
24. telomerase
25. processivity
26. telomeres
27. mutagen

a. _____ The ability of a polymerase to remain attached to a template, primarily due to the action of the β subunit.
b. _____ The partial unwinding of a DNA double helix to form two single stands where the replisome is formed.
c. _____ Short sections of DNA synthesized discontinuously and then ligated together.
d. _____ The proportion of adenine always equals thymine; the proportion of guanine always equals cytosine.
e. _____ The DNA strand on which replication occurs continuously from one initial primer.
f. _____ An enzyme that synthesizes the ends of chromosomes using an internal RNA template.
g. _____ Viruses that infect bacteria consisting of genetic material that is surrounded by a protein coat.
h. _____ Each strand of a DNA molecule can be used to specify the other by base-pairing.
i. _____ Any agent that increases the number of mutations above background levels.
j. _____ The covalent linkage between two adjacent thymine bases in the DNA caused by UV radiation.
k. _____ A single-ringed nitrogenous base, such as thymine or cytosine in DNA, or uracil or cytosine in RNA.
l. _____ The topological state of the DNA that determines how the double helix coils in space.
m. _____ A nonspecific form of repair in which a damaged region in the DNA is removed and replaced by DNA synthesis.
n. _____ Enzymes that can chew away at an end of a DNA molecule.
o. _____ A subunit of DNA consisting of a five-carbon sugar, a PO_4 group, a nitrogenous base.
p. _____ A model for DNA replication in which one strand of a parental duplex remains intact in the daughter strands.
q. _____ The DNA strand where replication occurs discontinuously and requires multiple priming events.
r. _____ Specialized structures that protect the ends of eukaryotic chromosomes from nucleases.
s. _____ A transfer of virulence from one cell to another that was described in the experiments by Frederick Griffith.
t. _____ A white, slightly acidic material extracted from nuclei, discovered by Miescher, known as DNA or RNA today.
u. _____ A two-ringed nitrogenous base, such as adenine or guanine.
v. _____ Enzymes that can break phosphodiester bonds between nucleotides internally.
w. _____ A single functional unit consisting of the complete chromosome plus the origin in prokaryotes.
x. _____ Functional units of DNA that contain the information to specify traits and are located on chromosomes.
y. _____ Linkage of a phosphate group to two sugars by means of a pair of ester bonds allowing DNA to form long chains.
z. _____ A multiprotein complex containing a primosome and two DNA pol III enzymes capable of DNA replication.
aa. _____ A short stretch of RNA or DNA approximately 10-20 base pairs long that anneals to the template strand.

LEARNING BY EXPERIENCE

The following two activities should be useful in understanding the concepts of this chapter.

1. Color this illustration. As you color each structure or molecule, review its function. Fill in the circle following the name of each object listed below with the color you will use on the illustration:

First subunit of DNA polymerase III ○   Single-strand binding proteins ○   Helicase ○
Primase ○   Second subunit of DNA polymerase III ○   RNA primer ○   DNA ligase ○
Okazaki fragment ○   DNA polymerase I ○

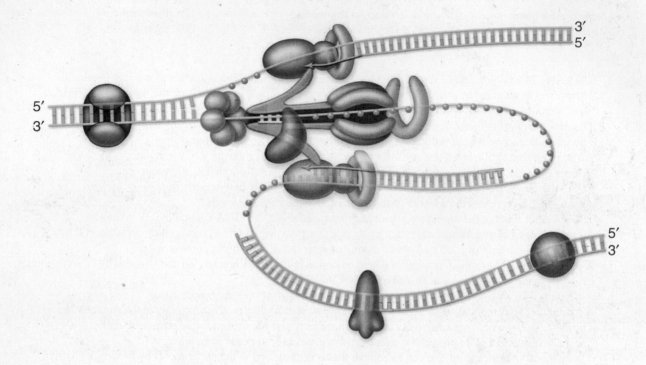

2. Using Chargaff's rules, print the base sequence of the complementary strand beneath the DNA strands shown here.

       a. CATGGTA   b. TTGGCAA   c. AGCTACG

EXERCISING YOUR KNOWLEDGE

Briefly answer the following questions in the space provided.

1. In the Avery experiments, removing nearly all of the protein from the dead S *Streptococcus* did not reduce the transforming activity. What properties of the transforming substance suggested that it was DNA?

2. How did Hershey and Chase conclude that the genetic information that bacteriophages use to infect bacteria is DNA, not protein?

3. Watson and Crick deduced the structure of DNA based on what was known from Chargaff's, and Franklin and Wilkins's experiments. What did these scientists discover and how was this interpreted in the Watson-Crick model?

4. When deoxyribose molecules bind in DNA formation, (a) what kind of reaction takes place? (b) What kind of a bond is formed? (c) Which carbons are involved in the respective molecules?

5. What is the relationship between the constant 2-nanometer diameter of DNA and the nature of base-pairing?

6. What is the evidence for the conclusion that DNA replication is semiconservative?

7. What is the role of the RNA primer in DNA replication?

8. Why does replication on the lagging strand occur away from the replication fork instead of toward it as in the leading strand?

9. Why is the single-strand binding protein needed in DNA replication?

10. What is the purpose of DNA gyrase in DNA replication?

Circle the letter of the one best answer in each of the following questions.

11. DNA pol. I, unlike the other DNA polymerases has 5' to 3' exonuclease activity that is essential during lagging strand replication to
    a. remove damaged Okazaki fragments.
    b. repair damaged template DNA.
    c. degrade template DNA.
    d. remove the RNA primers.
    e. remove overlapping segments of Okazaki fragments.

12. The two strands of DNA found in a double helix are_____
    a. semidiscontinuous.
    b. antiparallel.
    c. identical.
    d. topoisomers.
    e. linked by a phosphodiester bond.

13. Griffith infected mice with different strains of bacteria to demonstrate the presence of genetic material in bacteria. Which of the following best describes Griffith's explanation for one of his observations?
    a. Dead bacteria are less lethal than live ones.
    b. Genetic material transferred from dead type s bacteria into live type r bacteria transform them into bacteria capable of killing a mouse.
    c. Genetic material in type s bacteria allowed them to evade the immune system.
    d. Genetic material in type r bacteria transferred to dead type s bacteria restored their life and allowed them to kill mice again.
    e. High levels of the heat-killed type s bacteria localize to the lungs killing the mice.

14. The fact that some viruses use DNA to direct their heredity was demonstrated by finding
    a. radioactive sulfur from a bacteriophage in a bacterium.
    b. radioactive phosphorus from a bacterium in a bacteriophage.
    c. that radioactive phosphorus from a bacteriophage had mutated a bacterium.
    d. radioactive phosphorus from a bacteriophage in a bacterium.
    e. radioactive sulfur from a bacterium in a bacteriophage.

15. What functional group is found at the 5' end of a DNA strand?
    a. a phosphate group
    b. a hydroxyl group
    c. a carbonyl group
    d. a deoxyribose sugar
    e. a carboxyl group

16. In a nucleic acid, the bases are always attached to the _____ carbon of the sugar.
    a. 5'
    b. 4'
    c. 3'
    d. 2'
    e. 1'

17. In nucleic acids, the free hydroxyl group is attached to the _____ carbon of the sugar.
    a. 5'
    b. 4'
    c. 3'
    d. 2'
    e. 1'

18. Which of the following is NOT correct concerning the initiation of bacterial replication?
    a. It initiates at an *ori*C sequence.
    b. Two separate replisomes are loaded at the origin.
    c. The strands are separated at GC-rich regions.
    d. Replication proceeds biodirectionally.
    e. There is one unique termination site.

19. _____ is a _____ that forms ____H⁺ bonds with_____.
    a. Guanine, purine, 3, cytosine
    b. Thymine, purine, 2, adenine
    c. Adenine, purine, 3, thymine
    d. Cytosine, pyrimidine, 2, guanine
    e. Uracil, pyrimidine, 3, guanine

20. In the process of bonding two nucleotides, _____is released.
    a. a molecule of water
    b. a phosphate group
    c. a hydroxyl group
    d. an oxygen molecule
    e. a hydrogen molecule

21. What function does the β subunit of DNA polymerase III provide?
    a. priming activity
    b. topoisomerase activity
    c. helicase activity
    d. proofreading activity
    e. clamp binding activity

22. According to Chargaff's rules, if the DNA of a species contains 20% thymine, what percent of guanine will it contain?
    a. 80%
    b. 30%
    c. 60%
    d. 20%
    e. 40%

23. Which of the following is true of standard Watson-Crick base-pairing in a molecule of DNA?
    a. Purines base pair with purines.
    b. Pyrimidines base pair with pyrimidines.
    c. Purines base pair with pyrimidines.
    d. All bases can potentially base pair.
    e. More than one of the above are correct.

24. Which of the following statements best describes why synthesis of the lagging strand is discontinuous?
    a. DNA polymerase can synthesize DNA only in the 3'-5' direction.
    b. DNA polymerase requires a primer to initiate synthesis.
    c. DNA polymerase can synthesize DNA only in the 5'-3' direction.
    d. DNA polymerase is not a processive enzyme.
    e. DNA polymerase III has only 5'-3' exonuclease activity.

25. The main eukaryotic replication polymerase is a complex of two enzymes that work together known as_____ and _____.
    a. DNA pol beta, DNA pol delta
    b. DNA pol alpha, DNA pol beta
    c. DNA pol beta, DNA pol epsilon
    d. DNA pol delta, DNA pol epsilon
    e. DNA pol alpha, DNA pol delta

26. Which of the following statements best describes why DNA replication requires a helicase enzyme?
    a. The newly created daughter strand needs to be wound into a double helix.
    b. Separation of parental DNA strands creates positive supercoils in front of the fork.
    c. Complementary strands of the parental DNA need to be separated to create new daughter strands.
    d. Primers need to base-pair with the template for synthesis to begin.
    e. Single-strands of DNA because hydrophobic bases are exposed to water.

27. DNA replication is called semiconservative because _____ of the original duplex appears in the new duplex.
    a. none
    b. most
    c. half
    d. hardly any
    e. all

28. Since the first nucleotide cannot be linked in a newly synthesized strand in DNA replication, _____ is required.
    a. a DNA primer
    b. DNA polymerase
    c. ligase
    d. an RNA primer
    e. helicase

29. Excision repair is considered to be a nonspecific repair pathway because
    a. undamaged bases on the complementary strand of DNA are removed also.
    b. the bases on the complementary strand are used for resynthesis.
    c. it can be carried out by replicative polymerases alone.
    d. DNA replication itself activates this pathway.
    e. bases surrounding the damaged base are also removed from the DNA.

30. Which of the following features of the DNA helix contribute(s) to its stability?
    a. hydrogen bonding between bases
    b. the presence of a 3'-OH group
    c. the presence of a 2'-OH group
    d. proportion of the nitrogenous bases
    e. phosphodiester backbone

ASSESSING YOUR KNOWLEDGE

Answers to the questions in the following sections test your ability to synthesize information gained from the chapter and to solve challenging problems on an exam or in everyday life.

Challenging Your Understanding-Answers

1.

Leading

a. Replisomes loaded onto the origin
b. RNA primer synthesized
c. DNA polymerase III synthesizes until reaching a termination site.

Lagging

a. Replisomes loaded onto the origin
b. RNA primer synthesized
c. DNA polymerase III synthesizes the first Okazaki fragment.
d. RNA primer synthesized
e. DNA polymerase III synthesizes the second Okazaki fragment.
f. DNA polymerase III reaches the previously synthesized strand, releases β clamp.
g. Primer in front removed by DNA polymerase I and then replaced by DNA using the previous Okazaki fragment to prime
h. Nick between Okazaki fragments sealed by DNA ligase

2. For the DNA chain structure, refer to figures 14.3, 14.5, 14.8, and 14.10 in the text to complete this exercise.

Key Terms-Answers

a. 25, b. 18, c. 17, d. 9, e. 15, f. 24, g. 3, h. 10, i. 27, j. 23, k. 5, l. 21, m. 22, n. 14, o. 7, p. 11, q. 16, r. 26, s. 2, t. 6, u. 4, v. 13, w. 20, x. 1, y. 8, z. 19, aa. 12.

Learning by Experience—Answers.

1.	Compare your work to text figure 14.16.
2.	a. GTACCAT b. AACCGTT
	c. TCGATGC

Exercising Your Knowledge—Answers

As you check your answers, put a mark in the review (Rvw) column for the answers you missed. If you didn't miss any, congratulations—you have mastered the chapter! If you missed some, review the section (Sect.) in the text where this concept is discussed. In order to develop an efficient review strategy, it is important that you understand what types of questions you missed. The questions with asterisks test more for understanding of the **concepts**, whereas the others test more for **detail**. *See the preface for learning strategies for concepts and for details.*

	Sect.	Rvw.
*1. The elemental composition agreed with that of DNA, when spun at high speeds in an ultracentrifuge, it migrated to the same level as DNA, extracting lipids and proteins did not reduce transforming activity, protein-digesting enzymes did not affect transforming activity, nor did RNA-digesting enzymes, DNA-digesting enzymes destroyed all transforming activity.	14.1	
*2. Bacteriophages contain only DNA and protein. Bacterial cells were infected with phages containing either radiolabeled protein (^{35}S), or radiolabeled DNA (^{32}P). After infection, the viral particles were removed from the surfaces of the bacteria. The cell pellet was found to contain ^{32}P, but not ^{35}S indicating that the injected genetic material that reprogrammed the cell was DNA, not protein.	14.1	
*3. Chargaff found that the amount of adenine present in DNA always equals the amount of thymine, and the amount of guanine always equals the amount of cytosine. In the Watson-Crick model, this was explained because adenine will only properly hydrogen bond with thymine and guanine with cytosine. Because of this base-pairing, adenine and thymine will always occur in the same proportions in any DNA molecule, as will guanine and cytosine. Franklin and Wilkins demonstrated by X-ray diffraction that the DNA molecule has the shape of a helix, with a consistent diameter of 2 nm and a complete helical turn every 3.4 nm. In the Watson-Crick model, a DNA molecule was described to be made up of two chains of nucleotides that are antiparallel and intertwined into a double helix. The nitrogenous bases protrude to the interior of the helix and stabilize it by hydrogen bonding in the interior.	14.2	
*4. (a) The reaction is dehydration synthesis. (b) A phosphodiester bond is formed. (c) The phosphate end of the bond is attached to the 3′ carbon, and the other end attaches to the 5′ carbon of the other sugar.	14.2	
*5. The 2-nanometer diameter is maintained because a small pyrimidine always pairs with a larger purine instead of like with like.	14.2	
*6. DNA was first cultured in a medium containing ^{15}N, and then transferred to a medium containing ^{14}N. The next generation of DNA was intermediate in weight between that grown on ^{14}N medium and that grown on ^{15}N medium. Thus, half of the new molecules came from each culture.	14.3	
*7. Polymerase III cannot attach nucleotides directly to a chain that is already paired with the parent strand. It attaches them to an RNA primer, and they are later attached to the parent chain.	14.3	

*8. Polymerase III can only add nucleotides to the 3′ end of a DNA strand. The two strands are antiparallel, so the nucleotides must be attached in opposite directions.	14.4	
*9. Without the single-strand binder, the single strand might be cleaved or re-annealed.	14.4	
*10. DNA gyrase can relieve the torsional strain caused by unwinding and prevent supercoiling.	14.4	
11. d	14.4	
*12. b	14.2	
13. c	14.1	
*14. d	14.3	
*15. b	14.2	
*16. e	14.2	
*17. c	14.2	
*18. c	14.4	
*19. a	14.2	
20. a	14.2	
* 21. e	14.4	
*22. b	14.2	
*23. c	14.2	
*24. c	14.4·	
25. d	14.5	
26. c	14.4	
27. c	14.3	
28. d	14.4	
29. e	14.6	
30. a	14.2	

CHAPTER 15 GENES AND HOW THEY WORK

MASTERING KEY CONCEPTS

An important activity in this chapter is "navigating"—knowing where you are in what process. Similarities and differences are easily confused. Remember that this chapter is mostly about RNA and its activities. Of course, it takes DNA to get RNA, but thereafter it is RNA all the way. Don't confuse RNA rules and processes with those for DNA.

15.1 The Central Dogma traces the flow of gene-encoded information.

- **Overview**: Genetic information is passed from the DNA (genes) to an RNA copy by the process of **transcription**, to a protein by the process of **translation**. Thus, an organism's **genotype** is expressed in its physical traits as a **phenotype**.
- **Details**: Know the experiments and conclusions of Garrod and Beadle and Tatum.
  Garrod: inherited diseases are the result of enzyme deficiencies.
  Beadle and Tatum: DNA specifies particular enzymes, **one-gene/one polypeptide** hypothesis.

15.2 Genes encode information in three-nucleotide code words.

- **Overview**: The genetic code consists of three nucleotide sequences that are read as a **codon** to direct the incorporation of one amino acid into a protein. Four nucleotides (A, C, G, T, or U) arranged in different combinations produce **64 codons** — 61 that specify 1 of 20 amino acids, 3 that specify a stop codon.
- **Details**: Know the experiments of Crick and Brenner, and those of Nirenberg and Khorana.
  Crick and Brenner: three nucleotides in the DNA defines one codon and directs the incorporation of one amino acid into a protein. Codons are unspaced.
  Nirenberg and Khorana: Determined which amino acid was encoded by each of the 64 possible codons.

15.3 Gene expression

- **Overview**: DNA is transcribed to RNA by binding of **RNA polymerase** to the **promoter** of a gene. **mRNA** is translated into a protein using **tRNA** as an adaptor molecule. Transcription and translation both occur as three-step processes, initiation, elongation, and termination.
- **Details**: Know the mechanistic details of the three steps involved in transcription and again in translation. Know the differences between these steps in transcription and translation. Be able to distinguish between the functions of the different cellular RNA molecules.

15.4 Prokaryotic transcription

- **Overview**: The **holoenzyme** of RNA polymerase initiates transcription at DNA sequences called **promoters**. The RNA transcript is elongated by the addition of ribonucleotides to the 3' end of the growing strand. As soon as the 5' end of the RNA is available, translation begins, coupling transcription and translation in prokaryotes.
- **Details**: There is only one bacterial RNA polymerase. Know the difference between the **core polymerase** and the **holoenzyme**. Know the significance of the DNA sequences at **-35 nt.**, **-10 nt.**, the **start site**, and the **terminator site**.

15.5 Eukaryotic transcription

- **Overview**: Transcription is more complicated in eukaryotes than it is in prokaryotes. There are three different RNA polymerases, **RNA polymerase II** synthesizes **mRNA**. Unlike prokaryotes, eukaryotic transcription requires **transcription factors** to bind RNA polymerase to the promoter. RNA polymerase binding forms the **initiation complex**. The **primary transcript** is modified by the addition of a **5' cap** and a **3' poly-A tail,** and **introns** are removed by **splicing** to form the **mature mRNA**.
- **Details**: Know the **three different RNA polymerases** in eukaryotes and what molecules each polymerase is responsible for transcribing. Know the differences between the promoters for each. Know how eukaryotic initiation and termination differ from prokaryotes and how a **primary transcript** is modified to produce the **mature transcript**.

15.6 Eukaryotic pre-mRNA splicing

- **Overview**: Eukaryotic genes contain **exons**, or coding regions that are separated by **introns**, or noncoding regions, which have to be removed to form a **mature transcript**. **Pre-mRNA splicing** removes introns and joins together the exons in a large RNA-protein complex known as the **spliceosome**. **Alternative splicing** can produce more than one protein from a single gene.
- **Details**: Know the details of the **splicing reaction**. Know how **alternative splicing** can produce more than one protein from one gene.

15.7 Structure of tRNA and ribosomes

- **Overview**: tRNA molecules from a cloverleaf structure with an **anticodon loop** at the bottom and an acceptor stem at the 3' end. The appropriate amino acid is attached to the tRNA acceptor stem by 1 of 20 **aminoacyl-tRNA** synthetases in a **charging reaction**. The appropriate charged tRNA binds to the **ribosome** such that the anticodon loop of the charged tRNA can base-pair with the codon in the mRNA, which is held between the small and large ribosomal subunits. A **peptide bond** can then be formed between two amino acids being held by tRNAs at adjacent ribosomal sites.

- **Details**: Know the details of the **tRNA charging reaction**. Know the **three tRNA binding sites on the ribosome** and what role each plays in polypeptide synthesis.

15.8 Process of translation

- **Overview**: Initiation occurs by binding of the small subunit of the **ribosome** to the **RBS** in prokaryotes and to the **5' cap** in eukaryotes. The large ribosomal subunit is added to the small subunit, initiator tRNA and the mRNA. When formation of the ribosome is complete, the **initiator tRNA** is bound to the **P site**. As the ribosome translocates along the mRNA, peptide bonds are formed on the ribosome between the amino group of the incoming amino acid in the **A site** and the carboxyl end of the growing peptide in the **P site**.
- **Details**: Know the two differences between prokaryotic and eukaryotic translation initiation. Know the series of events required to add amino acids to a growing peptide. Know the arrangement of the ribosome sites relative to the mRNA. Know what happens at the termination of protein synthesis.

15.9 Summarizing gene expression

- **Overview**: Eukaryotic gene expression is more complex than prokaryotic gene expression due to **temporal and spatial separation of transcription and translation, required modifications of the primary transcript**, and the **presence of introns in the pre-mRNA**.
- **Details**: Focus on the specific differences between prokaryotes and eukaryotes in the processes of transcription and translation (table 15.2).

15.10 Mutations

- **Overview**: **Mutations** in **specific nucleotides of the DNA**, or **chromosomal mutations,** can have deleterious effects on the phenotype of an organism, although some mutations can be evolutionarily beneficial.
- **Details**: Know the different types of mutations that can occur in the DNA and the types of mutations that can occur to a chromosome. Understand what effect these mutations could have on a cell and an organism.

CHALLENGING YOUR UNDERSTANDING

Draw a flowchart detailing each of the three steps described in the text for prokaryotic and cukaryotic transcription and translation. Your chart should include details for initiation, elongation, and termination for both processes.

KEY TERMS

Match the numbered term with the definition that fits it best. Put the corresponding number in front of the appropriate definition.

1. nutritional mutants
2. one-gene/one-polypeptide hypothesis
3. retroviruses
4. central dogma of molecular biology
5. codons
6. reading frame
7. triplet-binding assay
8. degenerate
9. start codon
10. stop codon
11. transcription
12. translation
13. template strand
14. coding strand
15. mRNA
16. tRNA
17. core polymerase

18. holoenzyme
19. promoter
20. terminator
21. transcription unit
22. -35 nt sequence
23. -10 nt sequence
24. transcription bubble
25. operon
26. transcription factors
27. TATA box
28. primary transcript
29. mature mRNA
30. 5' cap
31. 3'poly-A tail
32. introns
33. exons
34. spliceosome
35. snRNPs
36. pre-mRNA splicing

37. alternative splicing
38. branch point
39. ribosome
40. aminoacyl-tRNA synthetase
41. acceptor stem
42. anticodon loop
43. initiator tRNA
44. peptidyl transferase
45. signal recognition particle
46. wobble pairing
47. ribosome binding sequence
48. A site
49. P site
50. E site
51. nonsense mutation
52. frameshift mutation
53. transition mutation
54. transversion mutation

a. _____ Increments of three nts read continuously without spacing where the first codon defines subsequent codons.
b. _____ The DNA-directed synthesis of RNA that results in a RNA molecule complementary to the template strand.
c. _____ The DNA strand that is copied when double-stranded DNA is transcribed into single-stranded RNA.
d. _____ Some amino acids are specified by more than one codon in the genetic code.
e. _____ Site on the DNA that is required for the recognition and binding of RNA polymerase.
f. _____ The RNA transcript used to direct the synthesis of polypeptides.
g. _____ The region of DNA that is located between the promoter of a gene and its terminator sequence.
h. _____ Formed by addition of the σ subunit to the core polymerase allowing it to properly initiate synthesis.
i. _____ An enzyme that can synthesize RNA using DNA as a template, but can not initiate synthesis accurately.
j. _____ Cells with these mutations will grow only on medium that is supplemented with additonal nutrients.
k. _____ A series of three nucleotides read in sequence to direct the incorporation of one amino acid into a protein.
l. _____ One of the 6-bp sequences common to bacterial promoters that is recognized by RNA pol. holoenzyme.
m. _____ A ribosomal process in which a mRNA and charged tRNAs base-pair to allow formation of a peptide bond.
n. _____ The region containing the RNA polymerase, the DNA template, and the growing RNA transcript.
o. _____ The DNA strand not used as a template for transcription that has the same seq. as the RNA transcript.
p. _____ DNA seq. found upstream of the start site in eukaryotic promoters, resembles the -10 seq. found in prokaryotes.
q. _____ One of the 6-bp sequences common to bacterial promoters where the DNA helix is opened.
r. _____ Beadle and Tatum: a single defect in an enzyme is caused by a mutation at a single site on a chromosome.
s. _____ A single transcription unit, common to prokaryotes, in which functionally related genes are grouped.
t. _____ Nirenberg used this to test if defined three-base sequences could bind to the protein synthetic machinery.
u. _____ The codons UAA, UGA, and UAG that do not specify specific amino acids.
v. _____ Information passes in one direction from the DNA to an RNA copy, which directs the assembly of a protein.
w. _____ A class of viruses that can convert their RNA genome into a DNA copy with the enzyme reverse transcriptase.
x. _____ An adaptor molecule that interacts with mRNA and amino acids and plays a critical role in protein synthesis.
y. _____ Proteins used to recruit RNA polymerase II to eukaryotic promoters to initiate transcription.
z. _____ The codon AUG, which encodes the amino acid methionine.
aa. _____ A DNA sequence that signals RNA polymerase to end transcription.
bb. _____ More than one mature mRNA produced from a single primary transcript by the inclusion of different exons.
cc. _____ Activating enzyme that catalyzes the attachment of an amino acid with the appropriate tRNA molecule.
dd. _____ Sequences in this region of the tRNA cloverleaf structure base-pair with the codons in the mRNA.
ee. _____ The ability of a single tRNA molecule to "read" more than one codon in the mRNA.
ff. _____ The class of DNA mutation present if a cytosine nucleotide is substituted for an adenine nucleotide.
gg. _____ The ribosomal location where the tRNA carrying the next amino acid to be added binds.

hh. _____ A base substitution mutation that changes a transcribed codon to stop codon and results in a truncated protein.

ii. _____ Seq. in the 5' end of a prokaryotic mRNA that is complementary to the 3' end of the small subunit rRNA.

jj. _____ The ribosomal location where the tRNA that carried the previous amino acid added binds.

kk. _____ Forms a bond between the amino group of 1 amino acid and the carboxyl group of the growing chain.

ll. _____ Small nuclear ribonucleoprotein particles that recognize the intron-exon junction.

mm. _____ Coding sequences of a gene that are joined together to form the mature mRNA transcript.

nn. _____ Added to the 3' end of a transcript by poly-A polymerase to protect the mRNA from degradation.

oo. _____ The final processed form of the mRNA after 5' capping, 3' polyadenylation, and splicing.

pp. _____ A conserved adenine nucleotide within introns that base-pairs with snRNA and is important for intron removal.

qq. _____ The ribosomal location where the tRNA attached to the growing polypeptide chain is bound.

rr. _____ The class of DNA mutation present if one pyrimidine is substituted for a different pyrimidine.

ss. _____ The 3' end of a tRNA molecule ending in 5'-CCA-3' where an amino acid is attached.

tt. _____ A large complex, consisting of snRNPs and other proteins, responsible for the removal of introns.

uu. _____ An insertion, or deletion, of a single base in the DNA that causes an alteration in the reading frame.

vv. _____ Modification of the 5' end of a transcript by the addition of methylated GTP to the 5' PO_4 group.

ww. _____ Noncoding DNA sequences that interrupt the coding sequence of a gene.

xx. _____ The cellular organelle that has two subunits and three tRNA binding sites where protein synthesis takes place.

yy. _____ A cytoplasmic protein complex that binds polypeptides with a signal sequence and targets them to the ER.

zz. _____ The process of removing the introns from a primary transcript to form a mature mRNA.

aaa. _____ In prokaryotes, this tRNA is charged with a chemically modified methionine, N-formylmethionine.

bbb. _____ The original RNA synthesized by RNA polymerase before it undergoes processing.

LEARNING BY EXPERIENCE

1. Refer to table 15.1. To the right of each triplet below, write the associated amino acid. If none, describe the effect of the triplet.

a.   codon UUG

b.   codon CCG

c.   codon GGA

d.   anticodon GCC

e.   codon GUC

f.   codon AUG

g.   DNA triplet AAA

h.   codon AUG

i.   codon UGG

j.   anticodon UCA

2. For the following exercise, refer to the figure, or to table 15.1 to answer the questions below.

DNA:
Strand A   5' TTA GGA CCC TCT GGG GTT CAC CAG CGA CAT TCC GAT AGC 3'
Strand B   3' AAT CCT GGG AGA CCC CAA GTG GTC GCT GTA AGG CTA TCG 5'

mRNA:
            5' GCU AUC GGA AUG UCG CUG GUG AAC CCC AGA GGG UCC UAA 3'

a. Consider the DNA molecule and the mRNA molecule that is transcribed from it depicted above. Which strand of the DNA is the coding strand?

b. What is the amino acid sequence of the protein that would be translated from this mRNA?

3. For the following exercise, refer to the DNA sequence shown below and answer the questions that follow by figuring out the amino acid sequence of each of the DNA strands shown.

            DNA (coding strand): A-T-G-C-C-A-G-C-A-C-T-G-G-T-A-A-A-A-C-A-C-T-G-A

a. Compared to the DNA sequence shown, the following DNA sequence has what type of mutation present?
A-T-G-C-C-A-G-C-A-C-T-G-A-T-A-A-A-A-C-A-C-T-G-A

b. Compared to the DNA sequence shown, the following DNA sequence has what type of mutation present?
A-T-G-C-C-A-G-C-A-G-C-T-G-G-T-A-A-A-A-C-A-C-T-G-A

c. Compared to the DNA sequence shown, the following DNA sequence has what type of mutation present?
A-T-G-C-C-A-G-C-A-C-T-A-G-T-A-A-A-A-C-A-C-T-G-A

d. Compared to the DNA sequence shown, the following DNA sequence has what type of mutation present?
A-T-G-C-C-A-G-C-A-C-T-G-G-T-A-T-A-A-C-A-C-T-G-A

EXERCISING YOUR KNOWLEDGE

Briefly answer the following questions in the space provided.

1. What are the roles of the three forms of RNA?

2. Why is the phenomenon symbolized by DNA → RNA → Protein referred to as the Central Dogma?

3. Why are the terms *transcription* and *translation* appropriate for their respective processes?

4. (a) What is meant by the "reading frame"?
    (b) Why is it important?

5. What is the function of the TATA box?

6. What is the function of 5′ caps and 3′ poly-A tails?

7. Why do some activating enzymes need to recognize only one anticodon while others need to recognize several?

8. (a) What is a GC hairpin, and (b) how does it work?

9. In the initiation of transcription, what does RNA polymerase do?

10. How are introns dealt with before translation?

Circle the letter of the one best answer in each of the following questions.

11. RNA polymerase adds nucleotide triphosphates to a new RNA chain that are complementary to
    a. the template strand.
    b. the mRNA.
    c. the coding strand.
    d. the anticodon.
    e. the promoter sequence.

12. The function of tRNA is to
    a. provide a place for polypeptide synthesis.
    b. transport amino acids to the ribosome.
    c. travel to the ribosome to direct the assembly of polypeptides.
    d. transcribe DNA.
    e. translate DNA.

13. The work of H. Gobind Khorana used organic synthesis to produce which of the following
    a. mutated DNA molecules.
    b. amino acids.
    c. RNA molecules of defined sequence.
    d. RNA polymers with more than 1 nucleotide.
    e. DNA molecules of defined sequence.

14. In Beadle and Tatum's experiments, if the argE gene contained a mutation that inactivated the E enzyme, the *Neurospora* would fail to grow on
    a. ornithine.
    b. arginosuccinate.
    c. arginine.
    d. citrulline.
    e. glutamate.

15. A molecule of tRNA with the anticodon AAA will transport the amino acid
    a. phenylalanine.
    b. lysine.
    c. proline.
    d. glycine.
    e. arginine.

16. Which of the following must take place in eukaryotes, before a primary transcript can be translated?
    a. 5' capping
    b. 3' poly-A tail addition
    c. mRNA transport to the cytoplasm
    d. pre-mRNA splicing
    e. all of the above

17. In eukaryotes, _____ codons specify amino acids.
    a. 21
    b. 24
    c. 61
    d. 64
    e. 60

18. Peptidyl transferase activity of the ribosome resides in which of the following?
    a. the small subunit
    b. the rRNA
    c. the amino acids
    d. the large subunit
    e. the tRNA

19. Relative to the mRNA, how are the ribosome sites arranged 5' to 3'?
    a. A, P, E
    b. P, E, A
    c. A, E, P
    d. E, P, A
    e. E, A, P

20. A mutation that changes a thymine nucleotide to a guanine nucleotide is what type of mutation?
    a. frameshift
    b. transversion
    c. inversion
    d. translocation
    e. transition

21. A mutation occurring when one chromosome is broken and is attached to another chromosome is
    a. inversion.
    b. transversion.
    c. translocation.
    d. reversion.
    e. duplication.

22. In mitochondrial genomes, _____ is a "stop" codon.
    a. UGA
    b. UUU
    c. AUA
    d. UAA
    e. AGA

23. In the process of transcription,
    a. the base sequence of DNA is copied into RNA.
    b. a polypeptide is formed as specified by the genes in chromosomes.
    c. rRNA is specified by exons in DNA.
    d. a strand of mRNA is formed with base sequences complementary to those of DNA.
    e. mRNA is formed as coded by introns.

24. After a peptide bond is formed during translation, which of the following occurs?
    a. The ribosome moves relative to the mRNA.
    b. The mRNA dissociates.
    c. The tRNA in the P site is ejected.
    d. The large subunit dissociates.
    e. EF-Tu factor binds to the charged tRNA.

25. The 5' cap plays a key role in eukaryotic translation because of which of the following?
    a. It binds the initiator tRNA.
    b. It binds initiation factors.
    c. It binds to the ribosome-binding sequence.
    d. It has enzymatic activities.
    e. It binds the small ribosomal subunit.

26. In the process of translation,
    a. a strand of mRNA is formed with nucleotide sequences complementary to those of DNA.
    b. nucleotide sequences of tRNA are established.
    c. a polypeptide is formed in response to the rRNA nucleotide sequences.
    d. rRNA is synthesized with sequences complementary to those of tRNA.
    e. a polypeptide is formed as dictated by the nucleotide sequences in mRNA.

27. In prokaryotic transcription, the −35 sequence and the −10 sequence are
    a. coding strands.
    b. promoters.
    c. RNA polymerase.
    d. terminators.
    e. part of the template strand.

28. As polypeptides are formed at the ribosome, elongation continues until _____ is exposed.
    a. a release factor
    b. an intron
    c. a stop codon
    d. an exon
    e. polypeptidase

29. A spliceosome is formed from a cluster of
    a. spRNAs.
    b. smRNAs.
    c. ribosomes.
    d. nucleosomes.
    e. snRNPs.

30. For the process of pre-mRNA splicing to occur accurately, the spliceosome must recognize
    a. the 5' cap.
    b. the tRNA molecule.
    c. the DNA template.
    d. the intron-exon junctions.
    e. the DNA-mRNA hybrid.

ASSESSING YOUR KNOWLEDGE

Answers to the questions in this section test your ability to synthesize information gained from the chapter and to solve challenging problems on an exam or in everyday life.

Challenging Your Understanding—Answers

Prokaryotes

Transcription

Initiation: σ subunit of RNA pol. recognizes the -35nt and the -10 nt seq.→DNA helix opens at -10 nt region→transcription starts at +1.

Elongation: RNA pol. leaves the promoter→transcription bubble is formed and DNA is transcribed→DNA rewound as RNA pol. passes.

Termination: Terminator seq. signals stop to RNA pol.→RNA pol. releases the DNA.

Translation

Initiation: As soon as the 5' end of the transcript is available, translation begins by formation of the initiation complex containing mRNA, initiator tRNA charged with N-formylmethionine, small ribosome subunit →large ribosomal subunit added.

Elongation: Charged tRNAs brought to the ribosome base-pair with the mRNA→peptide bond formed→ribosome translocates.

Termination: Stop codon encountered in the mRNA→Stop codon recognized by release factors→Peptide chain dissociates.

Eukaryotes

Transcription

Initiation: Transcription factors bind to the TATA box→Other transcription factors associate→RNA pol. recruited to the promoter to form an initiation complex.

Elongation: RNA pol. leaves the promoter→transcription bubble is formed and DNA is transcribed→DNA rewound as RNA pol. passes.

Termination: Terminator seq, not as well defined as in prokaryotes, but exists and signal stop to RNA pol.→RNA pol. releases the DNA, but does not form the end of the mRNA because the chromosomes are linear.

Modification: Primary transcript is capped at the 5' end→3' poly-A tail is added by poly-A polymerase→primary transcript is spliced to join the coding regions→mature mRNA is transported from the nucleus to the cytoplasm.

Translation

Initiation: Formation of the initiation complex containing mRNA, initiator tRNA charged with methionine, small ribosome subunit ,and other protein factors →large ribosomal subunit added.

Elongation: Charged tRNAs brought to the ribosome base-pair with the mRNA→peptide bond formed→ribosome translocates.

Termination: Stop codon encountered in the mRNA→Stop codon recognized by release factors→Peptide chain dissociates.

Key Terms—Answers

a. 6, b. 11, c. 13, d. 8, e. 19, f. 15, g. 21, h. 18, i. 17, j. 1, k. 5, l. 22, m. 12, n. 24, o. 14, p. 27, q. 23, r. 2, s. 25, t. 7, u. 10, v. 4, w. 3, x. 16, y. 26, z. 9, aa. 20, bb. 37, cc. 40, dd. 42, ee. 46, ff. 54, gg. 48, hh. 51, ii. 47, jj. 50, kk. 44, ll. 35, mm. 33, nn. 31, oo. 29, pp. 38, qq. 49, rr. 53, ss. 41, tt. 34, uu. 52, vv. 30, ww. 32, xx. 39, yy. 45, zz. 36, aaa. 43, bbb. 28.

Learning by Experience—Answers

| 1a. Leucine |
| 1b. Proline |
| 1c. Glycine |
| 1d. Arginine |
| 1e. Valine |
| 1f. Methionine |
| 1g. Phenylalanine |
| 1h. none (stop) |
| 1i. Tryptophan |

1j. Serine	
2a. Strand B	
2b. Met-Trp-Leu-Val-Asn-Pro-Arg-Gly-Ser	
3a. missense	
3b. frameshift	
3c. silent	
3d. nonsense	

Exercising Your Knowledge—Answers

As you check your answers, put a mark in the review (Rvw.) column for the answers you missed. If you didn't miss any, congratulations—you have mastered the chapter! If you missed some, review the section (Sect.) in the text where this concept is discussed. In order to develop an efficient review strategy, it is important that you understand what types of questions you missed. The questions with asterisks test more for understanding of the **concepts**, whereas the others test more for **detail**. *See the preface for learning strategies for concepts and for details.*

	Sect.	Rvw.
*1. (a) mRNA defines the polypeptide to be formed. (b) tRNA delivers the appropriate amino acid to the ribosome. (c) rRNA, along with proteins, forms the ribosome.	15.3	
*2. The phenomenon is so named because it is true of all known organisms.	15.1	
*3. Transcription is appropriate because the process transfers the code from DNA to RNA, though in complementary fashion. Translation is appropriate because the code of RNA is read and used to define the appropriate amino acid.	15.3	
*4. (a) The reading frame refers to the selection of the correct triplet of nucleotides by selecting the correct beginning point. (b) If the beginning point is wrong, all nucleotides will be clustered into the wrong codons.	15.2	
*5. The TATA box is a promoter that starts the transcription process.	15.5	

	Sect.	Rvw.
*6. The 5′ caps and the 3′ poly-A tails protect transcripts from degradation.	15.5	
*7. For some amino acids, there is only one anticodon. For others, there are several.	15.3	
*8. (a) The GC hairpin is a structure composed largely of G and C nucleotides that terminates transcription. (b) It causes the RNA polymerase to pause over a section with which it bonds poorly. Because of the weakness of the bond, the RNA strand dissociates from the DNA, and transcription stops.	15.4	
*9. RNA polymerase (a) binds to a promoter binding site at the beginning of a gene, and (b) moves along the strand, adding RNA nucleotides to a growing strand. (c) When it reaches a "stop" signal, it disengages and releases the assembled RNA.	15.3	
*10. Introns are cut out of the strand, and the strand is spliced together before translation.	15.6	
*11. a	15.3	
*12. b	15.3	
13. c	15.2	
14. e	15.1	
15. a	15.2	
*16. e	15.5	
17. d	15.2	
*18. d	15.7	
*19. d	15.7	
20. b	15.10	
21. c	15.10	
22. e	15.2	
*23. d	15.3	
*24. a	15.8	
*25. e	15.9	
*26. e	15.3	
*27. b	15.4	
*28. c	15.8	
29. e	15.6	
30. d	15.6	

CHAPTER 16 CONTROL OF GENE EXPRESSION

MASTERING KEY CONCEPTS

The object of regulation of gene expression is the production of the right polypeptide in the right amount at the right time. All genes being fully active at the same time would waste energy and other resources. It would also result in undesirable excesses of many enzymes and the products of their action.

16.1 Gene expression is controlled by regulating transcription.

- **Overview**: Regulatory proteins repress transcription by blocking access of RNA polymerase to the **promoter,** or activate transcription by stimulating RNA polymerase binding to the promoter.
- **Details**: Know the differences between transcriptional programs in prokaryotes vs. eukaryotes.
  Prokaryotes: adjust to environmental changes
  Eukaryotes: protect **homeostasis**

16.2 Regulatory proteins read DNA without unwinding it.

- **Overview**: Regulatory proteins that affect gene expression interact with DNA through a specific sequence of bases, usually by "reading the **major groove**" of the DNA. A different regulatory domain on these proteins interacts with the transcriptional apparatus.
- **Details**: Know how the common **DNA binding motifs** found in proteins interact with DNA.

16.3 Prokaryotes regulate genes by controlling transcription initiation.

- **Overview**: Positive control mediated by **activators** that stimulate transcriptional initiation. Negative control mediated by **repressors** that decrease the initiation of transcription.
  Details: Know how the *lac* and *trp* **operons** are controlled.

16.4 Transcriptional control in eukaryotes operates at a distance.

  Overview: Eukaryotic transcription is more complex than prokaryotic transcription due to chromatin structure and spatial and temporal separation of transcription and translation. General factors are required for transcription but do not increase the **basal level of transcription** (for example, TFIID, TFIIE, TFIIF, TFIIA, TFIIB).

Specific transcription factors act in a tissue- and time-dependent manner to increase transcriptional levels above normal basal levels (for example, **activators**). **Activators** bind to enhancer sequences in DNA. Looping in the DNA allows **enhancers** to be close to promoters and signals can be sent through the general factors to enhance transcription. Activators can be affected by co-activators and mediators.

- **Details**: Know the difference between general vs. specific transcription factors.

16.5 Eukaryotic chromatin structure affects gene expression.

- **Overview**: Nucleosomes and the higher order of chromatin organization cause chromatin condensation making promoters inaccessible.
- **Details**: DNA or histone **methylation**, histone **acetylation,** and chromatin-remodeling complexes alter chromatin structure and affect gene expression.

16.6 Eukaryotic posttranscriptional regulation can alter gene products.

- **Overview**: Gene expression can be altered in several ways even after an mRNA transcript is already made.
- **Details**: Small RNAs, alternative splicing, RNA editing, mRNA degradation, mRNA transport, and the initiation of translation are all involved in posttranscriptional control of gene expression.

16.7 The degradation of some proteins in the cell is a regulated process.

- **Overview**: In addition to normal turnover of proteins, cells need a mechanism to get rid of old, unused, and misfolded proteins, as well as to regulate the turnover of some critical cellular proteins. **Proteases** in lysosomes and the **proteasome** degrade proteins.
- **Details**: **Polyubiquitination** marks proteins for degradation by the proteasome. This occurs in a **three-step process**.

CHALLENGING YOUR UNDERSTANDING

Draw a flowchart detailing each regulated step required for the production of a protein from a gene, and its subsequent degradation for both prokaryotes and eukaryotes. Your flowchart should start with DNA and end with protein degradation.

KEY TERMS

Match the numbered term with the definition that fits it best. Put the corresponding number in front of the appropriate definition.

1. promoter
2. homeostasis
3. transcriptional control
4. posttranscriptional control
5. major groove
6. structural (DNA-binding) motifs
7. helix-turn-helix
8. homeodomain
9. zinc fingers
10. leucine zipper
11. operators
12. repressors
13. activators
14. catabolite activator protein (cap)
15. basal transcription factors
16. specific transcription factors
17. enhancers
18. methylation
19. acetylation
20. RNA interference
21. microRNAs (miRNAs)
22. small interfering RNAs
23. chromatin-remodeling complexes
24. alternative splicing
25. ubiquitin
26. proteasome
27. lysosome

a. _____ A modification of the DNA or of the histone proteins that is associated with inactive regions of chromatin.
b. _____ A cellular organelle that degrades polyubiquinated proteins in a regulated fashion.
c. _____ DNA binding motif containing a recognition helix that fits into the major groove of a DNA molecule.
d. _____ A regulatory sequence found in the DNA that is bound by RNA polymerase to initiate transcription.
e. _____ DNA binding motif commonly mutated in the homeotic mutations in *Drosophila*.
f. _____ A multiprotein complex containing enzymes that can modify DNA and histones, and affect chromatin structure.
g. _____ An activator protein that uses cAMP as an effector and can stimulate transcription of catabolic operons.
h. _____ Cellular vesicles that contain digestive enzymes can nonspecifically remove old proteins.
i. _____ Regulatory sequences in the DNA that can prevent or decrease transcription when bound by certain proteins.
j. _____ The production of more than one protein from a single gene.
k. _____ A modification of the histone tails that allows DNA to be accessible for transcription.
l. _____ Regulatory sequences in the DNA bound by proteins that affect the basal level of transcription.
m. _____ The maintenance of a constant internal environment in the cells of a multicellular organism.
n. _____ A small RNA that blocks the translation of a mRNA with a complementary sequence.
o. _____ A 3-D substructure found in many proteins through which they interact with a specific DNA sequence.
p. _____ A 76-amino-acid peptide that is added to proteins as either a single molecule or as a chain.
q. _____ The regulation of gene expression by processes occurring after the primary RNA transcript is made.
r. _____ A deep groove found in a DNA molecule in which the nucleotides H^+ donors/acceptors are accessible.
s. _____ Small fragments of double-stranded RNA that act to inhibit the expression of RNAs from which it came.
t. _____ Allosteric, regulatory proteins that bind DNA and stimulate transcriptional initiation.
u. _____ Proteins required for transcription initiation, such as TFIID, TFIIE, TFIIF, TFIIA, TFIIB, TAFs.
v. _____ DNA binding motif in which two different protein subunits containing hydrophobic amino acids interact.
w. _____ A small RNA picked up by an enzyme complex called RISC that then degrades complementary mRNAs.
x. _____ Proteins that bind to regulatory sequences in the DNA and increase the basal level of transcription.
y. _____ DNA binding motif in which one or more zinc atoms are used to fit an α-helical region into the major groove.
z. _____ Gene expression controlled at the level of transcriptional initiation.
aa. _____ Regulatory proteins that bind to specific sites on the DNA and prevent or decrease transcription.

LEARNING BY EXPERIENCE

Color code the illustration that follows. Indicate your color code by filling the circle following the name of each object with the appropriate color. As you color, review the function of each object. Depending on how well you remember the material in chapter 15, you may need to review.

RNA polymerase ○   Primary transcript ○   Processed transcript ○ Introns ○   Exons ○   3′ poly-A tail ○   5′ Cap ○
Ribosome ○   tRNA at A site ○   tRNA at P site ○   tRNA at E site ○   Polypeptide ○   Codons ○   Anticodons ○

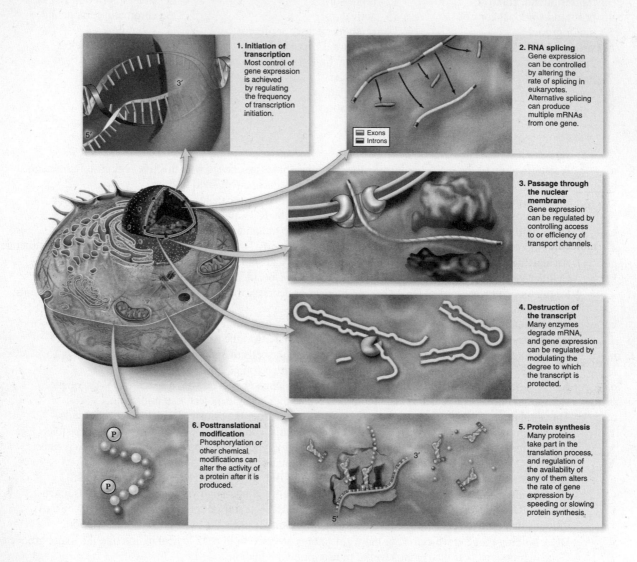

1. **Initiation of transcription**
Most control of gene expression is achieved by regulating the frequency of transcription initiation.

2. **RNA splicing**
Gene expression can be controlled by altering the rate of splicing in eukaryotes. Alternative splicing can produce multiple mRNAs from one gene.

☐ Exons
☐ Introns

3. **Passage through the nuclear membrane**
Gene expression can be regulated by controlling access to or efficiency of transport channels.

4. **Destruction of the transcript**
Many enzymes degrade mRNA, and gene expression can be regulated by modulating the degree to which the transcript is protected.

6. **Posttranslational modification**
Phosphorylation or other chemical modifications can alter the activity of a protein after it is produced.

5. **Protein synthesis**
Many proteins take part in the translation process, and regulation of the availability of any of them alters the rate of gene expression by speeding or slowing protein synthesis.

EXERCISING YOUR KNOWLEDGE

Briefly answer the following questions in the space provided.

1. Compare prokaryotes and eukaryotes as to the goals of gene expression control.

2. Why is it not necessary for DNA to be unwound for sequences of nucleotides to be read?

3. What is the specific single purpose for all of the binding motifs described?

4. Binding motifs are parts of what kind of larger molecule?

5. What is the mechanism by which the presence of tryptophan prevents *Escherichia coli* from producing its own tryptophan?

6. What is the mechanism by which *E. coli* is enabled to utilize other foods in the absence of glucose?

7. (a) Under what conditions will the catabolite activator protein bind to its binding site?
   (b) What conditions must exist for the *lac* operon to be transcribed once the CAP is bound?

8. What purpose is served by DNA methylation in eukaryotes?

9. How can mRNA transcripts be degraded despite the presence of a 3′ poly-A tail?

Circle the letter of the one best answer in each of the following questions.

10. _____ tend to cause RNAs to be degraded between transcription and translation.
    a. siRNAs
    b. dRNAs
    c. CAPs
    d. miRNAs
    e. Nucleotides

11. A common method by which gene expression is controlled in both prokaryotic and eukaryotic organisms is
    a. mRNA transport.
    b. transcriptional initiation.
    c. proteasomal degradation.
    d. alternative splicing.
    e. mRNA degradation.

12. Agents of posttranscriptional control include
    a. methyl groups.
    b. RISC.
    c. repressors.
    d. RNA pol II.
    e. all of these.

13. In order for the helix-turn-helix motif to bind to DNA, the _____ must fit into the major groove.
    a. homeotic switches
    b. zinc fingers
    c. operator
    d. recognition helix
    e. protein link

14. What is the most common protein structure used to insert into the major groove of the DNA helix?
    a. α-helix
    b. β-sheet
    c. γ-turn
    d. zinc atoms
    e. loop domain

15. In the zinc finger motif, what role do the zinc atoms play in the protein-DNA interaction?
    a. neutralize the negative charge of the DNA
    b. recognize a specific DNA sequence
    c. bind an amino acid to a nucleotide
    d. bind two protein subunits
    e. positioning the recognition helix

16. Transcription factors in the leucine zipper family can bind DNA only when _____.
    a. they are phosphorylated
    b. they are methylated
    c. they bind a second leucine zipper protein
    d. they do not bind a second leucine zipper protein
    e. they are acetylated

17. When tryptophan is present in the medium, the transcription of tryptophan-producing genes in *E. coli* is stopped by a helix-turn-helix regulator binding to a site within the
    a. *trp* repressor.
    b. *trp* operon.
    c. *trp* promoter.
    d. *trp* operator.
    e. *trp* polymerase.

18. When tryptophan is present in the environment of *E. coli*, the tryptophan binds to the
    a. *trp* operon.
    b. *trp* promoter.
    c. *trp* operator.
    d. *trp* repressor.
    e. *trp* polymerase.

19. Two copies of the helix-turn-helix acting on the same DNA molecule are separated by_____ of the DNA helix.
    a. three turns
    b. one-half turn
    c. two turns
    d. four turns
    e. one turn

20. In the function of the *lac* operon in *E. coli*, the *lac* genes are transcribed in the presence of lactose because
    a. RNA polymerase binds to the operator.
    b. the repressor protein binds to the operator.
    c. allolactose binds to the repressor.
    d. CAP does not bind to the operator.
    e. of the absence of cAMP.

21. In the absence of available glucose, *E. coli* is able to use foods other than glucose because falling levels of glucose cause an increase in
    a. cAMP.
    b. CAP.
    c. lactose.
    d. *glu* operons.
    e. tRNA.

22. In the absence of glucose, *E. coli* can import lactose to change into glucose and galactose because CAP binds to the
    a. cAMP.
    b. *lac* promoter.
    c. *lac* operon.
    d. operator.
    e. repressor.

23. The function of the core promoter is to _____.
    a. specify the translational start site
    b. define the reading frame
    c. specify the transcriptional start site
    d. regulate the amount of mRNA produced
    e. bind regulatory transcription factors

24. Which of the following is a component of the core promoter?
    a. enhancer
    b. activator
    c. repressor
    d. a TATA box
    e. none of the above

25. Enhancers can function at large distances from promoters because
    a. regulatory proteins bind large regions on the DNA.
    b. the DNA can loop.
    c. transcription can initiate several Kb upstream of the promoter.
    d. the signal can be transmitted down the DNA.
    e. regulatory proteins can initiate transcription.

26. Histone acetylation can affect transcriptional levels by
    a. preventing repressors from binding.
    b. activating RNA polymerase.
    c. tightening the association between the nucleosomes and the DNA.
    d. neutralizing the negative charge on DNA.
    e. opening the chromatin structure.

27. Transcription factors appear to be unable to bind to a promoter packaged in a nucleosome because
   a. activators are inhibited by that configuration.
   b. of inhibition of RNA polymerase.
   c. of histones positioned over promoters.
   d. nucleosomes are especially vulnerable to repressors.
   e. operators are placed in an inaccessible position.

28. The role of methylation of DNA is now viewed as
   a. interfering with DNA transcription by blocking base-pairing between cytosine and guanine.
   b. complexing with enhancers to prevent transcription.
   c. prevention of mutation.
   d. ensuring that genes that are turned off stay turned off.
   e. irrelevant to gene transcription.

29. Translation repressor proteins may shut down translation of processed mRNA transcripts by
   a. binding with the 3′ poly-A tails.
   b. resetting the reading frame.
   c. reinserting introns into the transcript.
   d. excising a short sequence of nucleotides.
   e. binding to the beginning of the transcript.

30. Addition of a polyubiquitin chain to a protein
   a. targets the protein to the proteasome.
   b. exports the protein from the nucleus.
   c. stabilizes the protein.
   d. increases binding of the protein to DNA.
   e. opens the chromatin structure.

31. The proteasome degrades
   a. nonfunctional organelles.
   b. misfolded proteins.
   c. stable proteins.
   d. proteases.
   e. all proteins.

ASSESSING YOUR KNOWLEDGE

Answers to the questions in the following sections test your ability to synthesize information gained from the chapter and to solve challenging problems on an exam or in everyday life.

Challenging Your Understanding—Answers

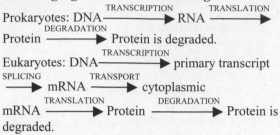

Prokaryotes: DNA —TRANSCRIPTION→ RNA —TRANSLATION→ Protein —DEGRADATION→ Protein is degraded.

Eukaryotes: DNA —TRANSCRIPTION→ primary transcript —SPLICING→ mRNA —TRANSPORT→ cytoplasmic mRNA —TRANSLATION→ Protein —DEGRADATION→ Protein is degraded.

Key Terms—Answers

a. 18, b. 26, c. 7, d. 1, e. 8, f. 23, g. 14, h. 27, i. 11, j. 24, k. 19, l. 17, m. 2, n. 21, o. 6, p. 25, q. 4, r. 5, s. 20, t. 13, u. 15, v. 10, w. 22, x. 16, y. 9, z. 3, aa. 12.

Learning by Experience—Answers

Compare your work to text figure 18.23. You may also want to review figure 15.20.

Exercising Your Knowledge—Answers

As you check your answers, put a mark in the review (Rvw.) column for the answers you missed. If you didn't miss any, congratulations—you have mastered the chapter! If you missed some, review the section (Sect.) in the text where this concept is discussed. In order to develop an efficient review strategy, it is important that you understand what types of questions you missed. The questions with asterisks test more for understanding of the **concepts**, whereas the others test more for **detail**. *See the preface for learning strategies for concepts and for details.*

	Sect.	Rvw.
*1. The prokaryote goal in gene expression is to adapt rapidly to changes. Gene expression in eukaryotes is geared to maintaining homeostasis.	16.1	
*2. The unique characteristics of each nucleotide are exposed in the major groove to which access is gained without unwinding.	16.2	
*3. The binding motifs make the regulatory proteins fit into the major groove.	16.2	
*4. The binding motifs are parts of regulatory proteins.	16.2	
*5. Tryptophan activates a repressor that binds to the operator site within the *trp* promoter.	16.3	
*6. Falling glucose levels cause an increase in cAMP production. cAMP binds to the catabolite activator protein (CAP), altering the shape of CAP and enabling it to bind to DNA near a promoter for the transcription of an appropriate gene.	16.3	
*7. (a) CAP will bind if glucose is absent. (b) The *lac* operon will be transcribed if lactose is present.	16.3	
*8. In eukaryotes, methylation of DNA makes genes that have been turned off stay turned off.	16.4	
*9. Even if the mRNA transcript has a 3′ poly-A tail, a sequence of A or U nucleotides nearby makes it vulnerable to degradation.	16.4	
10. a	16.6	
11. b	16.2	
12. b	16.6	
13. d	16.2	
14. a	16.2	
15. e	16.2	
*16. c	16.2	
*17. c	16.3	
18. d	16.3	
19. e	16.3	
*20. c	16.3	
21. a	16.3	
22. b	16.3	
23. c	16.4	
*24. d	16.4	
25. b	16.4	
26. e	16.5	
*27. c	16.5	
28. d	16.5	
29. e	16.6	
30. a	16.7	
31. b	16.7	

CHAPTER 17 BIOTECHNOLOGY

MASTERING KEY CONCEPTS

This chapter is about cutting-edge technology with which any modern biologist should be conversant. It represents the major thrust of biology for the foreseeable future and beyond.

17.1 Molecular biologists can manipulate DNA to clone genes.

- **Overview**: **Recombinant DNA** technology is based on the ability to manipulate DNA using **restriction endonucleases** to cut it at specific sites, **gel electrophoresis** to isolate specific fragments of the DNA, and **DNA ligase** to connect these fragments to other DNA molecules. Once ligated together, recombinant DNA molecules can be propagated in *E. coli* by **transformation,** which will allow independent clones to be isolated.

- **Details**: Know the two reasons why the identification of restriction endonucleases is significant. Know what is meant by **"sticky ends."** Know the difference between **Type I and Type II restriction enzymes**. Understand how gel electrophoresis is used to separate DNA fragments based on their size, and how DNA is visualized.

17.2 Molecular cloning

- **Overview**: **Molecular cloning** involves the isolation of a specific DNA fragment that typically encodes a protein product, followed by its ligation into a vector, either a **plasmid** or a **phage**, which can be propagated in a host cell, such as *E. coli* based on **selection** of a drug resistance marker present in the plasmid DNA, or the ability of a phage vector with recombinant DNA to assemble *in vitro*, infect a host, and propagate inside the host. **Genomic DNA libraries** can be created by partially digesting the DNA from an organism with a particular restriction enzyme and then cloning all of the fragments into a vector. This will produce a random collection of overlapping DNA fragments. **Reverse transcriptase** can be used to make a **cDNA library** containing DNA copies of only the expressed parts of genes made from the mRNA of an organism. The specific bacterial clone containing the gene of interest from a library can be identified by **molecular hybridization** with a radioactively labeled probe complementary to the gene.

- **Details**: Know the two components a plasmid must have in order for it to be useful. Understand how **blue-white screening** is used to determine whether a vector has an insertion or not. Understand the differences between plasmids and phage vectors. Know how DNA libraries can be produced in each. Understand the difference between a DNA library and a cDNA library. Know how to screen a library for a specific clone containing a sequence of interest.

17.3 Several techniques can be used to analyze DNA.

- **Overview**: Many techniques have been developed to characterize DNA. **Restriction site mapping** identifies the locations of cleavage sites for different restriction enzymes within a given sequence of DNA. **Southern blotting** is a technique used to determine if a specific DNA fragment is present among a collection of fragments. DNA is separated by electrophoresis, transferred to a filter, and probed with a single-stranded, radiolabeled probe complementary to a specific DNA fragment of interest. **Northern blotting** uses the same technique to analyze mRNA isolated from cells. The mRNA is separated by electrophoresis and probed with a single-stranded, complementary, radiolabeled probe to determine if a particular mRNA is expressed. **Western blotting** separates proteins by electrophoresis and probes for the presence of a specific protein using an antibody. **Restriction fragment length polymorphisms (RFLPs)** can be used to identify variations in the genes of different individuals. The **Sanger method of sequencing** utilizes the incorporation of **dideoxynucleotides** into the DNA to act as **chain terminators**. **Automated sequencing** uses the same method, but with **fluorescent dyes** instead of a radioactive label on the ddNTPs, and gels in thin capillary tubes, rather than large polyacrylamide gels. **PCR** is a technique that allows the amplification of a single DNA fragment from a small amount of template DNA using a series of denaturation, primer annealing, and synthesis reactions. The **yeast two-hybrid system** detects **protein-protein interactions**. By fusing one protein of interest to the **Gal4 DNA-binding domain** (bait), and the other to the **Gal4 activation domain** (prey). If the two proteins interact, the Gal4 DNA-binding domain will be brought together with its activation domain and restore Gal4 function to activate the expression of a reporter gene.

- **Details**: Understand the techniques of Southern, Northern, and Western blotting. Understand how RFLPs can be used as molecular markers for certain diseases and how they can provide a unique identification of an individual. Know the requirements for sequencing a DNA molecule by the Sanger method and by automated sequencing. Know the advantages of automated sequencing. Know the three steps of a PCR reaction. Understand how the yeast two-hybrid system identifies protein-protein interactions. Know how this technique can be used to identify unknown protein interactions.

17.4 Genetic engineering

- **Overview**: Recombinant DNA technology has given us the ability to introduce genes into organisms without conventional breeding (**transgenic**), and to determine the functions of different genes by either inactivating genes (**knockout**) or by replacing the wild-type copy of a gene with a copy that has specific mutations introduced by *in vitro* **mutagenesis**. By determining the defects in the mutant organism, or mutant cells, relative to the wild-type organism, or wild-type cells, the functions of a gene can be determined by **reverse genetics**.
- **Details**: Know how a knockout mouse of a particular gene can be constructed. Understand the techniques that can be used to determine the function of a gene.

17.5 Medical applications

- **Overview**: Genetic engineering and recombinant DNA technology have important medical implications. The techniques developed can be used to express medically important human proteins in bulk in bacteria for pharmaceutical purposes, to produce vaccines against communicable diseases, and to combat inherited genetic defects by the transfer of human genes (**gene therapy**).
- **Details**: Know how **subunit vaccines** and **DNA vaccines** work. Know the potential complications involved in gene therapy.

17.6 Agricultural applications

- **Overview**: New genes can be introduced into the chromosomes of broadleaf plants using **Ti plasmid** of the plant bacterium *Agrobacterium*. This method was used to make broadleaf plants resistant to the herbicide **glyphosate** by either inserting extra copies of **EPSP synthetase** into plants or by inserting a mutant form of EPSP synthetase that is not inhibited by glyphosate. Scientists have produced plants that are resistant to the insects that feed on them by inserting a gene encoding the **Bt toxin**. **Golden rice** has been genetically modified to contain enriched levels of β-**carotene** in endosperm. **Biopharming**, or plant genetic engineering, has been used to produce human proteins, recombinant subunit viruses, and antibodies in transgenic plants. The production of transgenic animals is in its early stages, but ethical issues concerning the use of animals, and issues raised over the consumption of genetically altered animals exist.
- **Details**: Know the benefits of making plants that are resistant to glyphosate. Understand why the Bt toxin is specific to insects. Understand why some people are against genetically modifying plants and animals.

CHALLENGING YOUR UNDERSTANDING

Outline the series of steps necessary to perform the techniques that can be used to determine the following:

1. If a small insertion was made at a specific location in the genome of an organism.

2. If a mRNA is expressed in a particular tissue.

3. If a mutation is present in a particular gene after *in vitro* mutagenesis.

4. Create a genomic library in a plasmid.

5. Knock out a particular gene in a mouse.

KEY TERMS

Match the numbered term with the definition that fits it best. Put the corresponding number in front of the appropriate definition.

1. restriction endonucleases
2. restriction sites
3. DNA ligase
4. vector
5. multiple cloning site (MCS)
6. recombinant DNA
7. cDNA library
8. genomic library
9. reverse transcriptase
10. hybridization
11. probe
12. polymerase chain reaction
13. Southern blot
14. restriction fragment length polymorphisms
15. DNA fingerprint
16. embryonic stem cells
17. dideoxynucleotides
18. subunit vaccines
19. DNA vaccines
20. Ti (tumor-inducing) plasmid
21. glyphosate
22. transgenic
23. biopharming
24. Northern blot
25. Western blot
26. knockout
27. *in vitro* mutagenesis

a. _____ An enzyme isolated from retroviruses that can make cDNA from a mRNA template.
b. _____ Allows the amplification of a single DNA fragment from a small amount of a complex mixture of DNA.
c. _____ Annealing of a complementary single-stranded probe to identify specific DNAs in complex mixtures.
d. _____ A biodegradable herbicide that kills most actively growing plants by inhibiting EPSP synthetase.
e. _____ Acts as a chain terminator when incorporated into the DNA because it lacks an OH at the 3' position.
f. _____ A technique in which mRNA from tissues or cells is identified by a complementary, radiolabeled probe.
g. _____ Spliced an influenza virus gene encoding an internal nucleoprotein into a plasmid that was injected into mice.
h. _____ A technique in which proteins are separated by electrophoresis and probed with a specific antibody.
i. _____ Cells derived from early embryos that can develop into different adult tissues.
j. _____ The ability to create base-pair substitutions at any site in a cloned gene to examine the effect on its function.
k. _____ A region of a plasmid that contains a number of unique restriction sites.
l. _____ The use of transgenic plants for medicinal or pharmaceutical purposes.
m. _____ A piece of DNA that other genes have been attached to, which can integrate into the DNA of broadleaf plants.
n. _____ Catalyzes the formation of a phosphodiester bond between adjacent PO_4 and -OH groups of nucleotides.
o. _____ Enzymes capable of cleaving DNA at specific sequences.
p. _____ An animal or plant containing a gene that has been introduced without the use of conventional breeding.
q. _____ A single DNA molecule made from two different sources.
r. _____ Point mutations found in a population that can eliminate or create restriction sites.
s. _____ A technique in which DNA fragments containing a specific sequence are identified by a radiolabeled probe.
t. _____ A collection of DNAs that represent the genes expressed in many different tissues or cells.
u. _____ A piece of DNA that carries a recombinant DNA molecule and can replicate in a host cell.
v. _____ The inactivation of a specific gene to assess the effect of the loss of its function in an organism.
w. _____ Specific DNA sequences that are cleaved by particular restriction enzymes.
x. _____ Genes encoding a part of the protein polysaccharide coat of a virus are spliced into the vaccinia virus genome.
y. _____ A collection of DNAs in a vector that together represent the entire genome of an organism.
z. _____ Sequences of repetitive DNA used as identity markers because they are not identical in different individuals.
aa. _____ A specific sequence of interest that is radiolabeled and used to find a complementary sequence in a mixture.

LEARNING BY EXPERIENCE
Try an exercise in simplification. Distill each stage in a genetic engineering experiment into a single sentence or, at most, two sentences.

1. Cleavage

2. Recombinant DNA production

3. Cloning

4. Screening

EXERCISING YOUR KNOWLEDGE

Briefly answer the following questions in the space provided.

1. How do the outcomes of screening procedures and those of selection differ?

2. Why are "sticky ends" of DNA sticky?

3. What is recombinant DNA?

4. (a) What is a vector? (b) What are two kinds of commonly used vectors?

5. In screening DNA clones, (a) what is a probe and (b) how is it used?

6. (a) What is the purpose of the polymerase chain reaction? (b) Why is temperature critical to the process?

7. Briefly describe how DNA fingerprinting can be used to identify an individual.

8. (a) What is cDNA? (b) How is it produced?

9. (a) What is EPSP synthetase? (b) Describe two ways in which broadleaf plants have been genetically engineered to make glyphosate-resistant plants. Why doesn't glyphosate affect humans?

10. What nutritional problem does transgenic "golden rice" solve?

Circle the letter of the one best answer in each of the following questions.

11. Which of the following is NOT one of the steps required to produce double-stranded cDNAs without introns?
    a. production of a mRNA-cDNA hybrid
    b. transformation into *E. coli*
    c. isolation of mRNA
    d. degradation of mRNA
    e. addition of DNA polymerase to make double-stranded cDNA

12. Which of the following characteristics is unique to the lambda vector and NOT true of plasmid vectors?
    a. Lambda requires live cells for replication.
    b. DNA can be inserted into it at specific sites.
    c. The lambda genome is linear.
    d. X-gal screening can be used to identify clones containing inserts.
    e. Drug selection is used to select for cells containing recombinant DNA

13. The most common host bacterium used in cloning is
    a. *E. coli.*
    b. *S. aureus.*
    c. *V. laevis.*
    d. *A. tumefaciens.*
    e. *B. thuringiensis.*

14. All fragments cut by most restriction endonucleases have
    a. complementary double-stranded ends.
    b. supplementary single-stranded ends.
    c. double-stranded "sticky" ends.
    d. complementary single-stranded ends.
    e. double-stranded supplementary ends.

15. When "sticky ends" are paired, they can be joined by
    a. restriction enzymes.
    b. Taq polymerase.
    c. nucleases.
    d. reverse transcriptase.
    e. DNA ligase.

16. Which of the following organisms were used in the production of "golden rice"?
    a. daffodils
    b. beans
    c. wild rice
    d. *Aspergillis*
    e. all of these

17. The second step in most engineering experiments is
    a. screening.
    b. production of recombinant DNA.
    c. cleavage of DNA.
    d. cloning.
    e. testing.

18. A library of DNA fragments results from the use of
    a. restriction endonucleases.
    b. λ virus.
    c. SNPs.
    d. recombinant DNA.
    e. DNA ligase.

19. In screening clones, it is common to use
    a. restriction enzymes.
    b. dyes.
    c. antibiotics.
    d. radiation.
    e. milipore filters.

20. In the screening process, clones that metabolize X-gal turn
    a. yellow.
    b. white.
    c. red.
    d. blue.
    e. green.

21. In a polymerase chain reaction, a synthetic sequence of nucleotides is involved in
    a. denaturing.
    b. heating.
    c. priming.
    d. copying.
    e. all of these.

22. The optimal temperature for Taq polymerase to extend primers is
    a. 40°C.
    b. 55°C.
    c. 58°C.
    d. 72°C.
    e. 94°C.

23. One of the most useful methods for identifying a specific gene is
    a. thin-layer chromatography.
    b. the Eastern blot.
    c. the Western blot.
    d. magnetic resonance imaging.
    e. the Southern blot.

24. A powerful way to identify an individual using a particular gene as a marker is the analysis of
    a. RFLPs.
    b. Northern blots.
    c. PCRs.
    d. Western blots.
    e. transgenic animals.

25. Which of the following is an example of reverse genetics?
    a. finding a mouse gene can direct eye formation in *Drosophila*
    b. observing a phenotype and isolating the gene that produces that phenotype
    c. isolating clones from a library using hybridization of a radiolabeled probe
    d. identifying a protein-protein interaction by a yeast two-hybrid screen
    e. mutating a cloned gene and substituting the mutant copy for the wild-type copy in an organism to assess its function

26. In making a piggyback vaccine for herpes, the gene for the identity marker of the herpes virus is spliced into the genome of the _____ virus.
    a. chickenpox
    b. rabbitpox
    c. cowpox
    d. opossum pox
    e. smallpox

27. Animals are not affected by Bt toxin in plant crops because
    a. while it is toxic to insects, it is a normal metabolite for animals.
    b. animals do not produce aromatic amino acids so Bt toxin can not be incorporated into metabolic pathways.
    c. it is destroyed by acids in the stomach.
    d. animals lack the enzymes to interact with it.
    e. animals have the enzymes to convert it to a nontoxic substance.

28. In attempts to confer special characteristics upon plants, genetic engineers find *Agrobacterium tumefaciens* to be an effective vector for use with
    a. corn.
    b. rice.
    c. wheat.
    d. soybeans.
    e. barley.

29. Which of the following is NOT one of the steps required to clone a piece of DNA using a plasmid vector?
    a. Assemble the plasmid vectors containing insert DNA *in vitro*.
    b. Cut a vector and an insert with a specific restriction enzyme to create "sticky ends."
    c. Isolate DNA fragments by gel electrophoresis.
    d. Transform ligated pieces of DNA into *E. coli*.
    e. Ligate vector and insert DNA with similar sticky ends together.

30. In the Sanger method of sequencing, the incorporation of dideoxynucleotides act as chain terminators because they do not have a
    a. 2'-H.
    b. 3'-OH.
    c. 2'-OH.
    d. 3'-H.
    e. 5'-PO$_4$.

ASSESSING YOUR KNOWLEDGE

Answers to the questions in the following sections test your ability to synthesize information gained from the chapter and to solve challenging problems on an exam or in everyday life.

Challenging Your Understanding—Answers

1. *If a small insertion was made in the genome of an organism.* Southern blot: DNA is isolated from several cells in which the insertion may or may not be present, as well as the starting cells where the insertion is for sure not present. These DNAs are cleaved into fragments with a restriction enzyme that cuts at known places surrounding the location of the insertion. DNA is separated by electrophoresis. The resulting bands are blotted onto nitrocellulose. The blots are hybridized with a radioactively labeled probe designed to be complementary to sequence in the fragment of interest (the fragment that will show whether the insertion is present in the genome) and detected by autoradiography.

2. *If a mRNA is expressed in a particular tissue.* Northern blot: mRNA is isolated from the several different tissues, including the tissue of interest and at least one tissue known to express the mRNA of interest and when possible, one known not to express the mRNA of interest. The mRNAs isolated from different tissues are separated by electrophoresis. The resulting bands are transferred to nitrocellulose. The nitrocellulose blot is hybridized with a radioactive probe that is complementary to at least part of the mRNA sequence of interest and detected by autoradiography.

3. *Determine if a mutation is present in a particular gene after* in vitro *mutagenesis.* Restriction digest if possible, and sequencing: In some cases, mutation of a gene will eliminate, or introduce a restriction site at the location in the DNA where the mutation is introduced. In these cases, DNA isolated from clones that potentially contain the mutation is digested with a specific restriction enzyme to suggest which clones may contain the desired mutation. If this is not possible, or to confirm the restriction enzyme digest, mutations can be detected by sequencing. Four reactions are set up for different template DNAs isolated from potential clones containing the mutation of interest. Each of these four reactions contains a different radiolabeled ddNTP, the other three dNTPs, a primer that anneals to a known location in the gene, template DNA, and polymerase. The radiolabeled ddNTPs will be incorporated and act as chain terminators to produce a series of fragments in each reaction tube. The fragments can be separated by size on a sequencing gel and then visualized by autoradiography. The

sequence can be read from the primer, starting with the smallest fragments to fragments that are each longer by one base. This method will confirm whether any of the clones contain the desired mutation.

4. *Create a genomic library in a plasmid.* The genome is randomly fragmented by partially digesting it with a restriction enzyme that cuts it relatively frequently. Partial digest allows random cutting of sites and not all sites will be cleaved. The random fragments are then inserted into a vector and introduced into host cells.

5. *Knock out a particular gene in a mouse.* Neomycin gene is inserted into the gene of interest to disrupt it and confer G418 resistance. This construct is introduced into ES cells. In some cells, the construct will recombine with the chromosomal copy of the gene and replaces the chromosomal copy with the copy disrupted by the neo gene. The ES cells are placed on G418-selection medium. If the neo gene is present, cells will live indicating that these cells have had a replacement event and contain a knocked out copy of the gene. ES cells containing the knocked out gene are injected into a blastocyst stage embryo, which is implanted into a female to complete development. Offspring of the female will contain one chromosome with the gene of interest knocked out. Genetic crosses between these offspring will produce mice that are homozygous for the knocked out gene in the next generation. These mice can be used to assess the phenotype of loss of the gene of interest.

Key Terms—Answers

a. 9, b. 12, c. 10, d. 21, e. 17, f. 24, g. 19, h. 25, i. 16, j. 27, k. 5, l. 23, m. 20, n. 3, o. 1, p. 22, q. 6, r. 14, s. 13, t. 7, u. 4, v. 26, w. 2, x. 18, y. 8, z. 15, aa. 11.

Learning by Experience—Answers

There are many ways that you could have responded to this challenge. Examples are given below.

1.	A restriction endonuclease is used to cleave the DNA into fragments that can be sorted by electrophoresis.
2.	DNA fragments are inserted into plasmids or viral vectors whose DNA has been cleaved by the same endonuclease.
3.	Plasmids or vectors are introduced to a cell (usually bacteria), which will produce many cells of the DNA clone.
4.	Clones with the desired genes are modified to resist an antibiotic or to possess unique nutritional capabilities. Such clones would be the only survivors when all clones are subjected to the antibiotic or put on a medium that only they can utilize.

Exercising Your Knowledge—Answers

As you check your answers, put a mark in the review (Rvw.) column for the answers you missed. If you didn't miss any, congratulations—you have mastered the chapter! If you missed some, review the section (Sect.) in the text where this concept is discussed. In order to develop an efficient review strategy, it is important that you understand what types of questions you missed. The questions with asterisks test more for understanding of the **concepts,** whereas the others test more for **detail.** *See the preface for learning strategies for concepts and for details.*

	Sect.	Rvw.
*1. All cells survive the screening process, while only the selected cells survive the selection process.	17.2	
*2. "Sticky ends" contain a single-stranded end complementary to the target fragment's single-stranded end with which it can pair.	17.1	
*3. Recombinant DNA is DNA that has been combined in the laboratory with that of another genome so as to produce a novel combination.	17.1	
*4. (a) A vector is a genome that carries foreign DNA into a host. (b) Two commonly used vectors are plasmids and viruses.	17.1	
*5. (a) A probe is a nucleic acid containing a known complementary sequence of nucleotides. (b) The probe is made radioactive and added to the clone library. It will hybridize with a complementary sequence in the clone and be detected by autoradiography.	17.2	
*6. (a) The process is used to produce large amounts of DNA. (b) DNA dissociates at about 98°C and reassociates at about 60°C.	17.3	
*7. DNA is isolated from two or more individuals and separated by electrophoresis. The resulting bands are blotted onto nitrocellulose and hybridized with a radioactive probe designed for DNA that is repetitive. The hybridization pattern is visualized by autoradiography. Since individuals in a population are polymorphic for these repetitive sequences, or molecular markers, they serve as DNA fingerprints to identify and distinguish between different individuals.	17.3	
*8. (a) cDNA is DNA made of intron-free genes. (b) mRNA corresponding to the desired gene is isolated. Using reverse transcriptase, the mRNA is transcribed into a single strand of DNA, which is a template to form a double strand of DNA.	17.2	

	Sect.	Rvw.
*9. (a) EPSP synthetase is an enzyme that plants require to produce aromatic amino acids, which are inhibited by the herbicide glyphosate. (b) To make glyphosate-resistant plants, scientists used a Ti plasmid to insert extra copies of the EPSP synthetase gene into plants allowing them to produce 20 times the normal level of EPSP synthetase and grow despite the presence of glyphosate. Second, they introduced a bacterial form of the EPSP synthetase gene into plants by the Ti plasmid. The bacterial form differs from the plant form by a single nucleotide and is not inhibited by glyphosate. Humans are unaffected by glyphosate because we do not make aromatic amino acids, but instead we get them from our diets.	17.6	
*10. Transgenic rice is higher in β-carotene and will solve the vitamin A deficiency problem in rice-dependent populations.	17.6	
11. b	17.2	
12. c	17.2	
13. a	17.2	
14. d	17.1	
15. e	17.1	
16. c	17.6	
17. b	17.2	
*18. a	17.2	
19. c	17.2	
20. d	17.2	
*21. e	17.3	
22. d	17.3	
23. e	17.3	
24. a	17.3	
*25. e	17.4	
*26. c	17.5	
27. d	17.6	
28. d	17.6	
29. a	17.2	
30. b	17.3	

CHAPTER 18 GENOMICS

MASTERING KEY CONCEPTS

This chapter is one of the most important ones for understanding life in today's world. Genomics and the related field, proteomics, hold the key to a better tomorrow for most people living today, and even more so for those yet to be born. There are no unimportant concepts here. Learn them as you go.

18.1 Genomes can be mapped both genetically and physically.

- **Overview**: **Genetic maps** use the recombination frequency between genes to determine their relative locations. **Linkage mapping** can determine the distance between two genes without knowing the DNA sequence, and can provide a link to phenotype, but the rules that govern this mapping have limitations. **Physical maps** are created using landmarks in the DNA sequence, such as restriction sites, chromosome banding patterns, or radiation hybrid maps. A physical map can be created by using restriction enzymes individually, or in combination with each other, to generate overlapping fragments of DNA that can be put back together into continuous fragments (**contigs**). Low-resolution **cytological maps** that can be used to characterize chromosome abnormalities and are generated by analyzing chromosome banding patterns or by fluorescent *in situ* hybridization using cloned DNA. **Radiation hybrid maps** allow sequences to be ordered based on the probability of a radiation-induced break occurring between two sites. Identifiable landmarks in the human genome, such as **sequence-tagged sites (STSs)**, or **short tandem repeats (STRs)** can be used to construct physical maps. STSs allow new genome sequences to be added into a known sequence, and STRs, which are short repeated sequences that vary in length among a population of individuals, can be used to identify an individual. **Details**: Know the important **landmarks** in a large sequence allowing physical maps to be constructed. Know the limitations of genetic mapping. Understand the problems in correlating **genetic and physical maps**.

18.2 Genome sequencing produces the ultimate physical map.

- **Overview**: **Yeast artificial chromosomes (YACs)** and **bacterial artificial chromosomes (BACs)** are used to clone large DNA inserts and to construct physical maps by restriction enzyme digest. Two methods, **clone-by-clone sequencing** and **shotgun sequencing**, or both approaches, have been used to sequence whole genomes. A combination of both approaches was used to sequence the human genome for which the "finished" sequence was published in 2004.
- **Details**: Know the disadvantages of YACs and BACs. Understand the clone-by-clone and the shotgun approaches to sequencing a genome.

18.3 Being more complex does not necessarily require more genes.

- **Overview**: The human genome contains only **25,000 genes** and only **1.5%** of human DNA consists of **protein-encoding sequences**—this includes single-copy genes, segmental gene duplications, multigene families, and tandem clusters. The rest of the genome consists of noncoding DNA, such as introns, structural DNA (constitutive heterochromatin), duplicated sequences, pseudogenes, and **transposable elements,** which are sequences that can move around in the genome and are repeated many times. Four different kinds of transposable elements, such as **long interspersed elements (LINES)**, **short interspersed elements (SINES)**, **retrotransposons**, and **dead transposons,** make up 45% of the human genome. **Expressed sequence tags (ESTs)** are markers of transcribed sequences in the genome that have been used to identify 87,000 cDNAs in different human tissues indicating that a number of mRNAs undergo **alternative splicing** to produce multiple gene products from a single gene.
- **Details**: Know the **different classes of DNA sequences** found in the human genome and the relative percentages of each. Understand how transposable elements move and how **haplotypes** facilitate locating disease-causing genes.

18.4 Genomics and proteomics

- **Overview**: **Comparative genomics** is being used to identify sequence similarities and differences between evolutionarily related organisms. To compare unsequenced genomes, the conserved arrangements of DNA segments in related genomes (**synteny**) can be determined by physical mapping techniques. **Functional genomics** is geared at inferring function using sequencing information. **DNA microarrays** allow the determination of active and inactive genes in specific tissues, or in response to specific environmental factors. **Proteomics** is aimed at assigning a function to all of the proteins encoded by a genome and to map all of the physical interactions between the proteins of a cell. **Protein microarrays** and **large-scale** yeast two-hybrid approaches are being used to analyze a large number of proteins at one time.

- **Details**: Understand how to prepare a DNA microarray. Understand what microarray analysis has revealed about gene expression patterns in cancer. Know the three ways a protein microarray can be probed.

18.5 Genomics is opening a new window on life.

- **Overview**: Genomics research can be used to determine the source of pathogens and to determine whether these viruses or bacteria have been genetically engineered to increase their lethality. Plant genetic engineering, based on the tools of genomics, is increasingly being used to increase the yield and the quality of crops. The increasing use of DNA-based identity information is controversial because this information can lead to discrimination of certain individuals who are genetically susceptible to develop a disease, or cancer. Ownership of this information and each individual's right to personal privacy will continue to be an ethical debate.

- **Details**: Understand the advantages and the disadvantages of the practical applications of genomics research.

CHALLENGING YOUR UNDERSTANDING

1. DNA was digested with one enzyme in reactions A and B and with both enzymes together in reaction A+B. Construct a physical map based on the restriction digest pattern shown by comparing the sizes of the fragments from the individual reactions with the sizes of the fragments in the combined reaction. Indicate the locations of the restriction sites and the distances between them.

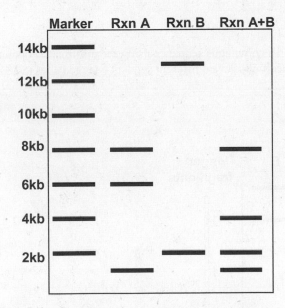

2. DNA was digested with one enzyme in reactions A and B and with both enzymes together in reaction A+B. Construct a physical map based on the restriction digest pattern shown by comparing the sizes of the fragments from the individual reactions with the sizes of the fragments in the combined reaction. Indicate the locations of the restriction sites and the distances between them.

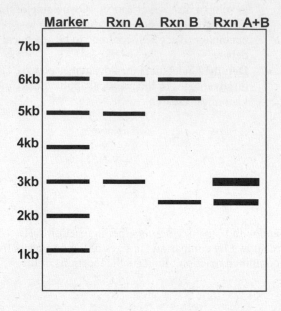

3. Create a physical map of the five clones by ordering them in a contiguous sequence using the information obtained from the electrophoresis of PCR products obtained using primers specific to seven different sequence-tagged sites (STSs).

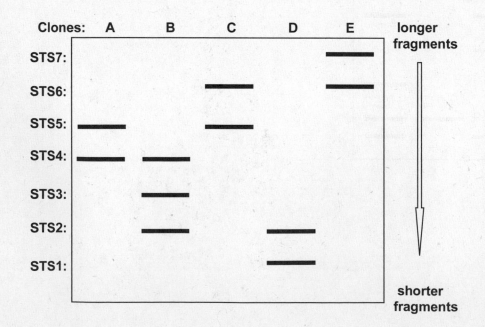

KEY TERMS

Match the numbered term with the definition that fits it best. Put the corresponding number in front of the appropriate definition.

1. genetic maps
2. physical maps
3. landmarks
4. contig
5. sequenced-tagged sites (STSs)
6. yeast artificial chromosomes (YACs)
7. bacterial artificial chromosomes (BACs)
8. consensus sequence

9. fluorescent *in situ* hybridization (FISH)
10. open reading frame (ORF)
11. transcriptome
12. expressed sequence tag (EST)
13. alternative splicing
14. single nucleotide polymorphisms (SNPs)
15. linkage disequilibrium
16. DNA microarray
17. synteny
18. functional genomics

19. proteomics
20. transposable elements
21. long interspersed elements (LINES)
22. short interspersed elements (SINES)
23. long terminal repeats (LTRs)
24. simple sequence repeats (SSRs)
25. comparative genomics
26. haplotypes
27. annotation

a. _____ A sequence that is consistent across all copies of multiple different sequenced clones.
b. _____ A one- to six-nucleotide sequence repeated thousands of times, making up 3% of the human genome.
c. _____ Sites in the DNA sequence of a population of individuals that differ by only a single nucleotide.
d. _____ The tendency for genes not to be randomized, which can be used to map their locations.
e. _____ The conversion of basic sequence information into a form that can be recognized based on landmarks.
f. _____ Retrotransposons that make up 8% of the human genome and reinsert by reverse transcriptase.
g. _____ Specific recognizable sequences in the genome, such as restriction sites, STSs, or ESTs.
h. _____ The study of all of the proteins encoded by the genome.
i. _____ Bits of DNA that are able to move from one location on a chromosome to another.
j. _____ The Alu element is one of these, which represents 10% of the human genome.
k. _____ A hypothesis-driven science aimed at assigning function to gene products.
l. _____ Vectors made in *E. coli* that accept inserts between 100 and 200kb long, maintained as a single copy.
m. _____ Constructed using landmarks in a DNA sequence, such as restriction enzyme sites, or the DNA sequence itself.
n. _____ Regions of chromosomes that are not being exchanged by genetic recombination.
o. _____ A small stretch of DNA that occurs only one time in the genome.
p. _____ The first generation of new vectors designed to allow larger pieces of DNA to be cloned.
q. _____ Ancient transposable elements, 6000bp long, that make up 21% of the human genome.
r. _____ The production of more than one protein from a single gene.
s. _____ A field of study based on the comparison of conserved regions of genomes among different organisms.
t. _____ The conserved arrangements of segments of DNA in related genomes.
u. _____ Hybridization of fluorescently labeled cloned DNA to whole chromosomes.
v. _____ Provide the relative locations of genes on a chromosome based on recombination frequency.
w. _____ Produced from one or both ends of short sections of sequenced cDNAs made from expressed mRNA.
x. _____ A chip in which fragments of DNA are deposited at indexed locations and hybridized with labeled mRNA.
y. _____ All of the RNA present in a cell or tissue, which is larger than the number of genes in the genome.
z. _____ A continuous piece of DNA, established by putting cut pieces of DNA back together based on size and overlap.
aa. _____ The coding region of a gene that begins with a start codon and ends with a stop codon.

LEARNING BY EXPERIENCE
Make a list of practical uses for genomic information.

EXERCISING YOUR KNOWLEDGE

1. How are genetic maps different from physical maps?

2. How may genetic and physical maps be linked?

3. How is the problem of large groups of geneticists working on the map of the same cloned DNA solved?

4. How are yeast artificial chromosomes constructed?

5. Why is the shotgun sequencing of genomes faster than the clone-by-clone method?

6. How do ESTs differ from other STSs?

7. How do only about 30,000 human genes produce over 80,000 proteins?

8. Explain synteny.

9. (a) What are microarrays, and (b) what is their value?

10. How does proteomics differ from genomics?

Circle the letter of the one best answer in each of the following questions.

11. Making a physical map includes the use of
   a. RFLPs.
   b. contigs.
   c. STSs.
   d. PCRs.
   e. all of these.

12. Distances between landmarks in physical maps are measured in kbs, which are _____ base pairs.
   a. 10
   b. 50
   c. 100
   d. 500
   e. 1000

13. In the construction of physical maps, the technique of _____ is used to separate fragments.
    a. gel electrophoresis
    b. sedimentation
    c. thin-layer chromatography
    d. mass spectrophotometry
    e. centrifugation

14. The artificial chromosome most commonly used now is
    a. SSR.
    b. BAC.
    c. STS.
    d. EST.
    e. YAC.

15. Artificial chromosomes are used as
    a. selectors.
    b. sequencers.
    c. cDNA sources.
    d. vectors.
    e. contigs.

16. Alu elements are part of which type of DNA sequence?
    a. LINEs
    b. SINEs
    c. LTRs
    d. dead transposons
    e. segmental duplications

17. Errors in shotgun sequencing are reduced by the assembly of a _____ sequence.
    a. rectified
    b. collated
    c. consensus
    d. tagged
    e. uniform

18. The human genome contains fewer genes than
    a. mice do.
    b. fruit flies do.
    c. rice does.
    d. nematodes do.
    e. none of these.

19. The coding region of a gene between a "start" and a "stop" codon is referred to as the
    a. SRS.
    b. PCR.
    c. ORF.
    d. EST.
    e. TCL.

20. The number of proteins produced by the human genome is greater than the number of genes because of
    a. alternative splicing.
    b. pseudogenes.
    c. EST amplification.
    d. LTRs.
    e. transposable elements.

21. Single copy genes silenced by mutation are called
    a. RFLPs.
    b. retrogenes.
    c. pseudogenes.
    d. homeogenes.
    e. heterochromatin.

22. Which of the following is not an example of noncoding DNA?
    a. retrotransposons
    b. tandem clusters
    c. SSRs
    d. heterochromatin
    e. pseudogenes

23. Which of the following is called heterochromatin?
    a. pseudogenes
    b. structural DNA
    c. segmental duplication
    d. LINE
    e. ALu

24. Sites where individuals differ by a single nucleotide are called
    a. LINEs.
    b. SINEs.
    c. SSRs.
    d. SNPs.
    e. RFLPs.

25. The tendency of genes not to randomize is called
    a. nondisjunction.
    b. transcription equilibrium.
    c. genetic stabilization.
    d. linkage disequilibrium.
    e. genome conservation.

26. Related organisms with genes in common are demonstrating
    a. symmetry.
    b. multigene families.
    c. tandem clusters.
    d. cognes.
    e. synteny.

27. Because translation of RNA may not coincide with transcription, proteomic scientists study
    a. hemiproteomes.
    b. translatomes.
    c. retrogenomes.
    d. microtomes.
    e. transcriptomes.

28. Diseases for which the pathogen's genomes are not known include
    a. smallpox.
    b. plague.
    c. Ebola.
    d. anthrax.
    e. tularemia.

29. How much of the human genome is made up of exons?
    a. 98.5%
    b. 45%
    c. 21%
    d. 5%
    e. 1.5%

30. In addition to microscope slides, _____ may be used for microarrays.
    a. silicone chips
    b. microvials
    c. jell sheets
    d. transistors
    e. microfiches

ASSESSING YOUR KNOWLEDGE

Answers to the questions in the following sections test your ability to synthesize information gained from the chapter and to solve challenging problems on an exam or in everyday life.

Challenging Your Understanding—Answers

1.

OR

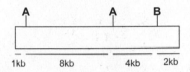

2.

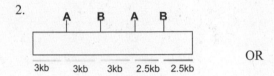

OR

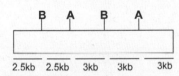

3. Clone order: D, B, A, C, E.

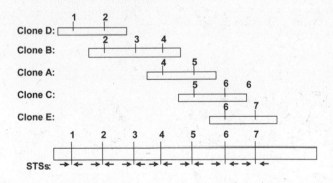

STSs:

Key Terms—Answers

a. 8, b. 24, c. 14, d. 15, e. 27, f. 23, g. 3, h. 19, i. 20, j. 22, k. 18, l. 7, m. 2, n. 26, o. 5, p. 6, q. 21, r. 13, s. 25, t. 17, u. 9, v. 1, w. 12, x. 16, y. 11, z. 4, aa. 10.

Learning by Experience—Answers

Lists will differ from one individual to another. Following is a typical list:
1. Better diagnosis of heritable diseases
2. Production of pharmaceuticals
3. Disease control
4. Forensic diagnosis
5. Evolutionary studies
6. Anthropology
7. Better agricultural breeding

Exercising Your Knowledge—Answers

As you check your answers, put a mark in the review (Rvw.) column for the answers you missed. If you didn't miss any, congratulations—you have mastered the chapter! If you missed some, review the section (Sect.) in the text where this concept is discussed. In order to develop an efficient review strategy, it is important that you understand what types of questions you missed. The questions with asterisks test more for understanding of the **concepts**, whereas the others test more for **detail**. *See the preface for learning strategies for concepts and for details.*

	Sect.	Rvw.
*1. Genetic maps give the distances between genes. Physical maps locate landmarks in the genome.	18.1	
*2. Genetic and physical maps may be linked by the segregation of RFLPs with a genetic trait.	18.1	
*3. The problem is solved by using sequence tagged sites (STSs).	18.1	
*4. Yeast artificial chromosomes (YACs) are constructed by using a yeast origin of replication and yeast centromere sequenced with foreign DNA.	18.2	
*5. The shotgun method does not require the numerous rounds of cloning that the clone-by-clone method does.	18.2	
*6. Most STSs involve the entire genome. ESTs identify only expressed genes.	18.3	
*7. Alternative splicing of RNAs result in more than one protein from the same RNA.	18.3	
*8. Synteny refers to the conserved (in common) arrangements of DNA segments in related genomes such as those of rice, corn, etc.	18.4	
*9. (a) Microarrays are DNA fragments deposited on a microscope slide. (b) Through the distribution of microarrays, several researchers can have access to the same genome.	18.4	
*10. Genomics deals with the identification of genes in a genome. Proteomics deals with the identification of the proteins produced by specific genes.	18.4	

*11. e	18.1	
12. e	18.1	
13. a	18.1	
14. b	18.2	
15. d	18.2	
16. b	18.3	
*17. c	18.2	
18. c	18.3	
19. c	18.3	
20. a	18.3	

21. c	18.3	
*22. b	18.3	
*23. b	18.3	
24. d	18.3	
25. d	18.3	
26. e	18.4	
*27. e	18.4	
28. b	18.5	
*29. e	18.3	
30. a	18.4	

CHAPTER 19 CELLULAR MECHANISMS OF DEVELOPMENT

MASTERING KEY CONCEPTS

Do not expect to get from this chapter a comprehensive knowledge of the development of each organism discussed. Each group of organisms will be discussed in detail in later chapters. Instead, try for a broad understanding of development in the sample organisms. The chapter is profusely illustrated; take advantage of that.

19.1 Developmental program works with impressive precision.

- **Overview**: **Development** is a systematic, gene-directed process that guides the changes that occur throughout the life cycle of an organism. Most multicellular organisms develop using molecular mechanisms that are fundamentally similar and include **growth**, **differentiation**, **pattern formation**, and **morphogenesis**.
- **Details**: Understand the descriptions of the four different stages involved in the development of multicellular organisms.

19.2 Development begins with cell division.

- **Overview**: Immediately following fertilization in animal cells, a diploid zygote undergoes a period of rapid, multiple mitotic divisions regulated by cyclin-Cdks called **cleavage**, in which the two gap/growth phases (G_1, G_2) are extremely short or eliminated producing a **blastocyst**. The inner cell mass of a blastocyst consists of embryonic stem cells (**ES cells**) that can give rise to any tissue in an animal. Plants develop by building their bodies outward from stem cells contained in **meristems**.
- **Details**: Understand the differences between cell division in early embryos and in adult cells. Understand when and how ES cells can be isolated.

19.3 Cell determination commits it to follow a developmental pathway.

- **Overview**: **Cell determination**, the molecular decision that commits a cell to a particular developmental pathway, occurs prior to any overt changes in the cell, and depends on a series of intrinsic or extrinsic events. Interactions between cells and the differential inheritance of **cytoplasmic determinants** are both involved in establishing a cell's fate. The molecular basis of determination is the activation of transcription factors. The cloning of the sheep **Dolly** demonstrated that determination in animals is reversible because the nucleus of a fully differentiated cell was reprogrammed to be **totipotent**. However, there are inherent problems in **reproductive cloning**, such as a low success rate and clones having age-associated diseases, but **therapeutic cloning** to replace damaged, or nonfunctioning cells or tissues in an individual with healthy ones remains promising because using the initial stages to reproductive cloning to produce patient-specific lines of ES cells, scientists have overcome the problem of passing the immune system's "self" check. **Stem cell research**, however, has raised profound ethical issues because it requires early embryos to be broken apart to generate human embryonic stem cells.
- **Details**: Understand the **standard test for determination**. Know the details of an example where cell determination is established by **cytoplasmic determinants** or by **inductive cell interactions**. Understand how Dolly the sheep was cloned, and how embryonic stem cells can be used in therapeutic cloning and the ethical issues in doing so.

19.4 Pattern formation establishes anterior-posterior and dorsal-ventral polarity.

- **Overview**: During the earliest events of development, the **anterior-posterior axis** (head-to-tail) and the **dorsal-ventral axis** (back-to-front) are established defining a bilaterally symmetrical body plan. Embryogenesis in *Drosophila* produces a **larva** from a fertilized egg, which undergoes a **metamorphosis** to produce a **pupa** that develops into a mature fruit fly. The transcription of maternal mRNA, provided in part from **nurse cells**, directs the initial course of development in *Drosophila*. The **syncytial blastoderm** contains numerous nuclei in one cytoplasm. These nuclei separate themselves evenly along the surface and membranes grow between them forming the **cellular blastoderm**, followed by formation of a segmented, tubular body. The anterior-posterior axis and the dorsal-ventral axis in *Drosophila* are determined by maternally expressed genes. The anterior-posterior is established by opposing protein gradients of the **morphogens**, **Bicoid** and **Nanos**, which act as cytoplasmic determinants. These two proteins control the translation of two transcription factors, **Hunchback** and **Caudal**, which direct anterior and posterior structures, respectively. **Gurken**, a soluble cell-signaling molecule, and **Dorsal**, a transcription factor, direct the formation of the dorsal-ventral axis. Sequential activation of the segmentation genes, **gap genes**, **pair-rule genes**, and **segment polarity genes**, whose products all act as transcription factors, produces the segmented body structure of the fly. These segments are given their identity by **homeotic genes** that are clustered together on a chromosome in a **bithorax complex**. A second cluster of homeotic genes, the **Antennapedia complex**, directs the anterior end of the fly. All of the homeotic genes produce proteins that contain a DNA-binding domain called a **homeodomain** (**homeobox** in the DNA). These genes are conserved in organisms throughout evolution. In plants, **MADS-box genes**, a family of transcription factors, dominate the control of development.

- **Details**: Know how Bicoid and Nanos protein gradients are established in *Drosophila* embryos and how these proteins affect Caudal and Hunchback expression, respectively, to establish the anterior-posterior axis. Know how protein gradients also establish the dorsal-ventral axis in *Drosophila*, and the overall importance of transcription factors in pattern formation. Understand the importance of homeobox genes and their organization in establishing segment identity in *Drosophila*.

19.5 Morphogenesis generates an ordered form and structure.

- **Overview**: **Morphogenesis** occurs as a result of changes in cell structure and behavior. To achieve this, animals regulate the number, timing, and orientation of **cell divisions**, **cell growth**, **changes in cell shape**, **cell migration**, and **cell death**. Cell-to-cell interactions mediated through **cadherins**, and cell to substrate interactions mediated by **integrin-**

ECM interactions are critical to **cell adhesion** and loss of adhesion, which is central to permitting cell migration. Since most plants are immobile, cell division and expansion are the primary morphogenetic processes.

- **Details**: Know the processes that animals regulate to achieve morphogenesis. Know the genes involved in apoptosis in *C. elegans*. Know the proteins involved in cell adhesion and how they contribute to cell migration.

19.6 The environment can affect development.

- **Overview**: In immobile seed plants, the **environment** affects essentially every step after embryogenesis, from seed dispersal to germination and flowering. Plant development is guided by **symbiotic relationships** and influenced by interactions with other organisms. The environment also affects animal development. Many environmental chemicals (**endocrine-disrupting chemicals, ECDs**) interfere with endocrine signaling, which is essential for normal development and homeostasis in all animals.

- **Details:** Know an example of how the environment affects plant development and an example of how it affects animal development. Know the three sources of endocrine-disrupting chemicals.

CHALLENGING YOUR UNDERSTANDING

1. Describe the standard test for determination using head and tail cells as an example. Indicate what happens in a normal cell, what happens when transplanted cells are not determined, and what happens if they are.

2. Describe what you think would happen in a chicken embryo if partially committed cells from the tip of the wing bud are transplanted to the identical looking base of the leg. Explain your answer.

KEY TERMS

Match the numbered term with the definition that fits it best. Put the corresponding number in front of the appropriate definition.

1. blastomeres
2. cleavage
3. stem cells
4. totipotent
5. pluripotent
6. blastocyst
7. meristems
8. cell determination
9. induction
10. somatic cell nuclear transfer (SCNT)
11. reproductive cloning
12. genomic imprinting
13. therapeutic cloning
14. larva
15. metamorphosis
16. polarity
17. nurse cells
18. oocyte
19. syncytial blastoderm
20. cellular blastoderm
21. lineage map
22. pupa
23. morphogens
24. gap genes
25. pair-rule genes
26. segment polarity genes
27. homeotic genes
28. biothorax complex
29. antennapedia complex
30. neurulation
31. gastrulation
32. apoptosis
33. necrosis
34. MADS-box genes
35. homeodomain
36. morphogenesis
37. *Hox* gene
38. endocrine-disrupting complex (EDC)

a. _____ The molecular decision-making process that commits a cell to a particular developmental pathway.
b. _____ A process in which mammary cells and egg cells are surgically combined.
c. _____ The passage from one body form to another that involves a radical shift in development.
d. _____ Structures that contain the groups of stem cells that form new parts of a plant.
e. _____ A developing egg, which grows at least in part with the help of nurse cells.
f. _____ Genes encoding transcription factors whose expression is activated by the gap genes.
g. _____ Genes that are expressed differently depending on parental origin.
h. _____ Indicates how each of the cells that make up an adult worm was derived from the fertilized egg.
i. _____ Proteins that form a concentration gradient and specify different cell fates along an axis.
j. _____ The first, tubular-shaped body type produced by many insects.
k. _____ A stage of development in *Drosophila* in which numerous nuclei are contained in a single cytoplasm.
l. _____ Cells that can become multiple different cell types during early cell divisions.
m. _____ A change in cell fate that occurs as a result of an interaction with an adjacent cell.
n. _____ Cells that help the egg grow by moving some of their maternally encoded mRNAs into the maturing oocyte.
o. _____ Genes expressed in 14 distinct bands, which subdivide each of the seven zones specified by pair-rule genes.
p. _____ The large number of small cells that the enormous mass of the zygote is subdivided into.
q. _____ A process that uses patient-specific lines of ES cells to replace injured tissues in an individual.
r. _____ Genes that map out the coarsest subdivision of the embryo along the anterior-posterior axis.
s. _____ The developmental stage in *Drosophila* in which metamorphosis occurs to produce an adult fly.
t. _____ Genes in which mutations cause a transformation in a body part making it look similar to a second body part.
u. _____ The acquisition of axial differences in developing structures.
v. _____ Cells that are set aside and continue to divide while remaining undifferentiated.
w. _____ The period of rapid cell division following fertilization in animal embryos.
x. _____ A ball of cells produced as a result of cleavage that consists of an outer layer and an inner cell mass.
y. _____ A process in which an animal that is genetically identical to another is created.
z. _____ A developmental stage in *Drosophila* where nuclei line up on the surface and membranes grow between them.
aa. _____ Stem cells that can become any cell type during early cell divisions.
bb. _____ A DNA-binding domain common to all of the homeotic genes.
cc. _____ Cell death due to injury in which cells typically swell and burst.
dd. _____ A compound that interferes with production, transport, or binding of endogenous hormones.
ee. _____ A tight cluster of homeotic genes that control the development of the thorax and abdomen of the fly.
ff. _____ The generation of ordered form and structure during embryonic development.
gg. _____ Developmental process in which the hollow ball of animal embryonic cells folds in on itself.
hh. _____ A homeobox-containing gene that specifies the identity of a body part.
ii. _____ A cluster of homeotic genes that direct the development of the anterior end of the fly.
jj. _____ The predominant homeotic gene family in plants containing a conserved DNA-binding domain.
kk. _____ Programmed cell death in which cells shrivel and shrink.
ll. _____ The developmental stage characterized by the formation of the neural tube.

LEARNING BY EXPERIENCE

1. Describe or draw a diagram to demonstrate how the combination of *macho-1* and FGF signaling leads to four different cell types in tunicate embryos.

2. Describe or draw a diagram to indicate how Bicoid, Nanos, Hunchback, and Caudal direct anterior-posterior development in the fly.

EXERCISING YOUR KNOWLEDGE

Briefly answer the following questions in the space provided.

1. How is the formation of the syncytial blastoderm of the fruit fly different from that of the blastula of vertebrates?

2. Distinguish between the cell cycles of an adult somatic cell and that of an early embryonic cell.

3. (a) What are stem cells? (b) How are stem cells used in therapeutic cloning?

4. Describe two ways in which a cell becomes committed to follow a particular developmental pathway.

5. Describe the successful aspects of reproductive cloning and its inherent problems.

6. Distinguish between determination and differentiation.

7. (a) Identify the unifying factor controlling the establishment of both A/P and D/V polarity in *Drosophila*. (b) Explain how this factor works.

8. What is the role of the *bicoid* gene in embryo development of the fruit fly?

9. Distinguish between necrosis and apoptosis.

10. (a) Describe how environmental endocrine-disrupting chemicals (EDCs) disrupt normal development. Indicate the potential sources of these chemicals. (b) Give an example of one EDC and how it functions.

Circle the letter of the one best answer in each of the following questions.

11. Internal structures of vertebrates form from the _____ pole of the zygote.
    a. vegetal
    b. endodermal
    c. mesodermal
    d. animal
    e. ectodermal

12. In early stages of vertebrate cleavage, successive blastomeres
    a. are equal in size to the original zygote.
    b. become smaller and smaller.
    c. grow larger and larger.
    d. migrate to positions of future development.
    e. begin immediate differentiation.

13. If two separated groups of cells—one, animal pole cells and the second, vegetal pole cells— are placed next to each other, some of the animal pole cells will develop into which of the following?
    a. epiderm
    b. endoderm
    c. neural tissue
    d. mesoderm
    e. notoderm

14. For somatic cell nuclear transfer to be successful, the egg and the donated nucleus must be
    a. at the same stage in development.
    b. from the same organism.
    c. at the same stage of the cell cycle.
    d. fused *in vivo*.
    e. unable to undergo cell division.

15. Misexpression of the *macho-1* mRNA leads to the formation of additional
    a. notochord cells.
    b. muscle cells.
    c. endoderm cells.
    d. nerve cord cells.
    e. mesenchyme cells.

16. Follicle cells on the side of the oocyte where Gurken is not released form which type of structures?
    a. posterior
    b. ventral
    c. anterior
    d. dorsal
    e. thoracic segments

17. Which of the following directly produces the segmented body plan of a fly?
    a. induction
    b. cell migration
    c. sequential activation of transcription factors
    d. programmed cell death
    e. *macho-1* and FGF signaling

18. Which of the following *Drosophila* proteins is NOT a transcription factor?
    a. Hunchback
    b. Caudal
    c. Gurken
    d. Dorsal
    e. Hairy

19. When the vertebrate develops into a hollow ball, it is called a
    a. fistula.
    b. blastula.
    c. gastrula.
    d. morula.
    e. planula.

20. The order of the *Drosophila* HOM genes along the chromosome is mirrored by which of the following?
    a. pattern of expression
    b. timing of expression
    c. sequential regulation of each other
    d. importance in development
    e. evolutionary lineage

21. In *C. elegans*, 131 cells always die during development. Inactivating mutations in the *ced-9* gene cause which of the following?
    a. All 1090 cells to live.
    b. 959 cells to die.
    c. It has no effect on the death program.
    d. All 1090 cells to die.
    e. 131 cells undergo necrosis.

22. Insect larvae go through four stages, called
    a. instars.
    b. resects.
    c. extras.
    d. metamorphs.
    e. cleavages.

23. Which of the following are the MADS-box genes NOT involved in?
    a. control of cell proliferation in animals
    b. transition from vegetative to reproductive growth in flowering plants
    c. patterning of animal embryos
    d. root development in plants
    e. tissue-specific gene expression in postmitotic animal muscle cells

24. Reproductive cloning fails because of
    a. reprogramming by the female donor.
    b. insufficient time for reprogramming.
    c. undersized offspring.
    d. postponement of cell division.
    e. reprogramming by the male donor.

25. Development of a syncytial blastoderm is characteristic of
    a. frogs.
    b. birds.
    c. insects.
    d. salamanders.
    e. starfish.

26. Which of the following is NOT an example of an endocrine-disrupting chemical?
    a. diethylstilbestrol (DES)
    b. dioxin
    c. atrazine
    d. glyphosate
    e. heavy metals

27. Which of the following processes are the primary morphogenetic processes in plants?
    a. cell division and cell expansion
    b. changes in cell shape and cell migration
    c. cell division and cell death
    d. cell growth and cell migration
    e. timing and orientation of cell divisions

28. Which of the following provides a route for nutrients to reach a developing plant embryo?
    a. meristem
    b. suspensor
    c. vascular tissue
    d. organizer
    e. ground tissue

29. The migration of cells during the developmental stages of an animal depends primarily on which of the following?
    a. orientation of cell divisions
    b. relative placement in the embryo
    c. osmotic expansion
    d. changing patterns of cell adhesion
    e. growth regulating hormones

30. The process of apoptosis is one in which cells
    a. are programmed to die, shrivel, and shrink.
    b. develop structures in the wrong places.
    c. die because of injury.
    d. are guided into appropriate locations in development.
    e. establish the polarity of an embryo.

ASSESSING YOUR KNOWLEDGE

Answers to the questions in this section test your ability to synthesize information gained from the chapter and to solve challenging problems on an exam or in everyday life.

Challenging Your Understanding—Answers

1. The standard test for determination is to move the donor cell(s) to a different location in a host embryo. If the cells of the transplant develop into the same type of cell as they would have before transplantation, they are already determined. If they develop into the same type of cell as the cells in the location where the cell was transplanted, it was not previously determined. Cells in the head of an embryo normally develop into head structures and those in the tail develop into tail structures. If tail cells are transplanted to the head and develop into head structures, they were not previously determined. If tail cells are transplanted to the head and develop into tail structures, they were previously determined. (Refer to figure 19.5 for a diagram of this description.)

2. If partially committed cells are transplanted from the tip of the wing bud to the identical-looking base of the leg, the cells will likely develop into the shoulder or upper part of the wing, rather than the wing tip. This is because the tissue has already been determined to be part of the wing, but it is not yet committed to being a particular part of the wing. Therefore, it can be influenced by signaling at the base of the leg to form an upper limb structure, rather than a limb tip structure. This chicken embryo will have an upper wing-like structure in place of its leg base.

Key Terms—Answers

a. 8, b. 10, c. 15, d. 7, e. 18, f. 25, g. 12, h. 21, i. 23, j. 14, k. 19, l. 5, m. 9, n. 17, o. 26, p. 1, q. 13, r. 24, s. 22, t. 27, u. 16, v. 3, w. 2, x. 6, y. 11, z. 20, aa. 4, bb. 35, cc. 33, dd. 38, ee. 28, ff. 36, gg. 31, hh. 37, ii. 29, jj. 34, kk. 32, ll. 30.

Learning by Experience—Answers

1. The differentiation of mesodermal cells in the tunicate embryo depends on the inheritance of the *macho-1* mRNA from the female parent and on FGF signaling. FGF binds to a receptor tyrosine kinase, which activates a Ras/MAP kinase cascade that ultimately activates a transcription factor, T-Ets, that turns on gene expression resulting in differentiation. *Macho-1* mRNA is only inherited by some cells and FGF is only bound to the surfaces of the marginal cells that directly border the endoderm precursor cells. Whether the mRNA is inherited or not, and whether the FGF signal is received or not will determine how these cells differentiate. If *macho-1* is expressed and the FGF signal is received, muscle-specific genes are suppressed and cells differentiate into mesenchyme precursor cells. If *macho-1* is expressed and the FGF signal is not received, cells differentiate into muscle precursor cells. If *macho-1* is not expressed and the FGF signal is not received, notochord-specific genes are suppressed and nerve cord-specific genes are activated. As a result, cells differentiate into nerve cord precursor cells. If *macho-1* is not expressed, but the FGF signal is received, cells differentiate into notochord precursor cells. (Refer to figure 19.8 for a diagram of this description.)

2. *Bicoid* and *nanos* mRNAs are cytoplasmic determinants. They are maternally inherited from the nurse cells that secrete the mRNAs into the maturing oocyte. These mRNAs are then differentially transported to opposite poles of the oocyte along microtubules by different motor proteins. The *bicoid* mRNA is anchored in the cytoplasm at the anterior end of the embryo, and the *nanos* mRNA is anchored in the cytoplasm at the posterior end of the embryo. Following fertilization, the mRNAs are translated into proteins creating opposing gradients of each at opposite poles of the embryo. The Bicoid and Nanos proteins control the translation of two other maternal messages, *caudal* and *hunchback*, which direct posterior and anterior structures, respectively. In the anterior pole of the embryo, the Bicoid protein binds to the *caudal* mRNA, inhibiting its translation, and preventing Caudal from activating the expression of genes that direct posterior structures. Likewise, Nanos protein binds to *hunchback* mRNA and prevents its translation in the posterior pole of the embryo. This prevents Hunchback from activating the expression of genes that direct anterior structures in the posterior pole of the embryo. (Refer to figure 19.15 for a diagram of this description.)

Exercising Your Knowledge—Answers

As you check your answers, put a mark in the review (Rvw.) column for the answers you missed. If you didn't miss any, congratulations—you have mastered the chapter! If you missed some, review the section (Sect.) in the text where this concept is discussed. In order to develop an efficient review strategy, it is important that you understand what types of questions you missed. The questions with asterisks test more for understanding of the **concepts,** whereas the others test more for **detail.** *See the preface for learning strategies for concepts and for details.*

	Sect.	Rvw.
*1. The syncytial blastoderm begins with a single cytoplasm containing many nuclei that are later separated by cell membranes. The blastula results from a series of cleavages that form a complete cell each time.	19.2	
*2. The cell cycle of an early embryonic cell lacks the two gap/growth phases, allowing the cleavage stage nuclei to rapidly cycle between DNA replication (S) and mitosis. Cyclin mRNA, which is present in large stores in the unfertilized egg, is translated periodically to allow passage from S phase into mitosis. Subsequent degradation of cyclin proteins leads to Cdk inactivation that allows the cell to complete mitosis. This is unlike an adult somatic cell in which S phase is preceded, and followed by a growth/gap phase, and different cyclin/Cdk complexes are required to be activated at three different times in the cell cycle. This activation requires the production of different cyclins at the appropriate times in the cycle to allow cell cycle progression.	19.2	
*3. (a) Stem cells are capable of developing into a variety of specialized cells. (b) Stem cells may be injected into an organ, where they will develop into cells of the same type as those surrounding them.	19.3	
*4. The first way a cell can become committed to follow a particular developmental pathway is by the differential inheritance of maternally produced cytoplasmic determinants. The second way is by cell-cell interactions in which a cell's fate is determined by an inductive cell interaction with an adjacent cell.	19.3	
5. In 1984, a sheep was cloned, followed by the cloning of pigs and monkeys using early embryo cells. Dolly the sheep, born in 1996, was the first reproductive clone to be generated from a fully differentiated animal cell. Dolly matured and gave birth to six lambs. Since Dolly's birth, one or more cats, rabbits, rats, mice, cattle, goats, pigs, and mules have been successfully cloned. Although reproductive cloning has had these successful results, it also has inherent problems because the efficiency in reproductive cloning is actually quite low and many clones that are born are either oversized or die shortly after from liver failure or infections. All of these problems are likely a result of too little time to reprogram the DNA and remodel the chromatin in the transferred donor nucleus. The reprogramming of the DNA that occurs in adult reproductive tissue usually takes months or years, but in reproductive cloning, it must occur within only a few hours.	19.3	

*6. Determination is the commitment of a cell to a particular developmental path. Differentiation is the specialization of a cell into a particular tissue.	19.3	
*7. (a) The unifying factor in the establishment of both A/P and D/V polarity in *Drosophila* is the creation of morphogen gradients in the embryo based on maternally expressed genes. (b) These morphogen gradients drive the expression of zygotic genes that pattern the embryo.	19.4	
*8. The *bicoid* gene causes production of Bicoid protein, which establishes the anterior end of the embryo.	19.4	
*9. Necrosis is the unprogrammed or accidental death of cells. Apoptosis is the programmed death of cells at a particular point.	19.5	
*10. (a) EDCs interfere with the production, transport, or receptor binding of endogenous hormones that are essential for normal development and homeostasis in animals. Environmental EDCs are derived from industrial wastes, agricultural practices, and the effluent of municipal sewage-treatment plants. (b) There are several examples of EDCs, including dioxins, heavy metals, PCBs, atrazine, and DDT. Dioxins suppress immune system function and impair spatial memory, learning, and other cognitive processes.	19.6	
*11. a	19.3	
*12. b	19.3	
*13. d	19.3	
*14. c	19.3	
15. b	19.3	
16. b	19.4	
*17. c	19.4	
18. c	19.4	
19. b	19.2	
*20. a	19.4	
21. d	19.5	
22. a	19.4	
*23. c	19.4	
24. b	19.3	
25. c	19.4	
26. d	19.6	
*27. a	19.5	
28. b	19.5	
29. d	19.5	
30. a	19.5	

CHAPTER 20 GENES WITHIN POPULATIONS

MASTERING KEY CONCEPTS

Only identical twins or clones have identical genetic information. An individual's unique genotype and phenotype make it either more or less likely to survive and reproduce than other members of its population, depending on how well adapted each is to the local environment. Such differences in reproduction are the essence of natural selection, which results in evolution. Mutation, gene flow, nonrandom mating, genetic drift, and selection can also cause changes in a population's allele frequencies over time.

20.1 Genes vary in natural populations.

- **Overview**: Individuals within natural populations contain **genetic variations**. **Darwin** proposed that **natural selection** of advantageous characteristics leads to evolutionary change in a population, while **Lamarck** proposed that the **inheritance of acquired characteristics** leads to the evolution of a species. In populations of insects and plants, high levels of genetic variability among their genes are due to **polymorphisms** at **enzyme-encoding loci**. Vertebrates have less polymorphic loci than plants and insects, but still have high levels of genetic variability due to relatively high percentages of **heterozygous loci**. DNA sequence analysis has also demonstrated the presence of a significant number of polymorphic sites in both the exons and the introns of genes within a specific population. The rate at which these polymorphisms occur cannot be explained simply by the occurrence of spontaneous mutations.
- **Details**: Understand the differences between Darwin's and Lamarck's theories of evolution. Know how populations display genetic variation.

20.2 Why do allele frequencies change in populations?

- **Overview**: **Hardy and Weinberg** discovered that sexual reproduction (meiosis and fertilization) does not cause allele frequencies to change over time in a population. They found that the original proportion of genotypes and phenotypes in large populations, where no selection, mutations, or gene transfers occur, will remain constant from one generation to the next, if mating occurs randomly. If this is not true, it suggests that one or more evolutionary processes are acting on a given population.
- **Details**: Understand how to use the **Hardy-Weinberg equation** to calculate the **genotype frequencies** in a population and how to predict frequencies in subsequent generations. Understand the situations in which a population may lack **Hardy-Weinberg equilibrium**, the

potential hypotheses that may explain why this occurs, and what it means.

20.3 Five agents can bring about evolutionary change.

- **Overview**: Changes in alleles or the proportions of genotypes can be brought about by **evolutionary processes**, such as **mutation**, **gene flow**, **nonrandom mating**, **genetic drift** in small populations, or the **pressures of natural selection** leading to a lack of Hardy-Weinberg equilibrium. **Mutation** is the ultimate source of genetic variation although a typical gene mutates only once per 100,000 cell divisions, and this rate is not affected by natural selection. **Gene flow** is a major factor promoting change among populations. It can occur by the drifting of gametes, mating of individuals belonging to adjacent populations, or the arrival of a new individual in a population whose genetic composition and characteristics are different from the existing population. **Nonrandom mating** increases the frequency of homozygous individuals (**assortative mating**) or the frequency of heterozygous individuals (**disassortative mating**) but does not affect allele frequency. In small populations, or in large populations that were much smaller at one time, the frequencies of particular alleles can change drastically by chance alone (**genetic drift**) because if the gametes of only a few individuals form the next generation, the alleles may not be representative of the entire parent population. In fact, advantageous alleles can be lost, and harmful alleles can increase as a result of genetic drift. **Natural selection**, like many other factors, can lead to evolutionary change if variation exists among the individuals of a population. If this variation results in differences in the number of surviving offspring in the next generation and is genetically inherited, it will lead to evolutionary change by natural selection, resulting in a population that is better adapted to its environment.
- **Details**: Understand the agents that bring about evolutionary change and how. Understand what is meant by the **founder effect** and the **bottleneck effect**. Know the three conditions that must be met for natural selection to occur. Understand the relationship between natural selection and evolution. Know three different examples of how natural selection has allowed organisms to become better adapted to their particular environments.

20.4 Fitness is a measurement of reproductive success.

- **Overview**: **Fitness**, or reproductive success, is

quantified as the number of surviving offspring in the next generation. It is a combination of survival, mating success, and the number of offspring per mating.
- **Details**: Understand how to **assign fitness values** given the number of phenotypes of each in a population. Know how to **calculate the difference in fitness**, and how to predict changes in phenotypes based on the **three components of fitness**. Understand how natural selection can affect the components of fitness and how these components can affect each other.

20.5 Genetic variation is determined by interactions among evolutionary forces.
- **Overview**: **Mutation rates** and **genetic drift counter selection** in that they act to remove variations from populations, while selection acts to increase the representation of alleles that enhance survival. **Gene flow** can spread a beneficial mutation, or can impede adaptation within a population by the flow of inferior alleles from other populations. The extent to which gene flow inhibits selection depends on the relative strengths of the two processes.
- **Details**: Understand the conditions under which genetic drift, or gene flow, can hinder the effects of natural selection.

20.6 Selection can maintain variation in populations.
- **Overview**: **Frequency-dependent selection** favors certain phenotypes in a population depending on how frequently or infrequently they occur. When common phenotypes have the advantage (**positive frequency-dependent selection**), variation is eliminated from a population. The rarer a genotype is, the more likely it will be selected against. When rare phenotypes have the advantage (**negative frequency-dependent selection**), variation is maintained, but as these rare genotypes become more common, their selective advantage will decrease. **Oscillating selection** maintains genetic variation by environmental changes that favor one phenotype at one time, and a second phenotype at another time. When heterozygotes are favored in a population (**heterozygote advantage**), natural selection maintains variation in the population.
- **Details**: Know an example of negative frequency-dependent selection, and an example of positive frequency-dependent selection. Understand the **relationship between the sickle cell allele and malaria**. Understand why the sickle cell allele is maintained among African populations but is being eliminated from African American populations.

20.7 Selection can act on traits affected by many genes.
- **Overview**: The interactions between genes are complex, and one trait is typically determined by the action of more than one gene. Selection changes a population based on which genotypes are favored. **Disruptive selection** eliminates individuals having an intermediate phenotype and partitions the population into two phenotypically distinct groups. Selection may also act to eliminate one of the extremes in an array of phenotypes (**directional selection**), or may act to eliminate both extremes from an array of phenotypes (**stabilizing selection**). Many traits, if not most, are influenced by more than one gene.
- **Details**: Understand how disruptive, directional, and stabilizing selection will affect a population.

20.8 Experimental studies of natural selection test evolutionary hypotheses.
- **Overview**: Differences in the guppy populations above and below waterfalls suggest that natural selection affects coloration, size, and the reproductive age of the fish differently in the two populations due to the existence or lack of predators. **Laboratory experiments** to explain these differences support the idea that **predation** can lead to rapid changes in guppy coloration and size. **Reproducing the experiment in nature** also demonstrated that a low predation population of guppies becomes more colorful, larger, and mature later.
- **Details:** Know how guppy populations above and below waterfalls are affected by natural selection. Understand how evolutionary changes can be tested in the laboratory and under natural conditions.

20.9 There are limits to what selection can accomplish.
- **Overview**: There are limits to the ability of selection to promote genetic change. These limits are the result of **pleiotropy**, or alleles having more than one effect on phenotype, **a lack of genetic variation** in a population, and **epistatic interactions between genes**, where the outcome of selection at one gene depends on which alleles are present at a second gene.
- **Details:** Understand the examples of how pleiotropy, lack of genetic variation, and epistasis set the limits for the genetic changes that selection can bring about.

CHALLENGING YOUR UNDERSTANDING—Part I

Indicate the five agents that lead to changes in allele frequencies during the evolutionary process.

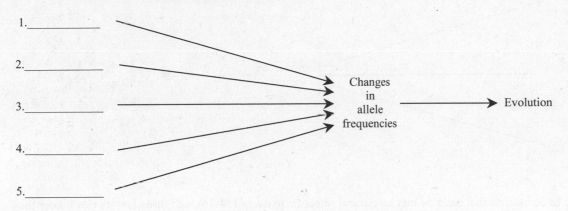

THE EVOLUTIONARY PROCESS

1._____

2._____

3._____

4._____

5._____

Changes in allele frequencies → Evolution

Indicate the five assumptions that must be met for the Hardy-Weinberg equilibrium to be achieved in a population.

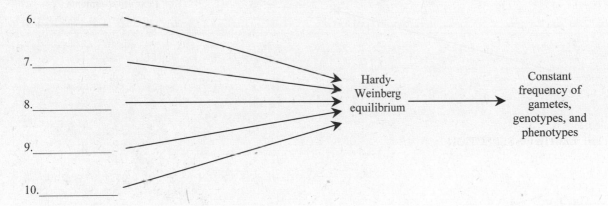

THE HARDY-WEINBERG PRINCIPLE

6._____

7._____

8._____

9._____

10._____

Hardy-Weinberg equilibrium → Constant frequency of gametes, genotypes, and phenotypes

CHALLENGING YOUR UNDERSTANDING—Part II

Indicate the three factors that contribute to the fitness of an individual.

MEASURING FITNESS

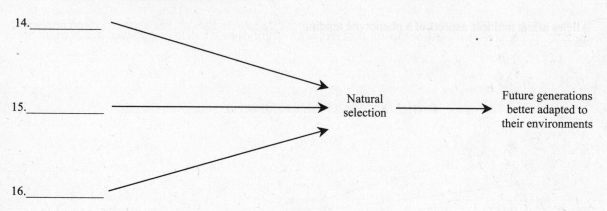

Indicate the three conditions that must be met for natural selection to occur (14-16), and three factors that hinder the ability of selection to produce evolutionary change (17-19).

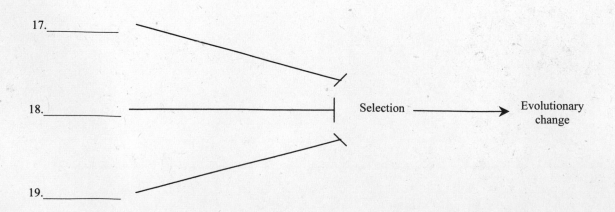

KEY TERMS

Match the numbered term with the definition that fits it best. Put the corresponding number in front of the appropriate definition.

1. natural selection
2. inheritance of acquired characteristics
3. evolution
4. polymorphic
5. heterozygosity
6. blending inheritance
7. Hardy-Weinberg equilibrium
8. allele frequencies
9. genotype frequencies

10. gene flow
11. assortative mating
12. disassortative mating
13. genetic drift
14. founder effect
15. artificial selection
16. natural selection
17. fitness
18. frequency-dependent selection

19. oscillating selection
20. heterozygote advantage
21. disruptive selection
22. directional selection
23. stabilizing selection
24. epistasis
25. pleiotropy
26. bottleneck effect
27. population genetics

a. _____ Calculated using the Hardy-Weinberg equation to find the rate at which a genotype is present in a population.
b. _____ In small populations, frequencies of particular alleles may change drastically by chance alone.
c. _____ A breeder selects for the desired characteristics of the offspring of a mating.
d. _____ Process in which phenotypically different individuals mate, producing an excess of heterozygotes.
e. _____ A phenomenon in which selection favors one phenotype at one time and another at a different time.
f. _____ The movement of alleles from one population to another.
g. _____ A diploid individual containing two different alleles of a particular gene.
h. _____ Individuals pass on bodily and behavioral changes acquired during their lives to their offspring.
i. _____ Previously rare alleles in a population are a significant fraction of a new population's genetic endowment.
j. _____ A locus that has more than one allele at a frequency greater than what would occur due to mutation alone.
k. _____ Alleles affect multiple aspects of a phenotype tending to set limits on how much a phenotype can be altered.
l. _____ A phenomenon in which the fitness of a phenotype depends on its frequency within a population.
m. _____ A loss of genetic variability resulting from only a few individuals in a population forming the next generation.
n. _____ The selective favoring of individuals in a population that have more than one copy of a particular allele.
o. _____ When selection acts to eliminate both extremes from an array of phenotypes.
p. _____ The study of the properties of different genes within a population.
q. _____ Individuals better suited to their environments are more successful passing advantageous traits to their offspring.
r. _____ A phenomenon in which selection acts to eliminate intermediate types in a population.
s. _____ A rate determined from the proportion of individuals possessing a particular phenotype in a population.
t. _____ When the phenotype of one gene masks the phenotype of a second gene.
u. _____ The frequencies of gametes, genotypes, and phenotypes remain constant from one generation to the next.
v. _____ A quantitation of reproductive success reflected as the number of surviving offspring in the next generation.
w. _____ Results from any process that causes a change in the genetic composition of a population.
x. _____ When selection acts to eliminate one extreme from an array of phenotypes.
y. _____ A type of nonrandom mating in which phenotypically similar individuals mate.
z. _____ Environmental conditions determine which individuals in a population produce the most offspring.
aa. _____ A theory that predicted that offspring would be phenotypically intermediate to each of their parents.

LEARNING BY EXPERIENCE

1. Both Charles Darwin and Jean-Baptiste Lamarck believed that species evolved, but they proposed different mechanisms for how and why evolutionary changes occur. Write an essay or stage a debate with a classmate explaining the evolutionary mechanisms proposed by Darwin and Lamarck.

2. Feral animals are animals that used to be domesticated but have reverted back to the wild. Populations of feral goats exist on many islands around the world, left by previous settlers or by sailors who wanted to establish a source of fresh meat for future visits. Consider a population of 100 feral goats in which 75 individuals are solid black (the dominant phenotype) and 25 individuals are black-and-white spotted (the recessive phenotype). Calculate the frequency of the black allele (B) and the spotted allele (b) in the population, as well as the frequency of each genotype (BB, Bb, and bb) in the population. Show your work.

3. Consider the effect of selection on the length of ears in a population of feral goats. For each graph below, draw the shape of the curve after many generations of the type of selection indicated. The dotted curve shows the starting distribution of the population. Draw your curve over it.

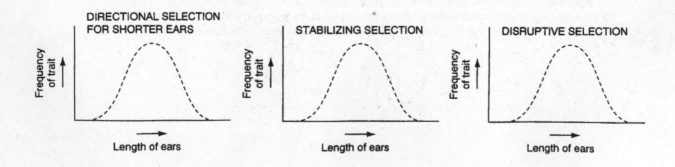

EXERCISING YOUR KNOWLEDGE

Briefly answer each of the following questions in the space provided.

1. Which procedure, protein electrophoresis or DNA sequencing, detects more genetic variation? What are the implications of this variation for understanding evolution?

2. What five factors can cause allele frequencies in a population to change? Which result(s) in adaptive evolutionary change?

3. The Hardy-Weinberg principle says that allele frequencies in a population don't automatically change over time, but we know they usually do. So why is the Hardy-Weinberg principle useful?

4. How are the founder effect and the bottleneck effect similar in terms of the implications for population genetics?

5. What factors or forces can counteract natural selection?

6. What is the difference between natural selection and evolution?

7. Does natural selection operate more efficiently on dominant or recessive alleles? Explain.

8. Does natural selection operate more efficiently on beneficial or deleterious alleles? Explain.

9. Why is "survival of the fittest" not the best way to explain the concept of evolutionary fitness?

10. Research has shown that adult male deer with large antlers tend to have more mating opportunities and produce more offspring than males with smaller antlers. Why hasn't natural selection led to male deer with huge antlers?

Circle the letter of the one best answer in each of the following questions.

11. Darwin proposed that the mechanism behind evolutionary change was
    a. heterozygosity.
    b. genetic drift.
    c. inheritance of acquired characteristics.
    d. polymorphism.
    e. natural selection.

12. How common is genetic polymorphism in natural populations?
    a. Essentially all loci are polymorphic.
    b. Essentially no loci are polymorphic.
    c. Depending on the species, all the loci are polymorphic or none of the loci are polymorphic.
    d. Depending on the species, somewhat more or somewhat less than half the loci are polymorphic.
    e. There is no way of knowing.

13. Which of the following types of organisms has the greatest degree of heterozygosity?
    a. plants with disassortative mating
    b. self-fertilizing plants
    c. invertebrates
    d. vertebrates
    e. They all have the same level of heterozygosity.

14. What percentage of the enzyme loci in a typical human are heterozygous?
    a. 0%
    b. 5%
    c. 15%
    d. 55%
    e. 100%

15. Assortative mating
    a. increases the proportion of homozygous individuals in a population.
    b. increases the rate of mutation.
    c. never occurs in plants.
    d. All of these are correct.
    e. None of these are correct.

16. What is the ultimate source of genetic variation?
    a. nonrandom mating
    b. gene flow
    c. mutation
    d. genetic drift
    e. selection

17. Which of the following factors is most likely to contribute to gene flow between populations?
    a. random mating
    b. migration
    c. genetic drift
    d. assortative mating
    e. mutation

18. In the Hardy-Weinberg equation, the term *2pq* represents the frequency of the
    a. dominant allele.
    b. recessive allele.
    c. homozygous dominant genotype.
    d. homozygous recessive genotype.
    e. heterozygous genotype.

19. Why is genetic polymorphism important to evolution?
    a. Individual variability provides the raw material for natural selection to act on.
    b. Genes cannot mutate unless they are polymorphic.
    c. Only heterozygous individuals are selected for natural populations.
    d. The Hardy-Weinberg equilibrium is less likely to be disturbed in polymorphic populations.
    e. Genetic polymorphism is *not* important to evolution.

20. Consider the following hypothetical situation: A virus kills most of the seals in the North Sea (for example, drops the population from 3000 to 60 individuals). In an effort to help prevent the species from going extinct, scientists catch 10 females and 4 males and use them to start a new population in the northwestern Pacific. Which of the following factors would most likely have the *least* impact on the population genetics of this species of seal?
    a. founder effect
    b. bottleneck effect
    c. genetic drift
    d. gene flow
    e. assortative mating

21. In a population of wildflowers, the frequency of the dominant allele for red flowers is 0.8. What is the frequency of the recessive white allele?
    a. 0.8
    b. 0.64
    c. 0.32
    d. 0.2
    e. 0.16

22. Referring to question 21, what is the frequency of homozygous, red-flowering plants in the population?
    a. 0.64
    b. 0.48
    c. 0.32
    d. 0.16
    e. 0.04

23. Referring to question 21, what is the frequency of homozygous white-flowering plants in the population?
    a. 0.64
    b. 0.48
    c. 0.32
    d. 0.16
    e. 0.04

24. Referring to question 21, what is the frequency of plants heterozygous for flower color in the population?
    a. 0.64
    b. 0.48
    c. 0.32
    d. 0.16
    e. 0.04

25. Is genetic drift likely to be a bigger factor for a population with a lot of individuals or for a smaller population?
    a. the bigger population
    b. the smaller population
    c. It will be the same for both.
    d. It is totally random and not related to population size.

26. The phenomenon in which environmental changes cause changes in the fitness of a particular phenotype is referred to as
    a. disassortative mating.
    b. heterozygote advantage.
    c. epistasis.
    d. frequency-dependent selection.
    e. oscillating selection.

27. A scientist measures the circumference of acorns in a population of oak trees and discovers that they range in size from 1cm to 3cm and that 2cm is the most common circumference. What would you expect the most common circumference to be after 10 generations of stabilizing selection?
    a. 1cm *and* 3cm
    b. 1cm *or* 3cm
    c. 2cm
    d. can't tell from the information provided

28. In evolutionary terms, the most fit individual is the one who
    a. is the strongest.
    b. is the biggest.
    c. lives the longest.
    d. has the greatest number of successful offspring.
    e. is the most intelligent.

29. The speed of thoroughbred racehorses provides a good example that selection
    a. can work only when genetic variability is present in the population.
    b. to avoid predators can be a powerful force.
    c. frequently works to match local climatic conditions.
    d. can result in resistance to antibiotics or pesticides.
    e. does not work on domesticated organisms.

30. Selection acts only on
    a. genotypes.
    b. phenotypes.
    c. dominant alleles.
    d. recessive alleles.
    e. heterozygotes.

ASSESSING YOUR KNOWLEDGE

Answers to the questions in this section test your ability to synthesize information gained from the chapter and to solve challenging problems on an exam or in everyday life.

Challenging Your Understanding—Part I, Answers

1. Mutation
2. Gene flow
3. Nonrandom mating
4. Genetic drift
5. Selection

(Answers 1-5 can be in any order.)

6. No mutations
7. No gene transfers
8. Random mating
9. Large population size
10. No selection

(Answers 6-10 can be in any order.)

Challenging Your Understanding—Part II, Answers

11. Survival
12. Mating success
13. Number of offspring per mating

(Answers 11-13 can be in any order.)

14. Variation exists.
15. Variation results in differences in the number of surviving offspring.
16. Variation is genetically inherited.

(Answers 14-16 can be in any order.)

17. Pleiotropy
18. Lack of genetic variation
19. Gene interactions

(Answers 17-19 can be in any order.)

Key Terms—Answers

a. 9, b. 13, c. 15, d. 12, e. 19, f. 10, g. 5, h. 2, i. 14, j. 4, k. 25, l. 18, m. 26, n. 20, o. 23, p. 27, q. 1, r. 21, s. 8, t. 24, u. 7, v. 17, w. 3, x. 22, y. 11, z. 16, aa. 6.

Learning by Experience—Answers

1. Darwin believed that natural selection was the mechanism that led to evolutionary change. Lamarck believed that inheritance of acquired characteristics was the mechanism. Neither had the benefit of knowing about genes, chromosomes, or the mechanics of meiosis. Darwin proposed that evolutionary change occurred in a population when certain advantageous inherited traits were passed on to future generations more than other less-advantageous traits were. Lamarck also believed that advantageous traits were passed on to future generations, but he believed the traits were acquired during the individual's lifetime because of circumstances and experiences, rather than being inherited.

2. If 25 of 100 individuals are spotted, and spotted is the recessive phenotype, the frequency of $bb = 0.25$ (= 25%). From the Hardy-Weinberg equilibrium, we know that $bb = 0.25$ is the same as saying that $q^2 = 0.25$ since q^2 is the frequency of the homozygous recessive genotype. Therefore, $q = 0.5$ (the square root of 0.25). In other words, the frequency of the recessive allele b is 0.5. If $q = 0.5$, then $p = 0.5$ too, since $p + q = 1.0$; $p = B$, so the frequency of the dominant allele B is 0.5. The frequency of homozygous dominant genotype is $BB = p^2 = 0.5 \times 0.5 = 0.25$, and the frequency of heterozygous genotype is $Bb = 2pq = 2 \times 0.5 \times 0.5 = 0.5$

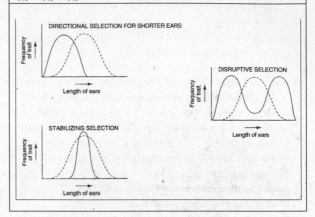

Exercising Your Knowledge—Answers

As you check your answers, put a mark in the review (Rvw.) column for the answers you missed. If you didn't miss any, congratulations—you have mastered the chapter! If you missed some, review the section (Sect.) in the text where this concept is discussed. In order to develop an efficient review strategy, it is important that you understand what types of questions you missed. The questions with asterisks test more for understanding of the **concepts**, whereas the others test more for **detail**. *See the preface for learning strategies for concepts and for details.*

	Sect.	Rvw.
*1. DNA sequencing detects more variation. These molecular techniques show that there is a lot of genetic variation in populations, material for natural selection to work on that leads to adaptive evolutionary change. The level of variation is greater than what would be expected from just mutation alone, lending support to the existence of natural selection as an evolutionary force.	20.1	
*2. Five factors = mutation, gene flow, nonrandom mating, genetic drift, and natural selection. Only selection produces adaptive evolutionary change that is tied to the local environment; the other factors produce random change or changes not related to the environment. Note: As Hardy and Weinberg demonstrated, the mechanics of meiosis and fertilization do not in and of themselves cause changes in allele frequencies.	20.3	

*3. The Hardy-Weinberg principle establishes the conditions under which allele frequencies do not change and allows us to calculate the frequencies of different genotypes and alleles, which can be of great use for medical, conservation, and other purposes. When allele frequencies do change, the Hardy-Weinberg principle provides a baseline against which the change can be compared to try and determine which of the conditions has not been met and therefore what factors are causing the change.	20.2	
*4. Both the founder effect and the bottleneck effect are likely to promote genetic drift, the random change in allele frequencies often seen in small populations due to chance events. Both result in very small populations, either because only a few individuals start the population in a new site (founder effect) or only a few individuals survive some catastrophe that befalls an established population (bottleneck effect). A population resulting from such a low number of individuals most likely will not be representative of the original stock population and will have less genetic diversity.	20.3	
*5. Mutation, genetic drift, and gene flow can all counteract natural selection and help maintain genetic polymorphism in a population. Gene flow, however, can also help reinforce natural selection, depending on the particular details.	20.5	
*6. Natural selection is a process or mechanism, while evolution is the product or the outcome. Individuals are selected for or selected against depending on their suite of characteristics relative to the local environment. Those selected for have a greater percentage of their genetic information represented in the next generation. As a result of this differential reproduction, populations change over time, or in other words, they evolve.	20.3	
*7. Selection acts more efficiently on dominant alleles than on recessive alleles because selection acts only on phenotypes. Selection can act on an allele only if it is physically expressed, and dominant alleles are physically expressed in both the homozygous dominant and the heterozygous genotypes. Recessive alleles, on the other hand, are phenotypically expressed only in the homozygous recessive genotype. Recessive alleles can be carried in the heterozygous genotype and cannot be acted on by selection then.	20.6	
*8. Selection can act equally efficiently on beneficial or harmful alleles. There can be selection for or against a trait. The greater the impact (positive or negative) of the allele, the stronger (more efficient) the selection pressure will be, and the more quickly the frequency of the allele will be increased or decreased in the population in future generations.	20.6	

*9. The key to understanding natural selection, evolutionary change, and fitness is recognizing that from an evolutionary point of view it's not how long you survive, but how much you reproduce relative to everyone else in the population and how successful your offspring and other descendants are. While it's true you have to be alive to be able to reproduce, you can survive to be the oldest individual in your population, but your fitness is zero if you have not reproduced; rather than "survival of the fittest," a better way to describe evolutionary fitness is "greater reproduction by the most well-adapted."	20.4	
*10. There are limits to what selection can accomplish; selection is acting on the entire phenotype of the deer, not just the one trait of antler size. Genes tend to interact, not operate in isolation, and a single gene may influence more than one trait. As the antlers get bigger, interactions may lead to other selection pressures that are negative. For example, huge antlers might be so big and heavy that it would be difficult for the buck to move or feed properly. Or it might require so much energy and calcium to make them that the buck is weak and his bones break easily	20.9	
11. e	20.1	
*12. d	20.1	
13. c	20.1	
14. b	20.1	
*15. a	20.3	
16. c	20.3	
17. b	20.3	
18. e	20.2	
*19. a	20.3	
*20. d	20.3	
21. d	20.2	
22. a	20.2	
23. e	20.2	
24. c	20.2	
25. b	20.3	
26. e	20.6	
27. c	20.7	
28. d	20.4	
*29. a	20.9	
30. b	20.7	

CHAPTER 21 THE EVIDENCE FOR EVOLUTION

MASTERING KEY CONCEPTS
We are surrounded by a great variety of evidence that evolution has occurred in the past and is continuing to occur in the species living on this planet. The fossil record and the anatomical record provide the evidence to demonstrate that selection can produce evolutionary changes in populations and species. Despite the overwhelming evidence supporting the evolutionary theory, some people continue to consider it controversial. Their objections, however, do not have scientific merit.

21.1 Evidence indicates that natural selection can produce evolutionary change.
- **Overview**: The ability of **natural selection** to change certain traits of a population has been clearly demonstrated in species such as **Darwin's finches**. Darwin collected 31 finches from three Galápagos Islands that were all similar to one another except for their beaks. These finches belonged to a closely related group of distinct species and Darwin proposed that their beaks had been shaped by natural selection as a result of the type of food available. More than a hundred years later, this hypothesis was tested and confirmed by **Peter and Rosemary Grant,** who measured the beak depths of individual ground finches for several years. They found that the average beak depth of the birds changed from year to year depending upon the amount of rainfall, which determined the type and the size of seeds available. By measuring the relation of the parent beak size to the offspring beak size, the Grants found that the depth of the beak was passed on to the next generation, regardless of environmental conditions, suggesting that beak sizes were due to genetic differences and were therefore a result of natural selection resulting in evolutionary change.
- **Details**: Know how rainfall affects the type and the size of seeds available and how this affects the beak shape in the ground finches of the Galápagos Islands. Understand how it was determined that the changes in beak depth actually do reflect natural selection.

21.2 Peppered moths and industrial melanism also support the idea of natural selection leading to evolutionary change.
- **Overview**: The **body color of the peppered moth**, ranging from light gray to black, is a genetic trait that reflects different alleles of a single gene, where the black allele is rare but dominant. Over time, black moths increased in populations around industrial centers to making up almost 100% of the population. **Tutt** proposed that the peppered moths were eliminated in polluted areas because they could be more easily seen on the soot-covered trees by the birds that ate them than the black-colored moths could be. **Kettlewell** tested this hypothesis and found that more black moths did survive in more polluted areas, while more light moths survived in less-polluted areas as a result of birds failing to detect the moths whose color matched the color of the trees. These experiments suggested that the birds that prey on the moths act as **agents of selection**, such that the less-visible moths in a particular population survive.
- **Details**: Understand how Kettlewell tested the hypothesis that the survival of light-colored peppered moths decreased in polluted areas because of **predation**. Know how the effects of **industrial melanism** began being reversed. Understand what agents of natural selection could be acting on the moth populations.

21.3 Human-initiated change is an example of artificial selection.
- **Overview**: **Human-imposed artificial selection** in which only individuals possessing a desired phenotypic trait are allowed to reproduce generation after generation can rapidly produce major changes in populations. These techniques have been utilized **in the laboratory**, **in agriculture**, and **in animal breeding**. Differences among breeds of dogs demonstrate that artificial selection can produce major changes in a population in a short period of time, suggesting that **natural selection** is a powerful agent influencing evolutionary change.
- **Details**: Understand how artificial selection can produce changes in populations. Specifically understand how artificial selection has affected the silver fox population. Know how artificial selection supports the idea that natural selection can produce major evolutionary changes.

21.4 Fossil evidence indicates that evolution has occurred.
- **Overview**: The **fossil record** provides the most direct evidence of the occurrence of evolution. It documents the course of life, and the waxing or waning of biological diversity through time. The age of a fossil is determined by dating the rocks in which it occurs. **Relative dating** determines the age of rocks according to their positions with respect to each other, while **absolute dating** uses **radioactive decay rates** of elements found in the rocks. **Intermediate fossils**, having some traits like their ancestors and others similar to their descendants, have bridged a number of **gaps in the fossil record**. The fossil record for horses demonstrates that while overall trends are

evident, the rate of evolution has not been constant, but has occurred in periods of great change that were separated by long periods with little change. These records also show that different lineages of horses have undergone simultaneous changes in evolution, but there are several exceptions to evolutionary trends.

- **Details**: Know the three events that must occur for **rock fossils to be created**. Understand why the process of fossilization and recovery of fossils rarely occurs. Understand how radioactive decay rates can be used to date rocks, and how the age of a fossil can be determined from this information. Understand why intermediate fossils have only some intermediate traits. Understand the detailed fossil record that exists for the horse.

21.5 Evidence for evolution can be found in other fields of biology.

- **Overview**: **Homologous structures, vestigial structures**, and **embryological development patterns** provide strong **anatomical evidence for evolution**. Homologous structures look different and have different functions in different organisms but are derived from the same body part of a common ancestor. Vestigial structures have no obvious function, but resemble the functional organs of an organism's ancestors. The early embryos of different organisms possess similar structures that change or disappear during development suggesting that organisms containing these structures are related.
- **Details**: Know different examples of homologous structures, vestigial structures, and developmental similarities that suggest that organisms are derived from a common ancestor.

21.6 Convergent evolution and the biogeographical record

- **Overview**: **Biogeography** indicates that natural selection has favored **convergent evolution**. Convergent evolution is the parallel evolutionary adaptations of distantly related organisms in similar environments but different geographical areas. This has occurred as a result of the organisms interacting with the environment in similar ways because of **similar selective pressures**. These interactions have made some groups of organisms phenotypically more alike, even though they are not derived from a common ancestor.
- **Details**: Understand how different groups of organisms demonstrate convergent evolution. Understand how the **continental drift** may have led to the separation of evolutionarily-related organisms.

21.7 The theory of evolution has proven controversial.

- **Overview**: Critics of Darwin's theory of evolution raise **seven major objections** to his conclusions. These arguments include the following: (1) Evolution is just a theory and not conclusively demonstrated. (2) There are no fossil intermediates. (3) Organisms are too complex for the random process of selection to have produced them. (4) Evolution violates the Second Law of Thermodynamics, which states that random events will increase disorder in a system. (5) Proteins are too improbable. (6) Natural selection does not imply evolution. (7) Complexity could not have evolved from simpler machinery. These objections do not hold up to scientific evidence or scientific processes.
- **Details**: Understand why each of the objections to Darwin's theory of evolution does not hold scientific merit.

CHALLENGING YOUR UNDERSTANDING—Part I

1. Indicate four pieces of evidence that suggest that natural selection can lead to evolutionary change. Some clues have been provided for the second and the fourth pieces of evidence.

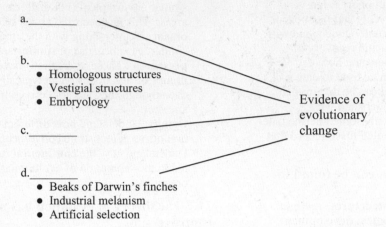

a._____

b._____
- Homologous structures
- Vestigial structures
- Embryology

c._____

Evidence of evolutionary change

d._____
- Beaks of Darwin's finches
- Industrial melanism
- Artificial selection

2. On the following graphs, draw a line to indicate the general trends that Peter and Rosemary Grant observed in successfully testing Darwin's hypothesis of natural selection. Explain why each of the trends was observed.

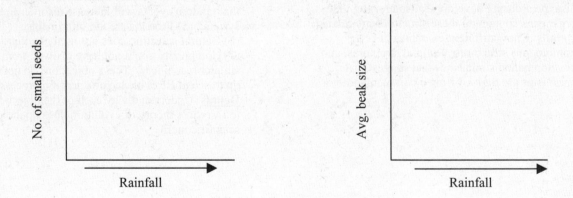

CHALLENGING YOUR UNDERSTANDING—Part II

3. On the following graphs, draw a line to indicate the general trends that Bernard Kettlewell observed in successfully testing Tutt's hypothesis of industrial melanism in the peppered moth populations in polluted areas. Explain why each of the trends was observed.

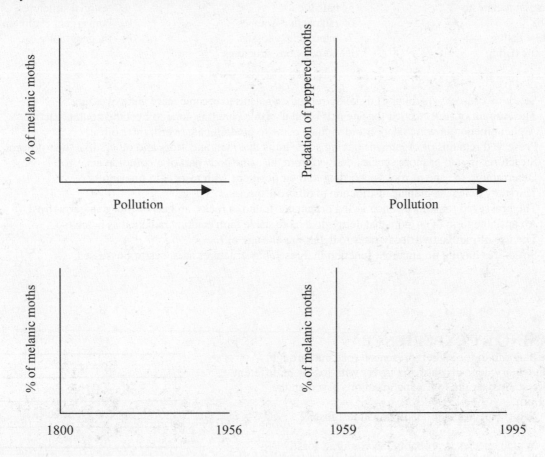

4. On the following graphs, indicate the amount of parent isotope remaining at each half-life, if at time zero you start with 4 mCi. List the amounts of parent isotope and daughter isotope present at each half-life below the graph.

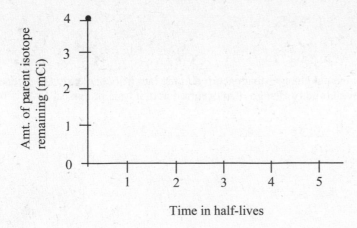

Parent isotope (mCi):
Daughter isotope (mCi):

KEY TERMS

Match the numbered term with the definition that fits it best. Put the corresponding number in front of the appropriate definition.

1. industrial melanism
2. fossils
3. relative dating
4. absolute dating

5. half-life
6. radioactive isotopes
7. intermediate fossils
8. homologous structures

9. vestigial structures
10. convergent evolution
11. biogeography

a. ____ Selection causes two groups of distantly-related organisms to become more alike over time.
b. ____ The amount of time needed for one half of an unstable parent isotope to become nonradioactive.
c. ____ A phenomenon in which darker individuals come to predominate over lighter ones.
d. ____ Preserved remains of organisms having some traits like their ancestors and others like their descendants.
e. ____ Structures in two or more species derived from the same body part of a common ancestor.
f. ____ Determining the age of rocks according to their positions with respect to one another.
g. ____ The study of the geographic distribution of different species.
h. ____ The preserved remains of once-living organisms found in rocks, amber, or Siberian permafrost.
i. ____ An unstable form of an atom that decays to a more stable form emitting radiation as it does so.
j. ____ The use of radioactive decay rates to determine the age of rocks.
k. ____ Structures having no apparent function that resemble structures an ancestor possessed.

LEARNING BY EXPERIENCE

1. The diagram to the right represents a road cut through sedimentary deposits showing layers with fossils of different species. Answer the following questions based on the diagram.

Species A
Species B, Species C
Species D, Species E
Species F

    a. Which species is probably the oldest fossil?

    b. Which species is probably the youngest fossil?

    c. Which fossil is most likely the same age as species C?

2. Explain the correlation between environmental changes that occurred in the late Miocene/early Oligocene epochs (20–25 million years ago) and evolutionary changes that occurred at that time in horses.

3. Describe what happened to the silver fox population within 40 years when scientists allowed only the most docile animals to reproduce. Why did more than just the behavior of the animals change?

4. Douglas Futuyma, an evolutionary biologist, has stated that "evolution is not random: some paths are more likely than others." Explain what he means.

EXERCISING YOUR KNOWLEDGE

Briefly answer each of the following questions in the space provided.

1. What are the three basic steps that occur when fossils are created?

2. Why are there gaps in the fossil record?

3. What changes have occurred in body size during the evolutionary history of the horse?

4. Describe how a scientist with a population of *Drosophila* containing individuals with a mean number of 85 bristles can create a population with a much lower mean number of bristles.

5. Describe how the anatomy of living organisms can reveal evidence of shared ancestry.

6. What lessons about evolution can we learn from artificial selection?

7. In the case of industrial melanism in the peppered moth, where did the dark moths come from?

8. Under what environmental conditions does convergent evolution occur?

9. What does biogeography tell us about evolution?

10. Are the objections of Darwin's critics based on scientific evidence?

Circle the letter of the one best answer in each of the following questions.

11. Which is a more accurate way of determining the age of rocks, absolute or relative dating?
    a. absolute dating
    b. relative dating
    c. They are equally accurate.

12. Compared to 20 million years ago, the diversity of horse species today is
    a. greater.
    b. less.
    c. the same.
    d. There were no horse species 20 million years ago.

13. Rocks can be aged by measuring the degree of decay of _____ in them.
    a. lanugo
    b. teosinte
    c. fossils
    d. radioactive isotopes
    e. vestigial structures

14. Which of the following fossils is transitional between dinosaurs and birds?
    a. *Biston betularia*
    b. *Geospiza fortis*
    c. *Archaeopteryx*
    d. *Hyracotherium*
    e. *Drosophila melanogaster*

15. The fossil record shows that approximately 200 million years ago oyster shells became
    a. asymmetrical.
    b. smaller and more curved.
    c. smaller and flatter.
    d. larger and more curved.
    e. larger and flatter.

16. How many genera (singular = genus) are there in the horse family today?
    a. 1
    b. 3
    c. 13
    d. 34
    e. 43

17. Who documented that industrial melanism had occurred in England?
    a. Gould
    b. Darwin
    c. Grant
    d. Lack
    e. Kettlewell

18. How many species of Galápagos finches are there?
    a. 1
    b. 7
    c. 14
    d. 28
    e. hundreds

19. In what type of environment would you expect melanic moths to be common?
    a. in a forest that has never been polluted
    b. in a polluted forest
    c. in a formerly polluted forest that has been cleaned up
    d. Melanic moths are never common.

20. Under what environmental conditions are big beaks advantageous for Darwin's finches?
    a. during cold weather
    b. during hot weather
    c. during wet weather
    d. during dry weather
    e. This is totally unpredictable.

21. Teosinte is believed to be the wild ancestor of
    a. corn.
    b. fruit flies.
    c. dogs.
    d. pigeons.
    e. silver foxes.

22. During artificial selection, selection pressure is exerted by
    a. the environment.
    b. predators.
    c. humans.
    d. domestic species.
    e. other members of the same species.

23. If pollution is cleaned up, what should happen over time to the color of moths living in the woods?
    a. Color patterns shouldn't change.
    b. Dark-colored moths should change to light colored.
    c. Light-colored moths should change to dark colored.
    d. Dark-colored moths should become more common.
    e. Light-colored moths should become more common.

24. As adults, humans have a vestige of a tail. It is called the
    a. lanugo.
    b. vermiform.
    c. placenta.
    d. coccyx.
    e. pharyngeal pouch.

25. During their early stages of development, the embryos of fish, reptiles, birds, and mammals look very similar. This suggests that fish, reptiles, birds, and mammals
    a. live in the same type of environment.
    b. have a common ancestor.
    c. have undergone convergent evolution.
    d. are no longer undergoing evolution.
    e. have gotten rid of all their vestigial structures.

26. The similarities between marsupials in Australia and placental mammals elsewhere are examples of
    a. industrial melanism.
    b. macroevolution.
    c. convergent evolution.
    d. the molecular record.
    e. vestigial structures.

27. The wing of a bat and the front flipper of a porpoise are examples of
    a. vestigial structures.
    b. homologous structures.
    c. melanic structures.
    d. all of these.
    e. none of these.

28. The vermiform appendix of humans and the fingernails of manatees are examples of
    a. vestigial structures.
    b. homologous structures.
    c. melanic structures.
    d. all of these.
    e. none of these.

29. Tutt hypothesized that which of the following acts as the agent of selection in the case of the peppered moth?
    a. tree color
    b. tree lichens
    c. industrial melanism
    d. birds
    e. pollution

30. Following a year with a lot of rainfall, Peter and Rosemary Grant found that which of the following types of ground finches were favored?
    a. large beaked
    b. gross beaked
    c. small beaked
    d. medium-size beaked
    e. blunt beaked

ASSESSING YOUR KNOWLEDGE

Answers to the questions in this section test your ability to synthesize information gained from the chapter and to solve challenging problems on an exam or in everyday life.

Challenging Your Understanding—Part I, Answers

1.
    a. Fossil record
    b. Anatomical record
    c. Biogeography
    d. Selection in action
(Answers a and c are interchangeable.)

2.

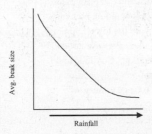

During droughts, plants produce few seeds and the small seeds are quickly eaten, leaving only large seeds. In wet years, plants flourish and produce a large number of small seeds.

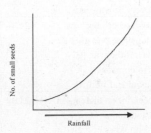

In dry years, selection favors finches with larger beaks because they are more efficient at cracking the large, tough seeds. During wet years, there are more small seeds available, and selection favors smaller beaks.

Challenging Your Understanding—Part II, Answers

3.

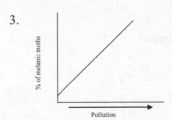

As pollution increases, the percentage of melanic moths increases by natural selection because the peppered forms were more visible to birds sitting on the soot-covered trees that had lost their lichens, than the black moths that blended in with the color of the trees.

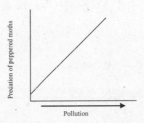

The predation of the peppered moths increased as pollution increased because these moths were more visible to the birds when they were sitting on the soot-covered trees than the melanic moths were.

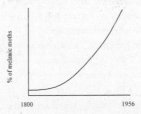

From the beginning of industrialization, the frequency of dark individuals in the moth populations around industrial centers increased, making up almost 100% of the population.

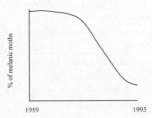

The melanic moth population began to decrease with the enactment of Clean Air Acts in England in 1956, and in the United States in 1959. By 1995, the frequency of dark moths around industrial centers dropped to 15% in England, and 15% in Detroit in 1994.

4.

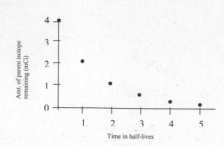

Parent isotope (mCi): 4, 2, 1, .5, .25, .125
Daughter isotope (mCi): 0, 2, 3, 3.5, 3.75, 3.875

Key Terms—Answers

a. 10, b. 5, c. 1, d. 7, e. 8, f. 3, g. 11, h. 2, i. 6, j. 4, k. 9.

Learning by Experience—Answers

1.   a. oldest = species F
   b. youngest = species A
   c. species B = same age as species C

2. In late Miocene/early Oligocene, grasslands replaced much of the forests in North America. Horses adapted to this new environment and became larger in size, with longer legs and fewer toes designed for more rapid running. This helped them escape predators and travel long distances. Forests had selected for smaller body size and multiple toes, providing agility in darting through the trees to escape predators. Their teeth also became larger and more complex, allowing them to more efficiently break down the tougher, grittier new diet (grass vs. leaves).
3. When only the most docile animals in each generation of silver foxes were allowed to reproduce, within 40 years, the silver foxes became exceptionally tame, allowing themselves to be petted, whimpering for attention, and sniffing and licking their owners. The foxes also began to exhibit traits like different color patterns, floppy ears, curled tails, and shorter legs and tails. These changes came about presumably because the genes responsible for docile behavior are closely linked to the genes that determine color patterns, ear shape, tail shape and size, and leg size, or because the genes for docile behavior affect these other traits as well.
4. Changes are not random. The process of natural selection favors traits that make an individual better adapted to its environment; thus it leads to changes in the population over time that result in the population being better adapted to its environment. The changes are also not random in that there are constraints on what changes can occur. The slate is not wiped clean with each evolutionary change, but rather the changes are added on to what has come before.

Exercising Your Knowledge—Answers

As you check your answers, put a mark in the review (Rvw.) column for the answers you missed. If you didn't miss any, congratulations—you have mastered the chapter! If you missed some, review the section (Sect.) in the text where this concept is discussed. In order to develop an efficient review strategy, it is important that you understand what types of questions you missed. The questions with asterisks test more for understanding of the **concepts**, whereas the others test more for **detail**. *See the preface for learning strategies for concepts and for detail.*

	Sect.	Rvw.
*1. First step: organism is buried in sediment without decaying or being scavenged. Second step: calcium in bone or other hard tissue is mineralized. Third step: surrounding sediment hardens into rock.	21.4	
*2. There are gaps in the fossil record because frequently the three basic steps (see previous question) don't occur, or even if they do, the fossils may be inaccessible to humans or are destroyed before they are found and studied.	21.4	
*3. The general trend has been for an increase in overall body size of horses and longer legs, especially in last 20–25 million years of their 55-million year history. Some of the earliest horses were the size of housecats. There were also some exceptions to the general trend, with some lineages becoming smaller in body size.	21.4	
*4. Each generation, pick out the 20% of the population with the lowest number of bristles and allow these flies to reproduce and establish the next generation. In the next generation, pick out the 20% of the population with the lowest number of bristles again and allow these flies to reproduce and establish the next generation. Continue to do this, until over many generations, a population with a significantly lower average number of bristles is established.	21.3	
*5. Although they do not necessarily share a common function, or even look similar anymore, homologous structures are indicative of shared ancestry because they all have the same basic bones suggesting that they were derived from the same body part of a common ancestor. Vestigial structures have no apparent function in some organisms anymore, but are still present. These structures resemble functional structures present in other organisms and thereby suggest that the group of organisms with these structures share a common ancestor. Embryos of related organisms are often very similar early on, but become more different as they develop further. Embryos can reveal evolutionary histories since embryos exhibit the characteristics of embryos of the ancestral species (e.g., pharyngeal pouches in human embryos and fish embryos). Relic developmental forms suggest that development has evolved.	21.5	

*6. Artificial selection, as seen with domesticated animals and plants, shows that selection can produce substantial and rapid changes in the traits of populations; it also demonstrates that in selecting for or against certain traits, other traits can tag along.	21.3
*7. The dark moths did not suddenly appear by mutation after the Industrial Revolution; instead, the dark moths already existed in the population, but in very low numbers since there was strong selection against being dark colored on the light-colored trunk trees. As the trees became darker due to pollution, it became advantageous to be a dark-colored moth; thus, they were selected for, survived more, reproduced more, and passed on more of their genetic information for dark color than did the light-colored moths. Over many generations, dark moths became more and more prevalent in the population.	21.2
*8. Convergent evolution, evolution of similar traits in unrelated species, occurs when the species experience similar environments and therefore similar selection pressures (for example, similar traits in marsupial mammals in Australia and placental mammals elsewhere).	21.6
*9. The geographic distribution of species (biogeography) provides more evidence of evolution; for example, species living on oceanic islands are most closely related to species on the nearest continent, reflecting their common ancestry.	21.6

*10. No; the objections are based on a lack of understanding of science terminology, how natural selection works, the completeness of the fossil record, and what valid statistical usage is.	21.7
11. a	21.4
*12. b	21.4
13. d	21.4
14. c	21.4
15. e	21.4
16. a	21.4
17. e	21.2
18. c	21.1
*19. b	21.2
*20. d	21.1
21. a	21.3
22. c	21.3
*23. e	21.2
24. d	21.5
*25. b	21.5
26. c	21.6
27. b	21.5
28. a	21.5
29. d	21.2
30. c	21.1

CHAPTER 22 THE ORIGIN OF SPECIES

MASTERING KEY CONCEPTS

We intuitively recognize the concept of species: No one would argue that a giraffe and an oak tree belong to the same species, and the distinction between an oak tree and a palm tree is also clear. A precise definition of species, however, is more difficult. We define species biologically on the basis of shared characteristics and degree of interbreeding, but there are many gray areas. Many mechanisms prevent hybridization between divergent populations and species, and thus help keep them separate. It appears that the rate of evolutionary change and formation of species can vary, sometimes occurring gradually and sometimes occurring in spurts. Human activities and resulting environmental changes are causing extinction or evolutionary change for many species.

22.1 Species are the basic units of evolution.

- **Overview**: **Sympatric** species live together in one area, but are phenotypically distinct and can distinguish their own species from other species. Within these groups of species, there are groups of individuals in different geographical areas that are distinctly different from other groups (**subspecies**). Where two groups of subspecies approach each other, they are typically connected by individuals that have characteristics that are intermediate to both groups.
- **Details**: Know the definition of sympatric species and subspecies. Understand the two phenomena that the definition of a species has to account for.

22.2 The biological species concept defines a species.

- **Overview**: **Mayr** defined a species as "groups of actually, or potentially interbreeding natural populations which are reproductively isolated from other such groups" (**biological species concept**). This definition implies that individuals that cannot mate with each other belong to different species (**reproductively isolated**), although they live together in the same area. Different species do not mate with each other under normal circumstances because they are subject to reproductive isolating mechanisms, some prezygotic and others postzygotic. These mechanisms prevent the genes of one species from entering the gene pool of another species. **Prezygotic isolating mechanisms**, such as the prevention of gamete fusion, geographic isolation, ecological isolation, behavioral isolation, temporal isolation, or mechanical isolation prevent zygote formation, while **postzygotic isolating mechanisms** prevent zygotes from developing into normal organisms that are capable of surviving and reproducing. However, in recent years, it has been found that **hybridization** between different plant species and different animal species is not as uncommon as

was once thought. Even so, species that interbreed still tend to remain distinct, questioning whether reproductive isolation is the only working force in nature acting to maintain different species. No single definition of a species or single explanation of what causes and maintains distinct species applies to all organisms.

- **Details**: Understand what is meant by the seven different reproductive isolating mechanisms of sympatric species. Understand the **criticisms of the biological species concept** and why reproductive isolation may not be the only force acting to maintain different species in nature.

22.3 Species maintain their genetic distinctiveness through barriers to reproduction.

- **Overview**: If two populations come in contact with each other and there are no barriers to reproduction, individuals from the two groups will mate, producing hybrids that will reproduce if they survive and are fertile. This promotes **gene flow** between the two populations. Over time, the differences between the two groups will fade and they will become one species. Conversely, the formation of two different species from one ancestral species occurs if two populations are reproductively isolated from each other. When reproductive isolation has only partially evolved, isolating mechanisms are **reinforced** by natural selection.
- **Details**: Understand how two species evolve from one and how two species can become one. Understand how reinforcement and gene flow affect speciation.

22.4 Genetic drift and natural selection play a role in speciation.

- **Overview**: **Reproductive isolation** can arise from random events such as **genetic drift**, **founder effects**, or **bottleneck effects**. **Natural selection** can also inadvertently lead to reproductive isolation because as organisms adapt to become better suited to their environments, two populations will tend to diverge from one another. Therefore, natural selection can directly increase or reinforce reproductive isolation.
- **Details**: Understand how genetic drift, the founder effect, and the bottleneck effect can cause reproductive isolation. Understand how natural selection can affect speciation.

22.5 The geography of speciation

- **Overview**: Populations that are geographically

isolated (**allopatric**) are more likely to undergo speciation because of a lack of gene flow, but isolation is not required for speciation to occur. Sympatric speciation can occur without isolation by **polyploidy** or, rarely, by **disruptive selection** in which two or more different phenotypes are maintained in a population.

- **Details:** Understand two mechanisms by which sympatric speciation can occur without isolation. Know the two different ways in which polyploid individuals come about.

22.6 Clusters of species reflect rapid evolution.

- **Overview**: The existence of clusters of closely related species that have evolved from a common ancestor to live in different environments (**adaptive radiations**) requires both adaptation to different environments and speciation. Hawaiian *Drosophila*, Galápagos finches, cichlid fishes, and alpine buttercups are examples of populations that have undergone adaptive radiation. Adaptive radiations have been favored by periodic isolation and by the occupation of habitats that have a vast number of resources and few predators.
- **Details**: Understand how different species of Hawaiian *Drosophila*, Galápagos finches, cichlid fishes, and alpine buttercups have evolved by adaptive radiation.

22.7 The pace of evolution is different for different species.

- **Overview**: Two hypotheses have been proposed to describe how evolutionary change affects speciation. **Darwin** proposed **gradualism,** which suggests that evolutionary change occurs slowly but gradually such that over millions of years, major changes have occurred. **Eldredge and Gould** proposed **punctuated equilibrium** in which short spurts of evolutionary change are separated by long periods of **stasis** due to a combination of the effects of stabilizing and oscillating selection. Studies of different species suggest that some evolve gradually, and others evolve by punctuated equilibrium.
- **Details**: Understand the two possibilities for how different species evolve and why it is believed that both are likely important.

22.8 Speciation and extinction have been recorded through time.

- **Overview**: Biological diversity and speciation have, in general, increased significantly since the Cambrian period and have steadily risen since that time. However, there have been five major **mass extinctions** in which the number of species has vastly declined. The cause of at least one of these extinction events was due to an asteroid hitting the Earth; others may have been caused by global climate changes. An important consequence of mass extinctions is that not all species are affected equally, and previously dominant groups may perish. The return of species diversity following a mass extinction is a slow process. We are now entering a **sixth major extinction event** due to human activity and the loss of resources may prevent a recovery or make it extremely slow.
- **Details**: Understand what happens to species diversity after mass extinctions and how speciation is recovered. Understand how mass extinctions can change the course of evolution.

22.9 Human-based changes will greatly affect the future of evolution.

- **Overview**: **Human-initiated changes** are affecting the environment in such a substantial way that these changes are directing natural selection. Global climate change, decreased population sizes, geographic isolation, and increases in mutation rates due to chemicals and radiation will lead to evolutionary change. Increased speciation may occur as a result of geographic fragmentation, but it is not likely to be able to counter the increased rate of extinction. Natural selection is the only agent driving evolutionary change in humans. Technological advances are likely to greatly affect this process.
- **Details**: Understand how human influences on the environment will affect the pattern of natural selection, and the populations of other species. Understand why natural selection is the major agent acting to bring about evolutionary change in humans.

CHALLENGING YOUR UNDERSTANDING

1. Consider the following relationship. According to the biological species concept, describe what keeps species A and species B distinct.

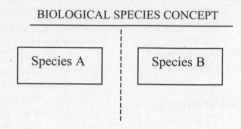

BIOLOGICAL SPECIES CONCEPT

Species A ┆ Species B

2. Consider the following relationship. Describe what will happen if isolating mechanisms have not evolved and what type of population will result.

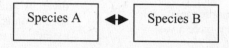

Species A ◄► Species B

3. Many scientists feel that the biological species concept does not fully define a species. Describe the criticisms of the biological species concept.

4. Consider the following graph of two species with similar body sizes. Circle the individuals in each species in the graph that are favored by natural selection and explain why. Indicate on the second graph what will happen to these two species as a result of displacement.

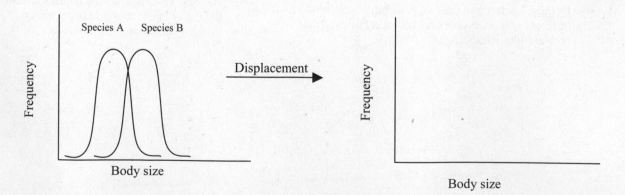

Species A   Species B

Frequency

Body size

Displacement →

Frequency

Body size

KEY TERMS

Match the numbered term with the definition that fits it best. Put the corresponding number in front of the appropriate definition.

1. biological species concept
2. sympatric
3. subspecies
4. gene pools
5. cladogenesis
6. reproductively isolated
7. reproductive isolating mechanisms
8. prezygotic isolating mechanisms
9. postzygotic isolating mechanisms
10. pheromones
11. key innovation
12. reinforcement
13. allopatric
14. polyploidy
15. autopolyploidy
16. allopolyploidy
17. adaptive radiations
18. character displacement
19. gradualism
20. stasis
21. punctuated equilibrium
22. mass extinctions

a. _____ Events that substantially, though briefly, reduce the number of species.
b. _____ Mechanisms that prevent the formation of a zygote and act as barriers to successful reproduction.
c. _____ Two species that are geographically separated from one another.
d. _____ Offspring having one copy of the chromosomes of two different species after these species hybridize.
e. _____ A new trait that evolves within a species allowing it to use resources that were previously inaccessible.
f. _____ Chemical signals that are emitted by organisms to attract members of the same species for mating.
g. _____ The evolution of divergent adaptations that minimizes competition between two species for resources.
h. _____ Individuals possessing more than two sets of chromosomes.
i. _____ Groups of actually or potentially interbreeding natural populations that are reproductively isolated.
j. _____ Long periods of little or no evolutionary change that are experienced by species.
k. _____ Barriers to successful reproduction that prevent the genetic exchange between species.
l. _____ The slow and steady accumulation of changes over long periods of time.
m. _____ Species that occur together in the same location but remain distinct phenotypically and behave separately.
n. _____ The process by which natural selection makes initially incomplete isolating mechanisms completely effective.
o. _____ Offspring having more than two sets of chromosomes that all came from a single species.
p. _____ The process by which one ancestral species becomes divided into two descendant species.
q. _____ Populations whose members do not mate with each other or who can not produce fertile offspring.
r. _____ A quick change in speciation followed by periods of no change due to stabilizing or oscillating selection.
s. _____ Closely related species recently evolved from a common ancestor that adapt to different environments.
t. _____ Groups of distinctive individuals within a single species that occur in different areas.
u. _____ Mechanisms that prevent the proper functioning of zygotes after they are formed.
v. _____ All of the alleles that are present in a population of individuals or a species.

LEARNING BY EXPERIENCE

1. For each of the following examples, write in the blank to the left the type of reproductive isolating mechanism that is in effect.

    _____ a. Two species of fireflies that live in the same area and are active at the same times use different light flashing patterns to attract their mates.

    _____ b. Mules are sterile.

    _____ c. One species of pine tree in California sheds its pollen in February; another species of pine growing in the same area reproduces in April.

    _____ d. Franklin's ground squirrels live in areas of North Dakota with vegetation that is at least 50 cm tall, and Richardson's ground squirrels live in grazed pastures and short grasslands in the same areas of North Dakota.

    _____ e. Pollen from one species of tobacco plant cannot form a pollen tube to reach the egg of a different species of tobacco even if the pollen lands on the stigma (the receptive female flower part).

    _____ f. In the wild, Asian elephants are found only in Asia, and African elephants are found only in Africa.

    _____ g. The male copulatory organs of one species of *Drosophila* will not physically fit the female organs of another species of *Drosophila*.

2. Match the following genera discussed in this chapter with the proper common name.

    _____ a. *Drosophila*   i. frogs
    _____ b. *Geospiza*   ii. oak trees
    _____ c. *Lactuca*   iii. Darwin's finches
    _____ d. *Quercus*   iv. fruit flies
    _____ e. *Rana*   v. wild lettuce
    _____ f. *Ranunculus*   vi. buttercups

3. What is a species? Is this a useful biological concept? Write an essay or stage a debate with classmates representing the different viewpoints.

EXERCISING YOUR KNOWLEDGE

Briefly answer each of the following questions in the space provided.

1. How distinct are different species compared to different populations of the same species?

2. Why is it advantageous to have prezygotic isolating mechanisms?

3. List several reasons why gamete fusion or fertilization may not occur even after successful mating between individuals from two different species.

4. Do reproductive isolating mechanisms usually arise for the express purpose of providing reproductive isolation?

5. Describe how human activities are affecting the environment and evolutionary processes.

6. Under what geographic conditions is speciation most likely to occur? Why?

7. Why does polyploidy result in instant speciation?

8. Why are so many examples of adaptive radiation known from islands (for example, finches in the Galápagos Islands, fruit flies in the Hawaiian Islands)?

9. What has happened to the diversity of life (the number of different species) since life began on Earth?

10. Do evolution and speciation occur slowly and gradually as proposed by Darwin or in spurts as proposed by Eldredge and Gould?

Circle the letter of the one best answer in each of the following questions.

11. Which of the following terms is analogous to "varieties?"
    a. subspecies
    b. species
    c. genus
    d. gene pools
    e. polyploids

12. Species that occur in the same area are called
    a. hybrids.
    b. polyploids.
    c. reinforcement.
    d. allopatric.
    e. sympatric.

13. Which of the following is key to the biological species concept?
    a. stasis
    b. geographical isolation
    c. reproductive isolation
    d. intermediate populations
    e. asexual reproduction

14. The sperm of species A dies when it comes in contact with secretions in the female reproductive tract of species B. This is an example of
    a. gradualism.
    b. punctuated equilibrium.
    c. periodic isolation.
    d. a prezygotic isolating mechanism.
    e. a postzygotic isolating mechanism.

15. Which of the following is particularly common for a species in a situation where few other species are present and there are resources available?
    a. polyploidy
    b. adaptive radiations
    c. punctuated equilibria
    d. natural selection
    e. gradualism

16. Behavioral isolation may occur if two species have different
    a. -sized and -shaped copulatory organs.
    b. courtship displays.
    c. times of the year that they are sexually active.
    d. habitat ranges.
    e. chemical compatibilities of their gametes.

17. Which of the following would be the most efficient reproductive isolating mechanism for an organism to have in terms of when in the reproductive process it had its impact?
    a. production of sterile hybrids
    b. mechanical isolation
    c. prevention of gamete fusion
    d. temporal isolation

18. Research has shown that leopard frogs in the *Rana pipiens* complex in the United States actually belong to four separate species instead of one. Some combinations of hybrids produce defective embryos. This is an example of
    a. postzygotic isolation.
    b. temporal isolation.
    c. behavioral isolation.
    d. ecological isolation.
    e. mechanical isolation.

19. The different species of *Rana* referred to in question 18 can be distinguished by
    a. their external physical appearance.
    b. their copulatory organs.
    c. their mating calls.
    d. the microhabitats they occupy.
    e. all of these.

20. Geographical isolation is associated with
    a. polyploidy.
    b. reinforcement.
    c. punctuated equilibria.
    d. sympatric speciation.
    e. allopatric speciation.

21. The term "isolating mechanism" is considered misleading by some scientists because they think it erroneously implies that the isolating traits
    a. evolved in isolation from all other traits.
    b. evolved strictly for the purpose of reproductive isolation.
    c. prevent hybridization from ever occurring.
    d. All of these are correct.
    e. None of these are correct.

22. Which of the following factors counteracts reproductive isolation?
    a. polyploidy
    b. natural selection
    c. gene flow
    d. speciation
    e. reinforcement

23. Which of the following factors can cause reproductive isolation?
    a. genetic drift
    b. founder effects
    c. population bottlenecks
    d. all of these
    e. none of these

24. Reinforcement continually improves which of the following?
    a. natural selection
    b. species diversification
    c. disruptive selection
    d. prezygotic isolation mechanisms
    e. adaptive radiations

25. Scientists estimate that approximately _____ of all plant species have a polyploid event in their history.
    a. one-tenth
    b. one-quarter
    c. one-third
    d. half
    e. three-quarters

26. Periods of stasis are associated with
    a. polyploidy.
    b. adaptive radiation.
    c. hybridization.
    d. gradualism.
    e. punctuated equilibria.

27. Under which of the following conditions would you expect rapid evolution of species to occur?
    a. among populations in similar habitats
    b. in large, randomly breeding populations
    c. in populations with few reproductive isolating mechanisms
    d. among populations experiencing the same stabilizing selection
    e. among populations exposed to climatic and other environmental changes

28. A single common ancestor is believed to have given rise to the approximately _____ species of *Drosophila* and *Scaptomyza* flies found in the Hawaiian Islands.
    a. 4,000,000
    b. 12,000
    c. 800
    d. 300
    e. 14

29. Which of the following statements about species and speciation is true?
    a. The Lake Victoria cichlids are the most diverse assembly of vertebrates known to science.
    b. Clusters of species present strong evidence for gradualism.
    c. The vegetarian finch in the Galápagos is famous for using twigs or cactus spines to help it obtain food.
    d. Adaptive radiation of buttercups in New Zealand occurred because New Zealand escaped most of the glaciation associated with the last Ice Age.
    e. Human activities are having little impact on speciation and extinction events today.

30. Do species ever hybridize?
    a. no, never
    b. yes, much more than originally thought
    c. plants yes, animals no
    d. plants no, animals yes
    e. only under the most extreme, unusual conditions

ASSESSING YOUR KNOWLEDGE

Answers to the questions in this section test your ability to synthesize information gained from the chapter and to solve challenging problems on an exam or in everyday life.

Challenging Your Understanding—Answers

1. According to the biological species concept, Species A and Species B are kept distinct by reproductive isolating mechanisms.

2. If isolating mechanisms have not evolved, Species A and Species B will mate freely, producing hybridized offspring. Over the course of time, differences between the two will disappear by genetic exchange and a single homogenized population will result.

3. The first criticism of the biological species concept is that it cannot explain hybridization among species of both plants and animals. Although hybrid offspring survive and reproduce, the two species tend to maintain their distinctiveness from each other, which is contrary to the biological species concept. Rather, this phenomenon is explained by natural selection. It has been proposed that hybridization has little effect on a population because alleles introduced by one species' gene pool are quickly eliminated from the gene pool of the other species by natural selection. Therefore, natural selection and ecological factors are acting to maintain the two distinct species, not an inability to mate. The biological species concept has also been criticized because it has no meaning for organisms that are asexual and reproduce without mating. Also, populations that are geographically separated in nature fail to encounter each other, so it is unknown whether these species would interbreed naturally. Finally, many species that coexist and do not naturally mate with one another, will do so in the laboratory. In this case, whether the two organisms actually represent two different species is a judgment call.

4.

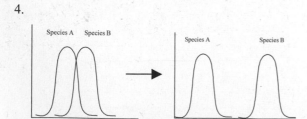

Natural selection in each species favors the individuals that are most different from the other species because they would not have to compete with the other species for resources. As a result, the two species will diverge in their use of resources and minimize competition between the two.

Key Terms—Answers

a. 22, b. 8, c. 13, d. 16, e. 11, f. 10, g. 18, h. 14, i. 1, j. 20, k. 7, l. 19, m. 2, n. 12, o. 15, p. 5, q. 6, r. 21, s. 17, t. 3, u. 9, v. 4.

Learning by Experience—Answers

1.	a. behavioral isolation
	b. postzygotic isolation
	c. temporal isolation
	d. ecological isolation
	e. prevention of gamete fusion
	f. geographical isolation
	g. mechanical isolation
2.	a. iv
	b. iii
	c. v
	d. ii
	e. i
	f. vi

3. It is hard to define a species precisely. The biological species concept defines species as "groups of actually or potentially interbreeding populations that are reproductively isolated from other such groups," but this definition works better for some organisms than others (for example, animals versus plants) and cannot be applied to organisms that reproduce asexually. We now also know there is much more hybridization going on between species than we originally thought, challenging the reproductive isolation criterion. Still, species is a very useful concept; it is the basis by which we classify the diversity of life on Earth, and it is the taxonomic unit of evolution.

Exercising Your Knowledge—Answers

As you check your answers, put a mark in the review (Rvw.) column for the answers you missed. If you didn't miss any, congratulations—you have mastered the chapter! If you missed some, review the section (Sect.) in the text where this concept is discussed. In order to develop an efficient review strategy, it is important that you understand what types of questions you missed. The questions with asterisks test more for understanding of the **concepts**, whereas the others test more for **detail**. *See the preface for learning strategies for concepts and for detail.*

	Sect.	Rvw.
*1. Different species are usually noticeably distinct. Even species that at first seem very similar to us in appearance usually have some distinctly different characteristics when we investigate more deeply (for example, mating calls or chemicals). Within a species, different populations may or may not be very distinct in different areas, but even if they are distinct, populations with intermediate traits are usually also present.	22.1	

*2. Reproduction is a costly process during which individuals invest time, energy, and materials and run the risk of injury or predation. Prezygotic isolating mechanisms prevent members of different species from taking risks or wasting time, energy, and materials on hybrid reproduction attempts that might not (and usually don't) result in successful offspring.	22.2	
*3. If the eggs and sperm have been shed into the environment, they may not attract each other. If there is internal fertilization, the female's reproductive tract may be a hostile environment for the sperm. In plants, the pollen tube may not be able to grow properly to reach the egg.	22.2	
*4. No; they usually arise for some other reason – for example, as the result of adaptation to a new environment. A trait that is selected because it makes the individual well adapted to the local environment may secondarily also serve to isolate the individual reproductively from other individuals who do not have the trait. Natural selection can reinforce reproductive isolating mechanisms, and random changes can also cause them.	22.3	
*5. A large proportion of the world's resources are being used up by human activities, leaving few resources available for adaptive radiation. Humans are also affecting global climate change and destroying the habitats of many other organisms that live in the wild, leaving populations small, isolated, and fragmented. Chemicals and radiation released into the environment as a result of human activity threaten to increase the mutation rates of all natural populations. As a result of these human-initiated problems, the number of species in the world is decreasing extremely rapidly. Extinction rates are increasing at an extremely quick rate. However, changes in the environment are causing changes in natural selection. Species that survive the environmental changes will evolve. Decreased population sizes will increase the possibility of genetic drift and geographic isolation of species that were once connected will remove gene flow, but may actually allow an increase in speciation rates as the species begin to adapt to their environments and evolve differences.	22.8 22.9	
*6. Geographically isolated (allopatric) conditions rather than sympatric (in the same area) conditions are more likely to lead to speciation. Different geographical areas will most likely have different environmental conditions, even at the micro level, and thus will have different selection pressures, resulting in different adaptations and traits being selected for. This will cause populations to diverge.	22.5	

*7. A polyploid individual cannot reproduce with nonpolyploids because of the mismatch in chromosome numbers, so there is instant reproductive isolation. For example, if plant species X has 14 chromosomes and polyploidy occurs, the new individuals with 28 chromosomes cannot reproduce successfully with individuals with 14 chromosomes, but only with those with 28 chromosomes.	22.5	
*8. Islands are geographically isolated from each other and the mainland, and geographic isolation is conducive to speciation. Because of their isolation, islands frequently provide a diversity of available niches to the first colonizers who arrive. There may be fewer competitors and predators.	22.6	
*9. Overall, the number of species has increased during the history of life on earth. But periods of mass extinction have temporarily greatly decreased the number of species and therefore the diversity of life on Earth. In the five previous mass extinctions, the number of species rebounded afterward and exceeded the original diversity levels, but there is concern that this may not be possible with the sixth event that humans are now causing.	22.8	
*10. The rate of evolution and speciation depends on the species and the circumstances. Some species have evolved gradually and others in spurts, but these are two ends of a continuum, and other species have fallen in between the two extremes or have shifted from one end to the other as environmental circumstances have changed.	22.7	
11. a	22.1	
12. e	22.1	
*13. c	22.2	
14. d	22.2	
15. b	22.6	
16. b	22.2	
*17. d	22.2	
18. a	22.2	
19. c	22.2	
20. e	22.3	
*21. b	22.3	
22. c	22.3	
23. d	22.4	
24. d	22.3	
25. d	22.5	
*26. e	22.7	
*27. e	22.7	
28. c	22.6	
29. a	22.6	
30. b	22.2	

CHAPTER 23 SYSTEMATICS AND THE PHYLOGENETIC REVOLUTION

MASTERING KEY CONCEPTS

Aside from naming an organism and determining its hierarchical classification is the question of the evolutionary relationships of groups. What we commonly call the family tree, biologists call the phylogeny. Scientists construct phylogenies to understand the evolutionary relationships among species. The questions considered in this section deal with how phylogenetics can be used to understand evolution.

23.1 Systematics is the reconstruction and study of evolutionary relationships.

- **Overview**: **Systematics** is the study of evolutionary relationships among organisms. These relationships are depicted in branching diagrams called **phylogenies**, where the intersection of two branches indicates an ancestor common to the organisms on each of the branches above the intersection. Intersection of branches closer to the top of the **phylogenetic tree** represents organisms that share a more recent common ancestor. Intersection of branches further down the tree represents organisms that share an older common ancestor. Similarities between organisms do not necessarily reflect evolutionarily related organisms because of selective pressures, oscillating selection, and convergent evolution. Variation in the rate of evolution also introduces complexities in assigning evolutionary relationships.
- **Details**: Understand how phylogenetic trees depict evolutionary relationships. Understand why changes in evolutionary rates, oscillating selection, and convergent evolution cause problems in predicting evolutionary relationships.

23.2 Cladistics constructs phylogenetic relationships based on shared derived characteristics.

- **Overview**: Due to the problems in assigning evolutionary relationships based on similarities between organisms, **cladistics** uses **shared derived characters** alone to determine evolutionary relationships. Cladistics distinguishes between similarities that are inherited from a common ancestor (**derived**) and similarities that arose prior to the common ancestor (**ancestral**). Characters are **polarized** by **outgroup comparisons**. All organisms derived from a common ancestor share characteristics (**synapomorphy**) and belong to a **clade**. A **cladogram** diagrams the relationship between organisms based on derived characters

and DNA sequence comparisons. Characters located between the intersection of two branches are shared by all of the organisms above it, but are not present in any of the organisms below it. Convergent evolution or evolution reversal can result in **homoplasy,** which complicates the process of assigning evolutionary relationships. In these instances, systematists rely on the **principle of parsimony,** which assumes that phylogenetic relationships most likely exist between organisms requiring the fewest evolutionary events to establish a relationship. If the rate of evolution on new character states is high, or if there is a limited number of character states, methods other than cladistics work better to assign evolutionary relationships. The timing of branching events can be estimated by reference to fossils, or by assuming a **molecular clock**.
- **Details**: Understand how shared derived characters are used to construct cladograms. Know why convergent evolution and evolutionary reversal complicated cladistic analysis. Understand the principle of parsimony and how to apply it. Understand when this principle can be misleading in reconstructing evolutionary relationships.

23.3 Systematics and traditional classification are not always congruent.

- **Overview**: **Taxonomic groups** are based on shared traits and are intended to reflect evolutionary relationships, but frequently they do not fit with phylogenetic information. The **phylogenetic species concept** defines a species as a population or set of populations with one or more set of derived characters. This concept, like the biological species concept, has inherent problems because it suggests that all differentiated populations are distinct species, and assumes that all species are monophyletic.
- **Details**: Understand what the difference is between **monophyletic**, **paraphyletic**, and **polyphyletic** groups. Understand how the phylogenetic species concept solves two of the problems inherent to the biological species concept but has problems of its own.

23.4 Phylogenetics is the basis of all comparative biology.

- **Overview**: **Phylogenetics** can be used to determine whether structures or behaviors among two or more organisms are derived from the same ancestral structure or behavior (**homologous**) or from different ancestral structures or behaviors (**homoplastic**). Phylogenetic analysis can also be used to determine the stepwise process by which complex characters evolve. For example, it is now known that feathery structures were first identified in animals that did not fly and later became modified to be aerodynamic in birds. Scientists can also use phylogenetic methods to distinguish between two competing hypotheses, and to suggest and explain patterns of species diversity. For example, a correlation has been identified between the timing of plant origins and the phylogenetic position of beetles that feed on conifers vs. those that feed on angiosperms.

- **Details**: Understand how parental care establishes an evolutionary relationship between dinosaurs, crocodiles, and birds. Understand how phylogenctic analysis can indicate if convergent evolution took place in two or more organisms. Understand how to use phylogenetic analysis to distinguish between two scientific hypotheses.

23.5 Phylogenetics can illustrate the evolution of a disease.

- **Overview**: Phylogenetic analysis can be used to determine the source of a disease, to follow its evolution, and to identify the source of infection of a particular individual. Using phylogenetics, **HIV** was found to be related and derived from **SIV**, a virus found in monkeys. HIV was found to have evolved multiple times to produce a number of different HIV strains, all most closely related to a particular SIV strain. Finally, HIV was found to have been acquired from different primate host organisms.

- **Details**: Know the three findings that were identified by phylogenetic analysis of HIV and SIV. Understand how the virus was likely transmitted from monkeys to humans, when this jump likely occurred, and why. Understand how phylogenetics can be used to identify the source of the infection in a particular individual.

CHALLENGING YOUR UNDERSTANDING—Part I

Given the following DNA sequence data, construct a cladogram that minimizes the amount of character evolution required. Indicate homoplastic and homologous evolutionary changes on the cladistic analysis, and then answer the questions below.

SITE	1	2	3	4	5	6	7	8	9	10
Species A	T	T	T	C	C	G	G	A	A	T
Species B	T	T	T	C	C	G	T	G	A	C
Species C	T	G	A	T	A	G	G	A	A	C
Species D	T	T	T	C	A	G	T	G	A	C
Outgroup	T	G	A	C	C	G	G	A	C	C

1. Cladogram:

2. How many evolutionary changes are required for the most parsimonious interpretation of the DNA sequencing data shown? _____

3. How many changes are homoplastic? _____   Which ones? _____

4. How many changes are homologous? _____   Which ones? _____

CHALLENGING YOUR UNDERSTANDING—Part II

Use the following cladograms to answer the questions below each one.

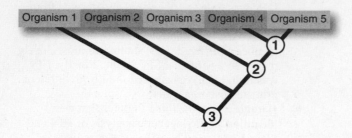

5. Which of the following organisms is organism 4 most closely related to? _____

6. Is organism 3 more closely related to organism 2 or to organism 4? _____

7. What do the nodes 1, 2, and 3 in the circles represent? _____

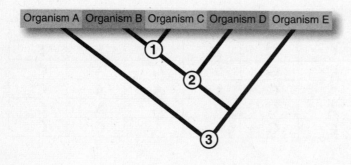

8. Which of the following organisms are most closely related to each other? _____   Why? _____

9. Circled node 2 demonstrates that which organisms share an older common ancestor? _____

10. The branch point at circled node 3 demonstrates what relationship among the organisms? _____

KEY TERMS

Match the numbered term with the definition that fits it best. Put the corresponding number in front of the appropriate definition.

1. systematics	9. clade	17. paraphyletic
2. phylogeny	10. synapomorphy	18. polyphyletic
3. convergent evolution	11. plesiomorphies	19. phylogenetic species concept
4. ancestral	12. symplesiomorphies	20. characters
5. derived	13. homoplasy	21. classification
6. cladistics	14. principle of parsimony	22. polarize
7. outgroup	15. molecular clock	
8. cladogram	16. monophyletic	

a. _____ A group consisting of the most recent common ancestor and all of its descendants.

b. _____ A shared character state that has not been inherited from a common ancestor with that character.

c. _____ How we place species and higher groups such as genus, family, class into the taxonomic hierarchy.

d. _____ Species that share a common ancestor, indicated by the possession of shared derived characters.

e. _____ The idea that a species should be defined as a group that has been evolving independently of other groups.

f. _____ Shared ancestral states that are not informative about phylogenetic relationships.

g. _____ Two species evolved independently with the same features due to similar habitats and selective pressures.

h. _____ Any aspect of the phenotype of a species, including morphology, physiology, behavior, and DNA.

i. _____ To determine whether particular character states are ancestral or derived.

j. _____ Favoring the hypothesis that requires the fewest assumptions to determine evolutionary relationships.

k. _____ A group consisting of the most recent common ancestor and some of its descendants.

l. _____ An evolutionary tree diagramming the relationships among organisms based on derived characters.

m. _____ Similar characteristics shared by a group that arose prior to the common ancestor of the group.

n. _____ The reconstruction and study of evolutionary relationships.

o. _____ Another term for an ancestral character state used in cladistics.

p. _____ A method using only shared derived characters to determine evolutionary relationships.

q. _____ Shared similar characteristics of a group that were inherited from the most recent common ancestor.

r. _____ An evolutionary tree that represents a hypothesis about patterns of relationships among species.

s. _____ A derived character shared by the members of a clade that is informative about phylogenetic relationships.

t. _____ A species that is related to but not a member of the group under study is used to assign character polarity.

u. _____ A timing method that assumes that the rate of evolution of a molecule is constant through time.

v. _____ A group that does not include the most recent common ancestor of all of the members of the group.

LEARNING BY EXPERIENCE

Imagine that you are a biologist exploring an unknown island. On that island, you find seven distinct-looking organisms. The morphological data that you collected from those seven organisms are arranged in the table shown below. A "1" indicates possession of the derived character state and a "0" indicates possession of the ancestral character state (the derived state for the character "no tail" is the absence of a tail, but for all other traits, absence of the trait is the ancestral state). Use this information to construct a cladogram for the seven organisms that you found. Indicate the derived characters between the cladogram branch points that are shared by all of the organisms above the branch but not present in any of the organisms below it. Answer the questions below.

Traits	Teeth	Hair	Lungs	Legs	No tail	Backbone
Organism 1	1	1	1	1	0	0
Organism 2	1	0	0	0	0	0
Organism 3	0	0	0	0	0	0
Organism 4	1	1	0	0	0	0
Organism 5	1	1	1	1	1	0
Organism 6	1	1	0	1	0	0
Organism 7	1	1	1	1	1	1

1. Cladogram:

2. Which organism represents the outgroup? _____

3. Which organism is most closely related to organism 7? _____

4. Which organism is most closely related to organism 3? _____

EXERCISING YOUR KNOWLEDGE

Briefly answer each of the following questions in the space provided.

1. How does the cladistic approach to classification differ from that of systematics?

2. Describe why similarity alone is not a good predictor of evolutionary relationships.

3. When are phylogenetic methods other than cladistics more effective?

4. What is an advantage of using methods based on statistical approaches, rather than cladistics, to determine evolutionary relationships?

5. Describe two ways in which branching events can be timed.

6. Describe an example in which systematics and taxonomic classification do not agree with each other.

7. (a.) What is the difference between the biological species concept and the phylogenetic species concept? (b.) What two problems of the biological species concept does the phylogenetic species concept solve?

8. Why is the phylogenetic species concept controversial?

9. (a.) How is it known that dinosaurs exhibited parental care? (b.) If dinosaurs are most closely related to crocodiles and birds, what does this say about the evolution of parental care as a behavioral trait?

10. Describe the evolution of structures over millions of years that now allow modern day birds to fly.

Circle the letter of the one best answer in each of the following questions.

11. Once a data set has been assembled, the first step in performing cladistic analysis of the data is to
   a. construct a cladogram.
   b. polarize the characters.
   c. determine how recently the species shared a common ancestor.
   d. identify symplesiomorphies.
   e. apply the principle of parsimony.

12. When the same character state is exhibited by several different outgroups, which of the following is true of polarity assignments?
   a. They are not useful.
   b. They minimize character evolution.
   c. They cannot be determined.
   d. They are most reliable.
   e. They contradict the principle of parsimony.

13. If frogs were most closely related to gorillas and humans rather than salamanders, two evolutionary changes in _____ and _____ would have had to occur, but _____ would have evolved only once.
    a. hair loss and loss of amniotic membranes; tail loss
    b. tail loss and hair loss; loss of teeth
    c. loss of teeth and tail loss; hair loss
    d. tail loss and hair loss; loss of amniotic membranes
    e. loss of teeth and loss of amniotic membranes; hair loss

14. Which of the following can phylogenetic analysis NOT be used for?
    a. distinguishing between competing hypotheses
    b. determining whether trait evolution involved homologous or homoplastic changes
    c. determining the precise time when an evolutionary event occurred
    d. identifying evolutionary sequences
    e. testing hypotheses about species diversity

15. Which of the following characters cannot be used to identify character variation between organisms?
    a. morphology
    b. physiology
    c. DNA
    d. behavior
    e. none of the above

16. Members of a clade always share
    a. homoplasies.
    b. symplesiomorphies.
    c. vestigial structures.
    d. analogous structures.
    e. synapomorphies.

17. The principle of parsimony is used when
    a. an outgroup cannot be identified.
    b. there are conflicts among characters.
    c. organisms have complex characters.
    d. rates of evolutionary change are rapid.
    e. statistical approaches fail.

18. Which of the following organism listed does NOT belong to the same monophyletic group as the others?
    a. bird
    b. bat
    c. *Velociraptor*
    d. crocodile
    e. *Tyrannosaurus*

19. Which of the following is an example of a paraphyletic group?
    a. crocodile, *Stegosaurus*, *Tyrannosaurus*, *Velociraptor*, hawk
    b. hawk, bat
    c. *Stegosaurus*, *Tyrannosaurus*, *Velociraptor*
    d. land plants, brown algae
    e. crocodile, *Stegosaurus*, *Tyrannosaurus*, *Velociraptor*

20. The dolphins flipper and the horses leg are an example of _____
    a. autology.
    b. homology.
    c. parsimony.
    d. homoplasy.
    e. analogy.

21. Phylogenetic analysis suggests that which of the following might be responsible for the diversity of beetles?
    a. soil modifications
    b. oscillating selection
    c. evolution of complex characters
    d. angiosperm specialization
    e. DNA divergence

22. Phylogenetics is the basis of all _____ because it examines the distribution of traits among organisms in the context of their phylogenetic relationships.
    a. natural selection
    b. classification
    c. comparative biology
    d. evolution
    e. species

23. Examination of the saber-toothed character state indicates that it likely evolved independently at least how many times?
    a. 2
    b. 3
    c. 4
    d. 5
    e. 6

24. The wings of birds and those of bees are an example of _____ structures.
    a. homologous
    b. synapomorphous
    c. homoplastic
    d. symplesiomorphous
    e. vestigial

25. Nondispersing larvae have evolved eight separate times from dispersing larvae, with no instances of _____
    a. evolution in the reverse direction.
    b. lower extinction rates.
    c. species diversification.
    d. geographic isolation.
    e. evolutionary increase.

26. Which of the following was NOT revealed by phylogenetic analysis of strains of HIV and SIV?
    a. HIV strains are more closely related to SIV strains than they are to each other.
    b. HIV is derived from SIV.
    c. Different strains of HIV represent independent transfers from different primate species.
    d. Humans acquired HIV from different primate hosts.
    e. SIV has been present in primates for millions of years.

27. The earliest HIV-positive result was found in a human blood sample from what year?
    a. 1920
    b. 1940
    c. 1959
    d. 1980
    e. 1998

28. SIV was most likely transmitted from chimps and monkeys to humans through which of the following processes?
    a. saliva exchange
    b. sexual intercourse
    c. butchering meat
    d. mosquito bites
    e. primate attacks

29. Genetic differentiation in strains of SIV suggests that it has infected primates for more than how many years?
    a. 10
    b. 100
    c. 1000
    d. 100,000
    e. 1,000,000

30. The fact that HIV rapidly mutates and infected individuals carry multiple genotypes can be used to determine which of the following?
    a. its SIV counterpart
    b. how HIV will affect future populations
    c. which mutations are deadliest
    d. the source of an infection
    e. prognosis regarding the severity of infection

ASSESSING YOUR KNOWLEDGE

Answers to the questions in this section test your ability to synthesize information gained from the chapter and to solve challenging problems on an exam or in everyday life.

Challenging Your Understanding—Part I, Answers
1. Cladogram:

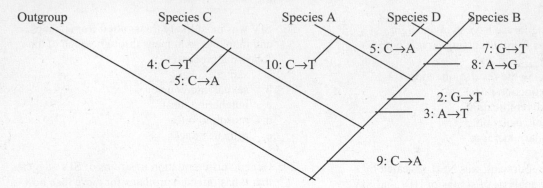

2. Eight evolutionary changes are required for the most parsimonious interpretation of the DNA sequencing data.
3. One change is homoplastic, 5: C→A.
4. Seven changes are homologous, 2: G→A, 3: A→T, 4: C→T, 7: G→T, 8: A→G, 9: C→A, 10: C→T.

Challenging Your Understanding—Part II, Answers
5. Organism 5
6. Organism 4
7. Nodes 1, 2, and 3 represent shared common ancestors of the organisms above this branch point.
8. Organisms B and C are most closely related because they share a common ancestor that was not an ancestor to the other organisms.
9. Organisms B, C, and D share an older common ancestor.
10. All of the organisms share a more distant common ancestor than the ancestors indicated by nodes 1 and 2.

Key Terms—Answers
a. 16, b. 13, c. 21, d. 9, e. 19, f. 12, g. 3, h. 20, i. 22, j. 14, k. 17, l. 8, m. 4, n. 1, o. 11, p. 6, q. 5, r. 2, s. 10, t. 7, u. 15, v. 18.

Learning by Experience—Answers
1. Cladogram:

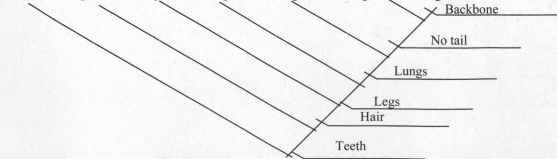

2. The outgroup is represented by organism 3.
3. Organism 5 is most closely related to organism 7.
4. Organism 2 is most closely related to organism 3.

Exercising Your Knowledge—Answers

As you check your answers, put a mark in the review (Rvw.) column for the answers you missed. If you didn't miss any, congratulations—you have mastered the chapter! If you missed some, review the section (Sect.) in the text where this concept is discussed. In order to develop an efficient review strategy, it is important that you understand what types of questions you missed. The questions with asterisks test more for understanding of the **concepts**, whereas the others test more for **detail**. *See the preface for learning strategies for concepts and for detail.*

	Sect.	Rvw.
*1. Cladistics is based on descent, emphasizing the presence of shared derived characteristics, whereas systematics relies solely on similarities to determine evolutionary relationships.	23.1	
*2. Similarity alone is not a good predictor of evolutionary relationships because species do not evolve at constant rates and evolution does not typically occur in a single direction. Therefore, differences between two species are not necessarily a function of how long the two species have been diverging. One species may have been subject to more selective pressures and may change a great deal over a short period of time, while the other species remains in the same habitat as its ancestor, and changes only a little over a very long period of time. Furthermore, convergent evolution can make two unrelated species have similar characteristics due to selective pressures of living in the same environment. Although these two species are not closely related, their similarities may lead you to believe that they are.	23.1	
*3. Phylogenetic methods, other than cladistics, are more effective in two instances. Either when the rate of evolution of character states is so high that the principle of parsimony does not hold, or when homoplasy dominates a character set such that the assumptions of the principle of parsimony are violated.	23.2	
*4. An advantage of using statistical approaches to determine evolutionary relationships, rather than cladistics, is that different assumptions about the rates of evolution can be used for different characters. When the rates of evolution are high, this method allows a more effective way to handle homoplasy than the principle of parsimony does.	23.2	
5. Branching events can be timed by either using fossils as references for the occurrence of events or by estimating the rate at which divergence of a particular character per unit time occurred. Assuming a molecular clock, this can then be used to determine the timing of other divergence events relative to it.	23.2	
*6. Phylogenetic evidence suggests that birds actually evolved from dinosaurs, but in the taxonomic system of classification, there are two separate groups for birds and for reptiles (Aves and Reptilia). This seems to indicate that birds and reptiles evolved independently and are not descended from a common ancestor. In this instance, phylogenetic analysis and the taxonomic system of classification do not agree.	23.3	
*7. (a.) The biological species concept defines a species as a group of organisms that are reproductively isolated, such that they can, and only do, naturally interbreed with other members of their group. The phylogenetic species concept defines a species as a group of organisms that have been evolving independently of other groups. (b.) The phylogenetic species concept, unlike the biological species concept can be applied to both asexual and sexual reproducing species. The biological species concept cannot be applied to asexual species because reproductive isolation is meaningless. The phylogenetic species concept also deals with whether geographically separated groups of organisms represent a species by determining whether organisms have lived independently and separated for a long enough period of time to develop their own characteristics. It does not define a species by reproductive isolation. In contrast, the biological species concept must be able to predict whether two groups of organisms would interbreed if they came in contact with each other, in order to determine if these two groups are both species. This can be a mere judgment call in many instances.	23.3	
*8. The phylogenetic species concept is controversial because many argue that first, it will lead to the recognition of every differentiated population of organisms as a species and second, it does not recognize paraphyletic species, but assumes that every species is monophyletic.	23.3	
*9. (a.) Fossils clearly indicate that dinosaurs squatted on their nests, in a manner similar to common day birds, incubating their eggs and then taking care of and protecting young dinosaurs once the eggs were hatched. From this record, we know that dinosaurs exhibited parental care. (b.) Dinosaurs, crocodiles and birds all exhibit parental care and are all closely related phylogenetically. Comparatively, this indicates that parental care is a homologous behavioral trait that was inherited from a common ancestor, rather than being a result of convergent evolution.	23.4	

*10. Many, many millions of years ago, dinosaurs evolved to have light bones. Dinosaurs further evolved to have wishbones, breastbones, and fewer fingers. From here, downy feathers, and then long arms with mobile wrists, and feathers with vanes, shafts, and barbs appeared on the Velociraptor. Further evolution produced organisms with long, aerodynamic feathers and arms that were longer than the organisms legs. Finally, as modern day birds have, there was the appearance of organisms with no teeth and short, feather-covered tails.	23.4	
*11. b	23.2	
*12. d	23.2	
13. a	23.2	
*14. c	23.2	
*15. e	23.2	
*16. e	23.2	
*17. b	23.2	
18. b	23.3	
19. c	23.3	
20. b	23.4	
21. d	23.4	
*22. c	23.4	
23. b	23.4	
24. c	23.4	
25. a	23.4	
*26. e	23.5	
27. c	23.5	
*28. c	23.5	
29. e	23.5	
*30. d	23.5	

CHAPTER 24 GENOME EVOLUTION

MASTERING KEY CONCEPTS

Technological advances now allow us to study genomes directly. These studies are beginning to reveal insights into how genomes evolve, and how genes can be conserved over time but can also be put to new uses.

24.1 Comparative genomics provides a tool for exploring evolutionary change at the DNA level.

- **Overview**: Sequencing the genomes of different organisms has introduced a powerful new approach to investigate evolutionary divergence by allowing comparisons of organisms at the DNA level in an attempt to connect changes in the DNA to morphological differences in organisms. Comparison of the human genome with the chimpanzee or the mouse indicates a high level of conservation, but comparison with the pufferfish does not. These differences are at least in part attributable to when the organisms diverged from each other. Humans and chimpanzees diverged about 5 million years ago, humans and mice diverged about 75 million years ago, while humans and pufferfish diverged 450 million years ago. Evolutionary changes occur at different rates in different genomes due to different generation times. Genetic differences or differences in gene expression between two related animals, two plant species, or plants and animals are likely to be responsible for the physiological and morphological differences between the organisms.
- **Details**: Know how the human genome compares to the genomes of mice, pufferfish, and chimpanzees, and how long ago humans diverged from each of these organisms. Know how the genomes of rice and *Arabidopsis* compare in terms of genome size and the number of genes. Understand how plant and animal genomes differ.

24.2 The evolution of whole genomes

- **Overview**: **Polyploidy** results from genome duplication in one species, or hybridization of the genomes from two different species and can lead to extensive genome changes. Polyploid events have given rise to tobacco species and domestic wheat species, and have occurred numerous times in the evolution of flowering plants. Polyploidy may be followed by the unequal loss of duplicated genes, or whole chromosomes from one parent or the other. This unequal loss is potentially due to different rates of genome duplication. Polyploidy can lead to gene silencing due to increased methylation of some genes, or can lead to an increase in

transposition events that can cause additional genetic alterations upon which evolution can act.
- **Details**: Understand how sequence comparison can be used to determine when polyploid events occurred. Know the changes that can arise in the genome of an organism due to polyploidy. Understand how tobacco and domestic wheat arose as a result of allopolyploid events.

24.3 Evolution within genomes involves gene duplication, rearrangements, or inactivation of genes.

- **Overview**: **Gene duplications**, **rearrangements**, and **gene inactivation** are three important ways that genomes of different organisms evolve. Duplication of segments of DNA, or of individual chromosomes, can contribute to the evolution of a genome because it provides the opportunity for different gene expression patterns that could result in new gene functions. Genome rearrangements have commonly occurred in different organisms and can provide a clue for how closely related two species are. In many related organisms, the order of the genes along the chromosomes has been preserved from the common ancestral species. This **conservation of synteny** can simplify the identification of homologous genes. Gene inactivation produces inactive **pseudogenes** that lead to a loss of function. For example, **OR gene inactivation** has led to a reduced sense of smell in humans. **Vertical gene transfer**, or the passage of genes from one generation to the next, is used to build phylogenies, but genes can also be swapped between species by **horizontal gene transfer**, which introduces complexities in the determination of evolutionary relationships. There is evidence of horizontal gene transfer between Archaea and Bacteria, as well as the presence of ancient transposons in humans that suggest that gene swapping occurred millions of years ago in the genomes of our distant ancestors as well.
- **Details**: Know the three potential fates of a duplicated gene. Understand where gene duplication is most likely to occur, what genes are most likely to be duplicated, and why this is a major evolutionary force. Understand the chromosomal differences between humans and living great apes. Know why conservation of synteny can be an important tool in identifying homologous genes. Understand the difference between human and primate OR genes. Understand how horizontal gene transfer has complicated our understanding of the Archaea, Bacteria, and Eukarya domain structure.

24.4 Gene function and expression patterns determine the differences between organisms.

- **Overview**: While the genomes of humans and mice, and humans and chimpanzees are strikingly similar, **different patterns of gene expression** and **posttranscriptional regulatory differences** in these organisms likely explain the morphological and behavioral differences between the organisms. The **FOXP2 gene** controls speech function in humans. Comparative genomics indicates that the human protein and the mouse protein differ by only three amino acids and the FOXP2 protein in chimpanzees and gorillas has only minimal additional changes. However, mice, chimps, and gorillas cannot speak, indicating that even small changes in homologous proteins can have a major impact on gene function in different organisms.
- **Details**: Understand how microarrays were used to detect differences between the gene expression patterns of chimpanzees and humans. Understand how small changes in the FOXP2 protein affect communicating signals in different organisms.

24.5 Nonprotein-coding DNA may regulate gene expression.

- **Overview**: **Retrotransposon DNA** that does not code for proteins is found in similar genomic locations in humans and mice. This DNA may code for **functional RNAs** that may play a critical role in gene expression, either by blocking translation of specific mRNAs or by targeting specific mRNAs for degradation.
- **Details:** Know how repetitive, nonprotein-coding DNA can affect gene expression.

24.6 Genome size does not correlate with the expected number of genes.

- **Overview**: Humans have a much smaller number of genes (25,000) than was originally expected (100,000). **Noncoding DNA**, such as **introns,** and **large segments of retrotransposon DNA** have increased the size of the human genome. In general, there is no correlation between genome

size and the number of genes it contains. Different plants have up to a 200-fold difference in the sizes of their genomes, but all of them still seem to have between 30,000 and 40,000 genes. Numerous polyploidy events cannot fully account for these differences, but other factors that may be involved are still being investigated by further sequencing projects.

- **Details**: Understand why there does not seem to be a correlation between genome size and gene number.

24.7 Genome analysis can provide information about disease prevention and treatment.

- **Overview**: Sequences conserved between human genes and the genes of pufferfish provide important information about amino acids that are critical to the functions of different proteins. Changes introduced at evolutionarily conserved sites are most likely to cause disease. The functions of conserved human genes and the effects of segmental duplications can be studied in experimental organisms. Genome sequencing and comparative analysis of the genomes of disease-causing parasites and pathogens can identify potential genes that could be targeted for drug development to treat or prevent the infections caused by these pathogens.
- **Details**: Understand how comparative genomics led to the identification of potential targets for drug development to treat malaria, Chagas' disease, African sleeping sickness, and *Leishmania* infections.

24.8 Whole genome sequences provide information that may lead to crop improvements.

- **Overview**: Genome sequencing of crop plants and beneficial microbes will provide information on how to improve crops by artificial selection, or how to improve crop yield by devising better methods of plant protection.
- **Details**: Understand examples of how genome analysis of model plants and pathogenic microbes can be used to improve crops.

CHALLENGING YOUR UNDERSTANDING

Fill in the blanks to demonstrate how the major concepts in the chapter relate to each other.

CAUSES OF GENETIC DIFFERENCES:

1. _____   4. _____
2. _____   5. _____
3. _____   6. _____

↓

7. Result: _____

DIFFERENCES BETWEEN SIMILAR GENOMES ARE DUE TO:

8. _____   9. _____   10. _____

↓

11. Result: _____
12. Even in organisms with highly _____.

13. Describe the similarities and the differences between the genomes of humans and mice, and the genomes of humans and chimpanzees.

14. Describe how it was experimentally demonstrated that the genomes of humans and chimpanzees have different patterns of gene transcription activity in their brain cells.

KEY TERMS

Match the numbered term with the definition that fits it best. Put the corresponding number in front of the appropriate definition.

1. nonsynonymous
2. synonymous
3. conservation of synteny
4. orthologues

5. paralogues
6. synthetic polyploids
7. paleopolyploids
8. aneuploidy

9. pseudogenes
10. vertical gene transfer
11. lateral gene transfer

a. _____ Hitchhiking genes from other species that can lead to phylogenetic complexity.

b. _____ Created by crossing plants closely related to ancestral species and then inducing chromosome doubling.

c. _____ Sequences of DNA that are similar to functional genes but do not produce a functional product.

d. _____ Two genes within an organism that have arisen from the duplication of a single gene in an ancestor.

e. _____ Mutations in coding DNA that do not alter the amino acids coded for in the sequence.

f. _____ The linear order of genes is the same because the common ancestral sequence has been preserved.

g. _____ The passage of genes from one generation to the next generation.

h. _____ Mutations in coding DNA that alter the amino acids coded for in the sequence.

i. _____ The duplication or loss of an individual chromosome, rather than an entire genome.

j. _____ The study of ancient polyploids to establish the time and patterns of polyploidy events.

k. _____ The conservation of a single gene from a common ancestor.

LEARNING BY EXPERIENCE

1. Arrange the following organisms in order, from those with the greatest number of genes to those with the least: fruit fly, human, mosquito, pufferfish, rice, yeast.

2. Arrange the following organisms in order, from those with the largest genome to those with the smallest: fruit fly, human, mosquito, pufferfish, rice, yeast.

3. Describe how wheat used in the production of pasta and domestic wheat have arisen.

4. Match the following scientific names discussed in this chapter with the more common proper name.

_____ a. *Anopheles gambiae*	1. pufferfish
_____ b. *Oryza sativa*	2. rat
_____ c. *Pan troglodytes*	3. budding yeast
_____ d. *Fugu rubripes*	4. rice
_____ e. *Mus musculus*	5. human
_____ f. *Saccharomyces cerevisiae*	6. mosquito
_____ g. *Arabidopsis thaliana*	7. mouse
_____ h. *Homo sapiens*	8. fission yeast
_____ i. *Rattus norvegicus*	9. wall cress
_____ j. *Schizosaccharomyces pombe*	10. chimpanzee

EXERCISING YOUR KNOWLEDGE
Briefly answer each of the following questions in the space provided.

1. If the human genome shares 99% of its genes with mice, why are humans and mice so different?

2. Is junk DNA really junk with no function?

3. Humans are very closely related to the other great apes but have one less chromosome. Why?

4. Do all genomes evolve at the same rate?

5. Have any genes been found that are unique to plants?

6. What two fates are most likely for duplicated genes? Which of the two is more likely?

7. Are gene duplication rates constant across different species?

8. What is the difference between vertical gene transfer and lateral gene transfer?

9. What accounts for the differences between the size of the genome and the number of genes in humans?

10. Describe the disease-prevention possibilities that were identified for malaria and *T. cruzi* by whole genome sequencing and comparative genomics.

Circle the letter of the one best answer in each of the following questions.

11. What percentage of genes do plants, animals, and fungi have in common?
    a. 30%
    b. 50%
    c. 70%
    d. 90%
    e. 95%

12. Which of the following is the wheat used in the production of pasta?
    a. a sterile hybrid species
    b. a fertile diploid species
    c. a sterile diploid species
    d. a fertile tetraploid species
    e. a fertile hexaploid species

13. Which of the following organisms has the most junk DNA?
    a. human
    b. mosquito
    c. Both have the same amount.
    d. Neither has any.
    e. We don't know—neither genome has been sequenced yet.

14. Which of the following statements is true?
    a. Larger genomes always have more genes than smaller genomes.
    b. Larger genomes always have fewer genes than smaller genomes.
    c. Genome size typically correlates with gene number.
    d. Gene number correlates with the complexity of the organism.
    e. None of the above is true.

15. Fruit flies have a lower level of transposons than humans because of which of the following?
    a. Transposons are not as active in fruit flies.
    b. Fruit flies eliminate unnecessary DNA faster than humans.
    c. Fruit flies have more coding DNA than humans.
    d. Fruit flies are not as complex as humans.
    e. None of the above.

16. Humans share approximately what percentage of their genes with mice?
    a. 5%
    b. 14%
    c. 27%
    d. 62%
    e. 99%

17. Which of the following has not contributed to the evolution of genomes?
    a. polyploidy
    b. horizontal gene transfer
    c. genome rearrangements
    d. duplicated DNA
    e. None of the above.

18. Which of the following organisms has had the fastest rate of chromosomal rearrangement?
    a. chicken
    b. mouse
    c. human
    d. All have had the same rate.
    e. Scientists do not know.

19. Compared to humans and pufferfish, which of the following is true about fruit flies and mosquitoes?
    a. They diverged more recently.
    b. They have undergone very little chromosomal rearrangement.
    c. They have much more noncoding DNA.
    d. All of these are true.
    e. None of these are true.

20. Of the genomes sequenced to date, what type of organism has the most genes?
    a. yeast
    b. fruit fly
    c. human
    d. mouse
    e. rice

21. Would a 3n polyploid be able to reproduce sexually?
    a. Yes, but only with itself.
    b. Yes, with any other 3n organism.
    c. No, because chromosomes have to pair up during meiosis, and three can't form a pair.
    d. No, because there would be too many genes involved.
    e. It depends on the particular organism.

22. Polyploidy is most common in what type of organisms?
    a. fungi
    b. vertebrates
    c. invertebrates
    d. plants
    e. protists

23. Which of the following types of human genes are likely to be duplicated?
    a. immune system genes
    b. growth and development genes
    c. cell-surface receptors
    d. all of these
    e. none of these

24. Approximately what percentage of the human genome consists of segmental duplications?
    a. 5%
    b. 15%
    c. 25%
    d. 50%
    e. 70%

25. About 70% of human OR genes are
    a. active pseudogenes.
    b. inactive pseudogenes.
    c. active genes.
    d. heterochromatin.
    e. domains.

26. Which of the following statements is true about lateral gene transfer in the history of life on Earth?
    a. It occurred early in the history of life.
    b. It occurred often.
    c. It helped simplify the tree of life.
    d. A and b are both correct.
    e. All of these are correct.

27. The FOXP2 gene in humans and chimpanzees differs by how many amino acids?
    a. 0
    b. 1
    c. 2
    d. 3
    e. 4

28. Nonprotein-coding DNA may produce RNAs that can do which of the following?
    a. prevent ribosomal function
    b. target some mRNAs for degradation
    c. block posttranscriptional modifications of proteins
    d. sequester splicing factors
    e. all of the above

29. Sequencing of the *P. falciparum* genome proved to be difficult because it has an unusually _____
    a. large proportion of heterochromatin.
    b. large genome.
    c. large number of segmental duplications.
    d. high proportion of adenine and thymine.
    e. large number of gene rearrangements.

30. Which of the following became the first biological control agent to have its genome sequenced?
    a. *Fugu rubripes*
    b. *P. fluorescens*
    c. *P. falciparum*
    d. *M. truncatula*
    e. *T. brucei*

ASSESSING YOUR KNOWLEDGE

Answers to the questions in this section test your ability to synthesize information gained from the chapter and to solve challenging problems on an exam or in everyday life.

Challenging Your Understanding—Answers

1. gene mutation
2. segmental duplication of DNA
3. chromosomal rearrangement
4. polyploidization
5. lateral gene transfer
6. chromosomal duplication
(Answers 1-6 can be in any order.)

7. Physical differences in genomes

8. Which genes are transcribed
9. Where they are transcribed
10. When they are transcribed
(Answers 8-10 can be in any order.)

11. Species differences
12. Conserved genes

13. Both the human and the mouse genomes have about 25,000 genes; 99% of these are shared between mice and humans. There are 300 genes unique to either mice or humans, most of the 150 genes found in mice, but not in humans, are associated with a sense of smell or reproduction. Humans have relatively the same size genome as mice. The human genome is 2900 Mb, while the mouse genome is 2600 Mb. Finally, retrotransposon DNA in humans and in mice is located in comparable regions of the genome. Differences include the fact that mouse DNA has mutated twice as fast as human DNA and chromosomal rearrangements have occurred twice as fast in mice as they have in humans. (There have been 171 chromosomal rearrangements between humans and mice.)

Both human and chimpanzee genomes have about 25,000 genes; only 1.06% of the two genomes have fixed differences in single nucleotides, and a 1.5% difference in insertions and deletions. The two genomes are relatively the same size—humans 2900 Mb and chimpanzees 3100 Mb. Chimpanzee DNA is 98.7% identical to human DNA, and protein-encoding sequences are 99.2% similar. The major difference between the two genomes is that they show very different patterns of gene transcription activity.

14. To look at the pattern of gene expression in human and chimpanzee brains, RNA was isolated from cells extracted from the brains of humans and chimpanzees, linked with a fluorescent tag, and hybridized to DNA microarrays containing up to 18,000 human genes under conditions in which DNA-RNA hybrids could form. If a RNA transcript is present in the brain cells, the DNA corresponding to the gene on the microarray fluoresces under UV light. The intensity of the signal correlates with the number of RNA copies present. From this experiment, it was found that the same genes are transcribed in humans and in chimpanzees, but the timing and the location of gene transcription was widely varied.

Key Terms—Answers
a. 11, b. 6, c. 9, d. 5, e. 2, f. 3, g. 10, h. 1, i. 8, j. 7, k. 4.

Learning by Experience—Answers

1.	mosquito, rice, pufferfish, human, fruit fly, yeast
2.	human, rice, pufferfish, mosquito, fruit fly, yeast
3.	Wheat used in the production of pasta arose from the hybridization of two different diploid genomes, followed by spontaneous chromosome doubling in some of these hybrid plants due to a failure of the chromosomes to separate in meiosis. Plants in which chromosome doubling occurred produced a fertile tetraploid species. Domestic wheat arose when this tetraploid species hybridized with a different diploid species, followed again by spontaneous chromosome doubling. These events produced a hexaploid species that is used today as bread wheat.
4.	a. 6 b. 4 c. 10 d. 1 e. 7 f. 3 g. 9 h. 5 i. 2 j. 8

Exercising Your Knowledge—Answers
As you check your answers, put a check mark in the review (Rvw.) column for the answers you missed. If you didn't miss any, congratulations—you have mastered the chapter! If you missed some, review the section (Sect.) in the text where this concept is discussed. In order to develop an efficient review strategy, it is important that you understand what types of questions you missed. The questions with asterisks test more for understanding of the **concepts**, whereas the others test more for **detail**. *See the Preface for learning strategies for concepts and for detail.*

	Sect.	Rvw.
*1. The genes are expressed at different times and perhaps in different tissues.	24.4	
*2. No; it is beginning to look like junk DNA may have functions and may be rich in regulatory RNA sequences.	24.5	
*3. Two ancestral ape chromosomes fused to make human chromosome 2.	24.3	
*4. No; some have undergone chromosome changes relatively slowly and others more rapidly. For example, chromosomal rearrangements have occurred twice as rapidly in mice as in humans.	24.1	
*5. Yes; about one-third of the genes in *Arabidopsis* and rice seem unique to plants; they have not been found in any animals or fungal genomes sequenced so far.	24.1	
*6. Duplicated genes tend to mutate and lose their function or mutate and gain a new function. Losing their function is more common.	24.3	
*7. No; for example, gene duplication in nematodes is about 10 times faster than in fruit flies.	24.3	
*8. Vertical gene transfer = passing genes from generation to generation; lateral gene transfer = transferring genes from one species to another.	24.3	
*9. There is no correlation between genome size and the number of genes in a genome. The human genome contains 75% fewer genes than was anticipated from its size (2900 Mb). The extra DNA is due to large expanses of retrotransposon DNA and to large introns, or noncoding sequences that interrupt the coding segments of the DNA.	24.6	
*10. Whole genome sequencing of *P. falciparum*, the parasitic protist that causes malaria, indicated that genes with related functions were clustered together, implying that they may share a common regulatory region that could be targeted to disable the protist. A link to chloroplast-like structures was also identified in *P. falciparum*. The apicoplast is a structure in *Plasmodium* that contains 12% of the parasitic proteins. This is the only locale where the parasite makes fatty acids. Drugs targeting the synthesis of these fatty acids, or chloroplast-specific herbicides that act against the apicoplast, could help prevent malaria. Sequencing of *T. cruzi* and comparative genomics identified 6200 genes in *T. cruzi* that are also present in *T. brucei* and *Leishmania major*, two other insect-borne pathogens. These genomic similarities are being used to direct the drug development efforts that are taking place to treat these diseases.	24.7	
*11. c	24.1	
12. d	24.2	
13. a	24.6	
*14. e	24.1	
15. b	24.3	
16. e	24.1	
17. c	24.3	

18. b	24.3	
19. a	24.1	
20. e	24.1	
*21. c	24.2	
22. d	24.2	
*23. d	24.3	
24. a	24.3	
25. b	24.3	
26. d	24.3	
27. c	24.4	
*28. b	24.5	
29. d	24.7	
30. b	24.8	

CHAPTER 25 EVOLUTION OF DEVELOPMENT

MASTERING KEY CONCEPTS

Technological advances now allow us to study genomes directly. These studies are beginning to reveal insights into how evolution and development are interconnected. This chapter focuses on how similar genes can produce different morphological structures in organisms depending on when and where they are expressed.

25.1 There is an evolutionary paradox in development.

- **Overview**: The **evolutionary paradox** of development is that sometimes genes have not changed, but their patterns of expression have. This is demonstrated by closely related sea urchins that undergo two different developmental patterns, one passing through a pluteus larva stage (indirect development), and the other developing directly into an adult. A small number of genes direct the development of plants and animals. Many of these genes encode transcription factors or signaling molecules. Alteration of these transcription factors, or signaling molecules, during evolution can affect gene expression by modifying when or where a gene is expressed. **Heterochronic mutations** alter the timing of developmental events, while **homeotic mutations** alter the spatial pattern of expression. Mutations in the regulatory region of a gene, or in the coding sequence itself, can affect the expression of the gene, or the function of the protein it produces respectively. The presence of these mutations in transcription factors, or signaling molecules, can change the cellular targets and alter development.
- **Details**: Understand how alterations in transcription factors or signaling molecules can affect development. Understand how heterochronic and homeotic mutations could alter development.

25.2 One or two gene mutations can cause a new phenotype.

- **Overview**: Mutations that improve the fitness of an organism at a specific time, in a particular environment, are selected for and lead to a change in the phenotype of an organism. A mutation in a single gene can change the developmental form of a species or the developmental function of a particular morphological characteristic. Broccoli and cauliflower arose from a common ancestor with a premature stop codon in the *CAL* gene, a gene required for meristems to transition from making branches to making flowers. Artificial selection for plants with many branches allowed broccoli and cauliflower to flourish. In cichlid fish, two genes are likely to be responsible for the length of their snouts, which have changed rapidly depending upon the available food sources in different environments allowing for some cichlids to be bottom feeders, others to be biters, and other to be rammers. In this way, natural selection has allowed rapid speciation of cichlid fish with different jaw sizes and shapes.

- **Details**: Understand the function of the CAL gene and the effect of introducing an early stop codon into this gene. Understand how phylogenetics was used to analyze the developmental pattern of evolution in *B. oleracea*. Understand how only a few genes can affect the overall size and shape of a cichlid fish.

25.3 Sometimes the same gene can evolve to have a new function in different organisms.

- **Overview**: Genes that have highly conserved sequences can have distinct functions in different organisms. The *Brachyury* gene encodes a transcription factor that is found in both vertebrates and invertebrates, but has different functions in different organisms likely because it activates different genes in different organisms. **Tbx5** is a transcription factor that regulates forelimb development in humans and wing development in birds. The expression of different genes in humans and birds is regulated by Tbx5. Changes in what genes are expressed and the timing of gene expression determine the development of different morphological structures.
- **Details**: Understand how the Brachyury and the Tbx5 proteins can cause dramatic morphological changes in different organisms.

25.4 Different genes can have convergent functions.

- **Overview**: Different developmental pathways can use the same set of genes for different functions. The *Distal-less* gene, typically involved in limb development, is also used for eyespot formation on butterfly wings. Similarly, different developmental pathways can use a single, existing regulatory program to perform different functions. Development of sensory bristles in *Drosophila* and of butterfly wing scales is initiated by the **achaete-scute transcription factor**. Bilaterally symmetrical flowers have arisen by convergent evolution. Some have used the *CYC* gene, and others have used different genes.
- **Details**: Know how the same genes can perform different functions, and how different genes can perform functions that result in similar phenotypes.

25.5 Duplicated genes can have divergent functions.

- **Overview**: Gene duplication in eudicots resulted in a gene that regulates petal development. A MADS box gene duplicated giving rise to two genes, **PI** and **paleoAP3**. *PaleoAP3* duplicated, giving rise to **AP3 and a duplicate AP3 gene**. This duplication of *AP3* correlated with petal development in eudicots. *ap3* and *pi* mutants fail to produce stamens or petals because AP3 and PI bind to each other and regulate the transcription of genes required for stamen and petal development. While the C-terminal end of PI can partially substitute for the C-terminal function of AP3 in stamen formation, the C-terminal end of AP3 is essential for petal formation.
- **Details**: Understand how gene duplication played a critical role in petal formation in eudicots. Understand the experiments that were done to determine what domains of AP3 and PI are required for stamen and petal development.

25.6 Functional analysis of genes across species is essential to identify gene functions.

- **Overview**: Sequence comparison alone cannot determine the functions of similar genes in different organisms. Function can be inferred from data obtained from sequencing, but actual experiments have to be performed to determine the actual function of genes.
- **Details**: Know what organisms are **good model systems** used to test gene functions.

25.7 Diversity of eyes in the natural world: A case study

- **Overview**: Complicated structures in organisms evolve by incremental improvements and natural selection. The eyes of organisms are analogous structures that have evolved independently numerous times (convergent evolution). The mouse **Pax6 gene** is a functional homologue of the *Drosophila eyeless* gene. **Walter Gehring** demonstrated that expression of the mouse Pax6 gene in the fly's leg could direct the formation of an eye on the leg of the fly. Pax6 was also expressed in regenerating eyespots of the ribbon worm, but was not required for eyespot regeneration in planaria. Consistent use of Pax6 and its homologues in eye development brings to question whether eye development actually did evolve independently many times, or whether eye development may have a single evolutionary origin in a common ancestor that had a rudimentary visual system. Descendants of this ancestor could have evolved more complex eyes over time.
- **Details**: Know how Walter Gehring demonstrated that the Pax6 gene directs eye development. Understand how the regeneration of eyespots in the ribbon worm was found to depend on Pax6, and how it is known that regeneration of eyespots in planaria does not depend on Pax6.

CHALLENGING YOUR UNDERSTANDING

1. The depicted transcription factor turns on the expression of depicted Gene A but has no effect on Gene B. Mark an X at all the positions of the following three depicted genes that show where mutations that can alter developmental patterns can occur.

2. List the evidence that supports the idea that development of animal eyes occurred once during evolution and then list the evidence that supports the theory that development of animal eyes occurred several independent times.

KEY TERMS

Match the numbered term with the definition that fits it best. Put the corresponding number in front of the appropriate definition.

1. homeobox
2. T box
3. heterochrony
4. homeosis

5. radially symmetrical
6. bilaterally symmetrical
7. functional genomics
8. transgenic

9. co-opting
10. pluteus larva

a. _____ A change in the place where a developmental event occurs in an embryo due to mutation of a gene or genes.

b. _____ An organism that in addition to its own DNA contains some new DNA.

c. _____ An object that will produce two identical halves if cut in half in any direction.

d. _____ A protein domain found in developmental transcription factors like *brachyury* and *Tbx5*.

e. _____ A domain of developmental transcription factors that binds to regulatory regions of genes.

f. _____ A change in the timing of a developmental event that arises from mutation of a gene or genes.

g. _____ An object that will produce two mirror images if cut in half at one specific place.

h. _____ An evolutionary process by which an old gene takes on a new function.

i. _____ A stage in the development of some sea urchins that creates a free-swimming organism.

j. _____ Performing experiments to determine differential functions of different versions of genes.

LEARNING BY EXPERIENCE

1. The Tbx5 transcription factor controls limb development in animals. Draw how this protein might control the expression of these five genes in animals that have very different limbs.

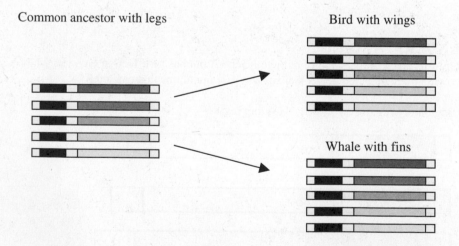

2. Draw an example of a radially symmetrical flower and a bilaterally symmetrical flower.

3. In the diagram of an animal embryo, color in the areas where you would expect to see the following genes expressed.

O *Pax6*   O *Brachyury*   O *Tbx5*

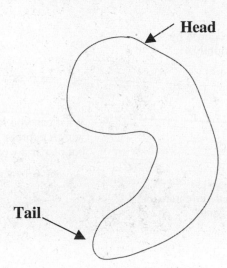

Head

Tail

4. Match each of the following genes with its developmental function.

_____ i. *Brachyury* gene   a. eye development
_____ ii. *Distal-less* gene   b. limb bud development
_____ iii. *Pax6* gene   c. notochord development
_____ iv. *Tbx5* gene   d. butterfly wing eye spot development

EXERCISING YOUR KNOWLEDGE

Briefly answer each of the following questions in the space provided.

1. Explain the difference between heterochronic and homeotic mutations.

2. Describe two types of mutations that can occur in the gene for a transcription factor that will alter its ability to properly regulate developmental patterns.

3. Propose a function for the protein produced by the *CAL* gene found in the cabbage family.

4. What might you expect to happen to a vertebrate that has a mutation in its *Brachyury* gene.

5. Explain how the *Tbx5* gene can promote the development of an arm in humans but a wing in birds?

6. What conditions might you find in an animal with a mutation in its *Tbx5* gene?

7. What was the original symmetry found in the earliest flowering plants and how did the other symmetry arise?

8. What can be determined by the experiment in which plants containing an *AP3* gene missing its C-terminus cannot produce stamens or flower petals?

9. What can you infer from the fact that ribbon worms express *Pax6* in their developing eyespots but planaria worms do not?

10. Why were scientists so surprised when gene sequencing revealed that the gene responsible for eye development in mice (*Pax6*) was very similar to the eye development gene in flies (*eyeless*)?

Circle the letter of the one best answer in each of the following questions.

11. Which of the following are transcription factor families ubiquitously involved in development?
    a. *Hox* genes
    b. *Brachyury* genes
    c. *CYC* genes
    d. MADS box genes
    e. Both a and d are correct.

12. If a mutation changes which cells in an embryo produce a particular signally receptor, the most likely change in development would be an example of which of the following?
    a. symmetrical change
    b. homologous change
    c. heterochronic change
    d. homeotic change
    e. convergent change

13. How can extremely similar organisms develop through very different stages?
    a. Genes may duplicate.
    b. Developmental patterns are random events.
    c. Several hundred genes must be mutated in order to produce developmental changes.
    d. Very minor changes in only a few genes can produce big developmental changes.
    e. Small genes can produce large changes.

14. What event led to the development of broccoli and cauliflower?
    a. mutation of a flower producing gene
    b. mutation of a leaf producing gene
    c. mutation of hundreds of genes
    d. mutation of *Hox* genes
    e. selective breeding of cabbage plants

15. What led to the establishment of broccoli and cauliflower as common plants in society?
    a. natural selection because they are more fit
    b. continual mutation
    c. artificial (human) selection by cultivation
    d. well-documented phylogeny
    e. beneficial genes

16. Cichlid fish have one of three morphologically different jaws. These three varieties result from what?
    a. different genes
    b. slightly different versions of one or two genes
    c. environmental effects during development
    d. global warming
    e. lethal mutations

17. The *Tbx5* gene belongs to which gene family?
    a. Hox transcription factors
    b. MADS box transcription factors
    c. cell signaling molecules
    d. T-box transcription factors
    e. cell surface receptors

18. The *Brachyury* gene is an example of a gene that
    a. has been co-opted to different functions throughout evolution.
    b. has been duplicated many times.
    c. is only responsible for one phenotype.
    d. is only found in mammals.
    e. has retained its function throughout evolution.

19. How could the *Distal-less* gene create eyespots in butterfly wings and limbs in other animals?
    a. Some genes mutated to allow *Distal-less* to activate them.
    b. *Distal-less* gained mutations to allow it to activate different genes.
    c. A gene mutated to cause *Distal-less* to be expressed in other cells.
    d. The regulatory sequence of *Distal-less* mutated to allow it to be expressed in other cells.
    e. All of the above are possibilities.

20. The formation of bilateral symmetry in flowering plants is an example of what?
    a. convergent evolution
    b. divergent evolution
    c. natural selection
    d. homoplastic evolution
    e. Both a and c are correct.

21. Why is radial symmetry considered to be convergent evolution?
    a. *CYC* gene mutated in some radially symmetric flowering plants.
    b. Flowering plants were originally bilateral.
    c. Several genes contribute to radial symmetry.
    d. One gene is responsible for radial symmetry.
    e. Gene duplication

22. What type of transcription factor is encoded by the *AP3* gene?
    a. Hox transcription factor
    b. MADS box transcription factor
    c. T box transcription factor
    d. cell signaling molecule
    e. cell surface receptor

23. The gene family of flowering plants that includes the *AP3* gene and promotes petal and stamen formation arose through which of the following?
    a. gene duplication
    b. convergent evolution
    c. divergent evolution
    d. cladogenesis
    e. homoplastic evolution

24. Sequence comparisons between different organisms identify differences in specific genes. What is needed to demonstrate that these sequence differences are the cause of phenotypic differences?
    a. a correlation
    b. at least two mutations per gene
    c. experiments to demonstrate a functional difference
    d. two organisms with the same mutation
    e. Both b and d are correct.

25. Why do biologists believe that animal eyes developed independent of each other homoplastically?
    a. The eyes of several different animals are very different.
    b. All animals have eyes.
    c. Some animals don't have eyes.
    d. A half-developed eye is not advantageous.
    e. The eyes of ribbon worms are very similar to the eyes of mammals.

26. What might a fish look like that has a mutation in its *Pax6* gene?
    a. abnormal head
    b. no fins
    c. no spine
    d. no eyes
    e. no scales

27. What observation(s) suggest(s) that eye development occurred just once in history?
    a. Insect and mammal eyes are very similar.
    b. *Pax6* sequence is extremely conserved.
    c. *Pax6* function is conserved.
    d. Some cavefish do not express *Pax6*.
    e. Both b and c are correct.

28. Can the actual function of a gene be determined by sequencing it?
    a. Yes—sequencing provides all the necessary information.
    b. The function can be inferred but not known for sure by sequencing.
    c. No—knowing the gene sequence has nothing to do with its function.
    d. Yes—but only if the gene is more than 10% homologous to another gene.
    e. No—because sequencing is highly inaccurate.

29. Walter Gehring is famous for
    a. doing the first complete gene sequencing.
    b. discovering the existence of apicoplasts.
    c. creating a transgenic fruit fly that had an eye form on its leg.
    d. studying sea urchin development.
    e. founding the field of bioinformatics.

30. The *Pax6* gene plays a role during the development of which organism?
    a. fruit fly
    b. ribbon worm
    c. mouse
    d. cavefish
    e. all of these

ASSESSING YOUR KNOWLEDGE

Answers to the questions in this section test your ability to synthesize information gained from the chapter and to solve challenging problems on an exam or in everyday life.

Challenging Your Understanding—Answers

1.

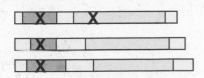

2.   Single developmental event:
The sequence and function of *Pax6* is conserved in diverse animals and *Pax6* from mice can promote eye development in fruit flies.

   Multiple convergent events:
Eye structure is very different in different animals. No evidence exists for an ancestor common to all animals with eyes that had some form of a light-sensing organ.

Key Terms—Answers

a. 4, b. 8, c. 5, d. 2, e. 1, f. 3, g. 6, h. 9, i. 10, j. 7

Learning by Experience—Answers

1.

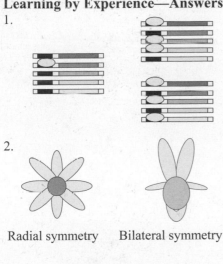

2.

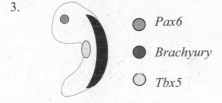

Radial symmetry   Bilateral symmetry

3.

- ⬤ *Pax6*
- ⬤ *Brachyury*
- ◯ *Tbx5*

4. i - c,   ii - d,   iii - a,   iv - b

Exercising Your Knowledge—Answers

As you check your answers, put a check mark in the review (Rvw.) column for the answers you missed. If you didn't miss any, congratulations—you have mastered the chapter! If you missed some, review the section (Sect.) in the text where this concept is discussed. In order to develop an efficient review strategy, it is important that you understand what types of questions you missed. The questions with asterisks test more for understanding of the **concepts**, whereas the others test more for **detail**. *See the Preface for learning strategies for concepts and for detail.*

	Sect.	Rvw.
*1. Heterochronic mutations change WHEN developmental events occur in the embryo while homeotic mutations change WHERE they occur in the embryo.	25.1	
*2. A change in the coding sequence may create a new protein that has an altered ability to activate transcription of other genes or a change in the regulatory region of the gene may alter the amount of the transcription factor produced.	25.1	
*3. The CAL protein most likely functions by causing flower buds to mature into flowers since inactivation of this gene in broccoli and cauliflower leads to immature flower buds.	25.2	
*4. If this organism survives, it would most likely have an abnormal notochord, vertebrae, or tail.	25.3	
*5. The *Tbx5* gene encodes a transcription factor. It activates the expression of a DIFFERENT SET of genes in each of these organisms. Therefore, humans and birds will express a different set of proteins in the region of the developing embryo where the analogous limb structure should form.	25.3	
*6. Abnormal, short, undeveloped, or nonfunctional forelimbs. In humans, this syndrome is known as Holt-Oram syndrome.	25.3	
*7. The original flowering plants had radial symmetry. Bilateral symmetry arose several times independently by the creation of new functions of different genes. Some bilateral plants used the *CYC* gene for this function.	25.4	
*8. The C-terminal portion of the protein encoded by the *AP3* gene is necessary for both stamen and flower petal formation.	25.5	
*9. The development of using *Pax6* to create the lens of animal eyes occurred sometime AFTER the divergence of ribbon and planaria worms.	25.7	
*10. Insects and vertebrates diverged more than 500 million years ago and have very different types of eyes (for example, simple eyes versus compound eyes). Originally, biologists thought the different types of eyes had evolved independently many times. They also thought the common ancestor had no ability to detect light. Both of these assumptions are being reconsidered because of the commonality of the *Pax6* gene in different organisms.	25.7	

11. e	25.1	
12. d	25.1	
*13. d	25.1	
*14. a	25.2	
*15. c	25.2	
16. b	25.2	
17. d	25.3	
*18. a	25.3	
*19. e	25.4	
20. e	25.4	
*21. a	25.4	
22. b	25.5	
23. a	25.5	
*24. c	25.6	
*25. a	25.7	
*26. d	25.7	
*27. e	25.7	
*28. b	25.6	
29. c	25.7	
30. e	25.7	

CHAPTER 26 THE TREE OF LIFE

MASTERING KEY CONCEPTS

Early humans probably named things in their environment using whatever they devised for language. For their relatively small world, this would suffice. It is acceptable to have local names for things of only local interest, but it hardly serves the needs when information is shared. With civilization, came much wider knowledge of the world and the things in it. Communication also increased, and a need became evident for some standardization in the naming process.

26.1 Life originated from organic molecules assembling into functional cells.

- **Overview**: There are **eight basic properties** that all organisms share that are fundamental to life. Organisms consist of one or more **cells**; they respond to **stimuli**; they use **metabolic processes** to grow; they **develop**; they **reproduce**; they have **regulatory mechanisms** and maintain constant internal conditions (**homeostasis**); and they possess **DNA,** which is used to carry, pass on, and record heritable changes in the genetic information of an organism. Life originated from the assembly of organic molecules into functional units. Life on Earth may have originated in meteors or in cosmic dust (**panspermia**). Life on Earth originated between 3.8 and 2.5 billion years ago, when the ocean and air temperatures were very high, and the Earth had a **reducing atmosphere** very different from today's atmosphere. **Miller and Urey** tried to reproduce in the laboratory the oceanic conditions that existed when life originated. They found that molecules with biological significance were formed under these conditions. Cells later could have formed from these organic molecules. Fossils indicate that most of the early life on Earth consisted of single-cell, prokaryotic organisms. By way of evolution, these organisms diversified.

- **Details**: Know the fundamental properties of life that all organisms possess. Know the conditions under which life originated on Earth. Understand how Miller and Urey set up an experiment to reproduce the conditions in the oceans that existed when life originated, what compounds were produced in this experiment, and what conclusions can be made about the origins of life on Earth from this experiment. Have a general idea of the major events in the geological time scale and the evolution of life on Earth.

26.2 Biologists name organisms in a systematic way.

- **Overview**: Until the mid-1700s, **polynomial names**, written in Latin, were used to describe organisms. **Carolus Linnaeus** adopted a two-part, or **binomial**, naming system to designate different species in the 1750s. The first part of the binomial name is the **genus** (capitalized), and the second part is the **species** (lower case). By this taxonomic classification system, no two organisms anywhere in the world have the same name. Besides being classified into a genus and a species, organisms are classified into **five higher order taxonomical groups** based on shared characteristics. From the largest group to the smallest group, this classification includes the **kingdom, phylum, class, order, family**, genus, and species. There are problems with the Linnaean taxonomic system. First, this system is based on similar traits among organisms, but it does not distinguish whether these traits are ancestral or derived. Second, the Linnaean system does not take evolutionary relationships into account and, therefore, many higher taxonomic groups are not monophyletic naturally.

- **Details**: Know the difference between polynomial and binomial naming, and why this change was needed. Know the names of the levels and the order, both descending and ascending, of the hierarchical classification system. Understand the conflict between the Linnaean taxonomic system and phylogenetic classification.

26.3 Organisms are grouped into domains and kingdoms.

- **Overview**: The **taxonomic system** includes **six kingdoms**, four kingdoms of eukaryotic organisms, including **Animalia, Plantae, Fungi**, and **Protista**, and two kingdoms of prokaryotic organisms, **Archaea** and **Bacteria**. A taxonomic level higher than the kingdom level, consisting of three **domains**, is being increasingly recognized due the differences between **Archaea, Bacteria**, and eukaryotes (**Eukarya**). The first domain consists of bacteria, which are very diverse and are the largest group of organisms on Earth. The second domain is Archaea, which comprises the organisms most closely related to the Eukarya and are classified as **methanogens, extremophiles**, and **nonextreme archae** based on their environments or metabolic pathways. Eukaryotes are the third domain. These are organisms with complex, compartmentalized cells. Some organelles in eukaryotic cells, such as mitochondria and chloroplasts, arose by **endosymbiotic** processes. Organisms classified as protists are primarily unicellular, while organisms in the Animalia, Plantae, and Fungi kingdoms are multicellular, each having evolved from a protist ancestor. Eukaryotes can be distinguished from prokaryotes by three characteristics, **compartmentalization**, **multicellularity**, and **sexual reproduction**. **Viruses** are composed of a protein coat surrounding a DNA- or RNA-based genome. Viruses cannot reproduce by themselves, but use the cellular machinery of a host cell to propagate. Viruses cannot be taxonomically classified because they are not organisms but rather are more like chemicals.

- **Details**: Know the general features of the three domains and the six kingdoms in the taxonomic system. Know the characteristics of Archaea that distinguishes these organisms from those classified as Bacteria. Know the three general Archaea categories and the characteristics that define each group. Know the three characteristics that distinguish eukaryotes from prokaryotes.

26.4 Protists as a group are not monophyletic.

- **Overview**: Any eukaryotic organism that cannot be classified as an animal, plant, or fungus, is classified as a protist. Therefore, the kingdom **Protista** is not monophyletic or based on evolutionary relationships.
- **Details**: Understand why the kingdom Protista is the weakest distinction in the classification system.

26.5 Land plants originated from an ancestral green alga.

- **Overview**: The origin of land plants from a green algal ancestor occurred only once in the history of evolution. Land plants are members of the **Streptophyta** along with green freshwater algae and other multicellular green plants. The **Charales** contain the closest relatives of land plants. A new kingdom of green plants, the **Viridiplantae**, consisting of two groups of green algae, the **Chlorophyta** and the Streptophyta, has been proposed. **Angiosperms** (flowering plants) are derived from the *Amborella* **shrub** that contains moss mitochondrial protein genes, which arose by horizontal gene transfer.
- **Details**: Understand the origin of land and flowering plants. Understand why the new kingdom Viridiplantae is proposed.

26.6 The evolutionary relationships among animals are being further elucidated by molecular data.

- **Overview**: Annelids and arthropods are two phyla whose members belong to the **protostome group**. Within this group annelids are classified as **lophotrochozoans**, and arthropods are classified as **ecdysozoans**. Comparisons of rRNA sequences from arthropods and annelids suggest that segmentation in each organism may have arisen independently. Segmentation arose independently again in the **deuterostomes**. The *Hox* **genes**, present in an ancient ancestor of the lophotrochozoans, the ecdysozoans, and the deuterostomes, evolved independently three times in a descendant from each group to regulate segmentation. The *Distal-less* **gene** is a single *Hox* gene that is responsible for **uniramous** appendages in insects, and **biramous** appendages in crustaceans. In the past, the single-branched or two-branched appendages have been used as evidence to taxonomically separate insects and crustaceans, but molecular data now indicate that this distinction is likely not valid because both arise by the action of the *Distal-less* gene. The class **Mammalia** is divided into three major subgroups, **monotremes**, **marsupials**, and **placental mammals** (**eutherians**). Of these three groups, the group consisting of the placental mammals is the largest. One defining characteristic of mammals is that they have **mammary glands** to feed their young. The placental mammals are divided into four major groups. Within these groups, the origins and the relationships of the organisms are being discovered based on morphological information from fossils and molecular data.

  Details: Understand how it is known that segmentation likely arose two independent times within the protostomes and again in the deuterostome group. Know the role of the *Hox* genes in segmentation. Know how mammals are grouped. Understand how relationships among animals are being elucidated and why this information is beneficial.

CHALLENGING YOUR UNDERSTANDING

Write in the six kingdoms of life across the top row of this table. Then fill in the rest of the table indicating which of the kingdoms display each of the characteristics listed on the left. Fill in this table as completely as possible before looking back at your textbook.

Kingdoms						
Prokaryote or Eukaryote						
Unicellular or Multicellular						
Chloroplasts						
Mitochondria						
Photosynthetic						

KEY TERMS

Match the numbered term with the definition that fits it best. Put the corresponding number in front of the appropriate definition.

1. genera
2. species
3. taxonomy
4. taxon
5. family
6. order
7. class
8. phylum
9. kingdom

10. Animalia
11. Plantae
12. Fungi
13. Protista
14. Archaea
15. Bacteria
16. domains
17. methanogens
18. extremophiles

19. nonextreme archaea
20. endosymbiosis
21. viruses
22. biramous
23. uniramous
24. eutherians
25. Viridiplantae
26. binomial
27. polynomial

a. ____ The placental mammals, they make up over 90% of the Mammalia class.
b. ____ Archae that can grow in very high or low temperatures or pHs, or in high salt or at high pressure.
c. ____ Taxonomic level consisting of groups of organisms belonging to orders with common properties.
d. ____ Eukaryotic organelles, like the mitochondria and chloroplasts, arose by engulfing prokaryotic cells.
e. ____ One group of archae that obtain their energy by using H_2 gas to reduce CO_2 to CH_4.
f. ____ A group of complex "parasitic" chemicals consisting of genetic material wrapped in a protein coat.
g. ____ A newly proposed green plant kingdom, including the green algal branches Chlorophyta and Streptophyta.
h. ____ Eukaryotes that do not fit in the Animalia, Plantae, or Fungi kingdoms are placed in this kingdom.
i. ____ Archea that grow in the same environments as bacteria.
j. ____ Two-part names that have become our standard way of designating different species.
k. ____ A kingdom and a domain of organisms with cell walls lacking peptidoglycan, and genes with introns.
l. ____ Having a single-branched structure such as the appendages found in insects and myriapods.
m. ____ Taxonomic levels higher than kingdom that each form a phylogenetic clade.
n. ____ A group of organisms at a particular level in a classification system.
o. ____ A eukaryotic kingdom containing organisms with multicellular forms and single-celled yeasts.
p. ____ Basic units by which organisms are grouped, represented by the first word of a binomial name.
q. ____ A eukaryotic kingdom containing multicellular organisms that includes all mammals.
r. ____ Having a two-branched structure such as the appendages of crustaceans.
s. ____ A level of taxonomic classification consisting of groups of organisms belonging to similar families.
t. ____ One of the great groups, such as Animalia, Plantae, Fungi, Protista, Archaea, or Bacteria in taxonomy.
u. ____ A "many names" system in which a series of descriptive terms was added to the name of a genus.
v. ____ A eukaryotic kingdom that includes angiosperms and other land plants.
w. ____ A taxonomic level of classification consisting of classes of organisms with similar characters.
x. ____ The science of classifying living organisms to give order and organization to life.
y. ____ A highly diverse kingdom and a domain containing the most abundant organisms on Earth.
z. ____ The scientific name for an organism; this group is represented by the second word in a binomial name.
aa. ____ A taxonomic level of classification consisting of genera with similar characters.

LEARNING BY EXPERIENCE

1. Place the following evolutionary events in order from earliest to most recent.

    I.   A.   Appearance of gymnosperm plants
            B.   Appearance of vascular plants
            C.   Appearance of flowering plants

    __ __ __

    II.   A.   Appearance of amphibians
            B.   Appearance of land plants
            C.   Appearance of Cyanobacteria
            D.   Appearance of fish
            E.   Appearance of dinosaurs

    __ __ __ __ __

    III.   A.   Appearance of multicellular organisms
            B.   Appearance of animals
            C.   Appearance of prokaryotes
            D.   Appearance of eukaryotes
            E.   Appearance of oxygen in the atmosphere

    __ __ __ __ __

2. Consider the eight levels of taxonomic classification. How many levels of classification are shared by the following pairs of organisms?

    a. pine tree and gorilla
    b. squirrel and mouse
    c. squirrel and fox
    d. fern and whale

3. Write in the three domains of life across the top row of this table. Then list the kingdoms of life that fit into each domain below it. Fill in this table as completely as possible before looking back at your textbook.

EXERCISING YOUR KNOWLEDGE

Briefly answer each of the following questions in the space provided.

1. Why is the binomial system preferred over the polynomial system?

2. What is the value of having all scientific names in the Latin language?

3. Once *Baeomyces roseus* is mentioned in a publication, how would the name be printed thereafter?

4. (a) Would it be more correct to say "classes may contain several orders" or "orders may contain several classes"? (b) Why?

5. (a) When was Latinizing of names of living things begun, and (b) why?

6. Why is the kingdom Protista considered to be the weakest area of the classification system?

7. What is the reason for the domain classification level?

8. (a) What is the evidence that segmentation arose independently? (b) What is the most likely genetic explanation of the independent appearance of segmentation in arthropods and annelids?

9. Now that archaebacteria have been found living alongside eubacteria, how do scientists know that those bacteria are archaebacteria?

10. Why are viruses not included in any schemes for classifying organisms?

Circle the letter of the one best answer in each of the following questions.

11. Which of the following is NOT true of Miller and Urey's experiments?
    a. They assembled a reducing atmosphere excluding O_2.
    b. They used electrodes to discharge sparks to simulate lightning.
    c. They placed cosmic dust into ocean water and heated it to 100°C.
    d. Glycine and alanine were produced.
    e. Within a week, 15% of CH_4 was converted into other carbon compounds.

12. In the early 1700s, the classification system used was
    a. polynomial.
    b. pentanomial.
    c. binomial.
    d. trinomial.
    e. tetranomial.

13. The oldest level of taxonomic classification is
    a. class.
    b. family.
    c. genus.
    d. phylum.
    e. species.

14. In writing or printing scientific names, it is permissible to abbreviate the _____ name.
    a. species
    b. phylum
    c. order
    d. family
    e. genus

15. In printing scientific names, only the _____ is capitalized.
    a. family
    b. class
    c. species
    d. kingdom
    e. genus

16. Which of the following is NOT a characteristic of organisms in the Archaea domain?
    a. They have identifiable signature sequences in their DNA.
    b. Their growth is inhibited by antibiotics.
    c. Lipids in the cell membranes have a branched structure.
    d. They can live in extreme environments.
    e. They have introns present in some of their genes.

17. Chloroplasts are energy-harvesting organelles derived from which of the following?
    a. halobacteria
    b. cyanobacteria
    c. flavobacteria
    d. purple nonsulfur bacteria
    e. gram-positive bacteria

18. Viruses are not considered to be alive due to which of the following characteristics?
    a. They consist only of DNA or RNA and protein.
    b. They are not included in the taxonomic classification system.
    c. They do not contain regulatory mechanisms.
    d. They require a host cell to reproduce.
    e. They lack structures to respond to their environments.

19. Which of the following is NOT true of the kingdom Protista?
    a. Organisms lack a nuclear envelope.
    b. Organisms can be photosynthetic, heterotropic, or both.
    c. Most organisms have a unicellular phase in their life cycles.
    d. It consists of eukaryotic organisms.
    e. Organisms have a cytoskeleton.

20. The _____ are excluded from the kingdom Virdiplantae.
    a. Charales
    b. land plants
    c. Chlorophyta
    d. red algae
    e. Mesostigmatales

21. Which of the following is the closest living relative of land plants?
    a. red algae
    b. Charales
    c. Coleochaetales
    d. *Amborella*
    e. mosses

22. By what mechanism did *Aborella* acquire mitochondrial genes from three different moss species?
    a. inherited from a common ancestor
    b. endosymbiosis
    c. horizontal gene transfer
    d. convergent evolution
    e. hybridization

23. Of the six kingdoms now recognized,
    a. two are plants and four are animals.
    b. four are eukaryotes and two are prokaryotes.
    c. four are macroscopic and two are microscopic.
    d. two are eukaryotes and four are prokaryotes.
    e. two are carnivores and four are herbivores.

24. Most unicellular eukaryotes are grouped into
    a. fungi and protists.
    b. fungi and eubacteria.
    c. only kingdom Protista.
    d. only kingdom Fungi.
    e. kingdoms Fungi, Protista, and Eubacteria.

25. Which gene is responsible for initiating uniramous or biramous appendage development?
    a. *AP3*
    b. *CYC*
    c. *Tbx5*
    d. *Pax6*
    e. *Distal-less*

26. A kingdom that is also a domain is
    a. Bacteria.
    b. Protista.
    c. Fungi.
    d. Prokaryota.
    e. none of these.

27. True multicellularity occurs only in
    a. animals.
    b. eukaryotes.
    c. plants and animals.
    d. plants, animals, and protists.
    e. plants, animals, and fungi.

28. Members of the kingdom Protista are
    a. monophyletic.
    b. semiphyletic.
    c. paraphyletic.
    d. polyphyletic.
    e. protophyletic.

29. Prokaryotic organisms make up
    a. Archaebacteria, Bacteria, and Protista.
    b. Archaebacteria and Protista.
    c. Protista and Bacteria.
    d. Protista.
    e. Bacteria and Archaebacteria.

30. Viruses are assigned to
    a. Archaebacteria.
    b. Protista.
    c. Eubacteria.
    d. Fungi.
    e. none of these.

ASSESSING YOUR KNOWLEDGE

Answers to the questions in this section test your ability to synthesize information gained from the chapter and to solve challenging problems on an exam or in everyday life.

Challenging Your Understanding—Answers

Kingdom	Archaea	Bacteria	Protista	Plantae	Fungi	Animalia
Prokaryote or Eukaryote	Pro	Pro	Euk	Euk	Euk	Euk
Unicellular or Multicellular	Uni	Uni	Most Uni	Multi	Multi	Multi
Chloroplasts	No	No	Yes	Yes	No	No
Mitochrondria	No	No	Yes	Yes	Yes	Yes
Photosynthetic	Some	Some	Some	Yes	No	No

Key Terms—Answers

a. 24, b. 18, c. 7, d. 20, e. 17, f. 21, g. 25, h. 13, i. 19, j. 26, k. 14, l. 23, m. 16, n. 4, o. 12, p. 1, q. 10, r. 22, s. 6, t. 9, u. 27, v. 11, w. 8, x. 3, y. 15, z. 2, aa. 5.

Learning by Experience—Answers

1. I: B, A, C; II: C, B, D, A, E; III: C, E, D, A, B
2. a.1, b.5, c.3, d.1
3.

Archaea	Bacteria	Eukarya
Archaea	Bacteria	Protista Plantae Fungi Animalia

Exercising Your Knowledge—Answers

As you check your answers, put a mark in the review (Rvw.) column for the answers you missed. If you didn't miss any, congratulations—you have mastered the chapter! If you missed some, review the section (Sect.) in the text where this concept is discussed. In order to develop an efficient review strategy, it is important that you understand what types of questions you missed. The questions with asterisks test more for understanding of the **concepts**, whereas the others test more for **detail**. *See the preface for learning strategies for concepts and for detail.*

	Sect.	Rvw.
*1. The advantage of the binomial system over the polynomial system is simplicity. The polynomial names are too cumbersome.	26.2	
*2. The use of Latin scientific names eliminates the need for scientists to master several foreign languages. Also, since Latin is no longer used as an active language by any cultures, the meanings of words and word parts are unlikely to change over time.	26.2	
*3. After the entire binomial has been used, the name could be printed as *B. roseus*.	26.2	

	Sect.	Rvw.
*4. (a) Classes may contain several orders. (b) Classes are higher in the hierarchy than orders.	26.2	
*5. (a) Though Latin may have been used earlier, it became common practice in the Middle Ages. (b) It was the language of scholars.	26.2	
*6. The kingdom Protista is considered to be the weakest area of the classification system because it reflects a major conflict between taxonomic classification and phylogenetic classification. This kingdom consists of several nonmonophyletic lineages having distinct evolutionary origins. All eukaryotic organisms that do not fit into one of the three other eukaryotic kingdoms are arbitrarily placed with the protists, regardless of evolutionary relationships.	26.4	
*7. The domain level is needed because some organisms are so different from all others that a level above kingdom is needed.	26.3	
*8. (a) Comparison of rRNA sequences indicate that annelids and arthropods are not closely related as was once thought implying that segmentation present in both of these groups of organisms likely arose independently twice and then again in the deuterostomes. (b) The most likely genetic explanation for the independent appearance of segmentation in both arthropods and annelids is that members of the *Hox* gene family, which were present in a common ancestor of the lophotrochozoans, ecdysozoans, and the deuterostomes, co-opted three times to evolve a role in segmentation.	26.6	
*9. Archaebacteria living alongside eubacteria are identified by signature sequences of DNA not shared by any other organisms.	26.3	
*10. Viruses are not organisms. They are acellular, lack metabolism, and do not reproduce themselves.	26.3	
11. c	26.1	
12. a	26.2	
13. c	26.2	
14. e	26.2	

15. e	26.2		
*16. b	26.3		
*17. b	26.3		
*18. d	26.3		
*19. a	26.4		
20. d	26.4		
21. b	26.5		
*22. c	26.5		

*23. b	26.3		
*24. c	26.3		
25. e	26.6		
*26. a	26.3		
*27. b	26.3		
*28. c	26.4		
*29. e	26.3		
*30. e	26.3		

CHAPTER 27 VIRUSES

MASTERING KEY CONCEPTS

Viruses—entities that cannot be called alive, much less organisms—have a remarkable impact upon our civilization. They are parasites that invade without motility, multiply without reproductive capacity, and defy us to cure the diseases they cause. Yet, they are useful as messengers in genetic engineering. They are a fascinating study.

27.1 Viruses consist of a nucleic acid core surrounded by a protein coat.

- **Overview**: All viruses contain a nucleic acid genome that is encased in a protein sheath or **capsid**. The viral genome can be DNA or RNA that is single- or double-stranded, but viruses do not contain cytoplasm and are not cellular. Viruses act as parasites to infect host cells in which they can replicate and propagate themselves by using the replication, transcription, and translation machinery of the cell. RNA viruses and **retroviruses** are replicated in the cytosol of the host cell, while DNA viruses are replicated in the nucleus. Viruses can infect almost any type of organism, including bacteria, fungi, protists, plants, and animals. Different viruses have distinctive shapes and sizes. Most viruses are **helical** (TMV) or **icosahedral** (adenovirus) in shape, but some complex viruses have a **binal symmetry** (T4 bacteriophage), and other animal viruses have an **envelope** surrounding the capsid (influenza).
- **Details**: Know the structure of different **virions**. Know the shapes, sizes, genome identities, and replicative mechanisms used by different viruses. Understand what is meant by **negative-strand**, or **positive-strand viruses**.

27.2 Bacterial viruses exhibit two sorts of reproductive cycles.

- **Overview**: **Bacteriophage** are a structurally and functionally diverse group of viruses whose members can all infect bacterial cells. Phages **attach,** or **adsorb,** to the outer surface of the bacterial cell and inject their DNA into the cell (**penetration**). In the **lytic reproductive cycle**, the viral DNA is replicated and viral proteins are then made (**synthesis**) and **assembled** into viral particles. These particles **bud** through the cell wall to infect other cells, or are released in a manner that lyses the host cell. In the **lysogenic reproductive cycle**, bacteriophages do not immediately kill the host cells that they infect, but rather **integrate** into the host cell's genome producing a **prophage (lysogeny)**. In this way, the virus is replicated when the host cell replicates its own DNA and is present in the genome of all subsequent daughter cells.

Expression of the lysogenic phage is repressed by viral regulatory proteins. When a cell is stressed, the lysogenic phage can be **induced** to enter the lytic cycle. The viral genome is **excised** from the bacterial genome and the viral genes are expressed.
- **Details**: Understand the lytic and lysogenic reproductive cycles of bacteriophage. Know how it is determined whether **phage lambda** will be lytic or lysogenic. Understand how a lysogenic bacteriophage can convert the harmless bacterium *V. cholerae* into a toxin-producing form.

27.3 HIV is a complex animal virus that causes AIDS (acquired immune deficiency syndrome).

- **Overview**: **HIV** is closely related to simian immunodeficiency virus (**SIV**), a virus that infects chimpanzees. Humans infected with HIV have varying degrees of resistance to the virus due to genetic variation and selective pressure from the **smallpox virus,** which favored the propagation of a mutated *CCR5* gene that encodes a receptor for both smallpox and HIV. HIV targets and kills $CD4^+$ cells, such as **helper T cells,** that are normally responsible for initiating an immune response against foreign agents, allowing bacteria and viruses to cause **opportunistic infections**. When a person is infected with HIV, the **gp120 protein** on the surface of the viral particles binds to CD4 and one of two **coreceptors**, CCR5 or CXCR4. Once HIV binds to its receptor, it enters the cell by **endocytosis**. Inside the cell, it sheds its protective coat, and viral **reverse transcriptase**, an inaccurate enzyme, synthesizes a strand of DNA complimentary to the viral RNA genome (retrovirus). After synthesis of a second DNA strand, the double-stranded DNA is integrated into the host genome by a viral enzyme. After a period of latency, the DNA is transcribed and either translated or used as the genome for new viruses. Viral proteins are assembled into enveloped viral particles and bud out of the cell. HIV has a long **latent period** during which it integrates into the genome of $CD4^+$ T cells, and macrophages. **HIV testing** looks for the presence of an antibody against HIV. **AZT** and **protease inhibitors** are two drugs that are being used to inhibit HIV (**combination therapy**), but this therapy is expensive and demanding, and has side effects. Researchers are focusing on investigating a defective HIV strain containing a specific negative factor (*nef* gene), blocking replication of the virus by a factor called **CAF** ($CD8^+$ cell antiviral factor), disrupting the CCR5 receptor by mutations, or blocking the CCR5 receptor by **chemokines** to develop an AIDS vaccine.

- **Details**: Understand how HIV compromises the immune system of an infected individual, and why some people are more susceptible than others. Learn the **HIV infection cycle** in detail. Know how viruses are targeted to specific tissues and how HIV recognizes its target cell. Know the two different ways a virus can exit a host cell. Understand why HIV has a high mutation rate, and why this is beneficial to the virus. Understand how AZT and protease inhibitors act to inhibit HIV, but why this combination therapy is not a viable treatment plan. Know what other approaches to an AIDS vaccine are being pursued.

27.4 Nonliving infectious agents are responsible for many human diseases.

- **Overview**: Numerous human diseases are caused by viruses, including **influenza**, which is an enveloped, segmented RNA virus consisting of three different types A, B, and C. Differences in the **hemagglutinin (H)** and **neuraminidase (N)** proteins caused by mutation or recombination lead to different viral subtypes that can cause an epidemic if the combination of H and N subtypes have never been experienced before. These different viral subtypes require the development of new flu vaccines. **The bird flu** (H5N1) is highly contagious and transmitted between domestic birds. It has a high mortality rate in humans, but currently does not seem to be transmitted between humans. Because this virus could mutate and thereby allow human to human transmission, scientists are trying to develop a vaccine. **Emerging viruses**, like the **hantavirus** that caused a pneumonia outbreak in 1993, the **coronavirus** that caused the **SARS outbreak**, or the **filovirus** that causes **Ebola virus,** arise in one organism, but then are passed to another. Viruses, such as **human papillomavirus (HPV)**,

can also cause **cancer** by triggering the expression of oncogenes, or by disrupting genes, that control the cell cycle.

- **Details**: Know what diseases are caused by viruses. Know why different flu vaccines are necessary to protect against different viral subtypes. Understand the nature of emerging viruses and the sources of hantavirus and the coronavirus that caused SARS. Understand how viruses can cause cancer.

27.5 Infectious diseases can also be caused by prions and viriods.

- **Overview**: Brain diseases, such as **scrapie** in sheep, **mad cow disease** in cattle, or **Crutzfeldt-Jacob disease (CJD)** in humans cause brain cavities known as **transmissible spongiform encephalopathies (TSEs)** to form. TSEs can be spread by tissue transplants, food, or by injections of diseased tissue. **Variant CJD (vCJD)** is a newly discovered human disease that has arisen from eating the meat of cattle with mad cow disease. In the 1960s, **T. Alper and J. Griffith** proposed that the infectious material in TSE preparations was protein, not DNA, or RNA. This was confirmed in the 1970s by **S. Prusiner**, who called the infectious protein a **prion**. **Misfolded prion proteins** could cause normal prion proteins to misfold by contacting them. **Viroids** are naked pieces of tiny RNAs that can cause infectious disease in plants, but the mechanism by which they act is not currently well understood.

- **Details**: Understand how TSEs are spread. Understand what observation led Alper and Griffith to propose that protein, not DNA, or RNA was the infectious agent in TSEs, and how this was confirmed by Prusiner. Know what distinguishes the normal prion protein (PrP^c), from the disease-causing prions (PrP^{sc}). Know two possible mechanisms by which viroids could cause diseases in plants.

CHALLENGING YOUR UNDERSTANDING

Section 1. Consider the following diagram of the HIV genome. Label each of the genes with its appropriate name and describe the function of the proteins produced from genes A, B, and G.

A _____   F _____

B _____   G _____

C _____   H _____

D _____   I _____

E _____

Section 2. In Chapter 27, you learned the composition and shape of different viruses. Using this knowledge, label all of the arrows as one of the following viral components: capsid protein, tail, nucleic acid genome, envelope, or glycoprotein. Then, classify each as a bacterial, plant, or animal virus in the odd-numbered spaces and provide the name of one example virus of each class in the even-numbered spaces.

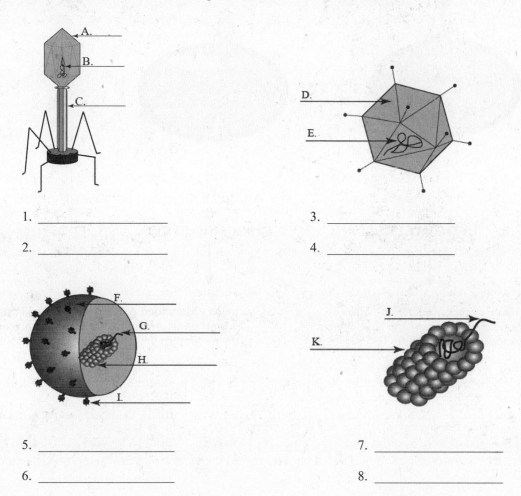

1. _____

2. _____

3. _____

4. _____

5. _____

6. _____

7. _____

8. _____

Section 3. For the following viruses, describe the nucleic acid present in the genome and the disease caused by each.

<table>
<tr><td></td><td align="center">Type of genome</td><td align="center">Disease caused</td></tr>
<tr><td>a. Influenza virus</td><td>_____</td><td>_____</td></tr>
<tr><td>b. HIV</td><td>_____</td><td>_____</td></tr>
<tr><td>c. Epstein-Barr virus</td><td>_____</td><td>_____</td></tr>
<tr><td>d. Enterovirus</td><td>_____</td><td>_____</td></tr>
<tr><td>e. Varicella zoster</td><td>_____</td><td>_____</td></tr>
<tr><td>f. Variola virus</td><td>_____</td><td>_____</td></tr>
<tr><td>g. Corona virus</td><td>_____</td><td>_____</td></tr>
<tr><td>h. Rhabdovirus</td><td>_____</td><td>_____</td></tr>
<tr><td>i. Filoviruses</td><td>_____</td><td>_____</td></tr>
<tr><td>j. Herpes simplex virus</td><td>_____</td><td>_____</td></tr>
<tr><td>k. Hepadnavirus</td><td>_____</td><td>_____</td></tr>
</table>

Section 4. After a virus has adsorbed to a host cell and injected its genome into the host cell, the virus can partake in one of two different cycles. To challenge your understanding of these two cycles, draw the events, including the host cell, viral particles, viral genome, and viral transcripts that you would observe in the lytic and lysogenic viral cycles.

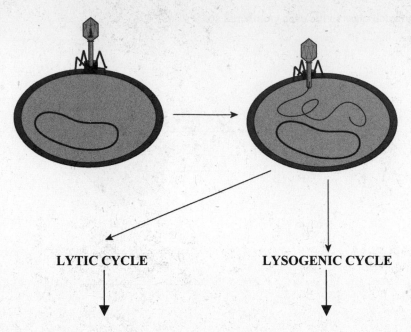

LYTIC CYCLE

LYSOGENIC CYCLE

KEY TERMS

Match the word on the left with the definition that fits it best on the right. Put the corresponding number in front of the appropriate definition.

1. capsid
2. envelope
3. host range
4. tissue tropism
5. latent
6. helical
7. icosehedral
8. bacteriophages
9. lytic cycle
10. virulent viruses

11. prophage
12. lysogeny
13. lysogenic cycle
14. induction
15. phage conversion
16. retrovirus
17. reverse transcriptase
18. combination therapy
19. chemokines
20. emerging viruses

21. hantavirus
22. Ebola virus
23. severe acute respiratory syndrome (SARS)
24. transmissible spongiform encephalopathies (TSEs)
25. prion
26. viriod
27. human immunodeficiency virus (HIV)

a. ____ A viral reproductive cycle in which the viral genome is integrated into the host cell's genome.
b. ____ A virus that infects bacterial cells. The T-even phages (T2, T4, etc.) are examples.
c. ____ A change in the characteristics of the host cell due to the integration of viral DNA in the lysogenic cycle.
d. ____ An enzyme that creates DNA from RNA and is used by many viruses that have an RNA genome.
e. ____ Viruses that cause the death of the host cell through lysis and release of new viral particles.
f. ____ A recently emerged, virally caused respiratory infection.
g. ____ A class of diseases that cause neurons to die leaving the brain with empty cavities and a spongy appearance.
h. ____ A phenomenon where some viruses will only target certain types of cells within a multicellular organism.
i. ____ Administering two or more treatments at the same time to improve the chances of eliminating a disease.
j. ____ A protein coating that encloses and protects the nucleic acid genome of a virus.
k. ____ Viruses that are produced in one organism and are transferred to a different organism.
l. ____ A state where a virus is dormant or inactive for a period of time and shows no signs or symptoms.
m. ____ A piece of RNA not protected by a protein coat that can cause disease in plants.
n. ____ A switch from the lysogenic viral reproductive cycle to the lytic cycle.
o. ____ The segment of a viral genome that is integrated into the DNA of the host cell.
p. ____ A lipid bilayer membrane derived from the host cell that encloses and protects some animal viruses.
q. ____ A protein that can transmit a disease from one organism to another.
r. ____ A virus containing single-stranded RNA for a genome and usually residing in rodents.
s. ____ The process of integrating a viral genome into the host cell's genome.
t. ____ Chemicals produced naturally in the human body that regulate immune cells and help block HIV infection.
u. ____ The viral reproductive cycle in which a virus causes an infected cell to lyse and release more viral particles.
v. ____ A 20-sided ball-shaped structure that is the capsid morphology of many viruses.
w. ____ A retrovirus that infects human immune cells and is responsible for causing the devastating disease AIDS.
x. ____ A very deadly human filovirus causing 90% lethality and found most frequently in outbreaks in Africa.
y. ____ The set of different cell types that a particular virus can use as a host cell.
z. ____ The structure of the capsid of viruses that that appear in the shape of a rod or a thread.
aa. ____ A class of viruses that contain RNA as their genome and use a special enzyme to create DNA from it.

LEARNING BY EXPERIENCE

In chapter 26, a list of characteristics of living things was presented and viruses were judged to be nonliving. Review this list and then use what you've learned about viruses in this chapter to state the evidence for and against viruses being living things. You may represent both positions or take one and have a classmate take the other. Briefly state the arguments below.

1. Cellular organization:

   a. Nonliving

   b. Living

2. Sensitivity:

   a. Nonliving

   b. Living

3. Growth:

   a. Nonliving

   b. Living

4. Development:

   a. Nonliving

   b. Living

5. Reproduction:

   a. Nonliving

   b. Living

6. Regulation:

   a. Nonliving

   b. Living

7. Homeostasis:

   a. Nonliving

   b. Living

EXERCISING YOUR KNOWLEDGE

Briefly answer each of the following questions in the space provided.

1. What is the basic structure of a virus?

2. Explain why viruses cannot replicate outside of a host cell.

3. How does a viral capsid differ from a viral envelope (a) in location and (b) in composition?

4. How does a lysogenic cycle differ from a lytic cycle?

5. (a) What enzyme is required to replicate HIV?
   (b) Why is it required?

6. How does HIV cause diseases to be more lethal to AIDS patients than to other people?

7. Once docked in the CD4 receptor or a macrophage, how does HIV gain entry?

8. Why does a macrophage serve as a continual HIV factory instead of being destroyed by the virus?

9. The Hong Kong flu virus was designated A(H3N2). What does that designation mean?

10. (a) What observation led Alper and Griffith to suggest that the infectious agent in TSEs was protein, not DNA or RNA?
    (b) How was this confirmed by Prusiner?

Circle the letter of the one best answer in each of the following questions.

11. Viruses are considered
    a. nonliving.
    b. primitive precursors of bacteria.
    c. a link between life and nonlife.
    d. primitive organisms.
    e. very small bacteria.

12. The suitable cells for the rabies virus to replicate in are
    a. connective tissue.
    b. skin cells.
    c. neurons.
    d. liver cells.
    e. respiratory cells.

13. The HIV viral genome is composed of
    a. double-stranded DNA.
    b. (+) single-stranded RNA.
    c. single-stranded DNA.
    d. (−) single-stranded RNA.
    e. both RNA and DNA.

14. Shingles is caused by which of the following viruses?
    a. Variola virus
    b. Varicella zoster
    c. Herpes simplex virus
    d. Flavivirus
    e. Coronavirus

15. Typically, viruses form _____ around their nucleic acid.
    a. an envelope
    b. a cell wall
    c. a capsid
    d. a cell membrane
    e. a capsule

250

16. *V. cholerae* is converted from a harmless form to a deadly form by introduction of a toxin-producing gene from which of the following?
    a. virulent virus
    b. lytic bacteriophage
    c. viroid
    d. lysogenic bacteriophage
    e. prion protein

17. The expression of early genes determines which of the following in phage lambda?
    a. where it integrates in the genome
    b. how the bacteriophage is assembled
    c. whether it is lytic or lysogenic
    d. when it's excised from the bacterial genome
    e. how rapidly the viral genome is replicated

18. The Epstein-Barr virus causes which of the following diseases?
    a. mononucleosis
    b. rubella
    c. measles
    d. yellow fever
    e. more than one of the above

19. A person infected with HIV may not develop AIDS if the virus has the defective _____ gene.
    a. *vpr*
    b. *gag*
    c. *pol*
    d. *nef*
    e. *env*

20. In AIDS patients, the virus homes in on the ____T cells.
    a. $CD1^+$
    b. $CD2^+$
    c. $CD3^+$
    d. $CD4^+$
    e. $CD5^+$

21. AZT inhibits which of the following to prevent HIV?
    a. docking on the CD4 receptor
    b. replication
    c. synthesis of viral proteins
    d. blocking the coreceptors
    e. function of the nef protein

22. ____ may prevent HIV replication by binding with the CXCR4 and CCR5 receptors.
    a. CD4
    b. The nef
    c. CAF
    d. Protease inhibitors
    e. Chemokines

23. Variability in the susceptibility to HIV infection is due in part to mutations in _____ that resulted from selective pressure of the smallpox virus.
    a. nef
    b. CCR5
    c. CXCR4
    d. CD4
    e. CD8

24. Viruses may contribute to what percentage of all human cancer cases worldwide?
    a. 1%
    b. 5%
    c. 15%
    d. 30%
    e. 50%

25. The hantavirus is transmitted to humans from _____ by fecal contamination.
    a. deer mice
    b. pack rats
    c. laboratory mice
    d. bats
    e. groundhogs

26. Different strains of the flu virus differ in which of the following?
    a. viral shapes
    b. nucleocapsid proteins
    c. mechanisms of replication
    d. envelope protein spikes
    e. viral sizes

27. An example of an emerging virus is
    a. herpes.
    b. polio.
    c. rubella.
    d. CJD.
    e. SARS.

28. Of the following viruses, the most lethal is
    a. influenza.
    b. Ebola.
    c. measles.
    d. herpes simplex.
    e. Epstein-Barr.

29. Which of the following is the causative agent of transmissible spongiform encephalopathies?
    a. protein
    b. double-stranded DNA
    c. hantavirus
    d. filovirus
    e. viroids

30. Disease-causing prions differ by normal prion proteins due to which of the following?
    a. different host organisms
    b. introduction of a stop codon
    c. alternative splicing
    d. introduction of a single point mutation
    e. misfolding

ASSESSING YOUR KNOWLEDGE

Answers to the questions in this section test your ability to synthesize information gained from the chapter and to solve challenging problems on an exam or in everyday life.

Challenging Your Understanding—Answers
Section 1
A. gag, capsid proteins to make capsid coat; B. pol, polymerase to replicate genome; C. vif; D. vpr; E. vpu; F. tat; G. env, envelope proteins like gp120 on the surface of the viral envelope; H. rev; I. nef.

Section 2
1. bacterial; 2.T2 or T4 bacteriophage; 3. animal; 4. adenovirus; 5. animal; 6. HIV; 7. plant; 8. TMV
A. capsid; B. nucleic acid genome; C. tail; D. capsid; E. nucleic acid genome; F. envelope; G. nucleic acid genome; H. capsid; I. glycoprotein; J. nucleic acid genome; K. capsid.

Section 3
a. − ssRNA, Flu; b. +ssRNA, AIDS; c. dsDNA, Mononucleosis; d. +ssRNA, Polio; e. dsDNA, Chicken pox; f. dsDNA, Small pox; g. −ssRNA, SARS; h. −ssRNA, Rabies; i. −ssRNA, Ebola; j. dsDNA, Herpes; k. dsDNA, Hepatitis B.

Section 4

LYTIC CYCLE	LYSOGENIC CYCLE
1. Synthesis	1. Integration

2. Assembly	2. Induction

3. Lysis & Release	3. Synthesis & Assembly

4. Lysis & Release

Key Terms—Answers

a. 13, b. 8, c. 15, d. 17, e. 10, f. 23, g. 24, h. 4, i. 18, j. 1, k. 20, l. 5, m. 26, n. 14, o. 11, p. 2, q. 25, r. 21, s. 12, t. 19, u. 9, v. 7, w. 27, x. 22, y. 3, z. 6, aa. 16

Learning by Experience—Answers

1.	a. Viruses lack a cell membrane and cannot be a cell.
	b. All viruses are contained by at least a capsid and sometimes an envelope. Doesn't that count?
2.	a. Viruses lack structures to sense their environment.
	b. The behavior of the bacterial virus shown in figure 26.3 indicates sensitivity and response to its environment.
3.	a. A virus has no metabolism of its own but depends upon its host for energy.
	b. No contest.
4.	a. A virus is not a multicellular organism and can have no such development.
	b. This is true, but there are unicellular life-forms that are considered living organisms.
5.	a. The virus cannot reproduce itself. Its replication is done by the host cell.
	b. No contest
6.	a. Viruses have no structures for self-regulation.
	b. This is true, but what about the delay of onset of activity after invading a host? Is that regulation?
7.	a. Viruses have no mechanism for maintaining homeostasis.
	b. No contest.

You may have different answers; the preceding are offered for thought. You might wish to consider whether we are looking upon this question with a bias. Is life, as we know it, all there is to life?

Exercising Your Knowledge—Answers

As you check your answers, put a mark in the review (Rvw.) column for the answers you missed. If you didn't miss any, congratulations—you have mastered the chapter! If you missed some, review the section (Sect.) in the text where this concept is discussed. In order to develop an efficient review strategy, it is important that you understand what types of questions you missed. The questions with asterisks test more for understanding of the **concepts**, whereas the others test more for **detail**. *See the preface for learning strategies for concepts and for detail.*

	Sect.	Rvw.
*1. A virus has a core of nucleic acid surrounded by protein.	27.1	
*2. Virions, or viral particles outside of a cell, are metabolically inert. They can replicate outside of a host cell because they lack most, if not all, of the enzymes required for nucleic acid replication, as well as the enzymes necessary for protein synthesis, including ribosomes. Viruses require the replication machinery, and the transcription and translation machinery of the host cell to reproduce.	27.1	

*3. (a) If present, the envelope surrounds the capsid. (b) Capsids are only proteinaceous, while envelopes also contain lipids and glycoproteins.	27.1	
*4. In the lysogenic cycle, the viral DNA is integrated into the host's genome.	27.2	
*5. (a) Replication of the HIV genome requires reverse transcriptase. (b) Transcription is usually from DNA to RNA. The HIV genome is RNA, so the process must be reversed.	27.3	
*6. HIV attacks macrophages and the CD4$^+$ T cells needed to activate the defense mechanism.	27.3	
*7. After gp120 binds to the CD4 receptor of a macrophage, it changes into a shape that allows it to bind to CCR5 receptor, which passes the gp120-CD4 complex into the cell.	27.3	
*8. HIV doesn't rupture the macrophage. It is passed out by exocytosis.	27.3	
*9. The Hong Kong flu virus was type A with 3 H molecules and 2 N molecules.	27.4	
*10. Alper and Griffith noticed that infectious TSE preparations were still infectious after they were treated with radiation that would normally destroy DNA or RNA. From this observation, they hypothesized that the infectious agent was actually protein. Prusiner confirmed this hypothesis when he tried to isolate nucleic acids or viruses from TSE preparations, but could not. Instead, he isolated a prion protein.	27.5	
*11. a	27.1	
12. c	27.1	
13. b	27.3	
14. b	27.2	
15. c	27.2	
*16. d	27.2	
*17. c	27.2	
18. a	27.2	
*19. d	27.3	
*20. d	27.3	
*21. b	27.3	
*22. e	27.3	
*23. b	27.3	
*24. c	27.4	
25. a	27.4	
*26. d	27.4	
27. e	27.4	
28. b	27.4	
*29. a	27.5	
*30. e	27.5	

CHAPTER 28 PROKARYOTES

MASTERING KEY CONCEPTS

Prokaryotes are the smallest and most numerous organisms. They exhibit considerable diversity in both structure and metabolism. Their relatively simplistic interior structure distinguishes them from eukaryotes. Yet despite the sparseness of their interior structure, prokaryotes are remarkably able to cope with life in diverse environments. Variation among prokaryotes is a major concern for our species because it can cause considerable healthcare problems due to the diseases that prokaryotes are associated with. However, there are redeeming qualities to prokaryotes, and in reality, we could not survive without them.

28.1 The first cells were probably prokaryotic.

- **Overview**: The fossil record, the composition of carbon-containing rocks, and the presence of organic compounds can be used to indicate when, where, and what type of organisms were present at the beginning of ancient life. **Microfossils** are fossilized forms of what seems to be present-day prokaryotes found in rocks 3.5 billion years old. **Stromatolites**, or sedimentary deposits, held in place by microorganisms are also indicative of ancient life dating back 2.7 billion years. Dating and analyzing carbon compounds in the oldest rocks indicate that carbon fixation occurred up to 3.8 billion years ago. The carbon isotope ratios of organic molecules, or **biomarkers** such as hydrocarbons isolated from rock formations, can be used to indicate the ancient origin of life as well.
- **Details**: Understand the methods being used to determine when ancient life began and what types of organisms were present.

28.2 Prokaryotes are distinctly different from eukaryotes.

- **Overview**: Prokaryotes differ from eukaryotes in a number of fundamental ways. Prokaryotes are primarily unicellular; generally small; lack a membrane-bound nucleus, internal compartmentalization, and membrane-bound organelles; undergo asexual reproduction by binary fission; have simple, rigid, spinning flagella; and can undergo either oxygenic or anoxygenic photosynthesis, or are **chemolithotropic**. Archaea and Bacteria are both groups of prokaryotes, but there are significant characteristic differences between the two groups. Archaean membranes contain ether linkages that can be branched and can form a monolayer rather than a bilayer. Bacterial

membranes contain ester linkages and are unbranched. The cell walls of Archaea lack **peptidoglycan**, and bacterial cell walls contain peptidoglycan. Archaean DNA replication is more similar to eukaryotes and Archaea have more than one RNA polymerase that are more similar to eukaryotic RNA polymerases, than to the single, bacterial RNA polymerase. Prokaryotes were typically classified based on whether they were photosynthetic, motile, unicellular, colony-forming or filamentous, undergo binary fission or form spores, and whether they were infectious human pathogens. Today, they are also classified by using molecular approaches to determine gene and RNA sequences, whole-genome sequences, amino acid sequences of key proteins, base composition of nucleic acids, and base-pairing between genomes from different species to determine how closely related they are.
- **Details**: Know the characteristics that distinguish prokaryotes from eukaryotes, and Archaea from Bacteria. Know the early classification characteristics and the molecular classification characteristics.

28.3 Prokaryotic cells are simple and categorized based on shape.

- **Overview**: Prokaryotes are **bacillus** or rod-shaped, **coccus** or spherical-shaped, or **spirillum** or long, helical-shaped. **Gram-positive bacteria** have a cell wall composed of a thick layer of cross-linked peptidoglycan chains and stain purple with **Gram stain**, while the cell wall of **gram-negative bacteria** is composed of multiple layers where the peptidoglycan layer is located between the plasma and the outer membrane consisting of **lipopolysaccharides**. Gram-negative bacteria do not retain the purple-colored Gram stain and are resistant to many antibiotics that target cell wall synthesis, such as penicillin. Some bacteria and archaea also contain a layer, known as the **S layer**, outside of the peptidoglycan layer (gram-positive) or outside of the outer membrane (gram-negative), which is involved in protection or surface adhesion. In addition, some bacteria are surrounded by a **capsule** that allows a prokaryotic cell to evade an immune response. Besides being diverse in shape, prokaryotic cells use different methods to move through their environments. Many prokaryotic cells have **flagella,** which act like propellers enabling the cell to move. Some gram-negative prokaryotes have **pili,** which are important for adhesion. Some prokaryotic cells can form highly resistant **endospores** that can germinate and return to normal cell growth after years or even decades.

While prokaryotes lack compartmentalization, they do have internal membranes that function in respiration and photosynthesis, a nucleoid region containing their DNA, and ribosomes.

- **Details**: Understand what information the Gram stain provides, how this test works, and the differences between the structures of the gram-positive and gram-negative cell walls. Understand what other features can be used to categorize prokaryotes.

28.4 Variation in prokaryotes arises by exchange of DNA or by mutation.

- **Overview**: Prokaryotes can acquire DNA by gene transfer through cell-to-cell contact (**conjugation**), by viruses (**transduction**), or from the environment (**transformation**). Horizontal gene transfer between two bacterial cells, such as **F plasmid** transfer, can occur by conjugation when the F plasmid attaches to the interior of the F^+ cell just below the **hollow pilus** at the **conjugation bridge**. This plasmid undergoes **rolling-circle replication**, and the second single strand of the plasmid is displaced into the F^- cell. The F plasmid can integrate into, and be excised from, the bacterial genome using **IS sequences** or insertion sequences present in the F plasmid and the *E. coli* genome. The **R plasmid** is a conjugative plasmid that has acquired antibiotic resistance genes that can lead to bacterial strains that are resistant to antibiotics, such as methicilin-resistant or vancomycin-resistant *S. aureus*. **Bacterial variation** can also arise by **mutations** that can spread rapidly in *E. coli* because it has a short doubling time. Horizontal gene transfer in bacteria also occurs by **bacteriophage**. **Generalized transduction** occurs when the phage packaging machinery stuffs bacterial DNA, rather than phage DNA, into a phage head. This will result in bacterial DNA being transferred and incorporated into the genome of the recipient cell. **Specialized transduction** occurs when a lysogenic phage that has integrated into the host chromosome is imprecisely excised taking some chromosomal DNA with it and resulting in loss of some phage genes. Specialized transducing phage particles integrate into the chromosome of the recipient cell. **Natural transformation** occurs when a bacterial cell dies spilling its contents into its surroundings and these contents are taken up by another cell. **Artificial transformation** can be used in the laboratory to clone or subclone a piece of DNA.
- **Details**: Understand how F plasmid conjugation occurs and how this could be used to map the order of the genes on the *E. coli* chromosome. Understand how antibiotic resistance can be transferred and the severe consequences. Be able to distinguish between generalized and specialized transduction. Understand how natural transformation occurs.

28.5 Prokaryotes acquire energy and carbon by four different mechanisms.

- **Overview**: Prokaryotes either obtain their energy from inorganic CO_2 (**autotrophs**) or obtain at least some carbon from organic molecules (**heterotrophs**). **Photoautotrophs** carry out oxygenic (cyanobacteria) or anoxygenic photosynthesis (purple and green sulfur bacteria). **Chemolithoautotrophs** obtain energy by oxidizing inorganic substances. **Photoheterotrophs** use light as a source of energy and organic molecules as a source of carbon. **Chemoheterotrophs** use organic molecules as both a source of carbon and a source of energy. Some bacteria, such as *Yersinia*, secrete proteins that are injected into other cells, and other bacteria infect plant cells.
- **Details**: Understand the various mechanisms prokaryotes use to obtain energy and carbon. Understand how some bacteria live as pathogens of other organisms.

28.6 Bacteria can spread by different methods in susceptible human populations.

- **Overview**: Human bacterial diseases can be spread by small drops of saliva or mucus in the air, by fetal contamination of food or water, or by insects or rodents. **Tuberculosis** caused by *Mycobacterium tuberculosis* results in an acute infection of the lungs, lymph, and meninges. Tuberculosis in the United States has been on the rise since the mid-1980s. It is easily transmitted through the air from person to person. TB is treated with antibiotics over many months, but due to the amount of time antibiotics have to be taken, there have been several outbreaks of **multidrug-resistant strains** (**MDR**). Teeth are susceptible to **bacterial biofilms** and bacteria in plaque that can cause **dental caries**. Bacteria can also cause **peptic ulcers** and **sexually transmitted diseases**, such as **gonorrhea**, **syphilis**, and **chlamydia**. Bioterrorists have used **anthrax** as a weapon to try to kill people by infecting them unknowingly.
- **Details**: Understand how tuberculosis is spread, the effects of the disease, how it is treated, and why multidrug-resistant strains have occurred. Understand how gonorrhea and chlamydia are caused, the effects of each, and how they are treated. Know the three stages of syphilis, the effect of this infection, and how it can be treated. Understand how bacteria can be used as a bioweapon.

28.7 Prokaryotes have beneficial effects on the atmosphere and the soil.

- **Overview**: Prokaryotes play an essential role in **chemical cycling**. Prokaryotes can act as **decomposers** to release the atoms of a dead organism back into the environment. Prokaryotes are also involved in **carbon fixation**, which contributes to oxygen production, **nitrogen fixation**, and **denitrification**, which is necessary to build and break down amino acids and other biological molecules containing nitrogen. Many bacteria live **symbiotically** with eukaryotic organisms and both organisms benefit (**mutualism**). For example, bacteria live in the digestive tract of animals or humans and produce vitamins or enzymes that allow digestion. Two other symbiotic relationships are **commensalism**, when only the bacterium benefits but the other organism is unharmed, and **parasitism**, when the bacteria benefits at the expense of the organism. Bacteria are beneficial to **genetic engineering** because they can be used to produce pharmaceutical agents. They can also be used for **bioremediation** and for the removal of toxic substances.

- **Details**: Understand the beneficial effects of prokaryotic organisms in recycling, fixation, genetic engineering, and waste treatment. Know the symbiotic relationships between prokaryotes and eukaryotes. Understand why some are more beneficial to one organism than they are to the other.

CHALLENGING YOUR UNDERSTANDING

1. Label each of the structures indicated on the bacterium shown below.

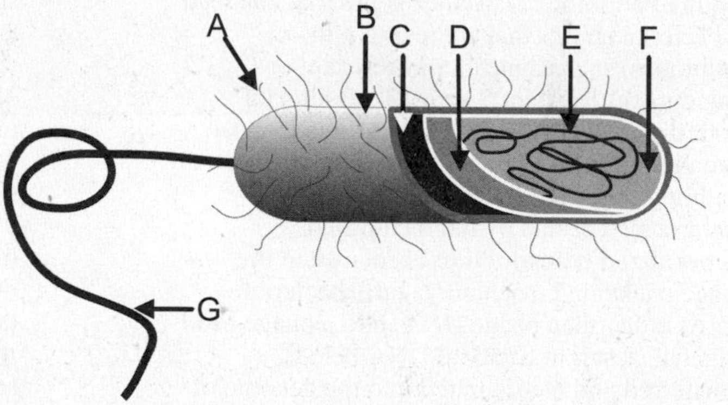

A. _____

B. _____

C. _____

D. _____

E. _____

F. _____

G. _____

2. For each of the following bacteria, describe the main reservoir for the bacteria and, if applicable, the host tissue that this bacteria invades. Then name the human disease caused by each.

	Reservoir/host tissue	Disease caused
A. *Yersinia pestis*	_____	_____
B. *Vibrio cholerae*	_____	_____
C. *Mycobacterium tuberculosis*	_____	_____
D. *Bacillus anthracis*	_____	_____
E. *Salmonella typhi*	_____	_____
F. *Streptococcus pneumonia*	_____	_____
G. *Borrelia burgdorferi*	_____	_____
H. *Neisseria gonorrhoeae*	_____	_____
I. *Mycobacterium leprae*	_____	_____
J. *Corynebacterium diphtheriae*	_____	_____

KEY TERMS

Match the numbered term with the definition that fits it best. Put the corresponding number in front of the appropriate definition.

1. bacillus
2. coccus
3. spirillum
4. endospores
5. nucleoid
6. cell wall
7. peptidoglycan
8. Gram stain
9. gram-positive

10. gram-negative
11. flagella
12. pili
13. autotrophs
14. heterotrophs
15. conjugation
16. transduction
17. transformation
18. dental caries

19. gonorrhea
20. syphilis
21. chlamydia
22. mutualism
23. commensalism
24. parasitism
25. bioremediation
26. F plasmid
27. R plasmid

a. _____ The transfer of DNA from one bacteria to another after cell-to-cell contact.
b. _____ Hairlike structures on the surface of gram-negative bacteria used for adhesion.
c. _____ A conjugative piece of DNA that contains an antibiotic resistance gene.
d. _____ A rigid multilayer network of proteins and polysaccharides that surround and protect bacteria.
e. _____ A group of bacteria that display a shape that is long and helical.
f. _____ Bacteria that don't stain purple in the presence of a special dye since their wall has very little peptidoglycan.
g. _____ Bacteria that acquire some of their carbon from inorganic CO_2 and some from organic molecules.
h. _____ An ecological relationship between species where one benefits while the other does not but is not harmed.
i. _____ Tooth decay that results from bacteria that live in plaque and produce an acid that decays teeth.
j. _____ An ecological relationship between two species in which both species benefit from each other.
k. _____ A group of bacteria that display a shape similar to a rod or bar.
l. _____ Bacteria that acquire all of their carbon from inorganic CO_2.
m. _____ A region of the bacterial cytoplasm where the genomic DNA is found.
n. _____ The use of living organisms to remove pollutants from the environment.
o. _____ A very destructive sexually transmitted disease that causes sores, rashes, and eventually brain/nerve damage.
p. _____ The process by which a bacteria picks up DNA from the environment.
q. _____ A polysaccharide that is unique to bacteria and is a component of bacterial cell walls.
r. _____ A group of bacteria that display a shape similar to a sphere or ovoid.
s. _____ An ecological relationship between two species in which one benefits and the other is harmed.
t. _____ Bacteria that stain purple in the presence of a special dye because their cell walls contain lots of peptidoglycan.
u. _____ The transfer of DNA from one bacteria to another in the absence of cell-to-cell contact but rather through viruses.
v. _____ A sexually transmitted disease caused by a bacteria that requires replicative help from a host (obligate parasite).
w. _____ A small, circular piece of DNA found in *E. coli* that can transfer to other bacteria during conjugation.
x. _____ Bacteria that have produced a thick wall around their cytoplasm to protect them from environmental stresses.
y. _____ A sexually transmitted disease that spreads to the eyes and internal organs if left untreated.
z. _____ A dye that binds to bacterial cell walls that contain lots of peptidoglycan and is used to classify bacteria.
aa. _____ A long, flexible protein tube found on the outer surface of bacteria and used to propel the bacteria through fluid.

LEARNING BY EXPERIENCE

Using information from this chapter, criticize the following statement: If we could eliminate all bacteria from the Earth, it would eliminate many diseases.

EXERCISING YOUR KNOWLEDGE

Briefly answer each of the following questions in the space provided.

1. How does bacterial photosynthesis differ from that of eukaryotes?

2. What makes tetracycline an effective antibiotic for bacterial infections in eukaryotes?

3. Why does a thicker coat of peptidoglycan in gram-positive bacteria result in a purple color when stained?

4. Describe what evidence is used to indicate when life began.

5. Prokaryotes are divided into Archaebacteria and Bacteria. What features distinguish these two groups of organisms?

6. Why is genetic recombination in bacteria not considered equivalent to sexuality in eukaryotes?

7. How do photoautotrophs and photoheterotrophs differ?

8. Explain the importance of type III genes to pathogenic bacteria.

9. Why does dietary sugar result in dental caries?

10. How are chlamydia different from other bacteria in terms of gene replication?

Circle the letter of the one best answer in each of the following questions.

11. Which of the following in NOT a charactcristic of the cell wall of gram-positive bacteria?
    a. Peptidoglycan network is thick around the cell.
    b. Outer membrane contains lipopolysaccharides.
    c. Lipoteichoic and teichoic acid protrude from the cell wall.
    d. resistant to antibiotics
    e. more than one of the above

12. Which of the following statements helps to explain how bacteria can become antibiotic-resistant?
    a. Genes can produce proteins that provide resistance.
    b. Spontaneous mutations can provide variations in gene function.
    c. Antibiotic use will select for bacteria that are resistant.
    d. Bacteria can receive an R plasmid.
    e. All of the above are correct.

13. Cell division in bacteria takes place mainly by
    a. conjugation.
    b. binary fission.
    c. sporulation.
    d. fragmentation.
    e. mitosis.

14. Some bacteria form a thick-walled _____ in response to poor nutrient conditions.
    a. endospore
    b. capsule
    c. sheath
    d. pilus
    e. autospore

15. Gram-negative bacteria do not stain purple as gram-positive do because they have
    a. too much glycoprotein.
    b. a polymer coating.
    c. less peptidoglycan.
    d. an additional polysaccharide.
    e. too much lipoprotein.

16. The genome of bacteria is normally in
    a. a nucleoid region.
    b. an endospore.
    c. a plasmid.
    d. a pilus.
    e. a heterospore.

17. Archaebacteria and bacteria differ in
    a. gene architecture.
    b. cell wall structure.
    c. gene translation machinery.
    d. plasma membrane structure.
    e. all of these.

18. Which of the following belong to the kingdom, Bacteria?
    a. *Halobacterium*
    b. *Methanococcus*
    c. Crenarchaeota
    d. Cyanobacteria
    e. *Thermoproteus*

19. We can expect that one out of every ____ bacteria will have a mutant characteristic.
    a. 100
    b. 200
    c. 500
    d. 1000
    e. 5000

20. Genetic recombination occurs in bacteria through the transfer of
    a. pili.
    b. plasmids.
    c. endospores.
    d. autospores.
    e. gametes.

21. Chemoautotrophic bacteria include
    a. halophiles.
    b. myxobacteria.
    c. spirochetes.
    d. sulfur bacteria.
    e. cyanobacteria.

22. Nitrifying bacteria are an example of
    a. photoautotrophs.
    b. photoheterotrophs.
    c. chemoheterotrophs.
    d. chemoautotrophs.
    e. none of these.

23. Plant diseases such as blights are caused by
    a. enterobacteria.
    b. actinomycetes.
    c. rickettsia.
    d. spirochetes.
    e. pseudomonads.

24. Photosynthetic bacteria that use water as an electron donor are known as
    a. bacteriavertae.
    b. chlorococci.
    c. chloroacteria.
    d. chromobacteria.
    e. cyanobacteria.

25. All of the following bacteria are heterotrophic bacteria except
    a. *Salmonella*.
    b. enterobacteria.
    c. cyanobacteria.
    d. pseudomonads.
    e. spirochetes.

26. In 1997, ____ was the leading cause of death by a single infectious agent worldwide.
    a. TB
    b. smallpox
    c. cholera
    d. diphtheria
    e. plague

27. The first stage of ____ is characterized by a chancre.
    a. gonorrhea
    b. genital herpes
    c. syphilis
    d. chlamydia
    e. HIV

28. The disease caused by ____ is sometimes called the "silent STD."
    a. Herpes simplex type 2
    b. *Chlamydia trachomatis*
    c. *Neisseria gonorrhoeae*
    d. *Treponema pallidum*
    e. *Streptococcus mutans*

29. Pelvic inflammatory disease (PID) in women is caused by
    a. *Leptotrichia bucallis.*
    b. *Treponema pallidum.*
    c. *Chlamydia trachomatis.*
    d. *Bacillus anthracis.*
    e. *Borrelia burgdorferi.*

ASSESSING YOUR KNOWLEDGE

Answers to the questions in this section test your ability to synthesize information gained from the chapter and to solve challenging problems on an exam or in everyday life.

Challenging Your Understanding—Answers

1. A. Pilus; B. Capsule; C. Cell wall; D. Plasma membrane; E. DNA genome; F. Cytoplasm; G. Flagellum
2. A. Rodent fleas, Plague; B. Human digestive tract, Cholera; C. Human lung, lymph system, and brain meninges, Tuberculosis; D. Animals, Anthrax; E. Humans, Typhoid fever; F. Human lungs, Pneumonia; G. Ticks, deer, and rodents, Lyme disease; H. Humans, Gonorrhea; I. Human skin, Leprosy; J. Human respiratory system; Diphtheria

Key Terms—Answers

a. 15, b. 12, c. 27, d. 6, e. 3, f. 10, g. 14, h. 23, i. 18, j. 22, k. 1, l. 13, m. 5, n. 25, o. 20, p. 17, q. 7, r. 2, s. 24, t. 9, u. 16, v. 21, w. 26, x. 4, y. 19, z. 8, aa. 11.

Learning by Experience—Answers

> There are many problems with this statement. We could hardly survive without bacteria. We need their oxygen production and nitrogen fixation. Their role as decomposers is very important, as is their production of methane (natural gas) and sulfur. They are useful in food production and environmental cleanup of oil spills. Bacteria are also useful tools in genetic engineering.

Exercising Your Knowledge—Answers

As you check your answers, put a mark in the review (Rvw.) column for the answers you missed. If you didn't miss any, congratulations—you have mastered the chapter! If you missed some, review the section (Sect.) in the text where this concept is discussed. In order to develop an efficient review strategy, it is important that you understand what types of questions you missed. The questions with asterisks test more for understanding of the **concepts**, whereas the others test more for **detail**. *See the preface for learning strategies for concepts and for detail.*

30. The majority of prokaryotic species get their carbon and energy from where?
    a. photosynthesis
    b. oxidation of inorganic compounds
    c. organic molecules
    d. geothermal vents
    a. chloroplasts

	Sect.	Rvw.
*1. While eukaryotes carry on a form of photosynthesis for which oxygen is always given off, bacteria have several forms of photosynthesis and may give off sulfur, sulfate, or oxygen.	28.2	
*2. Tetracycline binds with bacterial ribosomes, blocking protein synthesis. It does not bind with eukaryotic ribosomes.	28.3	
*3. The thicker peptidoglycan coat of the gram-positive bacteria retains more of the purple dye than does that of the gram-negative bacteria.	28.3	
*4. Microfossils are the only direct evidence of ancient life. Rocks that are 3.5 to 1 billion years old contain microfossils that resemble prokaryotes because they are small, unicellular, and have little internal structure. Isotopic data support the idea that microfossils are the remains of once-living organisms because they contain carbon molecules. Carbon compounds in rocks can be dated and analyzed to indicate when life began. Using this approach, carbon fixation appears to have occurred as much as 3.8 billion years ago. Organic molecules, such as hydrocarbons, can also be used as evidence of ancient life. Analysis of hydrocarbons from rock formations coupled with analysis of the carbon isotope ratios from these rock formations indicate that life may have began earlier than 3.5 billion years ago.	28.1	
*5. Archaea and Bacteria differ in plasma membranes, cell walls, DNA replication, and transcription machinery. Archaean membrane lipids contain ether linkages and the hydrocarbons can be branched, but bacterial membrane lipids contain ester linkages and are unbranched. Bacterial cell walls are composed of peptidoglycan, while archaeal cell walls contain pseudomurein but not peptidoglycan. Initiation of DNA replication and gene expression in Archaea is more similar to eukaryotes than to bacteria. Archaea have more than one RNA polymerase that do not closely resemble the single bacterial RNA polymerase.	28.2	
*6. The exchange of bacterial genetic material is less regular than in eukaryotes and does not involve equal participation by the partners.	28.4	
*7. While both photoautotrophs and photoheterotrophs use sunlight for energy, photoheterotrophs get their carbon from the products of other organisms rather than from carbon dioxide.	28.5	
*8. Type III genes enable the bacteria to bind to or enter host cells.	28.5	
*9. Oral bacteria ferment the sugar into lactic acid, which causes loss of calcium in the teeth and results in the breakdown of enamel.	28.6	

*10. Chlamydia depend upon the host cell for genetic replication.	28.6	
*11. e	28.3	
*12. e	28.4	
13. b	28.2	
14. a	28.3	
*15. c	28.3	
16. a	28.3	
17. e	28.2	
18. d	28.2	
19. b	28.4	
20. b	28.4	
21. d	28.5	
*22. d	28.5	
23. e	28.5	
*24. e	28.5	
25. c	28.5	
26. a	28.6	
*27. c	28.6	
28. b	28.6	
29. c	28.6	
30. c	28.5	

CHAPTER 29 PROTISTS

MASTERING KEY CONCEPTS

The kingdom Protista is by far the most diverse of any eukaryotic kingdom. Eukaryotes that are not animals, plants, or fungi are all lumped together in this kingdom. This represents a taxonomic problem because the phyla within this kingdom are only distantly related, and their evolutionary pathways are uncertain. It is now clear that the origin of eukaryotes likely began with ancestral protists. Compartmentalization distinguishes protists and other eukaryotes from bacteria and archaea.

29.1 The kingdom Protista includes many organisms that are not evolutionarily related.

- **Overview**: The kingdom Protista is paraphyletic and contains many organisms that are not evolutionarily related. Molecular approaches are now being used to determine which protists are related and which are more closely related to the organisms in different kingdoms. As this reorganization takes place, the kingdom Protista and subdivisions within it are not well defined. Recent data suggest that there are 15 major protist phyla organized into **seven monophyletic groups** with shared characteristics. One of these groups is the green algae (**Chlorophyta**), which are now recognized to be in the same clade as land plants. The other six groups include **Diplomonads/Parabasalids, Euglenozoa, Alveolata, Stramenopila, Rhodophyta**, and **Choanoflagellida**.
- **Details**: Understand the problem in defining protists. Know the general characteristics of organisms in the kingdom Protista.

29.2 Eukaryotic cells evolved through infolding of membranes, endosymbiosis, and horizontal gene transfer.

- **Overview**: Microfossils indicate that the first eukaryotes appeared **1.5 billion years ago**. Eukaryotic cells likely evolved from prokaryotes through **membrane infoldings**, **endosymbiosis**, and numerous **horizontal gene transfer events**. The membranes of the nucleus and the endoplasmic reticulum in eukaryotes likely resulted from infoldings of the prokaryotic plasma membrane. Endosymbiotic relationships between prokaryotes and ancestral eukaryotes gave rise to **mitochondria** and **chloroplasts**. The evolution of mitochondria likely involved the engulfing of aerobic bacteria, while chloroplasts arose from the engulfing of photosynthetic bacteria. Centrioles and large, motile cells may also have arisen by endosymbiosis. The fact that mitochondria, chloroplasts, and centrioles contain their own DNA supports the idea that these organelles may have been independent organisms at one time.

Today, these organelles require nuclear genes to direct their replication and division. Mitosis and cytokinesis also may have evolved because some fungi and protists use division processes that seem to be not fully evolved, intermediate mechanisms to mitosis and cytokinesis.
- **Details**: Understand how the internal membrane structure and organelles, such as the mitochondria and chloroplasts, arose. Understand how chloroplasts arose in red and brown algae.

29.3 Protists are highly variable eukaryotes with no unifying characteristics.

- **Overview**: The cell surfaces of protists vary among different organisms from delicate exteriors, such as the plasma membrane alone, to sturdier exteriors, where the ECM is deposited outside of the membrane or forms a cell wall. Protists can move primarily through the use of **flagella, cilia,** or **pseudopods** (lobopodia, filopodia, or axopodia) that allow movement by a rolling motion. Some protists are phototrophs, others are heterotrophs (**phagotrophs** or **osmotrophs**), and still others use a combination of both phototrophic and heterotrophic mechanisms (**mixotrophs**). Most protists reproduce asexually, although some can undergo sexual reproduction. Protists are believed to have given rise to **multicellularity**, which likely arose by single-celled eukaryotes living in close association with each other and assuming different duties.
- **Details**: Understand the different variations of the cell surfaces, mechanisms of motility, nutrition, and reproduction in protists.

29.4 Diplomonads and parabasalids are flagellated protists lacking mitochondria.

- **Overview**: **Diplomonads** and **parabasalids** have early eukaryotic ancestors. Diplomonads are unicellular protists with **two nuclei** and flagella, but are lacking mitochondria. Parabasalids have **undulating membranes** and flagella, but like diplomonads, they lack mitochondria. Some parabasalids live in **symbiotic relationships** with termites and bacteria.
- **Details**: Know the general characteristics of diplomonads and parabasalids.

29.5 Euglenozoa is a diverse group in which some members have chloroplasts.

- **Overview**: Organisms in the **Euglenozoa** group were once categorized as animals. One-third of these organisms have acquired chloroplasts by endosymbiosis and are autotrophic; the rest are heterotrophic. Euglenoids have a flexible pellicle in the plasma membrane that allows the organisms to change their shape. They also have two flagella and a **reservoir** that help the euglenoids to regulate osmotic pressure. Reproduction occurs by mitosis. An example of a euglenoid is *Euglena*. Another major group of Euglenozoa is the **kinetoplastids,** which contain unique individual mitochondria in each cell with **minicircle** and **maxicircle DNA** and **guide RNA-mediated DNA editing**. An example of a kinetoplastid is **trypanosome**. Trypanosomes can cause Leishmaniasis and Chagas' disease in humans. They can be transmitted through skin contact with urine or feces, by blood transfusions, or through insect bites, such as from the tsetse fly. Sequencing of the genomes of three kinetoplastids revealed a common set of core genes that are now being targeted for drug development to prevent these diseases.

- **Details**: Know the characteristics of euglenoids and kinetoplastids. Understand how disease-causing kinetoplastids are transmitted and potential targets for drug development.

29.6 Alveolata are protists with submembrane vesicles.

- **Overview**: All **Alveolata** (**dinoflagellates**, **apicomplexans**, and **ciliates**) have **alveoli**, or flattened, stacked vesicles located below their plasma membranes that are likely involved in membrane transport. Dinoflagellates are photosynthetic, have two flagella, and are unicellular. Dinoflagellates reproduce asexually by a unique form of mitosis, although under stress they can reproduce sexually. The DNA of dinoflagellates, unlike other eukaryotes, is not complexed with histone proteins. Dinoflagellates can produce toxins in the sea that are detrimental to fish, birds, and marine mammals. Apicomplexans contain an **apical complex** that allows these spore-forming parasites to enter their hosts. *Plasmodium* is an apicomplexan that causes malaria. *Plasmodium* undergoes sexual reproduction in mosquitoes to produce **sporozoites** that mosquitoes inject into humans. These sporozoites reproduce asexually in humans releasing **merozoites** into the bloodstream. Merozoites develop into gametocytes that infect other mosquitoes. Ciliates are unicellular, heterotrophic protists with a large number of cilia that contain a **micronucleus** and a **macronucleus** required for sexual and asexual reproduction, respectively. *Paramecium* is an example of a ciliate. *Paramecium*, like other ciliates, undergo conjugation in which two mature cells fuse and exchange micronuclei. These two micronuclei (n) fuse with the old micronuclei (n) to form diploid micronuclei (2n) that divide by mitosis to form two diploid micronuclei. One becomes the micronucleus, the other becomes the macronucleus.

- **Details**: Know the general characteristics of dinoflagellates, apicomplexans, and ciliates. Understand the life cycle of *Plasmodium* and what efforts have been taken to eradicate malaria. Know how the process of conjugation occurs in *Paramecium*. Understand how "killer" strains came about.

29.7 Stramenopila are protists with fine hairs.

- **Overview**: Flagella of the **Stramenopiles** (**brown algae**, **diatoms**, **oomycetes**) have fine hairs on them. Brown algae have life cycles that alternate between multicellular **sporophyte** (diploid) and gametophyte (haploid) stages. Diatoms are photosynthetic, unicellular organisms that produce **chrysolaminarin**. Some diatoms have **raphes** lined with fibrils to allow movement. Oomycetes are water molds that live either as parasites or as **saprobes** and were once categorized as fungi. The zoospores of oomycetes have two characteristic unequal flagella and are produced asexually.

- **Details**: Understand the life cycle of the brown alga. Know the unique characteristics of the members of the stramenopiles.

29.8 Rhodophyta is the red algae.

- **Overview**: **Red algae** greatly vary in size and contain the photosynthetic pigments **phycoerythrin**, **phycocyanin**, and **allophycocyanin** arranged in **phycobilisomes**. These algae lack flagella and centrioles. Chloroplasts indicate that red algae may be related to green algae, but DNA sequence comparisons of the RNA polymerase II gene indicate Rhodophyta emerged before the lineage that gave rise to plants. It is also possible that different host cells engulfed the same bacteria, explaining the similarities in their chloroplasts.

- **Details**: Know the unique characteristics of red algae. Understand the source of controversy over the origins of the red algae.

29.9 Choanoflagellida are the closest relatives of animals.

- **Overview**: **Choanoflagellates** have a **contractile collar** that surrounds a single flagellum. Choanoflagellates use their collars to strain bacteria out of water to feed on. This structure is identical to the structure found in sponges indicating a close relationship between choanoflagellates and sponges.

- **Details**: Know the unique feature of the choanoflagellates and the evidence to support that they are related to sponges.

29.10 Some protists lack a clade.

- **Overview**: **Amoebas** have similar characteristics but may have actually arisen independently more than once. **Rhizopoda** have pseudopods that allow them to move. Members of the phylum **Actinopoda** (**radiolarians**) have glassy exoskeletons. Members of the phylum **Foraminifera** have pore-studded shells (**tests**) that vary in composition and appearance, with **podia** that emerge out of the test openings. **Plasmodial slime molds** move as a mass of slime in a form known as the **feeding phase**, engulfing and digesting bacteria, yeasts, and small organic particles. Mature **sporangium** produce spores when plasmodium stop moving. **Cellular slime molds** act as separate amoebas and can form **slugs** during starvation.

- **Details**: Know the unique characteristics of amoebas, radiolarians, and foraminifera.

CHALLENGING YOUR UNDERSTANDING

1. Match the following characteristics with the corresponding group of protists that have that characteristic.

Characteristics	Organismal groups
_____ a. Apical complex	1. Red algae
_____ b. Two nuclei with flagella	2. Choanoflagellates
_____ c. Guide RNAs edit DNA	3. Euglenoids
_____ d. Phycobilisomes	4. Plasmodial slime molds
_____ e. Micro- and macronucleus	5. Chrysophyta (Diatoms)
_____ f. DNA is NOT complexed with histones.	6. Cellular slime molds
_____ g. Raphes	7. Kinetoplastids
_____ h. Reservoir with two flagella	8. Diplomonads
_____ i. Silica exoskeleton with podia	9. Brown algae
_____ j. Contractile collar	10. Parabasalids
_____ k. Undulating membranes	11. Amoebas
_____ l. Multicellular sporophyte/gametophyte	12. Dinoflagellates
_____ m. Mass slime feeding phase	13. Radiolarians
_____ n. Structures of zoospores	14. Apicomplexans
_____ o. Moving slug formation	15. Ciliates
_____ p. Cytoplasmic streaming	16. Oomycetes

2. Label each of the structures indicated on the ciliate protist shown below.

A. _____

B. _____

C. _____

D. _____

E. _____

F. _____

G. _____

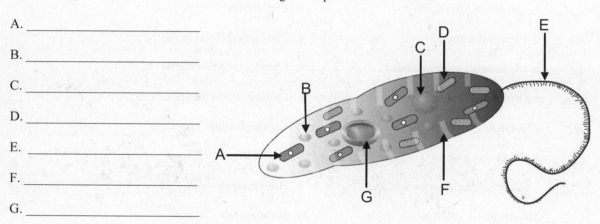

3. Label each of the structures indicated on the euglenoid protist shown below.

A. _____

B. _____

C. _____

D. _____

E. _____

F. _____

G. _____

4. Draw a flowchart that depicts how the malaria-causing parasite *Plasmodium falciparum* cycles through mosquitoes, human liver cells, and human blood cells. Draw a bold arrow that shows the stage that causes the severe symptoms of malaria.

KEY TERMS

Match the numbered term with the definition that fits it best. Put the corresponding number in front of the appropriate definition.

1. endosymbiosis
2. phototrophs
3. phagotrophs
4. osmotrophs
5. ciliate
6. budding
7. schizogony
8. apicomplexes

9. cytoproct
10. stramenopiles
11. brown algae
12. diatom
13. oomycetes
14. rhodophyta
15. plasmodium
16. sporangium

17. saprobes
18. phycobilisomes
19. micronucleus
20. macronucleus
21. raphe
22. pellicle

a. _____ A pore on the surface of ciliates that allows the excretion of waste particles.
b. _____ Phagotrophic protists that ingest soluble forms of food (liquids).
c. _____ Protists including brown algae, diatoms, and oomycetes that have fine hairs on their flagella.
d. _____ Division where the genome is replicated several times so that many individuals are produced at once.
e. _____ Protists that are either parasites or saprobes, live in the water or in plants, and caused the Irish potato famine.
f. _____ Red algae, a protist that uses alternative photosynthetic pigments instead of chlorophyll.
g. _____ Complex, rigid structures in which spores are produced and stored during times of environmental stress.
h. _____ A common protist that spends part of its life cycle as a multicellular seaweed.
i. _____ Organisms that obtain their energy through photosynthetic means.
j. _____ The smaller of two genome-containing organelles found in all ciliates that is sometimes dispensable.
k. _____ Protein strips within the plasma membrane of euglenoids to help it change shape.
l. _____ Photosynthetic structures in red algae that contain alternative photosynthetic pigments.
m. _____ A large, slimy, nonwalled mass of cytoplasm with many nuclei that has the ability to move along surfaces.
n. _____ The process of one cell living inside a host cell and performing beneficial functions for that host cell.
o. _____ Organisms that get their nutrition from ingesting dead organic matter.
p. _____ Spore-forming, parasitic protists that include the malaria-causing protist, *Plasmodium*.
q. _____ The larger of two genome-containing organelles found in all ciliates that is essential for life.
r. _____ Unicellular, heterotrophic protists that have many tiny beating hairs on their surface for specialized functions.
s. _____ A long groove along the length of a diatom that aids in movement.
t. _____ Heterotrophic protists that get their food through ingestion of visible food particles.
u. _____ A unicellular, photosynthetic protist that creates a hard shell made of silica to protect itself.
v. _____ A process of asexual reproduction where the daughter cell is considerably smaller than the parent cell.

LEARNING BY EXPERIENCE

For each of the following Phyla, cite any diseases, environmental effects, or human uses listed in the text that they participate in.

1. Euglenophyta

2. Alveolata

3. Stramenopila

4. Rhodophyta

5. Chlorophyta

6. Choanoflagellida

EXERCISING YOUR KNOWLEDGE

Briefly answer the following questions in the space below.

1. What characteristics of nonsulfur purple bacteria make them likely endosymbiotic sources of mitochondria?

2. Why is the evolutionary path of chloroplasts less clear than that of mitochondria?

3. Why is the kingdom status of protists problematic?

4. (a) Describe two characteristics of choanoflagellates that demonstrates that they are close relatives of animals. (b) Explain why.

5. Amoebas have pseudopodia and forams have podia. Explain the difference.

6. How are the chromosomes of dinoflagellates unique among eukaryotes?

7. Describe the diatom's shell.

8. Explain why the cellular slime molds are an early model for multicellularity.

9. Why are tsetse fly–transmitted trypanosome diseases so hard to control?

10. What distinguishes oomycetes from other protists?

Circle the letter of the one best answer in each of the following questions.

11. Which of the following groups was once considered to be animals?
    a. Choanoflagellates
    b. Diplomonadia
    c. Stramenopila
    d. Euglenozoa
    e. Alveolata

12. Which of the following organisms lacks chloroplasts?
    a. kelp
    b. dinoflagellates
    c. nori
    d. diatoms
    e. none of the above

13. Which of the following is among the earliest free-living eukaryotes to possess mitochondria?
    a. diplomonads
    b. euglenoids
    c. diatoms
    d. parabasalids
    e. oomycetes

14. Which of the following produces a unique carbohydrate called chrysolaminarin?
    a. brown algae
    b. slime molds
    c. apicomplexans
    d. diatoms
    e. red algae

15. Which of the following do NOT have a pellicle that allows the organism to change its shape?
    a. *Plasmodium*
    b. *Euglena*
    c. ciliates
    d. *Paramecium*
    e. none of the above

16. The poisonous "red tides" result from blooms of
    a. diatoms.
    b. dinoflagellates.
    c. red algae.
    d. foraminifera.
    e. euglenoids.

17. The Stramenopila includes the
    a. green algae.
    b. brown algae.
    c. red algae.
    d. extinct algae.
    e. all of these.

18. Which of the following organisms has a unique
    form of mitosis in which the permanently
    condensed chromosomes divide longitudinally
    within a permanent nuclear envelope?
    a. dinoflagellates
    b. apicomplexans
    c. diatoms
    d. ciliates
    e. oomycetes

19. Which of the following organisms were once
    considered to be fungi?
    a. apicomplexans
    b. oomycetes
    c. diatoms
    d. ciliates
    e. brown algae

20. *Paramecium* is a common
    a. ciliate.
    b. euglenoid.
    c. diatom.
    d. chlorophyte.
    e. sporozoan.

21. The White Cliffs of Dover are made up largely
    of
    a. plasmodia.
    b. dinoflagellates.
    c. euglenoids.
    d. diatoms.
    e. foraminifera.

22. Trypanosomiasis, or "sleeping sickness," is
    caused by a member of the
    a. dinoflagellates.
    b. oomycetes.
    c. apicomplexes.
    d. radiolarians.
    e. kinetoplastids.

23. In conjugation of the ciliate *Paramecium*, _____
    are exchanged.
    a. macronuclei
    b. heterocysts
    c. zoogonia
    d. micronuclei
    e. stigmas

24. Malaria results from a mosquito injecting the
    ____of *Plasmodium* into the human bloodstream.
    a. sporocyst
    b. glycoprotein coat
    c. merozoites
    d. gametocytes
    e. sporozoites

25. The great Irish potato famine in the middle
    1800s was caused by
    a. alveolas.
    b. stramenopiles.
    c. streptophytes.
    d. euglenophytes.
    e. slime molds.

26. The pellicle of euglenoids is formed
    a. within the plasma membrane.
    b. around the plasma membrane.
    c. around the central vacuole.
    d. as part of the cell membrane.
    e. as an extension of the stigma.

27. The name kinetoplastids refers to the unique
    a. flagellum.
    b. cytoproct.
    c. contractile vacuole.
    d. stigma.
    e. mitochondria.

28. Which lineage lacks flagella and centrioles?
    a. Alveolata
    b. Stramenopila
    c. Rhodophyta
    d. Choanoflagellates
    e. Parabasalids

29. The function of the micronucleus in *Paramecium* is
    a. sensory.
    b. motility.
    c. metabolism.
    d. sexual.
    e. all of these.

30. Which of the following is NOT a characteristic
    of the plasmodial slime molds?
    a. moves by streaming
    b. unicellular
    c. secrete glassy exoskeletons
    d. multinucleate
    e. form spores

ASSESSING YOUR KNOWLEDGE

Answers to the questions in this section test your ability to synthesize information gained from the chapter and to solve challenging problems on an exam or in everyday life.

Challenging Your Understanding—Answers

1. 14, 8, 7, 1, 15, 12, 5, 3, 13, 2, 10, 9, 4, 16, 6, 11

2. A. Posterior contractile vacuole; B. Food vacuole; C. Micronucleus; D. Macronucleus; E. Anterior contractile vacuole; F. Gullet; G. Cilia

3. A. Chloroplast; B. Paramylon granule; C. Contractile vacuole; D. Mitochondrion; E. Flagellum; F. Pellicle; G. Nucleus

4.

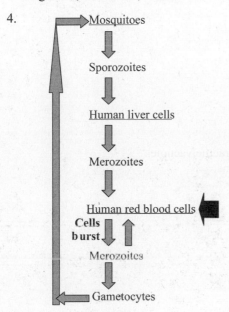

Key Terms—Answers

a. 9, b. 4, c. 10, d. 7, e. 13, f. 14, g. 16, h. 11, i. 2, j. 19, k. 22, l. 18, m. 15, n. 1, o. 17, p. 8, q. 20, r. 5, s. 21, t. 3, u. 12, v. 6.

Learning by Experience—Answers

1. African sleeping sickness East Coast fever Leishmaniasis Chagas' disease
2. luminescence toxic red tide malaria
3. food and shelter for marine organisms beauty potato blight
4. food cosmetics
5. None listed

6. beauty geological markers limestone formation cell differentiation research parasitic decomposition

Exercising Your Knowledge—Answers

As you check your answers, put a mark in the review (Rvw.) column for the answers you missed. If you didn't miss any, congratulations—you have mastered the chapter! If you missed some, review the section (Scct.) in the text where this concept is discussed. In order to develop an efficient review strategy, it is important that you understand what types of questions you missed. The questions with asterisks test more for understanding of the **concepts**, whereas the others test more for **detail**. *See the preface for learning strategies for concepts and for detail.*

	Sect.	Rvw.
*1. Nonsulfur purple bacteria are aerobic, carry out oxidative metabolism, and have membrane folds similar to those of the inner membrane of mitochondria.	29.2	
*2. There are three distinctly different kinds of chloroplasts, but they share the same kind of DNA.	29.2	
*3. Protists are a very diverse group of organisms that are only distantly related and have no evident common evolutionary path.	29.1	
*4. (a,b) Choanoflagellates possess a contractile collar with closely placed filaments surrounding a single flagellum. This exact contractile collar structure is also found in sponges, which are considered to be animals. In addition, choanoflagellates have a receptor tyrosine kinase that is highly homologous to a receptor tyrosine kinase found in sponges. These two similarities support that the two groups of organisms are evolutionarily related.	29.9	
*5. A pseudopodium is extended, and the body flows into it. Forams extend podia that act like tentacles, but the body remains in the test.	29.10	
*6. Chromosomes of dinoflagellates lack histones and do not form nucleosomes.	29.6	
*7. The diatom shell is a double shell of opaline silica. The shells are like small boxes with lids and are highly ornamented.	29.7	
*8. Under normal conditions, individual organisms act as separate amoebas, moving and ingesting food. When food becomes scarce, individuals aggregate to form a moving "slug" by following cAMP pulses. These cells differentiate creating an early model for multicellularity.	29.10	
*9. Trypanosomes contain over a thousand antigen genes but express only one at a time. They rearrange the antigens expressed during the asexual cycle, making their antigen expression unpredictable.	29.5	

*10. Oomycetes are distinguished from other protists by the structure of their zoospores, which have two flagella—one pointing forward and one pointing backward.	29.7	
11. d	29.5	
12. e	29.6-29.8	
13. b	29.5	
14. d	29.7	
15. a	29.6	
16. b	29.6	
17. b	29.7	
18. a	29.6	
19. b	29.7	

20. a	29.6	
21. e	29.10	
22. e	29.5	
*23. d	29.6	
*24. e	29.6	
*25. b	29.7	
26. a	29.5	
27. e	29.5	
28. c	29.8	
*29. d	29.6	
*30. c	29.10	

272

CHAPTER 30 OVERVIEW OF PLANT DIVERSITY

MASTERING KEY CONCEPTS

Considering the diversity of plants in the world, the scope of this chapter is large. It describes the innovation needed first to colonize land and second to dominate the competition. The farther up the ladder of success, the more complex the organism.

30.1 Freshwater green algae gave rise to all land plants.

- **Overview**: Green algae and land plants shared a common ancestor over a billion years ago and are now classified as the **Viridiplantae**. Red and brown algae are not part of this group, but mosses, liverworts, ferns, gymnosperms, and angiosperms are. There are two major clades of green algae, the **chlorophytes**, whose members never lived on land, and the **charaphytes**, including the **streptophyta,** which gave rise to land plants. Land plants have adapted to prevent water loss (**desiccation**) by the secretion of a waxy **cuticle** and the use of **stomata** for gas diffusion, which can be opened or closed to prevent water loss. Land plants can be categorized on the presence or absence of **tracheids,** which are specialized cells used for transporting water and minerals. The evolution of leaves for larger photosynthetic surfaces, and the shift to a dominant diploid generation and strong structural support have allowed larger land plants and trees to evolve.
- **Details**: Know the common characteristics of land plants. Understand what adaptations have been made by plants to allow them to survive on land.

30.2 The plant life cycle is haplodiplontic.

- **Overview**: Plants, unlike humans, have multicellular haploid and diploid stages (**haplodiplontic**) in their life cycles. Gametes are produced in plants by mitotic division of the **gametophyte** (n). Once a zygote is formed, it undergoes mitosis to produce a diploid **sporophyte**. Four haploid spores are produced by meiosis in the **sporangia**. These spores undergo mitosis resulting in a multicellular, haploid gametophyte. In this way, there is an alternation between the diploid generation (sporophyte) and the haploid generation (gametophyte). The size of the gametophyte is limited in most plants, while the sporophyte can become very large. In addition, the proportion of time spent in each generation can differ.
- **Details**: Understand the life cycle of a multicellular plant. Know why the size of the gametophyte generation is limited in all plants.

30.3 Chlorophytes are aquatic green algae.

- **Overview**: *Chlamydomonas* is a primitive from of green algae. It is a unicellular, biflagellated organism that reproduces asexually and sexually. *Chlamydomonas* has given rise to other genera of green algae, such as ***Chlorella***, a nonmotile, unicellular green algae, and ***Volvox***, a motile, colonial green algae, where individual cells specialize for reproduction thereby maintaining individual functions similar to multicellular organisms. *Ulva* is a multicellular chlorophyte that has a haplodiplontic life cycle, although it is not an evolutionary ancestor of land plants.
- **Details**: Understand the life cycles of *Chlamydomonas* and *Ulva*. Understand how *Chlorella* and *Volvox* were derived from *Chlamydomonas*.

30.4 Charophytes are green algae related to land plants.

- **Overview**: **Charophytes** are a clade of streptophytes that includes the **charales** and the **coleochaetales** lineages, both possessing similarities to land plants. Coleochaete have **plasmodesmata**, which are also found in land plants, and Chara are much larger and undergo mitosis and cytokinesis like land plants. Currently it is believed that the Charales is the group that is most closely related to the land plants.
- **Details**: Know the similarities of the charales and the coleochaetales to land plants.

30.5 Bryophytes are nontracheophyte green plants.

- **Overview**: **Bryophytes** are the closest living descendants of the first land plants. They lack **tracheids** but have conducting cells for transport. Many bryophytes have a close symbiotic relationship with fungi (**mycorrhizal associations**). There are three distinct clades of bryophytes: **liverworts**, **hornworts**, and **mosses**. Liverworts are lobed or leafy and resemble mosses. They undergo sexual and asexual reproduction and have a gametophyte that stands upright. Some liverworts have air chambers with a pore at the top in which there are rows of photosynthetic cells. Hornwort sporophytes are embedded in gametophyte tissue, are photosynthetic, and have stomata. Moss gametophytes are leafy structures surrounding an axis that is anchored by a **rhizoid** that can absorb water. Their gametophytes are photosynthetic and haploid. Female and male gametangia can develop on the same or on different plants. The **archegonium** produces a single egg (n), while the **antheridium** produces multiple sperm (n). The egg and sperm fuse to form a diploid zygote that divides mitotically to form a **sporophyte**, whose base is embedded in the **gametophyte** that provides the sporophyte with nutrition. Spores are produced in the **sporangium** and released. Although bryophytes are unspecialized, they can survive in a variety of different environments.

- **Details:** Know the unique features of liverworts, hornworts, and mosses. Understand the structures and the life cycle of a typical moss.

30.6 Tracheophyte plants have vascular transport systems.

- **Overview:** *Cooksonia* is the first known vascular plant, which lived approximately 420 million years ago. This plant stood upright and had sporangia at the tips of its branched stems. Early land plants developed vascular tissues consisting of water-conducting **xylem** and food-conducting **phloem** primarily in their sporophytes. Vascular plants also possess a cuticle and stomata to make them better adapted to live on land. Today, there are three clades of vascular plants: **lycophytes**, **pterophytes**, and **seed plants**. These plants live almost everywhere, except on the highest mountains and on the tundra. Over time, the gametophytes of plants have been reduced in size, and seeds produced by **heterosporous** plants appeared. Fruits form around the seeds to protect them and to attract animals to disperse them. Flowering plants (angiosperms) evolved to attract pollinators.
- **Details:** Know the unique structural features of tracheophyte plants. Know the seven living phyla of vascular plants.

30.7 Lycophytes are the club mosses.

- **Overview:** **Club mosses** are a sister group of the vascular plants. Many have become extinct, but, today, they are still abundant in areas that are tropical or moist. Club mosses resemble the bryophytes, but the two are not related to each other.
- **Details:** Know the characteristics and the evolutionary relationship of the lycophytes to the other vascular plants.

30.8 Pterophytes consist of ferns and their relatives.

- **Overview:** A common ancestor of the pterophytes gave rise to two clades, one consisting of a lineage of **ferns** and **whisk ferns**, and the other consisting of a second line of **ferns** and **horsetail ferns**. Whisk ferns are homosporous, they have green stems that lack leaves and roots, and they form symbiotic relationships with fungi for nutrients. The gametophytes of the whisk ferns are the only ones that develop some vascular tissue. Horsetails are also homosporous and have some relatives that were treelike. Their stems are ribbed and jointed arising from **rhizomes** with

roots. Their stems can be either photosynthetic or nonphotosynthetic, but the leaves are nonphotosynthetic. Ferns are abundant and may be the closest relative of seed plants. Sporophytes and gametophytes are both photosynthetic, but the gametophyte lacks vascular tissue, and the sporophyte is highly differentiated and contains vascular tissue. Ferns have rhizomes and fronds that are exposed as they mature. Ferns have distinctive sporangia arranged in clusters called **sori**. Diploid cells in the sporangia produce haploid spores by meiosis. These spores undergo mitosis to form gametophytes. A sperm (n) or an egg (n) produced from the same or different plants fuse to form a zygote (2n). Like other pterophyta, the sperm of ferns are motile and require water for fertilization. The sporophyte develops out of the gametophyte.

- **Details**: Know the characteristics that distinguish whisk ferns, horsetails, and ferns. Know the structures and the life cycle of a typical fern.

30.9 Seed plants evolved from spore-bearing plants called progymnosperms.

- **Overview**: **Progymnosperms** are the ancestors of **gymnosperms** and **angiosperms**. In these plants, the **seed coat** protects the embryo, allows easy dispersal, and permits an embryo to remain alive but dormant until environmental conditions favor its germination and growth. Seed plants produce male gametophytes (**pollen grains**) and female gametophytes, which produce an egg. Sperm can be moved to the egg by way of a **pollen tube**, or by the wind or a pollinator.
- **Details**: Know the benefits of producing seeds. Understand how fertilization occurs in seed plants.

30.10 Gymnosperms are plants with "naked seeds."

- **Overview**: **Gymnosperms** lack flowers and fruits, but have **cones,** which distinguish them from angiosperms. The **ovule** of gymnosperms becomes a **seed** that rests, at least partially exposed, on a shoot or a leaf. **Conifers**—consisting of pines, firs, spruces, and others—are the largest group of gymnosperms. Pines form pollen-bearing and seed-bearing cones. Pollen dispersed by the wind, produces sperm that is delivered to the egg by pollen tube growth. The zygote develops into an embryo within a seed that is dispersed and can form a tree when the conditions are right. **Cycads** produce cones, have a life cycle that is similar to pines, but look like palm trees. **Gnetophytes** are the only gymnosperms with **vessels** in their xylem, a characteristic common to angiosperms. The three genera of gnetophytes are widely varied in structural appearance and in location. Only one living species of **ginkgophytes** still exists. It is **dioecious** and produces seeds with fleshy outer coverings.

- **Details**: Understand the unique features of gymnosperms. Know the characteristics of the coniferophytes, cycadophytes, gnetophytes, and ginkgophytes. Know the structures and the life cycle of a typical pine.

30.11 Angiosperms are flowering plants.

- **Overview**: **Angiosperms** are distinct from gymnosperms because they have **flowers**, and their ovules are enclosed in an ovary located at the base of the **carpel** that develops into a **fruit**. The extinct plants, *Archaefructus,* may be the oldest known angiosperms, but *Amborella* is the closest living relative. Flowers have **four whorls** from the outside in consisting of **sepals**, **petals**, **stamens** (consisting of **anthers** and **filaments**), and the **gynoecium**, consisting of one or more **carpels**. The carpel consists of the

ovary, a stalk extending upward called the **style**, and a **stigma** at the tip. Most pollination takes place between two different flowering plants as the result of specific pollinators, such as insects or wind, but **self-pollination** can also occur. If the stigma receiving the pollen grain is receptive, **double fertilization** occurs because there are two functional sperm in the pollen tube. One sperm and the egg fuse to form a zygote, and the other sperm and two polar nuclei form a triploid endosperm nucleus that forms an **endosperm** to provide additional nutrients for the embryo.

- **Details**: Know the unique features of the angiosperms. Know the different structures of a flower. Understand the typical life cycle of an angiosperm. Understand why angiosperms have been so successful.

CHALLENGING YOUR UNDERSTANDING

1. Complete the following map to show the phylogenetic relationship of plants to each other.

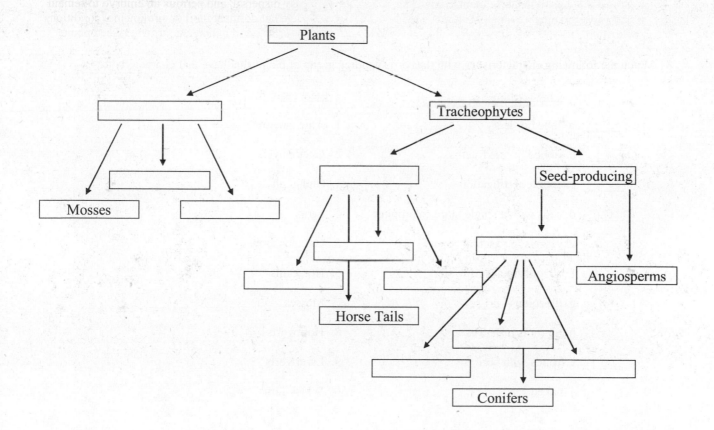

2. Draw a generalized flowchart that shows the life cycle of plants. Show depictions of sporophytes, gametophytes, spores, and gametes and include the ploidy of each stage. Also show where mitosis and meiosis produce spores or gametes.

3. Match the following characteristics with the corresponding group of plants that have that characteristic.

Characteristics	Plant groups
_____ a. lobed or leafy	1. Angiosperms
_____ b. ribbed, jointed stems	2. Gnetophytes
_____ c. double fertilization	3. Ginkgophytes
_____ d. cells with a single large chloroplast	4. Ferns
_____ e. vessels in vascular tissues	5. Gymnosperms
_____ f. rhizoids to absorb water	6. Horsetails
_____ g. dioecious	7. Mosses
_____ h. no roots or leaves	8. Hornworts
_____ i. fronds with sori	9. Liverworts
_____ j. naked seeds	10. Whisk ferns

KEY TERMS

Match the numbered term with the definition that fits it best. Put the corresponding number in front of the appropriate definition.

1. nontracheophytes
2. tracheophytes
3. seeds
4. desiccation
5. cuticle
6. stomata
7. diplontic
8. haplodiplontic
9. sporophyte
10. gametophyte
11. sporangia
12. sporocyte (spore mother cell)
13. spores
14. gametangia
15. bryophytes
16. rhizoids
17. archegonia
18. antheridia

19. homosporous
20. vascular tissues
21. heterosporous
22. ovule
23. nucellus
24. micropyle
25. xylem
26. phloem
27. dioecious
28. pedicel
29. sepals
30. petals
31. stamens
32. androecium
33. anther
34. filament
35. gynoecium
36. carpels

37. ovary
38. gymnosperms
39. angiosperms
40. primordium
41. whorls
42. fruit
43. stigma
44. style
45. integument
46. polar nuclei
47. egg
48. synergids
49. antipodals
50. embryo sac
51. pollen grains
52. pollination
53. double fertilization
54. endosperm tissue

a. _____ Multicellular organisms that constitute the diploid generation in plants and produce spores by meiosis.
b. _____ As the most ancient land plants, they lack tracheid cells limiting their ability to regulate internal water.
c. _____ Plant structure where meiosis produces haploid spores from a diploid sporocyte.
d. _____ Plants that contain structures made of tracheid cells that transport water and nutrients.
e. _____ Plants that produce only one type of spore rather than both micro- and megaspores.
f. _____ Plants in which the male and female reproductive structures are produced on different plants.
g. _____ Part of the female gametangia in seed-producing plants that becomes the actual seed.
h. _____ Plants that do not contain tracheid cells for transporting water and nutrients.
i. _____ Resistant structures developed by some land plants to protect their embryos from drought or harsh conditions.
j. _____ Small openings on the surfaces of plants that can open and close to allow gas exchange.
k. _____ Multicellular organisms that constitute the haploid generation in plants and produce gametes by mitosis.
l. _____ Plant structure where mitosis produces haploid gametes from a haploid gametophyte.
m. _____ Male gametangia found in the gametophytes of seedless plants where sperm are produced by mitosis.
n. _____ Plant structures that efficiently transport water and nutrients throughout the plant.
o. _____ A life cycle, like that of plants, in which both the haploid and diploid generations are multicellular.
p. _____ The tissue of the female ovule in which the embryo sac develops.
q. _____ A type of plant vascular tissue that conducts sucrose and hormone signals throughout the plant.
r. _____ A waxy substance secreted by land plants on their exposed surfaces to prevent water loss.
s. _____ Plants, like the seed-producing plants, that produce both microspores and megaspores.
t. _____ Haploid cells that are produced by meiosis and are the first cells of the plant gametophyte generation.
u. _____ A primitive form of roots found in mosses that attach to substrates and absorb water inefficiently.
v. _____ An opening in the ovule through which the pollen tube grows.
w. _____ A life cycle, like that of humans, in which only the diploid generations are multicellular.
x. _____ Diploid cells of the sporophyte generation that undergo meiosis to produce haploid spores.
y. _____ Female gametangia of seedless plant and gymnosperm gametophytes where eggs are produced by mitosis.
z. _____ A type of vascular tissue that conducts water and minerals upward in a plant.
aa. _____ A problem faced by land plants, the process drying out by losing water to the air through evaporation.
bb. _____ The base of the carpel that houses ovules and later develops into a fruit.
cc. _____ The male portion of a flower where pollen, the male gametophyte, is produced.
dd. _____ A group of seed-bearing plants that do not produce flowers and are more ancient than flowering plants.
ee. _____ Process in angiosperms where one sperm fertilizes an egg and a second fertilizes the two polar nuclei.
ff. _____ Fleshy, nutritious structure that surrounds the seed(s) of flowering plants for the purpose of seed dispersal.
gg. _____ The stalk of the male reproductive structure in flowers that supports the pollen-bearing anther.

hh. ____ A haploid cell produced from the megaspore in the ovule of flowering plants that is nearest the micropyle.

ii. ____ Two haploid nuclei in a flowering plant's female gametophyte that produce the endosperm.

jj. ____ A stalklike structure that connects the stigma and the ovary in flowering plants.

kk. ____ Food supply of some angiosperm seeds that is produced by fertilization of polar nuclei.

ll. ____ A whorl in a flower that contains all the male reproductive structures.

mm. ____ The uppermost part of the female reproductive structure of flowering plants that captures pollen.

nn. ____ The whorl of a flower containing all the female reproductive structures that produce gametophytes.

oo. ____ A bulge at the end of a flowering plant stalk that will develop into a leaf, shoot, or flower.

pp. ____ Cells from the megaspore that have no function and migrate to the end of the ovule opposite the micropyle.

qq. ____ Two haploid cells that form by mitosis during expansion of the megaspore and reside next to the egg.

rr. ____ Green, leaflike structures that form the outermost circle surrounding a flower.

ss. ____ The haploid male gametophyte of seed-bearing plants that is produced from microspores.

tt. ____ The process of transferring pollen to a stigma in angiosperms or to an ovule in gymnosperms.

uu. ____ Female reproductive structures of flowers that produce and house the female gametophytes.

vv. ____ Flower structure that is the female gametophyte and contains the eight nuclei from the megaspore.

ww. ____ A group of seed-producing plants that can produce flowers and fruit.

xx. ____ Rings of leaflike structures or reproductive structures that make up a flower.

yy. ____ The top end of the male reproductive structure that bears pollen for dispersal.

zz. ____ The outermost layer of an ovule in seed-bearing plants that will eventually become the seed coat.

aaa. ____ A ring of usually three or five colored leaflike structures whose purpose is attracting pollinators.

bbb. ____ A bud at the end of a flowering plant stalk that will develop into a flower.

LEARNING BY EXPERIENCE

Briefly describe each structure indicated in the following table.   For the gametophytes, seek out the mature form.

PLANT	SPOROPHYTE	FEMALE GAMETOPHYTE	MALE GAMETOPHYTE
1. MOSS			
2. FERN			
3. PINE			
4. FLOWER			

EXERCISING YOUR KNOWLEDGE

Briefly answer each of the following questions in the space provided.

1. What determines whether a structure is a member of the gametophyte generation?

2. What have been the trends in the evolution of the gametophyte generation?

3. (a) What problem did plants create as they prevented desiccation? (b) How was the problem solved?

4. What are two reasons that it is better to have the sporophyte generation become vascular and grow tall than to have the gametophyte generation do so?

5. Why is the development of vascular tissue important to plants?

6. What is the importance of plants becoming heterosporous?

7. What are three benefits of a hard seed coat?

8. How are pine needles adapted to cold climates where water may be frozen and unavailable?

9. Why are seed-producing ginkgo trees victims of sex discrimination in this country in that they are excluded in landscaping in favor of pollen-producing trees?

10. Describe how carpels are believed to have evolved.

Circle the letter of the one best answer in each of the following questions.

11. Unlike animals, the gametes of plants are produced by
    a. differentiation.
    b. meiosis.
    c. mitosis.
    d. fusion.
    e. binary fission.

12. The first member of the sporophyte generation is
    a. the zygote.
    b. a spore.
    c. an embryo.
    d. a sperm.
    e. a pollen grain.

13. In plant life cycles, which of the following sequences is correct?
    a. sporophyte, mitosis, spores, gametophyte
    b. spores, meiosis, gametophyte, mitosis
    c. gametophyte, meiosis, gametes, zygote
    d. zygote, sporophyte, meiosis, spores
    e. gametes, zygote, mitosis, spores

14. The first member of the gametophyte generation is
    a. an egg.
    b. a spore.
    c. the zygote.
    d. an embryo.
    e. a sperm.

15. Which of the following do not have nutritionally independent gametophytes?
    a. mosses
    b. liverworts
    c. gnetophytes
    d. hornworts
    e. bryophytes

16. The most abundant plants in the Arctic are
    a. mosses.
    b. liverworts.
    c. hornworts.
    d. conifers.
    e. angiosperms.

17. Mosses characteristically have usually colorless projections called
    a. rhizoids.
    b. mycorrhizae.
    c. rhizomes.
    d. roots.
    e. root hairs.

18. Which of the following does not have nutritionally independent sporophytes?
    a. Cycadophyta
    b. Psilophyta
    c. Gnetophyta
    d. Hepaticophyta
    e. Sphenophyta

19. Which of the following is not a tracheophyte plant group?
    a. Gnetophyta
    b. Anthocerotophyta
    c. Psilophyta
    d. Sphenophyta
    e. Cycadophyta

20. Ferns have horizontal stems called
    a. mycorrhizae.
    b. fronds.
    c. rhizomes.
    d. setae.
    e. rhizoids.

21. Seedless vascular plants include
    a. Anthophyta.
    b. Ginkgophyta.
    c. Cycadophyta.
    d. Lycophyta.
    e. Gnetophyta.

22. Female and male pine cones are typically produced where on pine trees?
    a. on different trees
    b. male cones near the bottom, female cones near the top of the same tree
    c. female cones near the bottom; male cones near the top of the same tree
    d. anywhere on the same tree
    e. male cones below ground, female cones above ground

23. Which of the following have motile sperm within a pollen tube?
    a. Coniferophyta
    b. Psilophyta
    c. Anthophyta
    d. Sphenophyta
    e. Cycadophyta

24. Which of the following is part of the gynoecium?
    a. anther
    b. filament
    c. carpel
    d. stamen
    e. sepal

25. The ____ultimately matures into a fruit.
    a. integument
    b. ovary
    c. carpel
    d. archegonium
    e. ovule

26. Which of the following is a part of the androecium?
    a. calyx
    b. petal
    c. corolla
    d. stamen
    e. sepal

27. The seeds of flowering plants are contained in
    a. the style.
    b. the archegonium.
    c. the androecium.
    d. the pollen tube.
    e. the carpel.

28. Ovules are completely enclosed by sporophyte tissue at the time of pollination in the
    a. cycads.
    b. ginkgos.
    c. gnetophytes.
    d. conifers.
    e. angiosperms.

29. Where do the gametophyte generations of angiosperms live?
    a. inside flowers
    b. at the base of plants
    c. at locations separate from the sporophytes
    d. inside pine cones
    e. inside seeds

30. Which of the following takes part in double fertilization and becomes an endosperm?
    a. synergid cells
    b. egg cell
    c. antipodal
    d. primary endosperm nucleus
    e. polar nuclei

ASSESSING YOUR KNOWLEDGE

Answers to the questions in this section test your ability to synthesize information gained from the chapter and to solve challenging problems on an exam or in everyday life.

Challenging Your Understanding—Answers

1.

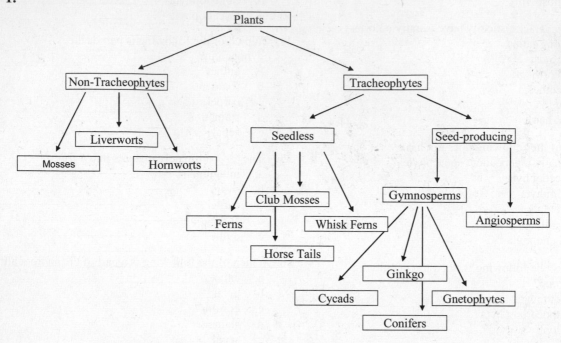

2.

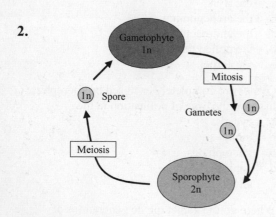

3. 9, 6, 1, 8, 2, 7, 3, 10, 4, 5

Key Terms—Answers

a. 9, b. 15, c. 11, d. 2, e. 19, f. 27, g. 22, h. 1, i. 3, j. 6,
k. 10, l. 14, m. 18, n. 20, o. 8, p. 23, q. 26, r. 5, s. 21,
t. 13, u. 16, v. 24, w. 7, x. 12, y. 17, z. 25, aa. 4,
bb. 37, cc. 31, dd. 38, ee. 53, ff. 42, gg. 34, hh. 47,
ii. 46, jj. 44, kk. 54, ll. 32, mm. 43, nn. 35, oo. 40,
pp. 49, qq. 48, rr. 29, ss. 51, tt. 52, uu. 36, vv. 50,
ww. 39, xx. 41, yy. 33, zz. 45 aaa. 30, bbb. 28.

Learning by Experience—Answers

PLANT	SPOROPHYTE	FEMALE GAMETOPHYTE	MALE GAMETOPHYTE
MOSS	Capsule on top of the gametophyte	Vertical axis with leaflike structures and egg in archegonium	Like the female gametophyte except with antheridia
FERN	Frond with rhizome	Small, thin, fly-sized heart shape with egg in archegonium	Antheridium with sperm on the same plant as the one with archegonia
PINE	Tree	Megaspore with eggs in archegonia	Germinated pollen grain with two sperm
FLOWER	Tree, shrub, or herb	Embryo sac with 8 nuclei in 7 cells	Mature pollen grain with pollen tube and sperm

Exercising Your Knowledge—Answers

As you check your answers, put a mark in the review (Rvw.) column for the answers you missed. If you didn't miss any, congratulations—you have mastered the chapter! If you missed some, review the section (Sect.) in the text where this concept is discussed. In order to develop an efficient review strategy, it is important that you understand what types of questions you missed. The questions with asterisks test more for understanding of the **concepts**, whereas the others test more for **detail**. *See the preface for learning strategies for concepts and for detail.*

	Sect.	Rvw.
*1. If the structure is haploid, it is gametophyte; if diploid, it is sporophyte.	30.1	
*2. The trends have been the reduction in size of the gametophyte and the increase in protection for the embryo.	30.2	
*3. (a) Water vapor and carbon dioxide are both gases. If water vapor can't escape, carbon dioxide for photosynthesis can't enter. (b) The problem was solved by the development of stomata that limit water loss while permitting carbon dioxide to enter.	30.1	
*4. (a) A tall gametophyte makes fertilization by a swimming sperm improbable. (b) Spore dispersal is more efficient from a tall sporophyte.	30.2	
*5. Vascular tissue enables plants to grow taller and compete more successfully for sunlight.	30.6	
*6. Heterospory allows specialization of male and female gametophytes for their different roles.	30.6	
*7. Benefits from a hard seed coat are (a) protection from desiccation, (b) dispersal mechanisms, and (c) dormancy.	30.9	
*8. Pine needles have a thick cuticle and recessed stomata to protect them from cold.	30.10	

	Sect.	Rvw.
*9. The ginkgo seed coat stinks.	30.10	
*10. Leaflike structures with ovules along their margins rolled the edges inward and fused.	30.11	
11. c	30.1	
*12 a	30.2	
*13. d	30.2	
*14. b	30.2	
15. c	30.5	
16. a	30.5	
17. a	30.5	
18. d	30.5	
19. b	30.5	
20. c	30.8	
21. d	30.7	
22. b	30.10	
23. e	30.10	
24. c	30.11	
25. b	30.11	
26. d	30.11	
27. e	30.11	
*28. e	30.11	
*29. a	30.11	
*30. e	30.11	

CHAPTER 31 FUNGI

MASTERING KEY CONCEPTS

For years, botanists studied fungi as unusual plants. It is now evident that they are not plants at all.

31.1 The fungi share several key characteristics.

- **Overview**: **Fungi** are classified into **six main groups**: the **chytridiomycetes**, **zygomycetes**, **glomeromycetes**, **ascomycetes**, **basidiomycetes**, and **deuteromycetes**. Analysis of DNA and protein sequences from fungi indicates that they are more closely related to animals than plants. All fungi share some basic common characteristics—they are **heterotrophs**; multicellular fungi are primarily **filamentous**; their cell walls contain **chitin**; they have a **dikaryon** stage (two nuclei in one cell) in some cells; and they undergo a **nuclear mitosis** where the nuclear envelope does not break down.
- **Details**: Know the six groups of fungi and the basic characteristics that all of these groups share.

31.2 The general biology of the fungi.

- **Overview**: Fungal bodies are composed of **hyphae filaments** that are continuous and contain cytoplasm and multiple nuclei, or are cells that are joined end to end and divided by **septa**. A mass of connected hyphae are called a **mycelium**. Proteins synthesized throughout the hyphae can be rapidly carried to the tips because of the free-flowing cytoplasm, promoting rapid growth. Like plants and some protists, fungal cell walls are composed of chitin, not cellulose. Unlike plant and animal cells, fungal cells or hyphae can contain one or more nuclei (mono-, dikaryotic). If these nuclei are distinctly different, they are **heterokaryotic**; if they are genetically similar, they are **homokaryotic**. Mitosis in fungi is distinctly different from other organisms as well because the spindle apparatus is formed within the nucleus, moving chromosomes to opposite poles of the nucleus (not the cell). Fungi can reproduce sexually when two haploid, compatible hyphae come together and fuse. They can also reproduce asexually. **Spores** can be produced by both reproductive methods and are dispersed by the wind, insects, or small animals. Fungi are heterotrophs that use **external digestion**. They release digestive enzymes into their surroundings and absorb the organic particles produced. Fungi can break down cellulose, lignin, and nematodes. Because fungi can break down such a wide variety of carbon-containing compounds, they may be valuable for **bioremediation**.
- **Details**: Understand the structure of fungi, their cell walls, cellular organization, and processes of mitosis, reproduction, and feeding. Know why fungi may be valuable for bioremediation.

31.3 Fungal phylogenies are rapidly changing.

- **Overview**: Some fungi have not been properly classified yet because of a lack of knowledge regarding characteristics, such as sexual reproduction. Molecular sequencing data now indicate that fungi are most closely related to animals. In the current classification of fungi, the Glomeromycota, Ascomycota, and Basidiomycota are monophyletic, but the Chytridiomycota and the Zygomycota are not. In addition to these, the Deuteromycetes are fungi, but their relationship to the others and to one another is not clear. The Microsporidia are parasites that may also belong to the Fungi kingdom.
- **Details**: Know the monophyletic and nonmonophyletic groups. Understand how the groups are related to each other.

31.4 Chytridiomycetes are aquatic fungi with flagellated zoospores.

- **Overview**: **Chytridiomycetes** are aquatic and have motile **zoospores**. They are the only group with **flagella** and are most closely related to the ancestral fungi.
- **Details**: Know the unique features of the chytrids. Understand the life cycle of *Allomyces*.

31.5 Zygomycetes are fungi that produce zygospores in the zygosporangium.

- **Overview**: **Zygomycetes** include bread molds, such as *Rhizopus*. Zygomycetes have multinucleate hyphae that lack septa except where they form sporangia or gametangia. A distinguishing characteristic is the formation of a diploid zygote nucleus when two haploid nuclei fuse during **karyogamy,** which is a key step in the sexual reproductive cycle. Other than these nuclei, all other nuclei of the zygomycetes are haploid. The diploid zygote nucleus develops into a **zygosporangium** where the **zygospore** will develop within. Haploid spores are released from the germinating zygosporangium after meiosis, followed by mitosis. During asexual reproduction, hyphae produce **sporangiophores** with **sporangia** at the tips that produce **spores**.
- **Details**: Know the unique characteristics of the zygomycetes. Understand the life cycle of *Rhizopus*.

31.6 Glomeromycetes are asexual plant symbionts.

- **Overview**: **Glomeromycetes** form hyphae that grow within plant roots permitting nutrient exchange (**arbuscular mycorrhizae**). They can not survive without this association, but its interaction with the host plant's roots is **mutualistic**. In this group, there is no evidence of sexual reproduction. Hyphae lack septa and zygospores. Sequence analysis of rRNAs indicates that the glomeromycetes are monophyletic.

- **Details**: Know the distinguishing characteristics of glomeromycetes. Understand why these fungi are no longer grouped with zygomycetes, but instead form their own monophyletic clade.

31.7 Ascomycetes are the sac (ascus) fungi.

- **Overview**: **Ascomycetes** include bread yeasts, common molds, *Penicillium* (penicillin-producing) and *Ophiostoma ulmi* (Dutch elm disease). Ascomycetes form a saclike **ascus** within which karyogamy occurs to produce a diploid nucleus. Asci differentiate in a structure know as the **ascocarp**. Meiosis, followed by mitosis, produces eight **ascospores** located inside the asci. Asexual reproduction occurs by **conidiae**, which are cut off from hyphae by **conidiophores**. Some ascomycetes reproduce asexually by fission, or budding. *Saccharomyces cerevisiae* belongs to this group, and is historically the most important yeast in baking, brewing, and wine making. It is also widely utilized as a model organism for genetic research.
- **Details**: Know the unique features of the Ascomycetes. Understand the life cycle of this group. Know the wide range of uses for these fungi.

31.8 Basidiomycetes are the club (basidium) fungi.

- **Overview**: **Basidiomycetes** include mushrooms, toadstools, shelf fungi, and plant pathogens, such as rusts and smuts. They are named for their characteristic sexual reproductive structure, the **basidium**, where karyogamy occurs. Meiosis follows to produce four **basidiospores** located externally at the tips of the basidium. After spore germination, a **primary mycelium** (monokaryon) is formed. Fertilization leads to the production of a **secondary mycelium** (dikaryon).
- **Details**: Know the distinguishing characteristics and the life cycle of the basidiomycetes.

31.9 Deuteromycetes are a polyphyletic group that includes most molds.

- **Overview**: **Deuteromycetes** include *Penicillium*, *Aspergillus*, and *Fusarium*. Deuteromycetes are difficult to classify because sexual reproduction has not been observed in these fungi. However, genetic recombination, or **parasexuality,** where distinct nuclei within a heterokaryotic hyphae exchange portions of chromosomes, has been observed to occur.
- **Details**: Understand why deuteromycetes are difficult to classify. Understand how parasexuality occurs.

31.10 Fungi are ecologically important.

- **Overview**: Fungi, along with bacteria, are the organisms primarily responsible for **decomposition**. Fungi can break down cellulose and lignin, and the bodies of other organisms to release carbon, nitrogen, and phosphorus. Fungi also interact with a wide range of other species in **symbiotic relationships**. **Endophytic** fungi live in the intercellular spaces of plants, in **parasitic** or **commensal** relationships. Lichens are also an example of mutualistic or parasitic symbiotic relationships between fungi and a photosynthetic host, such as cyanobacteria, or green algae. Specialized hyphae penetrate the cell wall of the photosynthetic organism to transfer nutrients into the fungi. Fungi protect the photosynthetic partner from strong light and desiccation. 90% of plant roots are associated with fungi in **mycorrhizal relationships** that are **mutualistic**. Fungi function as an extension of the plant root increasing the surface area for absorption and aiding in mineral transfer from the soil. In return, the plant supplies the fungus with organic carbon. In **arbuscular mycorrhizae**, the fungal hyphae penetrate the cell wall of the roots. The **glomeromycetes** are the fungal component in arbuscular mycorrhizal associations. In **ectomycorrhizae**, the fungi only surround the roots. **Basidiomycetes** and **ascomycetes** participate in these associations with hosts such as pine trees, oaks, willows, and others. Fungi also form symbiotic relationships with animals. Ruminant animals host fungi in their gut, and tripartite symbioses have been identified between fungi, ants, and plants.
- **Details**: Understand why fungi are such an important component in our ecosystem. Understand why they likely played a critical role in allowing plants to colonize land. Know why symbiotic relationships with fungi are beneficial for plants and animals.

31.11 Fungi can be parasitic or pathogenic.

- **Overview**: A major problem in treating fungal pathogens, or parasites, is that they, like plants and animals, are eukaryotes. Drugs have to be targeted at distinct fungal characteristics. Fungal pathogens have devastating effects on plants, and crops, and can also affect the animals that feed on them by producing toxins within them. Human diseases, such as ringworm, athletes' foot, thrush, and yeast infections are also fungal in origin. Mold allergies are also common in humans. Decline in the amphibian population correlates with the presence of a particular chytrid fungi that causes **chytridiomycosis**.

- **Details**: Know the detrimental effects that fungal infestation can have on plants, animals, and humans. Understand the problems associated with treating or preventing fungal parasites or pathogens. Know what observations have been made to link the declining amphibian population with the fungal chytrid *Batrachochytrium dendrobatidis*.

CHALLENGING YOUR UNDERSTANDING

1. Fill in the phylogenetic relationship between the five phyla of fungi. Then indicate which phyla the following five common fungi are part of: mushrooms, toadstools, yeast, common bread mold, morels.

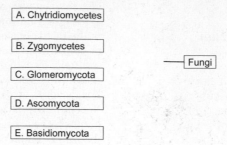

2. Match the following characteristics with the corresponding group of fungi or fungi-containing organisms that have that characteristic.

Characteristics	Fungal groups
_____ a. form arbuscular mycorrhizae	1. Chytridiomycota
_____ b. photosynthetic symbiotic association	2. Zygomycota
_____ c. molds; some produce antibiotics	3. Glomeromycota
_____ d. Sexual reproduction is most common.	4. Ascomycota
_____ e. aquatic, flagellated fungi	5. Basidiomycota
_____ f. most common fungi	6. Deuteromycetes
_____ g. hyphae lack septa; form zygosporangia	7. Lichens

3. Label the following mycelium with these structures: septum, hyphae, nuclei, dikaryotic cell.

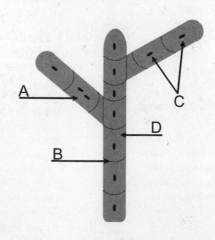

KEY TERMS

Match the numbered term with the definition that fits it best. Put the corresponding number in front of the appropriate definition.

1. mycology
2. hyphae
3. septa
4. mycelium
5. monokaryotic cells
6. dikaryotic cells
7. heterokaryotic cells
8. homokaryotic cells
9. yeast
10. symbioses
11. lichen
12. mycorrhizae
13. zygosporangium
14. sporangiophores
15. basidium
16. basidiospores
17. basidiocarp
18. ascus
19. ascocarps
20. ascospores
21. conidia
22. conidiophores
23. arbuscular mycorrhizae
24. ectomycorrhizae
25. karyogamy
26. endophytic
27. chytridiomycosis

a. ____ Often found in fungal hyphae, these cells contain two haploid nuclei that exist independently of each other.
b. ____ Fungi that live inside of plants in spaces between the plants cells.
c. ____ Ascus-forming fungi that are used in bread making, beer brewing, and wine making.
d. ____ Sexual reproductive structure unique to zygomycetes that is formed from the fusion of two haploid hyphae.
e. ____ Derived from the Greek word *mykes*, it means the study of fungus.
f. ____ An association between fungal hyphae and plant roots where the fungus penetrates into the plant root.
g. ____ Haploid fungal spores that are produced by meiosis in an ascus and protected by a tough wall.
h. ____ An association between a fungus and plant roots where the fungus surrounds the root but does not penetrate it.
i. ____ Specialized hyphae found in ascomycetes that allow conidia to be released from their ends.
j. ____ Spores produced by sexual reproduction in basidium and released externally on the ends of basidium.
k. ____ Long, slender filaments that form the body of fungi and are composed of cells that may contain multiple nuclei.
l. ____ An association between a specific fungus and amphibians where the fungus acts as a parasite.
m. ____ A mutualistic symbiotic relationship between a fungus and the roots of a plant.
n. ____ A saclike structure in which sexual reproduction takes place in ascomycetes fungi.
o. ____ A process in fungal sexual reproduction where two haploid nuclei fuse to form one diploid nucleus.
p. ____ Interactions between two different species that are beneficial for at least one of the individuals.
q. ____ Fungal spores formed asexually by mitosis and released from the ends of special hyphae in ascomycetes.
r. ____ Club-shaped sacs on the underside of familiar mushrooms where karyogamy and meiosis occur.
s. ____ Multinucleate cells that are derived from genetically identical individuals so that all the nuclei are identical.
t. ____ Multinucleate cells that are derived from genetically different individuals so that the nuclei are different.
u. ____ A familiar mushroom composed of dikaryotic hyphae and holding basidia on its underside.
v. ____ A mass of connected hyphae of a fungus that grows into the soil, wood, or other material and begins digesting it.
w. ____ Cells, like those found in plants and animals, that have only one nucleus per cell.
x. ____ Large, visible fungal structure composed of many asci and often resembling one or more cups.
y. ____ An organism composed of a symbiotic relationship between a fungus and a photosynthetic organism.
z. ____ Walls in fungus hyphae that divide the hyphae into separate cells, or segments, connected end to end.
aa. ____ Erect stalks produced by fungi (like bread mold) that support asexual production of spores in sporangium.

LEARNING BY EXPERIENCE
Fungal respiratory and food allergies are among the most common allergies. Make a list of the foods or food substances containing or produced by fungi identified in the text. It would be interesting to read labels in your kitchen and see what foods you couldn't eat or drink if you had such an allergy.

1.

2.

3.

4.

5.

6.

7.

8.

9.

10.

11.

12.

EXERCISING YOUR KNOWLEDGE

Briefly answer the following questions in the space provided.

1. What five characteristics of fungi eliminate them from the plant kingdom?
   a.
   b.
   c.
   d.
   e.

2. How are nutrients transported through septate hyphae?

3. What are two ways in which fungal mitosis differs from that of other organisms?

4. Describe food acquisition by fungi.

5. What unique reproductive feature distinguishes zygomycetes from other phyla of fungi?

6. In what two ways are conidia different from asexual spores of the zygomycetes?

7. What unique character indicates that Chytridiomycota are the closest to the ancestral fungi?

8. The ascomycetes were named for a unique structure. Describe it.

9. Compare the nuclear content of the primary mycelium of basidiomycetes to that of the secondary mycelium and to the basidiocarp.

10. How are yeasts reproductively different from most ascomycetes?

Circle the letter of the one best answer in each of the following questions.

11. Fungi have been incorrectly classified as plants because of their
    a. type of chlorophyll.
    b. immobility.
    c. cell wall composition.
    d. mitotic activity.
    e. gametes.

12. Cell walls of fungi are composed primarily of
    a. lignin.
    b. cellulose.
    c. chitin.
    d. protein.
    e. glycoprotein.

13. Fungi differ from plants in their
    a. cell walls.
    b. sexuality.
    c. food acquisition.
    d. mitotic division.
    e. all of these.

14. Fungi regulate the formation of microtubules during mitosis with
    a. basal bodies.
    b. centromeres.
    c. centrioles.
    d. spindle plaques.
    e. heterochromatin.

15. Mitosis in multicellular fungi usually involves the division of
    a. only the nucleus.
    b. only the cell.
    c. both the cell and the nucleus.
    d. hyphae.
    e. the nuclear envelope.

16. Fungi are capable of breaking down the _____ that strengthens the cell walls of their food source.
    a. cellulose
    b. lignin
    c. starch
    d. chitin
    e. proteins

17. Some endophytic fungi protect their host plants by producing
    a. alkaloids.
    b. celluloids.
    c. ketoids.
    d. saccharides.
    e. histones.

18. Zygomycete hyphae are unique in that they
    a. have perforated septa.
    b. are monokaryotic.
    c. are dikaryotic.
    d. lack septa.
    e. have solid septa.

19. In the zygomycetes, most spores are produced by
    a. somatic meiosis.
    b. mitosis.
    c. syngamy.
    d. zygotic meiosis.
    e. sporic meiosis.

20. Asexual reproduction occurs within sporangia in
    a. yeasts.
    b. basidiomycetes.
    c. ascomycetes.
    d. zygomycetes.
    e. all of these.

21. How do plants usually benefit from arbuscular mycorrhizae?
    a. carbon fixation by the fungus
    b. resistance to harsh conditions
    c. increased water uptake by the plant
    d. production of nitrogen by the fungus
    e. production of phosphorus by the fungus

22. Male gametes of ascomycetes enter the female gametangium by way of a(an)
    a. ascogonium.
    b. antheridium.
    c. trichogyne.
    d. ascopore.
    e. ascocarp.

23. Most yeast reproduction occurs by
    a. budding.
    b. conidia.
    c. syngamy.
    d. ascospores.
    e. basidiospores.

24. The _____ are not basidiomycetes.
    a. toadstools
    b. puffballs
    c. morels
    d. shelf fungi
    e. mushrooms

25. Which of the following fungi does not exhibit any sexual reproduction?
    a. *Saccharomyces* yeast
    b. common bread mold
    c. mushrooms
    d. *Penicillium* mold
    e. chytridiomycetes

26. The cells of the secondary mycelium of basidiomycetes have _____ nuclei.
    a. many
    b. 16
    c. 8
    d. 4
    e. 2

27. The worldwide decline of amphibians correlates with the presence of
    a. a chytrid.
    b. an ascomycete.
    c. a basidiomycete.
    d. a zygomycete.
    e. a yeast.

28. *Aspergillus flavus* produces dangerous substances called
    a. carcinotoxins.
    b. aflatoxins.
    c. cryptotoxins.
    d. ectotoxins.
    e. betatoxins.

29. What fungi, or form of fungi, are able to survive the harshest environmental conditions?
    a. mushrooms
    b. bread molds
    c. mycorrhizae
    d. lichens
    e. yeasts

30. The fungal components of lichens are mostly
    a. basidiomycetes.
    b. imperfect fungi.
    c. ascomycetes.
    d. zygomycetes.
    e. mycorrhizae.

ASSESSING YOUR KNOWLEDGE

Answers to the questions in this section test your ability to synthesize information gained from the chapter and to solve challenging problems on an exam or in everyday life.

Challenging Your Understanding—Answers

1.

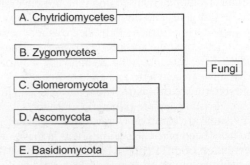

    B. common bread molds; D. yeasts, morels;
    E. mushrooms, toadstools;

2. a. 3, b. 7, c. 6, d. 5, e. 1, f. 4, g. 2.

3. A. dikaryotic cell; B. septum; C. nuclei; D. hyphae.

Key Terms—Answers

a. 6, b. 26, c. 9, d. 13, e. 1, f. 23, g. 20, h. 24, i. 22, j. 16, k. 2, l. 27, m. 12, n. 18, o. 25, p. 10, q. 21, r. 15, s. 8, t. 7, u. 17, v. 4, w. 5, x. 19, y. 11, z. 3, aa. 14.

Learning by Experience—Answers

1. yeasts	
2. morels	
3. truffles	
4. bread	
5. beer	
6. wine	
7. mushrooms	
8. cheese	
9. citric acid (often contained in carbonated beverages)	
10. soy sauce	
11. miso	
12. most fermented substances	
You may think of others.	

Exercising Your Knowledge—Answers

As you check your answers, put a mark in the review (Rvw.) column for the answers you missed. If you didn't miss any, congratulations—you have mastered the chapter! If you missed some, review the section (Sect.) in the text where this concept is discussed. In order to develop an efficient review strategy, it is important that you understand what types of questions you missed. The questions with asterisks test more for understanding of the **concepts**, whereas the others test more for **detail**. *See the preface for learning strategies for concepts and for detail.*

	Sect.	Rvw.
*1. a. heterotrophic, b. filamentous bodies, c. unusual reproduction, d. chitin cell wall, e. nuclear mitosis	31.1	
*2. Cytoplasmic streaming carries nutrients through pores in the septa.	31.2	
*3. a. Mitosis occurs within the nuclear membrane. b. Spindle plaques replace centrioles in function.	31.2	
*4. Fungi are heterotrophs, secreting enzymes into their surroundings and absorbing the digested product.	31.2	
*5. The formation of a zygosporangium around the zygote is a unique feature of zygomycetes.	31.5	
*6. a. Conidia are formed at the ends of hyphae, whereas zygomycete spores are formed in a sporangium. b. Conidia may be multinucleate, whereas zygomycete spores are haploid.	31.7	
*7. The chytrids are aquatic, as were the earliest plants and animals.	31.4	
*8. The ascomycetes are named for their ascus, which is a microscopic, saclike structure, walled off at the end of a hypha.	31.7	
*9. The primary mycelium is monokaryotic. Different primary mycelia may contain different mating strains. The secondary mycelium is dikaryotic and heterokaryotic. The basidiocarp, being formed from the secondary mycelium, is also dikaryotic and heterokaryotic.	31.8	
*10. Most yeast reproduction is by budding.	31.7	
11. b	31.1	
12. c	31.1	
13. e	31.2	
*14. d	31.2	
*15. a	31.2	
16. b	31.2	
17. a	31.10	
*18. d	31.5	
*19. b	31.5	
20. d	31.5	
*21. e	31.6	
*22. c	31.7	
23. a	31.7	
24. c	31.7	
25. d	31.9	
26. e	31.8	
*27. a	31.11	
28. b	31.11	
29. d	31.10	
30. c	31.10	

CHAPTER 32 OVERVIEW OF ANIMAL DIVERSITY

MASTERING KEY CONCEPTS

The scope of this chapter is not as great as that of the next three. However, it is fundamental to your understanding of the following chapters.

32.1 Animals have some general features.
- **Overview**: All animals are **heterotrophs** that must obtain energy and organic molecules by ingesting other plants or animals. Animals are **multicellular** and **lack cell walls**. Animals are active and **mobile** due to the evolution of muscle tissues and nervous systems. Animals vary in size, form, and habitat. Most animals **reproduce sexually** producing haploid gametes by meiosis that can directly fuse with another gamete to form a zygote. All animal embryos undergo a similar **pattern of development**, and cells are organized into **specialized tissues and organs**.
- **Details**: Know the general characteristics of animals.

32.2 The animal body plan evolved as a result of five key transitions.
- **Overview**: There are five identifiable key transitions that are responsible for the evolution of different body forms in animals. These include the evolution of **tissues**, **bilateral symmetry**, a **body cavity**, different **patterns of development**, and **segmentation**. Cell differentiation in animals allowed the evolution of tissues and organs, which are groups of cells and groups of tissues that carry out specialized functions in an organism. Bilateral symmetry evolved from radial symmetry allowing organisms to form anterior, posterior, ventral, and dorsal structures, leading to **cephalization**, and allowing animals with bilateral symmetry to be more mobile. The presence of three germ layers—the **ectoderm**, **endoderm**, and **mesoderm**—and the evolution of a body cavity have allowed the development of specialized organ systems in animals, and the evolution of more complex organisms. In **protostomes**, cell division occurs by **spiral cleavage**, the mouth develops before the anus from the **blastopore**, and development is **determinate** in that the fate of each embryonic cell is determined before cleavage begins. In **deuterostomes**, cell division occurs by **radial cleavage**, the blastopore develops into the anus, and development is **indeterminate** in that any of the early embryonic cells can develop into a complete organism. Segmentation is also an evolutionary advancement with two major advantages, it allows one segment to replace a second segment (**redundant system**) if necessary because all of the segments have the same functions, and it allows more flexibility in locomotion.

- **Details**: Understand how the evolution of tissues and organs, bilateral symmetry, a body cavity, different patterns of development, and segmentation led to advantageous evolutionary advances. Recognize the developmental differences between the protostomes and the deuterostomes.

32.3 The traditional classification of animals distinguishes 36 phyla.
- **Overview**: The kingdom **Animalia** is divided into two branches: the **Parazoa** and the **Eumetazoa**. Animals are classified into the Eumetazoa branch based upon the presence of tissues, organs, and defined symmetry. These organisms are further subdivided by the type of symmetry, and the absence or presence of the three different embryonic germ layers. Animals that have an ectoderm and endoderm but lack mesoderm are **diblastic**, while animals with all three germ layers are **triblastic**. Further divisions are based on characteristics that seem to have been particularly important in the evolution of different phyla, such as whether the organisms are protostomes or deuterostomes. The 36 phyla have been distinguished by comparing similar features and developmental patterns.
- **Details**: Understand how animals are classified. Know the major groups that animals are divided into.

32.4 Some organisms give a new look to the metazoan way of life.
- **Overview**: There are some organisms, such as the **myzostomids**, which are difficult to classify based on their characteristics. These organisms are parasites of the echinoderms, and have no body cavity and incomplete segmentation. They have traditionally been classified as annelids. Molecular evidence from sequencing DNA encoding key proteins of the myzostomids now indicates that they may not be related to annelids at all, and are actually most similar to flatworms. This evidence questions the validity of classifying organisms based on key morphological characters. **Molecular systematics,** in which unique sequences in certain genes are compared in order to group related organisms, is a revolutionary advance in classifying organisms that may greatly affect earlier classification schemes derived from comparing similar morphological traits.
- **Details**: Understand why DNA sequencing data are leading to advancements in our understanding of how animals are related, and a restructuring of some of the traditional phylogenetic classifications that were assigned.

32.5 The animal tree of life is rooted in evolutionary developmental biology.

- **Overview**: Most taxonomists accept that parazoans and eumetazoans have a common ancestor that was likely a colonial flagellated protist. Fossils indicate that there was a rapid increase in animal diversity during the Cambrian period, known as the **Cambrian explosion**, with no significant changes in body plans since that time. These changes seem to be attributable to changes in the timing and location of *Hox* gene expression.

- **Details**: Know the three hypotheses for the origin of metazoans from protists. Understand why the colonial flagellate hypothesis is the most likely. Understand the possible explanations for the increase in animal diversity during the Cambrian period.

CHALLENGING YOUR UNDERSTANDING

Fill in the following flowchart to indicate the major features, body plan transitions, types of symmetry, body cavities, and developmental patterns in animals.

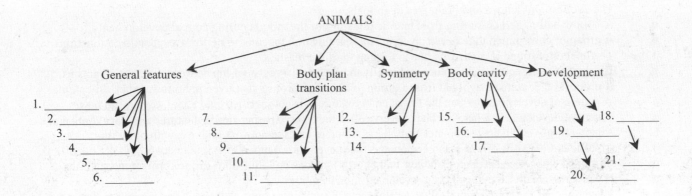

KEY TERMS

Match the numbered term with the definition that fits it best. Put the corresponding number in front of the appropriate definition.

1. Parazoa
2. Eumetazoa
3. vertebrates
4. invertebrates
5. ectoderm
6. mesoderm
7. endoderm
8. cephalization
9. acoelomates
10. pseudoelomates
11. pseudocoel
12. coelomates

13. circulatory system
14. open circulatory system
15. closed circulatory system
16. morula
17. blastula
18. gastrula
19. blastopore
20. archenteron
21. protostomes
22. deuterostomes
23. cleavage
24. spiral cleavage

25. radial cleavage
26. determinate development
27. indeterminate development
28. segmentation
29. molecular systematics
30. multinucleate hypothesis
31. colonial flagellate hypothesis
32. polyphyletic hypothesis
33. Cambrian explosion
34. tissue
35. coelom

a. ____ A network of vessels found only in coelomates that brings nutrients to organs and removes waste from them.
b. ____ A proposal that animals evolved from an ancestral protist with many nuclei in one cell.
c. ____ The evolution of a head and brain area in animals.
d. ____ A hollow ball of cells resulting from mitotic divisions of the morula during animal development.
e. ____ A group of cells joined together in an organism that function together to perform a specialized function.
f. ____ The opening formed in a gastrula due to folding in of the blastula.
g. ____ The use of DNA sequence differences to identify the evolutionary relationship between different organisms.
h. ____ A proposal that animals evolved from a group of ancestral protists that lived in hollow, spherical colonies.
i. ____ A pattern of development where the fate of embryonic cells is not specified until after cleavage has begun.
j. ____ Pattern of development where the fate of every cell in the embryo is specified in the egg before cleavage begins.
k. ____ A network of vessels in coelomates that allows blood to exit the network and mix with body fluids.
l. ____ An efficient network of vessels in coelomates that never allows blood to exit the network.
m. ____ An animal embryo consisting of a hollow ball of cells with one end folded inward to form an internal sac.
n. ____ The progressive division of cells in a developing animal embryo.
o. ____ A layer of cells in animal embryos that develops into the outer coverings of the body and nervous system.
p. ____ A layer of cells in animal embryos that develops into the digestive organs and intestines.
q. ____ A layer of cells in animal embryos that develops into the skeleton and muscles.
r. ____ Bilaterally symmetrical animals in which the blastopore of the developing embryo becomes the mouth.
s. ____ Bilaterally symmetrical animals in which the blastopore of the developing embryo becomes the anus.
t. ____ An event where most of the animals evolved in a geologically short period of time.
u. ____ Multicellular animals like sponges that lack symmetry, tissues, and organs but do display cell specialization.
v. ____ True multicellular animals that have symmetry, tissues, organs, and organ systems.
w. ____ Pattern of cell division in developing embryos where the newly formed cells are directly above each other.
x. ____ A pattern of cell division in embryos where newly formed cells are rotated with respect to the other cells.
y. ____ Animals that have no open body cavity.
z. ____ Animals that have a body cavity contained entirely within their mesoderm.
aa. ____ Animals that have a body cavity between their endoderm and mesoderm layers.
bb. ____ A proposal that sponges and eumetazoans evolved independently.
cc. ____ Animals that do not have a backbone.
dd. ____ The division of the developing animal body into repeating units.
ee. ____ A body cavity located between the endoderm and the mesoderm.
ff. ____ A fluid-filled body cavity located entirely within the mesoderm.
gg. ____ The primitive gut cavity formed inside of the gastrula by inward folding of a developing animal embryo.
hh. ____ Animals that have a backbone.
ii. ____ A solid ball of cells that results from mitotic divisions of zygote during animal development.

LEARNING BY EXPERIENCE

For the organisms listed across the top of the table, indicate whether each has the characteristics listed in the left-hand column, using table 32.2 and figure 32.5 as a guide. An "X" indicates possession of the derived character state, and a "0" indicates possession of the ancestral character state. (Note: Body cavity means possessing a pseudocoel or coelom, but a "true coelom" distinguishes between having a pseudocoel or a coelom.) Use this information to construct a cladogram for the seven organisms listed. Indicate the derived characters between the cladogram branch points that are shared by all of the organisms above the branch, but not present in any of the organisms below it. Hint: Two of the organisms will have to be listed on the same branch of the cladogram.

	Rotifers	Flatworms	Ctenophore	Nemertea	Sponges	Cnidarians	Choano-flagellates
Bilateral symmetry							
Body cavity							
Multi-cellular							
True tissues							
True coelom							

CLADOGRAM:

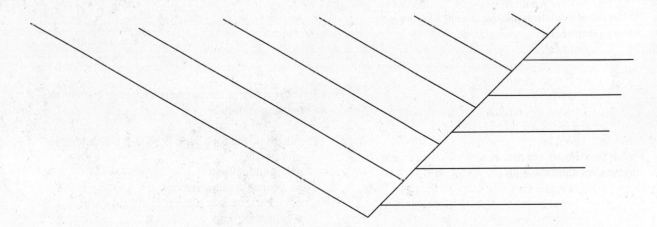

EXERCISING YOUR KNOWLEDGE

Briefly answer each of the following questions in the space provided.

1. What are the advantages of a closed circulatory system compared to an open one?

2. Some biologists describe animals as a tube within a tube. Explain why this makes sense?

3. To what development in body plan, largely related to the nervous system, did bilateral symmetry lead?

4. What other evolution did the advent of a body cavity permit?

5. What two tissues are associated with movement that makes animals unique?

6. What distinguishes Eumetazoa from Parazoa?

7. Why is there almost no alternation of haploid and diploid generations in animals as there is in plants?

8. Explain three hypotheses that have been proposed to explain how metazoans originated from protists and indicate which one appears to be most correct.

9. What developing field of study challenges traditional phylogenetics?

10. Describe how embryonic segmentation was beneficial for early animals.

Circle the letter of the one best answer in each of the following questions.

11. Which of the following is NOT a characteristic of animals?
    a. multicellular
    b. capable of movement
    c. characteristic pattern of development
    d. heterotrophs
    e. unique tissues

12. Which of the following represents major differences between animal cells and plant cells?
    a. types of symmetry
    b. types of nuclei
    c. presence of cell walls
    d. presence of chloroplasts
    e. Both c and d are correct.

13. What is the correct order of a developing animal embryo from earliest to latest?
    a. zygote, morula, blastula, gastrula
    b. zygote, blastula, morula, gastrula
    c. morula, zygote, gastrula, blastula
    d. zygote, gastrula, blastula, morula
    e. zygote, blastula, gastrula, morula

14. In deuterostomes, the blastopore becomes the
    a. mouth.
    b. nose.
    c. anus.
    d. respiratory system.
    e. brain.

15. Bilateral symmetrical animals can only be bisected in the _____ plane.
    a. anterior
    b. ventral
    c. sagittal
    d. dorsal
    e. posterior

16. Which of the following is characteristic of coelomic cavities?
    a. endoderm inside and mesoderm outside
    b. mesoderm inside and endoderm outside
    c. endoderm inside and endoderm outside
    d. endoderm inside and ectoderm outside
    e. mesoderm inside and mesoderm outside

17. Humans have what type of circulatory system?
    a. segmented
    b. beating
    c. open
    d. closed
    e. redundant

18. Which group of animals all display indeterminate development?
    a. parazoa
    b. acoelomates
    c. deuterostomes
    d. protostomes
    e. worms

19. Which group of animals all display radial cleavage?
    a. bilaterally symmetrical animals
    b. radially symmetrical animals
    c. pseudocoelomates
    d. protostomes
    e. deuterostomes

20. What is the most likely result if one cell were removed from a blastula of a developing protostome?
    a. Development would cease/embryo dies.
    b. Abnormal animal would develop.
    c. Normal animal would develop.
    d. Animal would be missing a body part.
    e. Animal would have extra body parts.

21. What is the most likely result if one cell were removed from a blastula of a developing deuterostome?
    a. Development would cease/embryo dies.
    b. Abnormal animal would develop.
    c. Normal animal would develop.
    d. Animal would be missing a body part.
    e. Animal would have extra body parts.

22. In embryonic development of bilaterally symmetrical animals, the hollow ball is referred to as the
    a. gastrula.
    b. blastula.
    c. morula.
    d. protostoma.
    e. spherula.

23. Spiral cleavage is characteristic of
    a. archestomes.
    b. deuterostomes.
    c. endostomes.
    d. protostomes.
    e. coelostomes.

24. How many layers of germ tissue do radially symmetrical animals have?
    a. 0
    b. 1
    c. 2
    d. 3
    e. 4

25. If you discovered a new sponge in the ocean that had three tissue layers and radial symmetry, how should you classify this organism?
    a. Parazoa
    b. Eumetazoa
    c. Chordata
    d. Bilateria
    e. Spirallia

26. Radially symmetrical animals can be bisected in
    a. only the sagittal plane.
    b. any two-dimensional plane.
    c. only the dorsal plane.
    d. only dorsal and anterior planes.
    e. only the ventral plane.

27. What information helped scientists realize that annelids and arthropods are less closely related than predicted by their segmentation?
    a. DNA sequence analysis
    b. molting pattern
    c. number of segments
    d. embryonic cleavage pattern
    e. Both a and b are correct.

28. Which phylum of animals consists of the greatest number of different species?
    a. Chordata
    b. Platyhelminthes
    c. Arthropoda
    d. Nematoda
    e. Annelida

29. Great diversification of animals occurred during the _____ explosion.
    a. Cambrian
    b. Devonian
    c. Silurian
    d. Permian
    e. Precambrian

30. Which of the following is a possible explanation for the fast animal diversification mentioned in question 29?
    a. extinction of the dinosaurs
    b. formation of the *Hox* gene
    c. formation of genes
    d. increased radiation from the Sun
    e. a large meteorite hit the Earth

ASSESSING YOUR KNOWLEDGE

Answers to the questions in this section test your ability to synthesize information gained from the chapter and to solve challenging problems on an exam or in everyday life.

Challenging Your Understanding—Answers

1-6. multicellular, heterotrophic, no cell wall, mobile, sexual reproduction (haploid gametes), embryonic development

7-11. tissues, bilateral symmetry, body cavity, developmental patterns, segmentation

12-14. none, radial, bilateral

15-17. none, pseudocoel, coelom

18. protostome; 21. determinate

19. deuterostome; 20. indeterminate

Key Terms—Answers

a. 13, b. 30, c. 8, d. 17, e. 34, f. 19, g. 29, h. 31, i. 27, j. 26, k. 14, l. 15, m. 18, n. 23, o. 5, p. 7, q. 6, r. 21, s. 22, t. 33, u. 1, v. 2, w. 25, x. 24, y. 9, z. 12, aa. 10, bb. 32, cc. 4, dd. 28, ee. 11, ff. 35, gg. 20, hh. 3, ii. 16.

Learning by Experience—Answers

	Rotifers	Flatworms	Ctenophore	Nemertea	Sponges	Cnidarians	Choano-flagellates
Bilateral symmetry	X	X	O	X	O	O	O
Body cavity	X	O	O	X	O	O	O
Multi-cellular	X	X	X	X	X	X	O
True tissues	X	X	X	X	O	X	O
True coelom	O	O	O	X	O	O	O

CLADOGRAM:

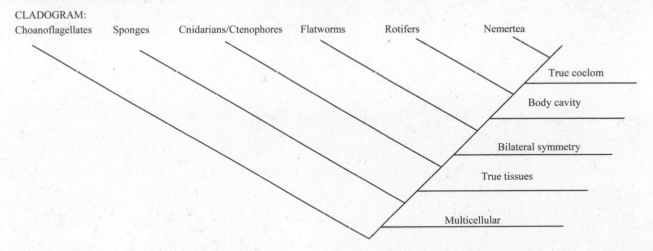

299

Exercising Your Knowledge—Answers

As you check your answers, put a mark in the review (Rvw.) column for the answers you missed. If you didn't miss any, congratulations—you have mastered the chapter! If you missed some, review the section (Sect.) in the text where this concept is discussed. In order to develop an efficient review strategy, it is important that you understand what types of questions you missed. The questions with asterisks test more for understanding of the **concepts**, whereas the others test more for **detail**. *See the preface for learning strategies for concepts and for detail.*

	Sect.	Rvw.
*1. In a closed circulatory system, blood carrying nutrients can move more quickly and efficiently because it is pressurized and does not rely on re-entry. Furthermore, circulation of blood and other body fluids can be controlled independently in a closed circulatory system.	32.2	
*2. Early animals, like worms, were tube shaped. Furthermore, all animals have some sort of gut where food is brought to be digested. This gut is like a tube through the middle of the body tube.	32.2	
*3. The development of bilateral symmetry led to cephalization.	32.2	
*4. The body cavity permitted the evolution of a more complex and efficient internal organ system.	32.2	
*5. Both muscles and nerves are associated with movement.	32.1	
*6. Eumetazoans display symmetry and have true tissues with highly specialized cells and organs.	32.3	
*7. Haploid animal cells fuse to form a zygote without first dividing by mitosis to create multicellular haploid organisms.	32.1	

	Sect.	Rvw.
*8. Multinucleate hypothesis: an ancient protist became multinuclear and at some point each nucleus became compartmentalized to form a multicellular animal. Colonial flagellate hypothesis: an ancient colony of protists formed a colony in the shape of a hollow sphere, which fused together to became a multicellular animal. Polyphyletic origin hypothesis: two different ancient protists gave rise to sponges and eumetazoans independently. The colonial flagellate hypothesis is most correct.	32.5	
*9. The comparison of DNA sequences through molecular systematics now challenges traditional phylogenetics.	32.4	
*10. Segmentation allowed redundancy and promoted movement. Redundancy: individual segments could regenerate whole bodies in the event of injury. Movement: segmentation allowed flexibility since each segment could bend or move independently of its neighboring segment.	32.2	
*11. b	32.1	
*12. e	32.1	
*13. a	32.1	
14. c	32.2	
15. c	32.2	
16. e	32.2	
17. d	32.2	
18. c	32.2	
19. e	32.2	
*20. a	32.2	
*21. c	32.2	
22. b	32.2	
23. d	32.2	
24. c	32.2	
*25. b	31.3	
26. b	32.2	
*27. e	32.4	
28. c	32.4	
29. a	32.5	
*30. b	32.5	

CHAPTER 33 NONCOELOMATE INVERTEBRATES

MASTERING KEY CONCEPTS

The scope of this chapter is considerable. How you approach it is important. The tips that follow should help you master it.

33.1 A revolution in invertebrate phylogeny

- **Overview**: There are significant disagreements about how animal phyla are related to each other. Molecular evidence is now emerging that can be combined with morphological data that we hope will clear up some of these disagreements. One change that these emerging data have led to is a reorganization of the protostome branch of animals. The major morphological characters that led to the traditional construction of the protostome phylogeny was the type of body cavity that an organism possesses, and whether its body is segmented. Sequencing data from rRNAs and other genes suggest that the protostomes should be separated into **spirilians** (nonmolting) and **ecdysozoans** (molting) because the other traits may be a result of convergent evolution. Spirilians are subdivided into the **Lophotrochozoans** and the **Platyzoa**. One major difference in this classification is the separation of the annelids and the arthropods that were once thought to be closely related because of their segmented body plans. Here, arthropods are grouped with other molting animals.
- **Details**: Understand the differences between the traditional classification of the protostomes, and the new classification. Recognize why this change is now being made.

33.2 Parazoans are animals that lack specialized tissues.

- **Overview**: **Parazoans**, such as **sponges (phylum Porifera)**, do not have tissues or organs, and, in addition, lack symmetry. They are, however, multicellular, and their cells are specialized to carry out different functions. Unlike other animals, sponge cells can differentiate, and then redifferentiate into other cell types. Sponges have a simple body structure, consisting of an outer epithelial layer, a protein-rich matrix of **mesohyl**, and internally flagellated cells called **choanocytes** that line the internal cavity. These choanocytes move water that enters by way of pores, through the sponge, allowing it to feed on the materials that it filters out. The water is then forced out through the **osculum**. Sponges reproduce asexually by the formation of new individuals from fragments when a sponge is broken apart, and sexually by the production of eggs and sperm.

- **Details**: Know the characteristics that distinguish the Parazoa. Know the body structure of the sponge, and how it feeds and reproduces. Understand why sponges are successful organisms.

33.3 Eumetazoans are animals with true tissues.

- **Overview**: **Eumetazoans** evolved ectoderm and endoderm that could give rise to true body tissues, and body symmetry. The phylum **Cnidaria**, including the **jellyfish** and sea anemones, and the phylum **Ctenophora**, containing the **comb jellies**, are the only two radially symmetrical eumetazoans left in existence. Cnidarians have distinct tissues, but no organs. They exist in two body forms: **polyps**, which are nonmotile, have a body opening opposite the point of attachment, and undergo both asexual and sexual reproduction, and **medusae**, which are motile, have tentacles surrounding their mouths, and reproduce sexually. Digestion in cnidarians, unlike sponges, occurs in the **internal gut cavity**, rather than in individual cells. Cnidarians have characteristic **cnidocytes** and specialized **nematocysts** on their tentacles and bodies to spear prey. No other group of organisms possesses these structures. There are four classes of cnidarians: **Hydrozoa**, **Scyphozoa**, **Cubozoa**, and **Anthozoa**. Members of the class Hydrozoa, including the genus *Hydra*, Portuguese man of war, and the genus *Obelia*, are primarily marine and colonial, reproduce asexually and sexually, and can be bioluminescent. Members of the class Scyphozoa, which the jellyfish belongs to, are transparent or translucent, and the medusa stage is dominant. Jellyfish are either male or female and undergo sexual reproduction, but polyps can still reproduce asexually. Members of the class Cubozoa are the box jellyfish characterized by a box-shaped medusae. The sea anemones and corals belong to the class Anthozoa, the largest of the cnidarian classes. **Planulae** (ciliated larvae) develop into polyps, and medusae are not formed by this class. Corals have an outer exoskeleton or needles made of calcium carbonate. The phylum Ctenophora includes comb jellies that are transparent, have retractable tentacles, and possess a specialized **colloblast** cell for catching prey. They have cilia for locomotion and true muscle cells derived from mesoderm tissue.
- **Details**: Know the unique characteristics of the cnidarians and ctenophores. Understand the

major evolutionary innovations of these groups relative to the sponges. Know the classes of cnidarians and the unique features of each. Understand the life cycle of the members in the genus *Obelia*.

33.4 The bilaterian acoelomates.

- **Overview**: The evolution of bilateral symmetry distinguishes **bilaterians** from cnidarians and ctenophores. The simplest are acoelomates, such as flatworms. **Flatworms** belong to the phylum **Platehelminthes**, the largest phylum of the bilaterian acoelomates. Flatworms have a defined head and a digestive cavity, but an incomplete gut with only one opening, so they cannot feed continuously. Flatworms lack a circulatory system, but do possess an excretory and osmoregulatory system, and a nervous system consisting of an anterior cerebral ganglion, a nerve cord, and two eyespots. Most flatworms are hermaphrodites and have an extreme capacity to **regenerate** if parts of their body are separated or lost. Flatworms are grouped according to whether they are free-living or parasitic. The class **Turbellaria** contains the free-living flatworms, such as the common **planaria**. Parasitic flatworms belong to the classes **Monogenea** and **Trematoda** (**fluke classes**), and **Cestoda** (**tapeworms**). Flukes lack cilia, eyespots, and sensory organs, but have mouths to eat, and epithelial layers that allow them to live within their hosts. Like flukes, many tapeworms are parasitic, but they absorb food through their epithelium and attach to their hosts by specialized attachment organs. Tapeworm bodies have a **scolex**, neck, and repetitive **proglottids** each of which is a complete hermaphroditic unit. **Ribbon worms**, belonging to the phylum **Nemertea**, are acoelomates, but are not closely related to the other acoelomates. Ribbon worms have **rhynchocoels**, fluid-filled sacs, to power their proboscis, a structure used to capture prey. They also have a **complete digestive system** with a mouth and an anus, and closed circulatory system. These features have led to the reclassification of the nemerteans in the Lophotrochozoa. **Cycliophora** make up an entirely new phylum of acoelomates with a unique form of sexual reproduction discovered by **Funch and Kristensen** in 1995.
- **Details**: Understand the body structure of the flatworm. Know what features make it more evolutionarily advanced than cnidarians or ctenophores. Know the four classes of flatworms and what distinguishes each group. Understand the life cycle of the oriental liver fluke. Know the body structure of the tapeworm. Understand why this is a frequent human parasite. Know what the basis was for reclassification of nemerteans. Know the unique features of the cycliophorans.

33.5 The pseudocoelomates

- **Overview**: Members of the phyla **Nematoda** and **Rotifera** are bilaterians that possess a **pseudocoel**, a cavity located between the mesoderm and endoderm. Members of the phylum Nematoda, consisting of vinegar eels, eelworms, and other roundworms, are bilaterally symmetrical and unsegmented, and possess a hydrostatic skeleton, and a thick cuticle. While nematodes lack respiratory organs, they have an advanced digestive system with a mouth, pharynx, intestine, and anus. Males and females are typically separate organisms that undergo sexual reproduction. Nematodes cause human diseases, such as **trichinosis**, **filariasis**, **intestinal roundworm**, and **pinworm infections**. Members of the phylum Rotifera are not related to the nematodes. They are a separate group of pseudocoelomates that are unsegmented and bilaterally symmetrical. Rotifers have a hydroskeleton, a complete gut, cilia, and well-developed organs, such as the **corona**, which is used for food gathering and locomotion.
- **Details**: Know the body structures and the unique characteristics of the nematodes and the rotifers. Understand what evolutionary advancements are present in these groups of organisms.

CHALLENGING YOUR UNDERSTANDING

Fill in the missing phyla or classes in the following flowchart to show how the groups of organisms discussed in the chapter relate to each other. (HINT: Some of the blanks have been filled in to give you a clue as to whether the other blanks should be filled in with a phylum or a class.)

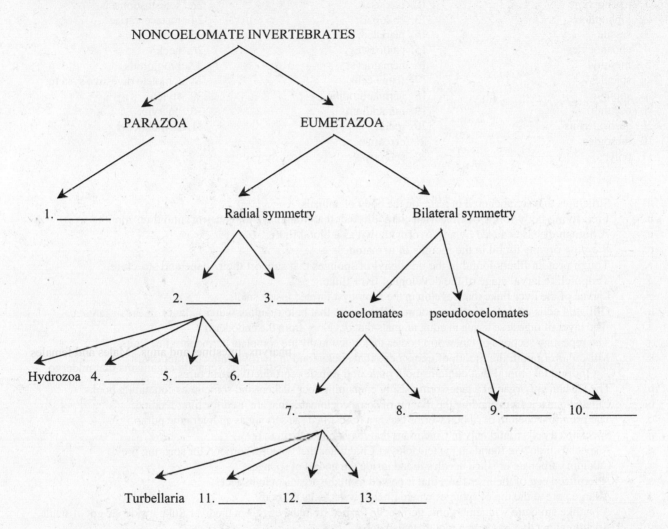

NONCOELOMATE INVERTEBRATES

PARAZOA   EUMETAZOA

1. _____

Radial symmetry   Bilateral symmetry

2. _____   3. _____

acoelomates   pseudocoelomates

Hydrozoa   4. _____   5. _____   6. _____

7. _____   8. _____   9. _____   10. _____

Turbellaria   11. _____   12. _____   13. _____

KEY TERMS
Match the numbered term with the definition that fits it best. Put the corresponding number in front of the appropriate definition.

1. trochophore
2. lophophore
3. sessile
4. choanocytes
5. mesohyl
6. spicules
7. spongin
8. osculum
9. gastrodermis
10. mesoglea
11. polyps

12. medusae
13. colloblast
14. planulae
15. cnidocytes
16. nematocyst
17. flame cells
18. hermaphroditic
19. miracidium
20. rediae
21. cercariae
22. sporocyst

23. schistosomiasis
24. metacercariae
25. scolex
26. neck
27. proglottids
28. complete digestive system
29. stylets
30. pharynx
31. rhynchocoel

a. _____ Structures that are anchored in place on the body of animals.
b. _____ Free-living body forms of Cnicarians like jellyfish that often have tentacles around their mouths.
c. _____ A human disease caused by a flatworm known as a blood fluke.
d. _____ Piercing organs found in the mouths of nematodes.
e. _____ Tough protein fibers found in the mesophyl of sponges that support their shape and structure.
f. _____ Tadpolelike larval stage of the developing liver fluke.
g. _____ Larvae of the liver fluke that develop in the sporocyst formed inside snails.
h. _____ Cilliated cells of the excretory system in flatworms that help regulate water balance in the organism.
i. _____ The layer of digestive tissue in adult animals that develops from the endoderm.
j. _____ The repeating sections of tapeworm bodies that individually are complete hermaphroditic units.
k. _____ Muscular organ in the mouth of nematodes that sucks food in by rhythmic contractions.
l. _____ An individual animal that contains both male and female reproductive structures.
m. _____ The attachment organ of a tapeworm usually containing four suckers and sometimes containing hooks.
n. _____ Ciliated tentacles surrounding the mouths of some coelomates that are used for filter feeding.
o. _____ The primitive coelom of ribbon worms that is a fluid-filled sac serving as an hydraulic pump.
p. _____ Specialized cells found only in Cnidarians that may deliver toxin to prey.
q. _____ A special cnidocyte found on the tentacles of Cnidarians that wields a harpoon for spearing prey.
r. _____ Calcium carbonate or silica needles found inside the bodies of sponges.
s. _____ A fertilized egg of the liver fluke that is passed from the organism in its feces.
t. _____ A large pore at the top of sponges where filtered water exits the body.
u. _____ A baglike structure with embryonic germ cells formed from the egg from the liver fluke inside the gut of snails.
v. _____ An animal gut that has both a mouth and an anus.
w. _____ Cyclindrical body forms of Cnidarians that are usually attached to a substrate.
x. _____ A free-living laval stage of coelomate protostomes.
y. _____ A free-swimming larval stage of cnidarians.
z. _____ Flagellated cells lining the interior of sponges and helping to move water through the sponge for feeding.
aa. _____ A protein-rich gel supporting mobile cells that is found between the choanocytes and outer tissue of sponges.
bb. _____ A special type of cell found in comb jellies that releases adhesive material to capture prey.
cc. _____ Laval stage of the liver fluke that develops in the muscle tissue of certain fish.
dd. _____ A layer of gel found between the epidermis and the gastrodermis of animals related to jellyfish.
ee. _____ The unsegmented part of a tapeworm body.

LEARNING BY EXPERIENCE

You have encountered numerous "firsts" in this chapter. To the right of each "first" listed below, name the phylum that first displayed the characteristic. ("First" may equal "most primitive" or, if that is not specified, let it equal the first mentioned in the textbook.) Use table 32.2 and the phylogenies at the beginning of each section of chapter 33 to complete this exercise.

1. Animal

2. Tissue

3. Symmetry

4. Bilateral symmetry

5. Cephalization

6. Anal opening

7. Body cavity

8. Internal digestion

9. Excretory system

10. Complete digestive system

EXERCISING YOUR KNOWLEDGE

Briefly answer each of the following questions in the space provided.

1. Explain how the phylum name Porifera relates to the feeding habits of sponges.

2. What is the role of spicules and sponging in sponges?

3. What function is performed by choanocytes in the sponge?

4. The bodies of both sponges and cnidarians have three layers. How do the middle layers differ?

5. How do cnidarians use nematocysts to acquire food?

6. What does the presence of choanocytes suggest about the evolution of sponges?

7. Why can flatworms that have a digestive cavity not feed continuously?

8. What is the nature of most flatworm reproduction?

9. Tapeworms are sometimes referred to as "degenerates" because they lack a digestive cavity and digestive enzymes. Why may the term "degenerate" not apply?

10. a. Why are rotifers called "wheel animals"?
    b. What functions are performed by the wheels?

Circle the letter of the one best answer in each of the following questions.

11. The _____ is a pseudoceolomate.
    a. starfish
    b. rotifer
    c. insect
    d. jellyfish
    e. bryozoan

12. In the phylogeny resulting from rRNA studies, lophophorates are assigned to
    a. Radiata.
    b. protostomes.
    c. deuterostomes.
    d. Ecdysozoa.
    e. Parazoa.

13. Cnidarian digestion is
    a. internal and extracellular.
    b. internal and intracellular.
    c. internal, extracellular, and intracellular.
    d. external and intracellular.
    e. external, extracellular, and intracellular.

14. Which of the following is characteristic of sponges?
    a. symmetry
    b. sexual reproduction
    c. tissues
    d. organs
    e. adult mobility

15. Which of the following is not a characteristic of cnidarians?
    a. tissues
    b. symmetry
    c. sexual reproduction
    d. asexual reproduction
    e. organs

16. Which of the following is characteristic of cnidarians?
    a. organs
    b. respiratory system
    c. blood vessels
    d. alternating haploid and diploid generations
    e. nervous system

17. Which of the following statements about nematocysts is incorrect?
    a. Stings from nematocysts may be fatal.
    b. The osmotic pressure of a nematocyst may exceed 100 atmospheres.
    c. Nematocysts turn inside-out when fired.
    d. Nematocysts are only used for getting food.
    e. Nematocysts may occur on the bodies of cnidarians as well as on tentacles.

18. A representative of the acoelomates would be
    a. earthworms.
    b. roundworms.
    c. smails.
    d. flatworms.
    e. squids.

19. The planulae of _____ develop only into polyps.
    a. Hydrozoa
    b. Ctenophora
    c. Scyphozoa
    d. Cnidaria
    e. Anthozoa

20. Ecdysozoans include
    a. nematodes.
    b. mollusks.
    c. flatworms.
    d. chordates.
    e. echinoderms.

21. Which of the following have an anal pore?
    a. ctenophorans
    b. flukes
    c. tapeworms
    d. free-living flatworms
    e. cnidarians

22. The nervous system of most flatworms can correctly be described as
    a. a brain.
    b. longitudinal nerve chords.
    c. a central nerve chord.
    d. a nerve ring.
    e. lacking.

23. Of the Eumetazoa listed below, the _____ are generally considered to be the most primitive.
    a. Chordata
    b. Rotifera
    c. Mollusca
    d. Ctenophora
    e. Nematoda

24. Sexually, most flatworms are
    a. parthenogenic.
    b. asexual.
    c. hermaphroditic.
    d. amorphous.
    e. aphrodisiac.

25. The largest phylum of pseudocoelomates is
    a. Cycliophora
    b. Platyhelminthes
    c. Cestoda
    d. Nematoda
    e. Rotifera

26. The phylum of the simplest animal to have a blood-filled circulatory system is
    a. Platyhelminthes.
    b. Nemertea.
    c. Nematoda.
    d. Rotifera.
    e. Porifera.

27. The phylum of the simplest animals to possess a complete digestive system is
    a. Nemertea.
    b. Rotifera.
    c. Onycophora.
    d. Ctenophora.
    e. Annelida.

28. In the new metazoan family tree, the traditional protostome group is broken into
    a. Parazoa and Ecdysozoa.
    b. Echinodermata and Hemichordata.
    c. Ecdysozoans and Spirilians.
    d. Parazoa and Lophotrochozoa.
    e. protostomes and deuterostomes.

29. The parasite that infects people who eat undercooked pork is
    a. *Clonorchis.*
    b. *Schistosoma.*
    c. *Trichinella.*
    d. *Caenorhabditis.*
    e. *Dugesia.*

30. Which of the following phyla was discovered most recently?
    a. Cycliophora
    b. Cnidaria
    c. Porifera
    d. Nematoda
    e. Platyhelminthes

ASSESSING YOUR KNOWLEDGE

Answers to the questions in this section test your ability to synthesize information gained from the chapter and to solve challenging problems on an exam or in everyday life.

Challenging Your Understanding—Answers

1. Porifera; 2. Cnidaria; 3. Ctenophora;

4-6. Scyphozoa, Cubozoa, Anthozoa;

7. Platyhelminthes; 8. Cycliophora;

9-10. Nematoda, Rotifera; 11-13. Monogenea, Trematoda, Cestoda.

Key Terms—Answers

a. 3, b. 12, c. 23, d. 29, e. 7, f. 21, g. 20, h. 17, i. 9, j. 27, k. 30, l. 18, m. 25, n. 2, o. 31, p. 15, q. 16, r. 6, s. 19, t. 8, u. 22, v. 28, w. 11, x. 1, y. 14, z. 4, aa. 5, bb. 13, cc. 24, dd. 10, ee. 26.

Learning by Experience—Answers

1. Porifera	
2. Cnidaria	
3. Cnidaria	
4. Platyhelminthes	
5. Platyhelminthes	
6. Cnidaria	
7. Nematoda	
8. Cnidaria	
9. Platyhelminthes	
10. Nemertea	

Exercising Your Knowledge—Answers

As you check your answers, put a mark in the review (Rvw.) column for the answers you missed. If you didn't miss any, congratulations—you have mastered the chapter! If you missed some, review the section (Sect.) in the text where this concept is discussed. In order to develop an efficient review strategy, it is important that you understand what types of questions you missed. The questions with asterisks test more for understanding of the **concepts**, whereas the others test more for **detail**. *See the preface for learning strategies for concepts and for detail.*

	Sect.	Rvw.
*1. Water is drawn into the interior through pores. Plankton is then gleaned from the water, which exits through the osculum.	33.2	
*2. Spicules and sponging fibers strengthen the body of the sponge.	33.2	
*3. Choanocytes propel water through the sponge pores and cavity.	33.2	
*4. The middle layer of the cnidarians, the mesoglea, contains muscle cells, which are lacking in sponges.	33.3	
*5. Cnidarians rapidly discharge a thread tipped with barbed spines and a chemical that paralyzes its prey. The thread is then retracted, drawing the prey into the cnidarian's mouth.	33.3	
*6. The similarities of choanocytes to flagellate protists suggest such an ancestor.	33.2	
*7. The digestive cavity has only one opening through which to ingest food and egest wastes. These two functions must be performed alternately, not continuously.	33.4	
*8. Most flatworms are hermaphroditic, having both male and female reproductive organs in each individual. However, they tend not to self-fertilize.	33.4	
*9. The reduction of those useless structures and processes is an adaptation to the environment in which the tapeworms are very successful.	33.4	
*10. a. The mouth is ringed with cilia, resembling the spokes of a wheel. b. The cilia propel the rotifer through the water and sweep food into its mouth.	33.5	
11. b	33.5	
12. b	33.1	
*13. c	33.3	
14. b	33.2	
*15. e	33.3	
16. e	33.3	
*17. d	33.3	
*18. d	33.4	
*19. e	33.3	
*20. a	33.1	
21. a	33.3	
22. b	33.4	
23. d	33.3	
*24. c	33.4	
25. d	33.5	
*26. b	33.4	
*27. a	33.4	
*28. c	33.1	
29. c	33.5	
30. a	33.4	

CHAPTER 34 COELOMATE INVERTEBRATES

MASTERING KEY CONCEPTS

The scope of this chapter is huge. Organizing it for study is vital. For each group of animals, you need to know the basic body plan and variations on this plan by various members of the group. You need to know how each organism discussed performs its life functions. Generalize where possible, but deal with specifics when necessary. Note the emergence of new characteristics.

34.1 Mollusks were among the first coelomates.

- **Overview**: The **coelom** allowed entirely new body plans to evolve. Coelomates have complex tissues and organs, and can grow to be much larger in size than the acoelomates, or the pseudocoelomates. The phylum **Mollusca** includes snails, oysters, clams, octopuses, and others. Mollusks are bilaterally symmetrical, with a coelom existing around the small spaces that are present around the heart, excretory organs, and part of the intestine. Mollusks may have a **differentiated head**, a **muscular foot** for locomotion, a **mantle** containing the respiratory organs, with **ctenidia** projections, and a concentrated **visceral mass** containing the digestive, excretory, and reproductive organs. Secretory action of the mantle produces the **shell** in some mollusks. Most mollusks have a **radula** for feeding, but this feature is absent in the bivalves, which use gills instead. Waste is removed from the coelomic cavity, into the mantle cavity, and out through the gills by **nephridia**. Most mollusks have a three-chambered heart and an **open circulatory system**, except for the Cephalopods. Most mollusks are male or female, some are hermaphrodites, but cross-fertilization is most common, and typically fertilization is external. There are eight classes of mollusks. Chitons (**class Polyplacophora**) are marine mollusks with a broad foot surrounded by the mantle cavity containing the gills. Snails, slugs, and others (**class Gastropoda**) typically have a shell, a pair or more tentacles, one set with eyes at the ends, and a foot for locomotion. Gastropods undergo **torsion,** which moves the mantle cavity and anus from the posterior closer to the front of the body, and therefore they are not bilaterally symmetrical. They also undergo the process of **coiling** or spiral winding of the shell. Clams, scallops, oysters, and others (**class Bivalvia**) are characterized by two lateral shells with a ligament serving as a hinge, and two **siphons**, **inhalant** and **exhalant,** for incoming and outgoing water. Bivalves are typically filter feeders and do not have distinct heads or radula. Octopuses and squids (class Cephalopoda) lack a shell, have a series of arms that have evolved from the foot, and have highly developed nervous systems and closed circulatory systems. Cephalopods have a siphon to bring in water and expel it, many have an **ink sac**, and some can change colors using their **chromatophores**.

- **Details**: Know the four different body plans of the mollusks and the class that each body plan is associated with. Know how the body plans differ from each other, the critical structures, and their locations. Understand the features that are unique to each class of mollusks.

34.2 Annelids were the first segmented animals.

- **Overview**: **Annelids** (phylum Annelida) are coelomates with bodies composed of specialized, repetitive segments that are separated internally by **septa**. Each segment has bristles of **chitin** on the exterior (**chaetae**) that help anchor the worm while it is moving. Annelids have a hydrostatic skeleton, and a closed circulatory system with five blood vessels that form a heart. They exchange oxygen and carbon dioxide through their body surfaces, and have an excretory system consisting of **nephridia**. There are three classes of Annelids, **Polychaeta** (marine worms), **Oligochaeta** (earthworms), and **Hirudinia** (leeches). Polychaetes have paddlelike projections (**parapodia**) on their segments. They are filter feeders, active swimmers, and predators. Mobile **trochophore larvae** are formed after fertilization that usually occurs externally in the water. Earthworms live underground. They have a mouth at one end and an anus at the other, and are hermaphroditic, but typically cross-fertilize. Fertilization and development of the eggs take place within a cocoon secreted by the **clitellum**. Leeches, like earthworms, are hermaphroditic and develop a clitellum. Leeches have **suckers** to attach to host organisms and suck their blood using vasodilators and anesthetics, but lack chaetae.

- **Details**: Know the structures of the annelids. Understand the advantages of segmentation. Know the three classes of annelids and the unique characteristics of each class.

34.3 Lophophorates appear to be a transitional group.

- **Overview**: **Lophophores** have **ciliated tentacles** surrounding their mouths that are used for both gas exchange and food collection. **Bryozoans** and **Brachiopoda** are two phyla of unrelated organisms that both possess a lophophore. Bryozoans are small "moss-like animals" that attach to various surfaces by way of a secreted **zoecium**. Members of a colony can also communicate with each other through pores in the zoecia, and polyps can be specialized to carry out different functions. Bryozoans are deuterostomes and can reproduce asexually by budding. Brachiopods are also deuterostomes and have two calcified shells. **Phoronids** secrete a chitinous tube to live in. They have lophophore tentacles that extend to catch food, but unlike brachiopods, phoronids develop as protostomes.

- **Details**: Know the unique characteristics of the Bryozoans and Brachiopods.

34.4 Arthropods are the most diverse of all animal groups.

- **Overview**: The phylum **Arthropoda** is the most successful of all of the animal phyla. Members of this phylum have segmented bodies, **jointed appendages**, chitinous **exoskeletons** in which the outer cuticle layer is shed in a process known as **ecdysis,** or molting, and **compound** or **simple eyes**. Arthropods have an open circulatory system with a long, muscular heart. The nervous system consists off two segmented ganglia and a brain. Air is taken in through openings in the exoskeleton (**spiracles**), and oxygen is transmitted throughout the body by **tracheae**. Other arthropods use gills, or exchange oxygen and carbon dioxide through their skin. Excretory systems vary, but many arthropods have **Malphigian tubules**. Within the phylum Arthropoda, there are four major classes, **arachnids**, **myriapods**, **crustaceans**, and **insects**. Arachnids, including spiders, ticks, scorpions, and others, have two body regions: the **prosoma** (anterior) and the **opisthosoma** (posterior). Arachnids have **chelicerae** that function as fangs or pincers, with **pedipalps** behind them. Arachnids are primarily terrestrial carnivores. **Book lungs** are the central component of their respiratory systems. Spiders (order Araneae) make their webs out of silk using **spinnerets**. These webs, or active hunting, are used to capture prey. Mites and ticks (order Acari) contain the largest number of species of arachnids. They feed on other organisms as predators or parasites. Centipedes (**class Chilopoda**) and millipedes (**class Diplopoda**) consist of segmented bodies with one or two pairs of leg per segment, respectively. Fertilization is internal and results in the laying of eggs. Centipedes feed on insects, while millipedes are herbivores. Crustaceans (**class Crustacea**) includes crabs, shrimps, lobsters (**decapod crustaceans**), barnacles (**sessile crustaceans**), and others. These organisms are primarily aquatic, have **biramous appendages**, two pairs of antennae, and **mandibles**. Most crustaceans pass through a **nauplius** developmental stage, which metamorphosizes through several stages to reach maturity. Decapod crustaceans have a **cephalothorax** and an abdomen with **swimmerets** on the ventral side. At the end, they have **uropod** appendages and some have a **telson**, or tail. Barnacles have free-swimming larvae that attach to other objects in the water to feed, and are hermaphroditic but cross-fertilize. Insects belong the extremely vast, diverse **class Hexapoda**. Insects consist of a **head**, **thorax** (with three pairs of legs), and **abdomen**. They typically have one pair of antennae, and one or two pairs of wings made of sheets of chitin and protein. Some groups, such as silverfish, fleas and lice, have lost their wings secondarily. The digestive tract in insects is a tube and excretion occurs through Malphigian tubules. Respiration occurs through the tracheae. Insects have **sensory setae** on their bodies and detect sound waves by **tympanal organs**. Many insects undergo some type of metamorphosis.

- **Details**: Know the structures and the unique characteristics of each class of arthropods. Know the advantages of jointed appendages and an exoskeleton. Know the arrangement of each of the major systems in arthropods. Know the unique features of spiders, mites and ticks, centipedes, millipedes, and crustaceans. Know the general features of insects.

34.5 Echinoderms are radially symmetrical as adults.

- **Overview**: **Echinoderms** are coelomates with an **endoskeleton** composed of **ossicles**, a deuterostome pattern of development, and a **water-vascular system** with tube feet and a muscular sac (**ampulla**) at the end of each one for feeding and locomotion. Echinoderms have **pentaradial symmetry** that shifts from bilateral symmetry in the larvae stage. The coelom is used for circulation, respiration, and waste removal. Reproduction can occur asexually by regeneration, but typically is sexual. Fertilization occurs externally in the water. There are five classes of echinoderms: **Asteroidea** (sea stars), **Ophiuroidea** (brittle stars), **Echinodea** (sea urchins), **Crinoidea** (sea lilies), and **Holothuroidea** (sea cucumbers). Sea stars have a central disc with arms in multiples of five. Brittle stars are the most abundant, most mobile echinoderms. They have slim, branched arms that they can use to swim. Unlike sea stars,

their tube feet lack ampullae and don't have
suckers. Sand dollars and sea urchins lack arms,
but still have five-part bodies.
- **Details**: Know the structures of sea stars and
  their unique features. Know how sea stars move.
  Know the classes of echinoderms, and examples
  and distinguishing characteristics of each.

CHALLENGING YOUR UNDERSTANDING

Fill in the missing classes of organisms that were mentioned in the chapter, and three characteristics of the
organisms of each phyla to demonstrate the similarities or the differences between the groups of organisms.
Examples of characteristics include unique body structures; unique developmental stages; or the type of circulatory,
digestive, excretory, nervous, or respiratory systems representative of the organisms in a particular phyla. At the
bottom, list some of the organisms that belong to each of the classes listed in the first part of the exercise.

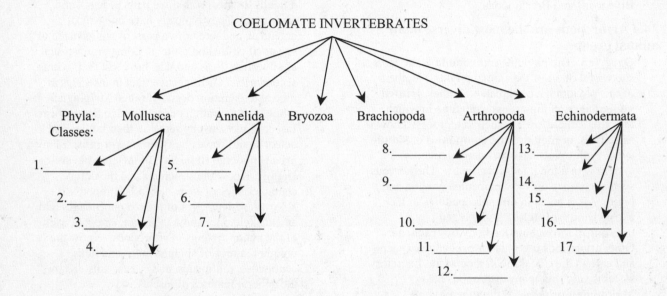

COELOMATE INVERTEBRATES

Phyla: Mollusca   Annelida   Bryozoa   Brachiopoda   Arthropoda   Echinodermata
Classes:

1._____   5._____   8._____   13._____

2._____   6._____   9._____   14._____
                                                                   15._____
3._____   7._____   10._____   16._____

4._____   11._____   17._____

                                                  12._____

Characteristics: Mollusks   Annelids   Bryozoa   Brachiopoda   Arthropods   Echinoderms

18._____   21._____   24._____   27._____   30._____   34._____

19._____   22._____   25._____   28._____   31._____   35._____

20._____   23._____   26._____   29._____   32._____   36._____

Organisms: <u>Mollusca</u>   <u>Annelida</u>   <u>Arthropoda</u>   <u>Echinodermata</u>

KEY TERMS

Match the numbered term with the definition that fits it best. Put the corresponding number in front of the appropriate definition.

1. visceral mass	18. phoronids	35. uropods
2. foot	19. exoskeleton	36. telson
3. mantle	20. tagmata	37. chelicerae
4. bivalve mollusks	21. cephalothorax	38. pedipalps
5. radula	22 ecdysis	39. book lungs
6. nephridia	23. compound eye	40. tympanum
7. nephrostome	24. ommatidia	41. metamorphosis
8. veliger	25. rhabdom	42. chrysalis
9. torsion	26. opisthosoma	43. echinoderms
10. coiling	27. ocelli	44. endoskeleton
11. ctenidia	28. tracheae	45. water-vascular system
12. annelid worms	29. tracheoles	46. nerve ring
13. septa	30. spiracles	47. tube feet
14. clitellum	31. Malphigian tubules	48. radial canals
15. parapodia	32. nauplius	49. madreporite
16. zoccium	33. mandibles	50. ampulla
17. chaetae	34. swimmerets	51. pentaradial symmetry

a. _____ Bristles of chitin on the segments of most annelids that help to anchor them during locomotion.

b. _____ A unique respiratory system present in most spiders that is a series of leaflike plates in a chamber.

c. _____ A special type of excretory structure used to remove nitrogenous wastes from the body of a mollusk.

d. _____ A larval form characteristic of crustaceans.

e. _____ Radial symmetry based on the presence of five axes like that found in echinoderms.

f. _____ Clams, oysters, and scallops that all have two lateral shells hinged together dorsally by a ligament.

g. _____ The shedding of the outer cuticle layer characteristic of the arthropods.

h. _____ Flexible, external extensions of the water-vascular system that are capable of attaching to surfaces.

i. _____ A flattened appendage at the end of the abdomen of lobsters and crayfish that form a compound paddle.

j. _____ A wall between two cavities.

k. _____ A rigid, external skeleton made of chitin and protein found in arthropods.

l. _____ A thin membrane associated with the tracheal air sacs that functions as a sound receptor in some insects.

m. _____ The spiral winding of the shell that is characteristic of gastropods and some cephalopods.

n. _____ Slender projections from the digestive tract serving as a unique excretory system found in insects.

o. _____ A resting stage immediately preceding the final molt into the adult form in an insect metamorphosis.

p. _____ Simple eyes with single lenses found in some arthropod groups.

q. _____ Biting jaws that likely originated in crustaceans from a pair of limbs that took on a chewing function.

r. _____ The internal organs in the body cavity of an animal.

s. _____ A muscular sac that contains fluid at the base of each tube foot.

t. _____ A compound body section of an arthropod resulting from embryonic fusion of two or more segments.

u. _____ A second free-swimming larval stage found in mollusks during which the foot, shell, and mantle appear.

v. _____ Appendages on the ventral surface of the abdomens of lobster and crayfish used for reproduction and swimming.

w. _____ Paired, fleshy, paddlelike lateral projections found on the segments of polychaetes.

x. _____ Small, branched, cuticle-lined air ducts that make up the respiratory system of most terrestrial arthropods.

y. _____ Any of five canals that connect to the ring canal of an echinoderm's water-vascular system.

z. _____ The first pair of appendages that often function as fangs or pincers in arachnids.

aa. _____ Independent visual units that are each covered by a lens and have a complex of eight retinular cells.

bb. _____ A muscular organ that serves as the primary mechanism of locomotion in mollusks.

cc. _____ Lophophorate invertebrates that secrete a chitinous tube in which they live.

dd. _____ Organisms such as sea stars and sea urchins that have a hard endoskeleton beneath delicate skin.

ee. _____ A tagma consisting of a distinct head fused with the thorax found in many crustaceans and chelicerates.

ff. _____ A sievelike plate on the animal's surface where water enters the water-vascular system.

gg. _____ The light-sensitive central core of an ommatidium.

hh. _____ A rasping, tonguelike organ used for feeding in mollusks.

ii. ____ A tiny chitinous chamber secreted by individual bryozoans that attaches to rocks or other substrates.

jj. ____ A central structure in the nervous system of echinoderms from which the branches arise.

kk. ____ The posterior region of arachnids that contains the reproductive organs.

ll. ____ Specialized portions of the mantle consisting of a system of filamentous projections rich in blood vessels.

mm. ____ Appendages that resemble legs, but typically have a sensory function and are not used for locomotion.

nn. ____ A thick epidermal sheet of skin covering the dorsal side of the body used to house organs in mollusks.

oo. ____ Hard, calcium-rich plates found beneath the surface of skin in echinoderms.

pp. ____ A visual organ found in many arthropods composed of many independent units with a lens, and retinular cells.

qq. ____ The tail spine of lobsters and crayfish.

rr. ____ A process in gastropods in which the mantle cavity and anus are moved toward the front of the body.

ss. ____ A change in body form that many insects undergo during their normal course of development.

tt. ____ Specialized openings in the exoskeleton that allow air to pass into the tracheae.

uu. ____ A thickened band on the earthworm's body through which they secrete a mucus cocoon that receives the eggs.

vv. ____ An open funnel from which a coiled tubule runs to the bladder, which connects to an excretory pore.

ww. ____ A fluid-filled hydraulic system found in echinoderms that provides body support and locomotion.

xx. ____ The smallest branches of the respiratory system of terrestrial arthropods used to transmit oxygen to cells.

yy. ____ A group of organisms with bodies composed of specialized, repetitive segments that are separated by septa.

LEARNING BY EXPERIENCE

Color the structures listed for figures 34.3 and 34.13 below. Fill in the circle at the end of each term to indicate your color code. As you color, review the functions of the structures.

Figure 34.3   Foot ◯   Mantle ◯   Gills ◯   Shell ◯   Gut ◯

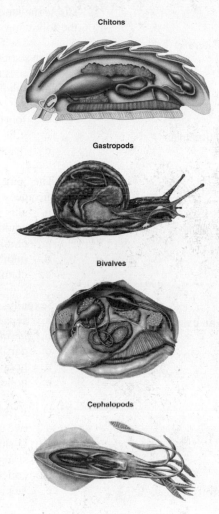

Chitons

Gastropods

Bivalves

Cephalopods

Figure 34.13   Dorsal blood vessel ◯   Hearts ◯   Pharynx ◯   Esophagus ◯   Intestine ◯   Nerve chord ◯

Mouth ◯   Brain ◯   Nephridium ◯   Male gonads ◯   Female gonads ◯   Septa ◯

EXERCISING YOUR KNOWLEDGE

Briefly answer each of the following questions in the space provided.

1. Describe mollusk excretion.

2. What led gastropods to become bilaterally asymmetrical?

3. What is the advantage of segmentation to an animal?

4. What are the advantages and disadvantages of the arthropod exoskeleton?

5. (a) What are tagmata? (b) What is an example of tagmatization?

6. Describe blood flow in insects.

7. Describe food digestion in carnivorous spiders.

8. Why are echinoderms described as having secondary radial symmetry?

9. Why is radial symmetry advantageous to echinoderms?

10. Describe the feeding habit of the sea star (Asteroidea).

Circle the letter of the one best answer in each of the following questions.

11. The secretory action of which of the following produces the shell of mollusks?
    a. radula
    b. gut
    c. foot
    d. gills
    e. mantle

12. The contemporary mollusk most resembling the ancestral mollusk is probably the
    a. slug.
    b. squid.
    c. chiton.
    d. nudibranch.
    e. clam.

13. Sexually, earthworms are
    a. separate sexed.
    b. hermaphroditic, but not self-fertilizing.
    c. parthenogenic.
    d. hermaphroditic and self-fertilizing.
    e. none of these.

14. The digestive tube of phoronids is
    a. two-way.
    b. U-shaped.
    c. straight.
    d. coiled.
    e. lacking.

15. Which of the following is NOT found in the prosoma of arachnids?
    a. legs
    b. chelicerae
    c. reproductive organs
    d. pedipalps
    e. none of the above

16. In the arthropod compound eye, each _____ is covered with a lens and linked to a light-sensitive core.
    a. ommatidium
    b. ocellus
    c. rhabdom
    d. retina
    e. labyrinth

17. The foremost appendages of a spider are
    a. pedipalps.
    b. maxillae.
    c. antennae.
    d. chelicerae.
    e. mandibles.

18. While most insects have four wings, the
    _____ have only two.
    a. termites.
    b. flies.
    c. fleas.
    d. damsel flies.
    e. crickets.

19. Which of the following is the largest group of
    arthropods?
    a. beetles
    b. flies
    c. bees, wasps, ants
    d. crustaceans
    e. myriapods

20. Lyme disease is caused by _____
    transmitted by ticks.
    a. fungal aflatoxins
    b. bacteria
    c. viruses
    d. trypanosomes
    e. protozoa

21. Which of the following is NOT a
    characteristic of all arthropods?
    a. distinct head
    b. jointed appendages
    c. book lungs
    d. ecdysis
    e. open circulatory system

22. Air first enters the insect body for respiration
    through the
    a. tracheoles.
    b. ossicles.
    c. spiracles.
    d. mouth.
    e. tracheae.

23. Which of the following insect structures is not
    homologous to the others listed?
    a. wings
    b. antennae
    c. legs
    d. mandibles
    e. chelicerae

24. When the insect heart contracts, the blood
    flows to the
    a. wings.
    b. head region.
    c. legs.
    d. thorax region.
    e. abdominal region.

25. The water-vascular system of a sea star
    surrounds its
    a. tube feet.
    b. stomach.
    c. anus.
    d. esophagus.
    e. ampulla.

26. After water enters the water vascular system
    of a sea star, it will first pass through the tube
    called a
    a. ring canal.
    b. ampullae.
    c. stone canal.
    d. papula.
    e. madreporite.

27. Most reproduction in echinoderms is
    a. sexual and external.
    b. hermaphroditic.
    c. asexual by fragmentation.
    d. parthenogenic.
    e. sexual and internal.

28. Some echinoderms, such as the _____,
    use their arms to swim.
    a. sea lilies
    b. sea stars
    c. brittle stars
    d. sea cucumber
    e. sea urchin

29. Sea urchins move by
    a. tentacles.
    b. flexible arms.
    c. movable spines.
    d. small pincers.
    e. extruded slime.

30. The _____ are the largest class of
    echinoderms in terms of numbers of species.
    a. brittle stars
    b. sand dollars
    c. sea urchins
    d. sea lilies
    e. sea stars

ASSESSING YOUR KNOWLEDGE

Answers to the questions in this section test your ability to synthesize information gained from the chapter and to solve challenging problems on an exam or in everyday life.

Challenging Your Understanding—Answers

Classes:
1-4. Polyplacophora, Gastropoda, Bivalva, Cephalopoda. 5-7. Polychaeta, Oligochaeta, Hirudinea. 8-12. Arachnida, Crustacea, Chilopoda, Diplopoda, Hexapoda. 13-17. Crinoidea, Asteroidea, Ophiuroidea, Echinoidea, Holothuroidea.

Characteristics:
Mollusca: radula for feeding, mantle secretes shell, foot for locomotion, trophophore larvae, open circulatory system, gills for respiration.

Annelida: segmented bodies, hydrostatic skeleton, respiration through skin, closed circulatory system, filter feeders (marine) or ingest soil (earthworms) or suckers (leeches).

Bryozoa: Lophophore for feeding and gas exchange, zoecium, colonies with specialized polyps.

Brachiopoda: Lophophore for feeding and gas exchange, dorsal/ventral valved shells, U-shaped gut.

Arthropoda: jointed appendages, exoskeleton, open circulatory systems, respiration by skin or gut, tracheae, book lungs, or gills, excretion by Malphigian tubules.

Echinodermata: endoskeleton, water-vascular system, tube feet, five-part body plan, respiration through skin.

Organisms:
Mollusca:
Polyplacophora: chitons
Gastropoda: snails, slugs
Bivalvia: clams, oysters
Cephalopoda: octopus

Annelida:
Polychaeta: clamworms
Oligochaeta: earthworms
Hirudinea: leeches

Arthropoda:
Arachnida: spiders
Crustacea: crabs, lobsters
Chilopoda: centipedes
Diplopoda: millipedes
Hexapoda: beetle, mosquito

Echinodermata:
Crinoidea: sea lilies
Asteroidea: sea stars
Ophiuroidea: brittle stars
Echinodea: sea urchins
Holothuroidea: sea cucumbers

(Other answers are possible for the characteristics, and the organisms.)

Key Terms—Answers

a. 17, b. 39, c. 6, d. 32, e. 51, f. 4, g. 22, h. 47, i. 35, j. 13, k. 19, l. 40, m. 10, n. 31, o. 42, p. 27, q. 33, r. 1, s. 50, t. 20, u. 8, v. 34, w. 15, x. 28, y. 48, z. 37, aa. 24, bb. 2, cc. 18, dd. 43, ee. 21, ff. 49, gg. 25, hh. 5, ii. 16, jj. 46, kk. 26, ll. 11, mm. 38, nn. 3, oo. 44, pp. 23, qq. 36, rr. 9, ss. 41, tt. 30, uu. 14, vv. 7, ww. 45, xx. 29, yy. 12.

Learning by Experience—Answers

> 1. Compare your work to textbook figures 34.3 and 34.13.

Exercising Your Knowledge—Answers

As you check your answers, put a mark in the review (Rvw) column for the answers you missed. If you didn't miss any, congratulations—you have mastered the chapter! If you missed some, review the section (Sect.) in the text where this concept is discussed. In order to develop an efficient review strategy, it is important that you understand what types of questions you missed. The questions with asterisks test more for understanding of the **concepts**, whereas the others test more for **detail**. *See the preface for learning strategies for concepts and for details.*

	Sect.	Rvw.
*1. Wastes pass through the coelom, where nephridia collect them with the ciliated nephrostome and pass them to the mantle cavity where they are expelled.	34.1	
*2. Uneven growth of the two sides has caused torsion, and loss of gills and nephridia on one side has led to coiling.	34.1	
*3. Segmentation permits specialization of different segments in different ways.	34.2	
*4. The exoskeleton provides a strong, flexible, and water-conserving surface to which muscles may be attached. The weight of the exoskeleton limits the size of an arthropod.	34.4	
*5. (a) Tagmata are fused segments. (b) Although there are others, the cephalothorax is a good example.	34.4	

*6. All blood is pumped toward the head region by the heart, which is shaped like a longitudinal vessel. Blood gradually seeps back through cavities between internal organs and is then pumped forward again.	34.4	
*7. Food digestion takes place in the body of the prey, into which the spider injects digestive enzymes. The spider then sucks out the digested juices.	34.4	
*8. The echinoderm larva is bilaterally symmetrical. The symmetry changes to radial as the animal develops.	34.5	
*9. Echinoderms are sessile or slow moving. Radial symmetry allows them to deal with their environment in all directions around them.	34.5	
*10. Sea stars use their tube feet to force a bivalve mollusk open slightly. The sea star extends its stomach through and into the bivalve shell, where it secretes enzymes and digests the prey. The stomach is then withdrawn into the sea star body.	34.5	

11. e	34.1	
12. c	34.1	
13. b	34.2	
14. b	34.3	
15. c	34.4	
16. a	34.4	
17. d	34.4	
18. b	34.4	
19. a	34.4	
20. b	34.4	
21. c	34.4	
22. c	34.4	
23. a	34.4	
24. b	34.4	
25. d	34.5	
26. c	34.5	
27. a	34.5	
28. c	34.5	
29. c	34.5	
30. a	34.5	

CHAPTER 35 VERTEBRATES

MASTERING KEY CONCEPTS

The emphasis is on advantageous evolutionary changes. Although the chapter is titled "Vertebrates," it also deals with nonvertebrate chordates. The chapter provides a sweeping survey of chordates and especially vertebrates.

35.1 Attaching muscles to an internal framework greatly improves movement.

- **Overview**: **Chordates** (phylum Chordata) include fishes, reptiles, amphibians, birds, and mammals. Like echinoderms, chordates are deuterostome coelomates. Chordates have four distinguishing characteristics at some point during development, a **hollow nerve cord**, **notochord**, **pharyngeal slits** or **pouches**, and a **postanal tail**. Most chordates have an **internal skeleton** and **muscles** arranged in segmented blocks that work against it, allowing mobility.
  Details: Know the characteristics of chordates.

35.2 Nonvertebrate chordates have a notochord but no backbone.

- **Overview**: The phylum Chordata is subdivided into three subphyla: the nonvertebrates, **Urochordata**, **Cephalochordata**, and the vertebrates, **Vertebrata**. Urochordata consists of tunicates and salps, immobile marine animals that are the most primitive of the chordates. Many tunicates secrete a **tunic**, or tough sac, around themselves and possess a notochord and nerve cord only in the larval form. Lancelets belong to the subphylum Cephalochordata. They are pointed at both ends and lack a distinguishable head. They have gill slits and are filter feeders. These organisms, like tunicates, have notochords, but in lancelets it persists in the adult form. They have discrete blocks of muscles, or **myomeres**. Lancelets are the closest living relatives of vertebrates.
- **Details**: Know the structures and characteristics of the larval and adult tunicate, and of the lancelets. Understand how each system in their bodies works.

35.3 The vertebrate chordates have a vertebral column and a distinguishable head.

- **Overview**: **Vertebrates** (subphylum Vertebrata) have two characteristic innovations relative to tunicates and lancelets, a **vertebral column** made up of cartilaginous vertebrae segments that replaces the notochord during embryonic development to protect the nerve cord, and a **well-defined head** with sensory organs, and a brain protected by a skull. In addition to these, vertebrates are also different because they have **neural crest cells** that are involved in the development of different structures, they have

internal organs and an **endoskeleton made of cartilage and bone**. Vertebrates evolved during the Cambrian period in the oceans. Amphibians invaded the land and gave rise to reptiles. Reptiles gave rise to birds and mammals, but these did not become abundant until after the Cretaceous mass extinction of the dinosaurs.
- **Details**: Know the distinguishing characteristics of vertebrates. Understand why an endoskeleton is advantageous. Know the order in which vertebrates evolved.

35.4 Fishes were the first vertebrates.

- **Overview**: **Fishes** were the first vertebrates, with a head and a primitive tail that they used to move through the water. Early fishes primarily were bottom feeders, until they evolved fins to help them move, bones for protection, jaws, and teeth. All fishes have some common characteristics, including an **internal skeleton** with a vertebral column, a **cartilaginous skull**, **jaws** and **paired appendages**, **internal gills**, a **single-loop circulatory system** that pumps blood, and the inability to synthesize aromatic amino acids (**nutritional deficiencies**). Sharks (class Chondrichthyes) have a highly evolved jaw, and were among the first vertebrates to have teeth. Sharks have a light, strong, cartilaginous skeleton that allows them to move very rapidly. The sensory organs of sharks exist in a **lateral line system** running beneath the skin's surface. Shark eggs are fertilized internally. Bony fishes evolved to have an internal skeleton made completely of bone. They are the most species-rich group of vertebrates due to adaptations such as the **swim bladder** that allows regulation of buoyancy and the gill cover, or **operculum,** that allows stationary fish to pass water over their gills. Amphibians likely evolved from lobe-finned fishes (class Sarcopterygii).
- **Details**: Know the common characteristics of almost all fishes. Know the major classes and how they differ from each other. Understand how fishes with jaws evolved and the innovations of bony fishes that have made them the most species-rich group of vertebrates.

35.5 Amphibians invaded the land.

- **Overview**: **Amphibians** are classified into three orders—**Anura** (frogs, toads), **Caudata** (newts, salamanders), and **Apoda** (caecilians) that share some common characteristics, such as **legs**, **lungs** supplemented by **cutaneous respiration**, **pulmonary veins**, and **partially divided hearts** to prevent mixing of aerated and nonaerated blood. In *Ichthyostega*, one of the earliest amphibians, the shoulder bones were no longer attached to the skull so they could support the weight of the animal. A rib cage formed to strengthen the backbone. In the Permian period, many amphibians had bony plates and armor-covered bodies and 60% became fully terrestrial (**Age of Amphibians**). The evolution of reptiles on land led to the mass extinction of terrestrial amphibians. Frogs and toads can live in a variety of environments but lay eggs in water. These eggs are fertilized externally and form tadpoles that undergo a **metamorphosis** to become adults. Frogs and toads lack tails. Salamanders live in water, or in moist places where they lay their eggs. Fertilization is internal and larval stage salamanders undergo a metamorphosis to become adults, which lack gills. Caecilians are burrowing amphibians, lacking legs, but possessing jaws and teeth.

- **Details**: Know the common characteristics of amphibians, the obstacles that these organisms had to overcome to invade the land, and how they successfully did so.

35.6 Reptiles improved on the innovations of amphibians.

- **Overview**: **Reptiles** evolved leg arrangements that could support their bodies better, their lungs and hearts became more efficient, they developed scales to prevent water loss, and their eggs evolved watertight coverings. All reptiles lay amniotic eggs with four membranes also found in birds and mammals. These include a **yolk sac, amnion, allantois,** and **chorion**. Reptiles have dry, watertight skin covered with scales, and thoracic breathing in which the air capacity is limited by the volume of the lungs, not by the mouth. Early reptiles that survived successfully for many years are the **synapsids**, including the pelycosaur, therapsids, and diapsids. The archosaurs (diapsids) gave rise to dinosaurs, crocodiles, birds, and the first bipedal land vertebrates. Dinosaurs were the most successful of all land vertebrates. Reptiles are **ectotherms** and have internal fertilization and a septum in their hearts that makes the circulatory system more efficient. There are four surviving orders of reptiles: **Chelonia** (turtles and tortoises), **Rhynchocephalia** (tuataras), **Squamata** (lizards, snakes), and **Crocodylia** (crocodiles and alligators). The bodies of turtles (mostly marine) and tortoises (mostly terrestrial) are encased in a **shell** consisting of a **carapace** (dorsal) and a **plastron** (ventral). Their eggs must be laid on land. Tuataras are lizardlike animals with a **parietal** third eye on top of their heads. These organisms are closely related to lizards and snakes. Lizards and snakes are characterized by changes in their head and jaw structures that permit greater mobility, and by males having paired copulatory organs. Most snakes and lizards are carnivores relying on

agility and speed to capture their prey. All crocodiles and alligators are also carnivores, living in or near the water in tropical regions. Crocodiles are closely related to birds, both of which are the direct descendants of dinosaurs.

- **Details**: Know the innovations that reptiles evolved to make them better suited than amphibians to live on the land. Know the three common characteristics of all reptiles. Know the four surviving orders of reptiles and their unique characteristics. Understand the similarities between crocodiles and birds.

35.7 The success of birds lies in the development of the feather.

- **Overview**: **Birds** are similar to reptiles in that they lay **amniotic eggs** and their lower legs and feet have **scales**, but birds are distinct because they **lack teeth**, have **vestigial tails, feathers,** and a **flight skeleton** with an enlarged breastbone. Fossils of *Archaeopteryx* indicate that it is an avian descendant of the dinosaurs. Birds have modified respiratory systems with air sacs and unidirectional air flow that makes gas exchange very efficient. The hearts of birds are divided into four chambers. They have rapid heartbeats and are **endothermic**. Together these characteristics are important innovations contributing to their ability to fly.

- **Details**: Know the characteristics that birds share with reptiles and those that are different.

35.8 Mammals have the smallest number of species of any of the vertebrate classes.

- **Overview**: **Hair** and **mammary glands** are two distinguishing characteristics of mammals. Hair maintains body temperature, functions as a sensory structure, and acts as protection and camouflage. Mammary glands allow mothers to nurse their newborns. In addition to these characteristics, all mammals are also **endothermic** with **four-chambered hearts** and **diaphragms** for efficient respiration. Developing embryos are carried internally allowing food, water, and oxygen to pass from the mother to the child by way of the **placenta**. Mammals also have **specialized teeth** that match their eating habits; **bacteria in their digestive tracts** that enable them to digest cellulose; and claws, fingernails, and hooves made of keratin. Mammals are divided into three groups: **monotremes** (Prototheria), **marsupials,** and **placental mammals** (Theria). Like reptiles, monotremes lay shelled eggs and have a **cloaca** for waste and reproductive products to leave the body. Like other mammals, monotremes have fur and mammary glands. Marsupials develop in a membranous, unshelled egg. Shortly before birth, a placenta forms. After birth, marsupials continue to develop in a **pouch**. In placental mammals, unborn embryos are nourished throughout development by the placenta and undergo substantial development before they are born, unlike marsupials.

- **Details**: Know the unique features of mammals. Know the differences between monotremes, marsupials, and placental mammals.

35.9 Primates gave rise to early humans.

- **Overview**: **Grasping fingers and toes**, and **binocular vision** are two innovations that allowed primates to successfully survive as tree-dwellers. Primates are split into two groups, the **prosimians** (lemurs, lorises, tarsiers) and the **anthropoids** (monkeys, apes, humans). Prosimians are nocturnal, while anthropoids are active during the day. **Hominoids** include apes and humans (**hominids**), whose common ancestor is likely an arboreal climber. Hominids evolved to become **bipedal**, while apes evolved knuckle-walking and many of the characteristics of each evolved from this difference. **Australopithecine** fossils indicate that these organisms were early hominids that walked upright. Why bipedalism evolved, however, is still a mystery. The genus *Homo* arose from australopithecine ancestors. Many *Homo* species arose in Africa and migrated to Asia and Europe. Modern humans include **Neanderthals**, which made tools, took care of their injured, and buried their dead, and **Cro-Magnons,** which had a complex social organization and full language capabilities. *Homo sapiens* (humans) are the only surviving *Homo* species. Humans have undergone **extensive cultural evolution**, rather than changing to meet the demands of the environment.

- **Details**: Know how primates evolved, and the differences between apes and hominids. Know the evolution of the genus *Homo* and the unique features of the *Homo sapiens*.

CHALLENGING YOUR UNDERSTANDING

Fill in the blanks in the following flowchart to indicate how the chapter concepts relate to each other.

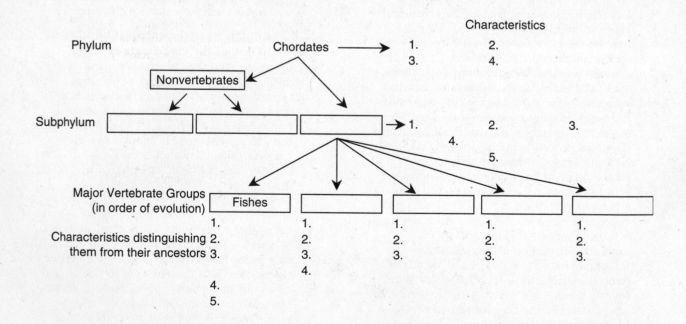

KEY TERMS

Match the numbered term with the definition that fits it best. Put the corresponding number in front of the appropriate definition.

1. chordates	10. vertebrates	19. ectothermic
2. nerve cord	11. swim bladder	20. endodermic
3. notochord	12. operculum	21. prosimians
4. pharyngeal slits	13. chorion	22. anthropoids
5. pharynx	14. amnion	23. hominoids
6. pharyngeal pouches	15. yolk sac	24. hominids
7. postanal tail	16. allantois	25. bipedal
8. tunic	17. synapsids	26. placenta
9. neural crest	18. diapsids	

a. _____ One of the two groups of the earliest primates that looked like a cross between a squirrel and a cat.

b. _____ Chordates in which the notochord develops into a column that encloses and protects the dorsal nerve cord.

c. _____ A dorsal rod of cartilage that runs the length of the body and forms the primitive axial skeleton in chordates.

d. _____ A group including the apes, humans, and their direct ancestors.

e. _____ A muscular tube that links the mouth cavity and the esophagus.

f. _____ A gas-filled sac that allows bony fishes to regulate their buoyant density and remain suspended at any depth.

g. _____ Organisms, such as reptiles, who obtain their heat from external sources.

h. _____ Provides food from the yolk for the embryo via blood vessels connecting to the embryo's gut.

i. _____ The property of walking upright on two legs.

j. _____ A unique group of embryonic cells that participate in the development of many different structures.

k. _____ Deuterostome coelomates with a nerve cord, notochord, pharyngeal slits, and a postanal tail at some point.

l. _____ Organisms with skulls that have two pairs of temporal holes behing the openings for the eyes.

m. _____ One of the two groups of the earliest primates that are diurnal, including monkeys, apes, and humans.

n. _____ The outermost membrane of the egg, which lies just beneath the porous shell.

o. _____ Structures present in the embryos of all vertebrates that disappear in animals lacking gills.

p. _____ A specialized organ that brings the bloodstream of the fetus into close contact with a mother's bloodstream.

q. _____ The membrane that surrounds a cavity into which waste products from the embryo are excreted.

r. _____ A flat, bony, external protective covering over the gill chamber in fish.

s. _____ A tough sac composed mainly of cellulose secreted by adult tunicates to surround their bodies.

t. _____ Animals who are able to generate their heat internally.

u. _____ Organisms whose skulls have a pair of temporal holes behind the openings for the eyes.

v. _____ A distinguishing characteristic of chordates, running lengthwise beneath the embryo's dorsal surface.

w. _____ A membrane that encases the developing embryo within a fluid-filled cavity.

x. _____ Any primate in the human family, Hominidae, of which *Homo sapiens* are the only living representatives.

y. _____ A characteristic of chordates, this structure extends beyond the anus , at least during embryonic development.

z. _____ Structures that connect the pharynx with the external environment.

LEARNING BY EXPERIENCE

Color code the figures below. Fill in the circle at the end of each term to indicate your choice of colors. As you color, review the functions of the structures.

Chorion ○

Amnion ○

Allantois ○

Yolk sac ○

Placenta ○

Umbilical chord ○

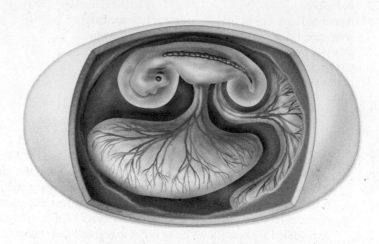

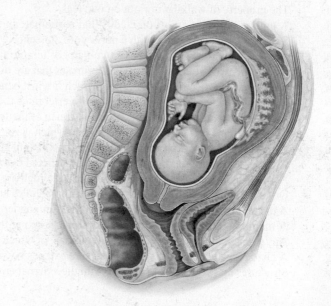

EXERCISING YOUR KNOWLEDGE

Briefly answer each of the following questions in the space provided.

1. What are the four major characteristics of chordates?

2. What evidence supports the view that rather than being degenerate fishes, lancelets are the closest ancestors of vertebrates?

3. What five characteristics separate vertebrates from other chordates?

4. How do fishes maximize oxygen absorption in the gills?

5. Sharks have to swim or they will sink. How do fishes solve the buoyancy problem?

6. How do bony fishes maintain a flow of water over the gills when at rest?

7. How is the amphibian circulatory system improved over that of the fishes?

8. What characteristics earned reptiles the title of the first truly terrestrial vertebrates?

9. What cardiac advance helped equip birds for flight?

10. What mammalian characteristics support endothermy?

Circle the letter of the one best answer in each of the following questions.

11. The notochord persists in the _____ adult.
    a. lancelet
    b. ray
    c. skate
    d. shark
    e. tunicate

12. Adult urochordates secrete a sac composed mainly of
    a. protein.
    b. cellulose.
    c. phospholipids.
    d. gelatin.
    e. pectin.

13. The story of vertebrate evolution started in the ancient seas of the _____ period.
    a. Cambrian
    b. Ordovician
    c. Devonian
    d. Silurian
    e. Carboniferous

14. More than half of the vertebrates are
    a. mammals.
    b. fishes.
    c. amphibians.
    d. birds.
    e. reptiles.

15. The propulsive fin of sharks and bony fishes is the _____ fin.
    a. pectoral
    b. dorsal
    c. pelvic
    d. ventral
    e. caudal

16. Sharks must constantly swim because they lack
    a. pectoral fins.
    b. a swim bladder.
    c. gills.
    d. lungs.
    e. a lateral line.

17. Not all amphibians have
    a. cutaneous respiration.
    b. pulmonary veins.
    c. lungs.
    d. a partially divided heart.
    e. legs.

18. Most paleontologists consider amphibians to
    have evolved from
    a. coelacanths.
    b. therapsids.
    c. rhipidistians.
    d. ray-finned fishes.
    e. lung fish.

19. The early amphibian *Ichthyostega* breathed by
    a. forward movement.
    b. muscular contractions around the swim
        bladder.
    c. rib cage movements.
    d. movement of the floor of the mouth.
    e. movement of the hind legs.

20. Amphibians bearing live young are
    a. caecilians.
    b. frogs.
    c. toads.
    d. salamanders.
    e. newts.

21. The earliest warm-blooded land animals were the
    a. pelycosaurs.
    b. therapsids.
    c. thecodonts.
    d. dinosaurs.
    e. microsaurs.

22. Which of the following were the most successful
    of all land vertebrates?
    a. pelycosaurs
    b. therapsids
    c. amphibians
    d. dinosaurs
    e. diapsids

23. Unique among reptiles, the _____ have a parietal
    eye.
    a. lizards
    b. crocodiles
    c. snakes
    d. turtles
    e. tuataras

24. The living animals that crocodiles most resemble
    are the
    a. snakes.
    b. turtles.
    c. lizards.
    d. birds.
    e. amphibians.

25. Which of the following is not a unique feature of
    birds?
    a. four-chambered heart
    b. hollow bones
    c. keeled breastbone
    d. constant direction of air flow through the
        lungs
    e. feathers

26. The most ancient group of living birds is
    composed of the
    a. woodpeckers.
    b. parrots.
    c. owls.
    d. ostriches.
    e. penguins.

27. Next to rodents, the largest order of mammals is
    made up of
    a. carnivores.
    b. bats.
    c. insectivores.
    d. primates.
    e. marsupials.

28. Mammals arose from the
    a. pelycosaurs.
    b. therapsids.
    c. thecodonts.
    d. dinosaurs.
    e. birds.

29. The fetal placenta and umbilical cord are formed
    from the
    a. chorion and amnion.
    b. chorion.
    c. chorion and uterus.
    d. amnion.
    e. chorion and allantois.

30. The major factor responsible for sharks and bony
    fishes replacing pioneer vertebrates was
    a. better jaws.
    b. better respiration.
    c. stronger bones.
    d. better swimming.
    e. better teeth.

ASSESSING YOUR KNOWLEDGE

Answers to the questions in this section test your ability to synthesize information gained from the chapter and to solve challenging problems on an exam or in everyday life.

Challenging Your Understanding—Answers

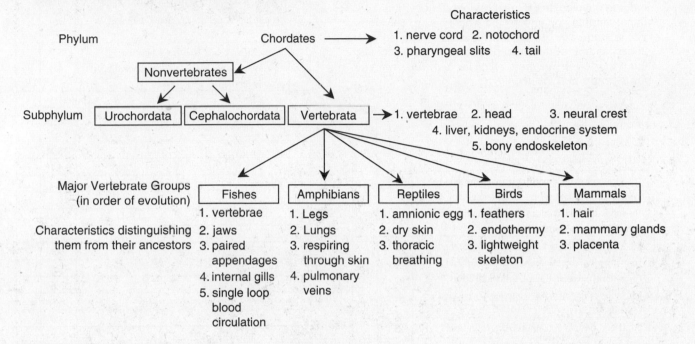

Key Terms—Answers

a. 21, b. 10, c. 3, d. 23, e. 5, f. 11, g. 19, h. 15, i. 25,
j. 9, k. 1, l. 18, m. 22, n. 13, o. 6, p. 26, q. 16, r. 12,
s. 8, t. 20, u. 17, v. 2, w. 14, x. 24, y. 7, z. 4.

Learning by Experience—Answers

Compare your work to textbook figures 35.17 and 35.30.

Exercising Your Knowledge—Answers

As you check your answers, put a mark in the review (Rvw.) column for the answers you missed. If you didn't miss any, congratulations—you have mastered the chapter! If you missed some, review the section (Sect.) in the text where this concept is discussed. In order to develop an efficient review strategy, it is important that you understand what types of questions you missed. The questions with asterisks test more for understanding of the **concepts**, whereas the others test more for **detail**. *See the preface for learning strategies for concepts and for detail.*

	Sect.	Rvw.
*1. The four major characteristics of chordates are (a) hollow dorsal nerve chord, (b) notochord, (c) pharyngeal slits, and (d) postanal tail.	35.1	
*2. The evidence supporting lancelets as the vertebrate ancestors are (a) feeding with cilia, (b) single-layered skin, (c) fossils predating fishes, and (d) molecular evidence.	35.2	
*3. The five characteristics separating vertebrates from other chordates are (a) vertebral column, (b) well-differentiated head, (c) neural crests, (d) well-developed diverse internal organs, and (e) endoskeleton.	35.3	
*4. Blood flow in the opposite direction from water flow maximizes oxygenation.	35.4	
*5. Bony fish have swim bladders that can be filled with air or emptied to adjust buoyancy.	35.4	
*6. By opening and closing the operculum and mouth in coordination, fishes achieve a bellows-like action that pumps water over the gills.	35.4	
*7. Amphibians have a pulmonary vein that causes blood to flow to the heart maintaining a higher pressure with more force as the blood is pumped to the body. The amphibian heart has separate chambers that reduce mixing of oxygenated blood with deoxygenated blood.	35.5	

	Sect.	Rvw.
*8. Reptiles earned the title of the first truly terrestrial vertebrates because of (a) better leg position, (b) thoracic breathing, (c) more efficient heart, (d) moisture-conserving skin, and (e) watertight eggs.	35.6	
*9. Birds have a four-chambered heart in which oxygenated blood and deoxygenated blood never mix.	35.7	
*10. Mammalian characteristics supporting endothermy are (a) hair, (b) four-chambered heart, and (c) a diaphragm.	35.8	
11. a	35.2	
12. b	35.2	
13. a	35.3	
14. b	35.4	
15. e	35.4	
*16. b	35.4	
17. e	35.5	
18. c	35.5	
19. d	35.5	
20. a	35.5	
21. b	35.6	
*22. d	35.6	
23. e	35.6	
*24. d	35.6	
*25. a	35.7	
26. d	35.7	
27. b	35.8	
28. b	35.8	
*29. e	35.8	
*30. d	35.4	

CHAPTER 36 PLANT FORM

MASTERING KEY CONCEPTS

This chapter is about plant structures and how they got that way.

36.1 Plant body development depends on the activities of meristems.

- **Overview**: **Vascular plants** have **root systems** that anchor the plant and allow it to penetrate the soil to obtain water and nutrients, and **shoot systems** consisting of stems and leaves, which are the principle photosynthetic structures of the plant. Roots and shoots have three basic types of tissue: **dermal**, **ground**, and **vascular**. Dermal tissue forms the outer protective covering of the plant, ground tissue supports and protects the plant, and also plays a role in storage, photosynthesis, and secretion. Vascular tissue carries liquid and nutrients throughout the plant. Development of the plant body depends on repeated cell divisions of the apical and lateral meristems. **Apical meristems**, located at the tips of the shoots and the roots, extend the plant above and below ground and produce the **primary plant body**. The apical meristems initiate the **protoderm**, **procambium**, and **ground meristem,** which give rise to the three tissue systems. **Secondary growth**, or an increase in the diameter of the roots and shoots, is due to the **lateral meristems**. Woody plants have two lateral meristems, the **cork cambium** and the **vascular cambium**.
- **Details**: Know the three types of plant tissues and their functions. Know how plant cell types can be distinguished.

36.2 Plants have three basic tissues, each composed of several cell types.

- **Overview**: **Dermal cells** arise from the **protoderm** and form dermal tissue, which forms the plant **epidermis**. The epidermis is typically one cell layer thick. The epidermis is typically covered by a waxy **cuticle**. Dermal tissue is also the tissue responsible for forming the bark of trees. **Guard cells** are specialized epidermal cells that flank **stomata,** which allow the passage of oxygen and carbon dioxide, and the diffusion of water in plants. **Trichomes** are another specialized cell in the epidermis that produces hairlike outgrowths. **Root hairs** are extensions of the epidermal cells that increase the surface area and absorption efficiency of the roots. Ground tissue consists of **parenchyma**, **collenchyma**, and **sclerenchyma cells**. Parenchyma cells function in food and water storage, photosynthesis, and secretion. Collenchyma cells provide support for plant organs and in the plant stem. Sclerenchyma cells

have secondary cell walls that commonly contain **lignin**. These cells are present either as **fibers** or **sclereids**. Fibers are long strands of cells and sclereids are branched cells. Both cell types provide support and protection to plant tissue. Vascular tissue, including **xylem** (water-conducting) and **phloem** (food-conducting), is derived from the **procambium**. Xylem distributes water, dissolved minerals, and inorganic ions throughout the plant and provides it with support. The conduction of food in plants is carried out by phloem tissue through **sieve cells** and **sieve-tube members**, two porous cell types. Sieve-tube members are associated with specialized parenchyma cells known as **companion cells**.
- **Details**: Know how each of the three different tissues functions in plants. Know the three specialized cells that occur in the epidermis and how they function. Know the three different cell types found in ground tissue and their functions. Know the two kinds of conducting tissues.

36.3 Root cells differentiate as they become distanced from the dividing root apical meristem.

- **Overview**: **Root caps** are composed of **columella cells** located on the inside, and **root cap cells** located on the outside. The main functions of the root cap are to protect the tissues behind it as the root grows down into the soil, and to sense gravity so that the roots are bent in the proper direction. The **zone of cell division** is located in the center of the root tip just behind the root cap. Cells at the edge of the apical meristem in this region undergo rapid division. Daughter cells of the apical meristem subdivide to form the protoderm, procambium, and ground meristem. Roots lengthen in the **zone of elongation** and no further increase in cell size occurs above this region. These lengthened cells become differentiated in the **zone of maturation** into epidermal cells on the outside, parenchyma cells that form the **cortex** beneath the epidermis, endodermal cells below the cortex, and **pericycle cells** located at the interior of the **endodermis**. Primary xylem and phloem cells are differentiated in discrete groups of cells located inside the endodermal layer. Modifications to the root systems in plants can give rise to **adventitious roots** that have a variety of different functions other than anchoring and absorption.
- **Details**: Know the location of the four main regions, cell types, and tissues present in developing roots. Recognize the difference between the zone of maturation in monocots and eudicots. Know the functions of adventitious roots.

36.4 Stems are the backbone of the shoot, transporting nutrients and supporting the aerial plant organs.

- **Overview**: The shoot apical meristem gives rise to stem tissue that has bulges (**primordial**) that can develop into leaves, flowers, or other shoots. Leaves are attached to a stem at **nodes** and typically are arranged alternately, opposite to each other, or whorled, with **internodes** between them. **Axillary buds** are formed at the axil of each leaf. Stems of plants lacking a cork cambium, such as monocots, and herbaceous eudicots are typically green and photosynthetic. Unlike eudicots, monocots lack a vascular cambium and cannot undergo secondary growth. In woody eudicots, the cork cambium gives rise to the outer bark. Patches of unsuberized cells beneath the stomata called **lenticels** allow gas exchange to continue after the cork is produced. Plants can form modified stems that have specialized functions such as increasing the storage and photosynthetic capabilities of the plant.
- **Details**: Know the structures unique to stems and their locations. Recognize the difference in the organization of the vascular tissue system in monocot and eudicot stems. Know the functions of the vascular and cork cambiums.

36.5 Leaves are adapted to support basic plant functions.

- **Overview**: **Leaves** are the primary sites where photosynthesis takes place in a plant. Their arrangement, form, size, and internal structure can vary greatly but are critically important to balancing water loss and gas exchange to maximize the photosynthetic capabilities of a plant. There are two different morphological groupings of leaves. **Microphylls** have one vein branching from the vascular cylinder of the stem that does not extend the length of the leaf, while **megaphylls** have many veins. The main monocot veins are typically parallel, and the leaves lack a **petiole**; eudicot veins form an intricate network in leaves with a flattened **blade** and a slim petiole. **Simple leaves** have blades that are undivided, but can have teeth, indentations, or lobes. **Compound leaves** are divided into **leaflets**. Leaves have an upper and a lower epidermis with **mesophyll** in between. Closest to the upper epidermis is the **palisade mesophyll** made of **chlorenchyma cells**, while the mesophyll closest to the lower epidermis is arranged in **spongy layers**. Modified leaves have adapted to allow a wide range of functions, such as underground photosynthesis (window leaves), plant reproduction (reproductive leaves), and reduction water loss and protection against predators (spines).
- **Details**: Know the external and internal structures of a leaf. Know the two explanations for the development of compound leaves. Know the modified functions of some leaves.

CHALLENGING YOUR UNDERSTANDING

1. In the following diagram of a three-year-old eudicot stem, label the primary and secondary xylem and phloem.

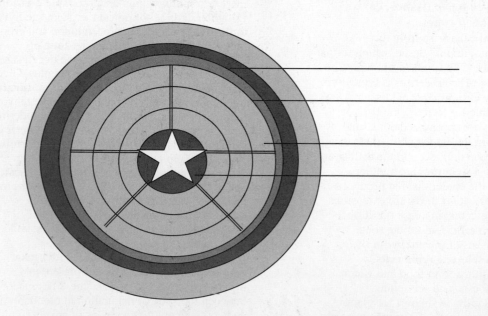

2. For the following flowcharts, fill in the blanks to indicate how the chapter concepts relate to each other.

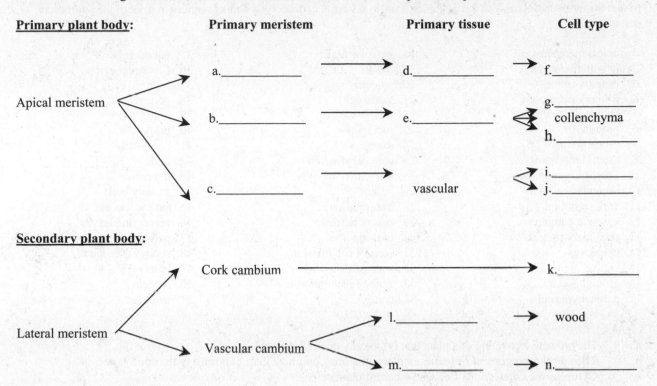

| **Primary plant body:** | **Primary meristem** | **Primary tissue** | **Cell type** |

Apical meristem

a._____ → d._____ → f._____

b._____ → e._____ → g._____
collenchyma
h._____

c._____ → vascular → i._____
j._____

Secondary plant body:

Lateral meristem

Cork cambium → k._____

Vascular cambium → l._____ → wood

m._____ → n._____

3. Draw a developing root. On your diagram, label the root cap, zone of cell division, zone of elongation, zone of maturation, epidermis, endodermis, apical meristem, and the ground and vascular tissue.

KEY TERMS

Match the numbered term with the definition that fits it best. Put the corresponding number in front of the appropriate definition.

1. apical meristems
2. lateral meristems
3. primary tissues
4. primary plant body
5. primary meristems
6. protoderm
7. procambium
8. ground meristem
9. intercalary meristems
10. secondary growth
11. cork cambium
12. vascular cambium
13. secondary tissues
14. epidermis
15. cuticle
16. ground tissue
17. parenchyma cells

18. vascular tissue
19. xylem
20. phloem
21. guard cells
22 trichomes
23. root hairs
24. stoma
25. collenchyma cells
26. sclerenchyma cells
27. lignin
28. transpiration
29. plasmodesmata
30. root cap
31. zone of cell division
32. zone of elongation
33. zone of maturation
34. cortex

35. endodermis
36. Casparian strips
37. stele
38. pericycle
39. pith
40. primordia
41. phyllotaxy
42. node
43. internode
44. axillary bud
45. simple leaves
46. compound leaves
47. palisade mesophyll
48. spongy mesophyll
49. bracts
50. suberin
51. lenticels

a. _____ The protective covering of a plant that is typically one cell layer thick.
b. _____ The spiral arrangement of leaves in plants that may optimize their exposure to the sun.
c. _____ Cytoplasmic connections between adjacent plant cells.
d. _____ Cells that divide to continually add more cells to the tips of stems and roots.
e. _____ Tissue made of tightly packed, cylindrical chlorenchyma cells located beneath the upper epidermis.
f. _____ Tissue system that arises in the stem internodes of some plants adding to the internode lengths.
g. _____ Tubular extensions of individual epidermal cells that occur behind the tips of growing roots.
h. _____ Region in the root where the cells produced by the primary meristems become longer increasing root length.
i. _____ Conducting tissues, such as xylem and phloem, that move fluids and dissolved substances through the plant.
j. _____ The ground tissue occupying the center of the stem or root within the vascular cylinder.
k. _____ An increase in the diameter of the stems or roots of vascular plants by division of the lateral meristems.
l. _____ A highly branched polymer that increases the rigidity of plant cell walls.
m. _____ Bands of suberin that surround each adjacent endodermal cell wall perpendicular to the root's surface..
n. _____ Leaves in which the blades are undivided, but may have teeth, indentations, or lobes of various sizes.
o. _____ Tissues derived from the apical meristems.
p. _____ A fatty substance impervious to water that the endodermal primary walls are impregnated with.
q. _____ Cellular or multicellular hairlike outgrowths of the epidermis.
r. _____ The primary meristem that gives rise to primary vascular tissues.
s. _____ The region or area of leaf attachment to the stem.
t. _____ A type of plant tissue involved in storage, photosynthesis, secretion, support, and protection.
u. _____ Large modified leaves that surround the true flowers and perform the same function as showy petals.
v. _____ Region of the root where cells differentiate into specific cell types.
w. _____ Tissues formed from the lateral meristems that make up the trunk, branches, and older roots.
x. _____ The extensions of the roots and stems derived from apical meristem tissues.
y. _____ The diffusion of water vapor into the intercellular spaces and out of the leaves into the surrounding air.
z. _____ All of the tissues interior to the endodermis.
aa. _____ Tissue located between the palisade mesophyll and the lower epidermis that has many air spaces within it.
bb. _____ Paired, sausage-shaped cells flanking the stomata that are required to open and close them.
cc. _____ A bud found in the axil of a stem and leaf that may develop into a new shoot or may become a flower.
dd. _____ The region of the root whose main function is to protect the delicate tissues behind it as growth extends it.
ee. _____ A lateral meristem that produces the outer bark of a tree.
ff. _____ The protoderm, procambium, and ground meristem produced by the apical meristem.
gg. _____ Cells with tough, thick walls that are present as fibers, or sclereids, and are important for plant strength.
hh. _____ Patches of unsuberized cells beneath the stomata that allow the interchange of gases through cork.

ii. _____ A lateral meristem located just beneath the back that produces secondary vascular tissue.

jj. _____ In vascular plants, these cells produce an increase in root and shoot diameter, or secondary growth.

kk. _____ The most common type of plant cell functioning in food and water storage, photosynthesis, and secretion.

ll. _____ Leaves in which the blade is divided into leaflets.

mm. _____ An epidermal opening where the passage of oxygen, carbon dioxide, and water vapor takes place.

nn. _____ The layer of cells forming the innermost layer of the cortex in roots and some stems of vascular plants.

oo. _____ The primary meristem that differentiates further into ground tissue.

pp. _____ Bulges produced intermittently by the shoot apical meristem that can develop into leaves, other shoots, or flowers.

qq. _____ The principal food-conducting tissue in vascular plants located toward the outer part of roots and stems.

rr. _____ Tough, flexible cells that provide support for plant organs and stems so they can bend without breaking.

ss. _____ A cylinder of parenchyma cells immediately adjacent and interior to the endodermis.

tt. _____ A waxy or fatty noncellular layer that covers the epidermis in young, exposed parts of the plant.

uu. _____ Region in young roots including the root apical meristem and adjacent cells where cells divide every 12-36 hours.

vv. _____ The primary meristem that forms the epidermis.

ww. _____ The principal water-conducting tissue of plants consisting of vessels and tracheids.

xx. _____ The area of the stem of a plant between two nodes.

yy. _____ The external primary ground tissue of a stem or root.

LEARNING BY EXPERIENCE

Complete the following table by filling in the function and components (variations as to type or as to cell types included).

TISSUE	(A) FUNCTION	(B) COMPONENTS
1. PARENCHYMA		
2. COLLENCHYMA		
3. SCLERENCHYMA		
4. XYLEM		
5. PHLOEM		
6. EPIDERMIS		

EXERCISING YOUR KNOWLEDGE

Briefly answer each of the following questions in the space provided.

1. What is the process by which meristems are continually replenished?

2. What is the maturation process for vessels?

3. What makes up the dermal system of plants that are limited to primary growth?

4. Compare the arrangement of vascular tissues in primary and secondary growth of stems.

5. How do trichomes and root hairs differ in structure?

6. What are special functions of parenchyma cells?

7. Describe the internal structure of a eudicot leaf.

8. What function is performed by the root cap other than protection?

9. What is the function of lenticels?

10. If you were to examine a rhizome, how could you tell whether it is a root or a stem?

Circle the letter of the one best answer in each of the following questions.

11. All of the following are derived from apical meristem except
    a. protoderm.
    b. vascular cambium.
    c. procambium.
    d. ground meristem.
    e. primary meristem.

12. Which of the following cells can contain chloroplasts?
    a. guard cells
    b. parenchyma
    c. monocot cortex
    d. all of the above
    e. none of the above

13. Which of the following is responsible for keeping leaf surfaces cool and reducing evaporation?
    a. guard cells
    b. parenchyma cells
    c. trichomes
    d. vessels
    e. tracheids

14. Rings in the stump of a tree reveal annual patterns of _____ growth.
    a. cortex
    b. vascular cambium
    c. dermal tissue
    d. cork cambium
    e. pith

15. Which of the following is not a basic plant tissue?
    a. pith
    b. ground tissue
    c. dermal tissue
    d. vascular tissue
    e. none of these

16. The gritty texture of pears is caused by
    a. sclerids.
    b. collenchyma.
    c. tracheids.
    d. parenchyma.
    e. pits.

17. Mature sclerenchyma cells are
    a. suberized and contain no living protoplasts.
    b. thin walled and often contain chloroplasts.
    c. lignified and contain living protoplasts.
    d. suberized and contain living protoplasts.
    e. lignified and contain no living protoplasts.

18. The form of conducting elements found almost exclusively in angiosperms is
    a. sieve cells.
    b. vessels.
    c. tracheids.
    d. sieve tubes.
    e. rays.

19. The outward cell division of the root apical meristem produces the
    a. root hairs.
    b. xylem.
    c. branch roots.
    d. root cap.
    e. pith parenchyma.

20. The outermost layer of the stele of a root is the
    a. cortex.
    b. endodermis.
    c. pericycle.
    d. pith.
    e. xylem.

21. Haustoria are a form of _____ roots.
    a. aerial
    b. adventitious
    c. buttress
    d. parasitic
    e. food storage

22. Which of the following is not a part of the outer protective layer of a mature stem?
    a. cork cambium
    b. phelloderm
    c. periderm
    d. cork
    e. epidermis

23. Wood consists of accumulated
    a. primary xylem.
    b. phloem.
    c. sclerenchyma.
    d. secondary xylem.
    e. secondary phloem.

24. The arrangement of _____ is directly related to the ability of a stem to undergo secondary growth.
    a. apical meristems
    b. ground tissue
    c. vascular tissue
    d. periderm
    e. collenchyma cells

25. The Irish potato is a
    a. bulb.
    b. tuber.
    c. corm.
    d. rhizome.
    e. stolon.

26. Which of the following is not part of the periderm?
    a. cork
    b. phelloderm
    c. cork cambium
    d. epidermis
    e. none of the above

27. Cactus stems may be modified into photosynthetic
    a. spines.
    b. cladophylls.
    c. tendrils.
    d. stolons.
    e. rhizomes.

28. The onion is an example of a
    a. tuber.
    b. rhizome.
    c. corm.
    d. bulb.
    e. stolon.

29. Venation of monocot leaves would best be described as
    a. palmate.
    b. alternate.
    c. parallel.
    d. pinnate.
    e. whorled.

30. When they emerge on a vascular plant, primordia are committed to becoming which of the following?
    a. shoots
    b. leaves
    c. flowers
    d. all of the above
    e. none of the above

ASSESSING YOUR KNOWLEDGE

Answers to the questions in this section test your ability to synthesize information gained from the chapter and to solve challenging problems on an exam or in everyday life.

Challenging Your Understanding—Answers

1.

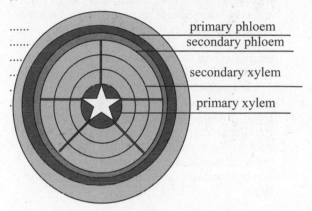

primary phloem
secondary phloem

secondary xylem

primary xylem

2. a. protoderm; b. ground; c. procambium; d. dermal; e. ground; f. epidermis; g-h. parenchyma, sclerenchyma; i-j. xylem, phloem; k. outer bark, l. secondary xylem; m. secondary phloem; n. inner bark.

3. Refer to figure 36.14 in the text.

Key Terms—Answers

a. 14, b. 41, c. 29, d. 1, e. 47, f. 9, g. 23, h. 32, i. 18, j. 39, k. 10, l. 27, m. 36, n. 45, o. 3, p. 50, q. 22, r. 7, s. 42, t. 16, u. 49, v. 33, w. 13, x. 4, y. 28, z. 37, aa. 48, bb. 21, cc. 44, dd. 30, ee. 11, ff. 5, gg. 26, hh. 51, ii. 12, jj. 2, kk. 17, ll. 46, mm. 24, nn. 35, oo. 8, pp. 40, qq. 20, rr. 25, ss. 38, tt. 15, uu. 31, vv. 6, ww. 19, xx. 43, yy. 34.

Learning by Experience—Answers

1.	(A) Photosynthesis, storage, secretion	
	(B) Spongy, palisade	
2.	(A) Support	
	(B) Fibers	
3.	(A) Rigidity	
	(B) Fibers, sclerids	
4.	(A) Water conduction	
	(B) Vessel elements, tracheids	
5.	(A) Food conduction	
	(B) Sieve cells, sieve-tube members, and companion cells	
6.	(A) Covering, gas regulation	
	(B) Guard cells, trichomes, root hairs	

Exercising Your Knowledge—Answers

As you check your answers, put a mark in the review (Rvw.) column for the answers you missed. If you didn't miss any, congratulations—you have mastered the chapter! If you missed some, review the section (Sect.) in the text where this concept is discussed. In order to develop an efficient review strategy, it is important that you understand what types of questions you missed. The questions with asterisks test more for understanding of the **concepts**, whereas the others test more for **detail**. *See the preface for learning strategies for concepts and for detail.*

	Sect.	Rvw.
*1. Each time a meristem cell divides, one cell becomes specialized but the other cell remains meristem.	36.1	
*2. Vessel cells secrete lignin into the cellulose wall, and the protoplast dies.	36.2	
*3. The dermal system of plants with only primary growth is made up of cuticle-covered epidermis.	36.2	
*4. In primary growth, xylem and phloem are together in the same bundle. In secondary growth, the xylem is toward the inside and the phloem is toward the outside.	36.4	
*5. Trichomes are one-celled to multicellular structures, whereas root hairs are extensions of epidermal cells.	36.2	
*6. Storage, nectar, and resin secretion are special functions of parenchyma.	36.2	
*7. A eudicot leaf has an upper and a lower epidermis. Just below the upper epidermis is the palisade mesophyll consisting of tightly packed rows of chlorenchyma cells. Between the palisade mesophyll and the lower epidermis is the spongy mesophyll that is loosely arranged and has many air spaces throughout the tissue.	36.5	
*8. The columella of the root cap senses gravity.	36.3	
*9. Lenticels permit gases to pass through bark to the living tissues inside.	36.4	
*10. The presence of scalelike leaves and axillary buds would indicate that a rhizome is a stem	36.4	
*11. b	36.1	
12. d	36.2	
*13. c	36.2	
*14. b	36.4	
15. a	36.2	
16. a	36.2	
*17. c	36.2	
18. b	36.2	
*19. d	36.3	
20. b	36.3	
21. d	36.3	
*22. e	36.4	
23. d	36.2	
24. c	36.4	
25. b	36.4	
26. d	36.4	
27. b	36.5	
28. d	36.4	
29. c	36.5	
30. d	36.4	

CHAPTER 37 VEGETATIVE PLANT DEVELOPMENT

MASTERING KEY CONCEPTS
There are two areas in this chapter where action is going on simultaneously: the embryo and the cells associated with it, and the old sporophyte providing the ovule, etc. The chapter starts with the embryo.

37.1 Plant embryo development establishes a basic body plan.
- **Overview**: Two sperm are released from the pollen tube into the embryo sac resulting in double fertilization in angiosperms. One sperm fuses with the egg to form the **zygote**, and the second sperm fuses with the polar nuclei to form a triploid primary endosperm nucleus. Cell division of the zygote produces the **embryo**, and a **suspensor** cell, while division of the triploid nucleus produces the **endosperm,** which serves as a nutrient source for the embryo. The vertical axis of the plant is established by the point of sperm entry and environmental signals, such as light and gravity. The radial axis is established by alternate synchronous cell divisions either parallel or perpendicular to the embryo surface. As a result, the three primary tissues are organized radially around the root-shoot axis. The *stm* and *hobbit* mutants in *Arabidopsis* established that root and shoot meristems are independently regulated. *STM* is required for shoot but not root meristem development, while *HOBBIT* is required for root, but not shoot meristem development. Primary meristems and **cotyledons**, or bulges in the heart-shaped embryo produced by the embryonic cells, differentiate while the embryo is in the **globular stage**. Changes in cell shape and the plane in which cells divide determine the form of a plant body (**morphogenesis**). During embryogenesis in angiosperms, a food supply is established, ovule tissue differentiates to form a hard covering around the embryo, and the carpel wall develops into the fruit. At the end of embryogenesis, a seed becomes **dormant** until germination when the apical meristems resume the addition of cells to the root and shoot tips.
- **Details**: Understand the stages of development in an angiosperm embryo and asymmetrical cell division in a *Fucus* zygote. Understand how the *STM, HOBBIT,* and *MONOPTEROS* genes function in meristem formation. Know three critical events that occur in angiosperms during embryo development.

37.2 The seed protects the dormant embryo from water loss.
- **Overview**: A **seed** contains a dormant embryo and stored food enclosed in an impermeable **seed coat** that develops from the outer layers of the **ovule**. The formation of seeds has several advantages. First, seeds can remain dormant until conditions favor the development of the plant. Second, seeds protect the young plant. Third, seeds contain stored food that nourishes the plant before photosynthesis can begin, and finally, seeds are vehicles for dispersal of plant embryos. Some seeds are sealed in tough cones that can only be opened by the heat of fire, others require inhibitory chemicals to be leached from their seed coats, while others need to be digested by birds or mammals before they germinate. These adaptations ensure that the conditions are right for the seeds to germinate.
- **Details**: Know the advantages of plant embryos forming seeds. Understand the conditions necessary for seeds to germinate. Know what types of adaptations some seeds use to ensure that the conditions are right for germination to begin.

37.3 Fruit formation enhances the dispersal of seeds.
- **Overview**: **Fruit** development, like seed development, is critical to the survival of angiosperm embryos. Fruit development can occur without seed development, but typically it accompanies the development of a seed coat around the embryo and endosperm. In this way, the seed matures within the developing fruit. Fruits are the **mature ovaries** of a plant. Three layers—the **exocarp**, **mesocarp**, and **endocarp**—can have different fates, which determine the type of fruit that a plant produces. Fruits enhance seed (embryo) dispersal. Colorful, fleshy fruits are dispersed by birds or other mammals that eat them and the seeds they contain. Fruits with hooked spines are dispersed by sticking to the fur of animals or to clothing. Some fruits are buried; others are dispersed by wind, water, or on the wings of birds.
- **Details:** Know why the formation of fruits is an important innovation in seed dispersal. Know the different methods by which seeds are dispersed inside fruits.

37.4 Germination initiates postseed development.
- **Overview**: The emergence of the **radicle** from the seed coat marks the beginning of **germination**. This occurs when the seed encounters water and the metabolic activities of the embryo resume. The absorption of water breaks the seed coat and allows the embryo access to oxygen. Seeds also require environmental signals in order to germinate. The seeds of many plants have to be held at low temperatures for a period of time (**stratified**) before they germinate. Digestion of metabolic

reserves, such as fats, oils, and starch, stored in **amyloplasts** are required for germination. Plant hormones signal the endosperm to produce α-**amylase**, an enzyme that breaks down the starch of the endosperm. These sugars are passed to the embryo through the **scutellum**. As the sporophyte emerges from the seed coat, it is oriented so the root grows down and the shoot grows up. Postembryonic growth is characterized by the shoot becoming photosynthetic.

- **Details**: Know the external and internal cues that trigger germination. Know how starch metabolism is initiated and inhibited. Know how the emerging root and shoots are protected.

CHALLENGING YOUR UNDERSTANDING

Fill in the blanks in the following flowchart to indicate how the chapter concepts relate to each other

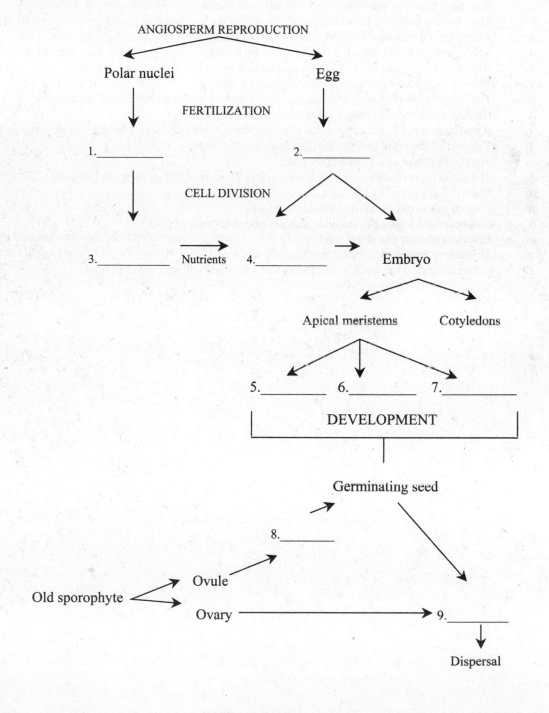

KEY TERMS

Match the numbered term with the definition that fits it best. Put the corresponding number in front of the appropriate definition.

1. suspensor	7. fruits	13. aleurone
2. endosperm	8. pericarp	14. coleoptile
3. embryo	9. stratified	15. coleorhiza
4. cotyledons	10. seed bank	16. integuments
5. morphogenesis	11. amyloplasts	17. radicle
6. seed coat	12. scutellum	18. germination

a. _____ The three layers of the ovary wall that can have distinct fates accounting tor the diversity of fruit types.

b. _____ The massive structure formed by modification of the cotyledon in cereal grains where food is stored.

c. _____ An elongated structure that links the embryo to the nutrient tissue of the seed.

d. _____ Seed leaves that store food in dicots or absorb it in monocots, providing nourishment during germination.

e. _____ An additional tissue layer in monocots that surrounds and protects the radicle.

f. _____ The ungerminated seeds in the soil of a particular area.

g. _____ The impermeable covering that encloses a seed with its dormant embryo and stored food.

h. _____ Holding seeds for periods of time at low temperatures.

i. _____ A nutrient source found in the seeds of angiosperms, which develops from the sperm fusing with the polar nuclei.

j. _____ The part of the plant embryo that develops into the root.

k. _____ The development of a plant's body form.

l. _____ The outer layer of endosperm in a seed that produces α-amylase to break down starch during germination.

m. _____ Mature ovaries or carpels.

n. _____ Formed as a result of cell division in the zygote.

o. _____ The outer cell layers of the ovule that develop into the seed coat.

p. _____ Colorless plastids that store starch.

q. _____ The resumption of growth and development of a seed.

r. _____ An additional tissue layer in monocots that surrounds and protects the shoot.

LEARNING BY EXPERIENCE

In the spaces provided, list (a) seed dispersal mechanisms and (b) an example of each.

1. (a)

    (b)

2. (a)

    (b)

3. (a)

    (b)

4. (a)

    (b)

5. (a)

    (b)

6. (a)

    (b)

7. (a)

    (b)

EXERCISING YOUR KNOWLEDGE

Briefly answer each of the following questions in the space provided.

1. What establishes the root-shoot axis?

2. Besides establishing the root-shoot axis, what important events occur during embryogenesis?

3. What does the suspensor do for the embryo?

4. What are the sources of (a) the dermal tissue, (b) the ground tissue, and (c) the vascular tissue?

5. How do cotyledons form?

6. From what does morphogenesis result?

7. What is the source of the seed coat?

8. What floral structure gives rise to the fruit?

9. What is the relationship between fruit color and seed dispersal?

10. How are the scutellum and aleurone involved in the nutrition of the embryo?

Circle the letter of the one best answer in each of the following questions.

11. After the zygote divides, the larger cell near the micropyle develops into the
    a. ground meristem.
    b. shoot apical meristem.
    c. suspensor.
    d. protoderm.
    e. root apical meristem.

12. The first cell division of the plant zygote is typically
    a. longitudinal.
    b. diagonal.
    c. radial.
    d. spiral.
    e. asymmetrical.

13. The suspensor formed in angiosperm seed development links
    a. root to shoot.
    b. stems to leaves.
    c. embryo to nutrients.
    d. cotyledon to epicotyl.
    e. endosperm to ectosperm.

14. A wild-type seedling depends on auxin-induced genes to
    a. inhibit *shootmeristemless*.
    b. activate *HOBBIT*.
    c. inhibit shoot formation.
    d. initiate root formation.
    e. inhibit *MONOPTEROS*.

15. In the angiosperm embryo, the cells near the suspensor are destined to form
    a. cotyledons.
    b. a root.
    c. endosperm.
    d. the plumule.
    e. a shoot.

16. The outermost cells in the plant embryo become
    a. vascular tissue.
    b. ovule.
    c. ground tissue.
    d. dermal tissue.
    e. apical meristem.

17. The ability of *Fucus* cells to remember where the rhizoid will form depends on which of the following?
    a. cell wall components
    b. location of the small bulge
    c. point of sperm entry
    d. external ion gradients
    e. asymmetrical divisions

18. As the spherical embryo develops, all of the tissues listed below develop except
    a. ground meristem.
    b. apical meristem.
    c. procambium.
    d. protoderm.
    e. integuments.

19. In plant embryo development, the bulk of the embryonic interior is
    a. epidermal cells.
    b. ground tissue.
    c. mesodermal tissue.
    d. vascular tissue.
    e. endodermal tissue.

20. In *stm* mutants,
    a. a root forms but shoots do not.
    b. shoots form but roots do not.
    c. neither roots nor shoots form.
    d. shoots form but do not produce leaves.
    e. the stem formed lacks chlorophyll.

21. Cotyledons are derived from
    a. nonmeristem embryo tissue.
    b. shoot apical meristem.
    c. protoderm.
    d. procambium.
    e. lateral meristem.

22. Water makes up about _____% of a mature seed.
    a. 1–3
    b. 5–20
    c. 25–40
    d. 45–60
    e. 75

23. When the seed coat forms, most of the metabolic activity
    a. slows down.
    b. accelerates.
    c. fluctuates.
    d. ceases.
    e. continues as before.

24. The seed coat forms from the
    a. cotyledons.
    b. ovary.
    c. hypocotyl.
    d. embryo dermal tissue.
    e. ovule.

25. In the seed, the gametophyte generation is represented by the
    a. endosperm.
    b. embryo.
    c. seed coat.
    d. meristems.
    e. none of these.

26. A tomato is an example of a
    a. legume.
    b. berry.
    c. drupe.
    d. hesperidium.
    e. samara.

27. A cherry is a
    a. legume.
    b. berry.
    c. drupe.
    d. samaras.
    e. multiple fruit.

28. When a cereal grain germinates, the food reserve of the _____ is used first.
    a. scutellum
    b. suspensor
    c. aleurone
    d. endosperm
    e. apical meristem

29. Food is stored in seeds in the form of
    a. starch.
    b. proteins.
    c. fats.
    d. oils.
    e. all of these.

30. When cereal grains germinate, α-amylase and other hydrolytic enzymes are secreted by the
    a. scutellum.
    b. suspensor.
    c. aleurone layer.
    d. endosperm.
    e. apical meristem.

ASSESSING YOUR KNOWLEDGE

Answers to the questions in this section test your ability to synthesize information gained from the chapter and to solve challenging problems on an exam or in everyday life.

Challenging Your Understanding—Answers

1. Triploid primary endosperm nucleus, 2. zygote, 3. endosperm, 4. suspensor, 5-7. protoderm, ground meristem, procambium, 8. seed coat, 9. fruit.

Key Terms—Answers

a. 8, b. 12, c. 1, d. 4, e. 15, f. 10, g. 6, h. 9, i. 2, j. 17, k. 5, l. 13, m. 7, n. 3, o. 16, p. 11, q. 18, r. 14.

Learning by Experience—Answers

1.	(a) animals eating fruits
	(b) berries
2.	(a) hooked spines
	(b) burgrass
3.	(a) winged fruits
	(b) maple
4.	(a) wind-catching devices
	(b) dandelion
5.	(a) flotation
	(b) coconut
6.	(a) buried by absent-minded squirrels
	(b) acorn
7.	(a) windborne dustlike seeds
	(b) orchid

Exercising Your Knowledge—Answers

As you check your answers, put a mark in the review (Rvw.) column for the answers you missed. If you didn't miss any, congratulations—you have mastered the chapter! If you missed some, review the section (Sect.) in the text where this concept is discussed. In order to develop an efficient review strategy, it is important that you understand what types of questions you missed. The questions with asterisks test more for understanding of the **concepts**, whereas the others test more for **detail**. *See the preface for learning strategies for concepts and for detail.*

	Sect.	Rvw.
*1. The root-shoot axis is established by root and shoot apical meristems under the influence of auxins.	37.1	
*2. The endosperm develops from the second fertilization during embryogenesis.	37.1	
*3. The suspensor links the embryo to the food supply and provides a pathway for the nutrients. The suspensor pushes the embryo into the food supply in gymnosperms.	37.1	
*4. (a) Protoderm forms the dermal tissue. (b) Most of the interior of the embryo becomes the ground tissue, and (c) the procambium forms the vascular tissue.	37.1	
*5. Cotyledons form as bulges of nonmeristem tissue (one in monocots and two in dicots) on the side of the embryo.	37.1	
*6. Morphogenesis results from changes in the planes and rates of cell division.	37.1	
*7. The seed coat forms from the integuments of the ovule.	37.2	
*8. The fruit is the ripened ovary.	37.3	
*9. Red and shiny black and blue fruits attract animals that eat them and disperse the seeds.	37.3	
*10. Food stored in the scutellum is one energy source during germination. The aleurone produces α-amylase to break down the starch in the endosperm.	37.4	
11. c	37.1	
12. e	37.1	
13. c	37.1	
14. d	37.1	
15. b	37.1	
16. d	37.1	
17. a	37.1	
18. e	37.1	
19. b	37.1	
*20. a	37.1	
*21. a	37.1	
22. b	37.2	
23. d	37.2	
*24. e	37.2	
*25. e	37.2	
26. b	37.3	
27. c	37.3	
28. a	37.4	
29. e	37.4	
30. c	37.4	

CHAPTER 38 TRANSPORT IN PLANTS

MASTERING KEY CONCEPTS

This chapter deals with how plants acquire nutrients from the environment and how they move and disperse those nutrients throughout the entire plant.

38.1 A water potential gradient from roots to shoots enables transport.

- **Overview**: Plants move water to the height of their stems through the **xylem** by way of the cohesion and adhesion of water, which pulls it upward as a result of **transpiration**. Water can move across plasma membranes by **osmosis** through the lipid bilayer, or by **aquaporins**. Organic molecules diffuse across membranes, or require protein transporters, or energy, to be passively or actively transported across a membrane. **Water potential** (Ψ_w), measured in units of pressure, **megapascals** (MPa), is used to describe which way water will move if a plant cell is placed in a solution. In a hypertonic solution (low water potential), a plant cell will lose water and shrink and the cell membrane will pull away from the cell wall (**plasmolysis**). In a hypotonic solution (high water potential), water will move into the plant by osmosis and increase its **turgor pressure** causing the cells to push against the cell wall (**turgid**). The water potential of a plant cell (Ψ_w) is the sum of its **pressure potential** (Ψ_p), or turgor pressure, and its **solute potential** (Ψ_s), the amount of pressure required to stop osmosis. Water moves into a cell or a solution with lower water potential. Water moves into the roots of a plant if the water potential of the soil is greater than that in the root. Evaporation in the leaves creates negative pressure which pulls water up the stem from the roots.
- **Details**: Know the two components of water potential. Understand how to determine water potential and whether water will move into or out of a cell.

38.2 Root hairs absorb water and transport minerals into plants.

- **Overview**: **Root hair** cells increase the absorptive surface of the root and have plasma membranes with protein transport channels that can move ions into plants against their concentration gradients using hydrogen ion gradients. Interactions between the roots of plants and mycorrhizal fungi also increase the absorptive surface. Water, dissolved minerals, and ions move from the root hairs to the vascular tissue by an **apoplast route**, a **symplast route**, or a **transmembrane route**. Passage through the cell walls is blocked by Casparian strips in the endodermis, forcing molecules to move through the plasma membranes or protoplasts of the endodermal cells to reach the xylem. This allows endodermal cells to regulate water and nutrient flow to the xylem. Once in the xylem, water and nutrients can be transported to other parts of the plant.
- **Details**: Understand the differences between the three transport routes in cells. Understand how transport through the endodermis is regulated.

38.3 Water and minerals move upward through the xylem.

- **Overview**: **Root pressure** occurs as a result of the accumulation of ions in the roots which causes water to continue to move into the root hair cells by osmosis, when transpiration in the leaves is low or absent. This will lead to the transport of water and ions upward through the xylem even when transpiration is not occurring. When root pressure is high, water can be lost from the leaves by **guttation**. The **cohesion-tension theory of the bulk flow** of water in the xylem is based on the **tensile strength** and adhesion of water moving continuously in small plant vessels and tracheids. The larger the vessel, the greater the volume of liquid that can be transported in a particular amount of time. **Cativation**, or a block in a vessel or tracheid by a gas-filled bubble, can break the continuity and cohesion of water and prevent water transport. Minerals also move through the vessels and tracheids of the xylem along with water in an upward flow.
- **Details**: Understand how root pressure affects transport. Know the two factors that explain the bulk flow of water in the xylem, and the effect of cativation.

38.4 Transpiration rates vary to balance water loss and gas exchange.

- **Overview**: The opening and closing of **stomata** balances water loss and gas exchange in plants. Stomata are opened when the solute concentration of **guard cells** increases causing water to enter by osmosis. During the day, sucrose accumulates in the guard cells as a result of photosynthesis. Active transport of this sucrose at night causes a loss in turgor pressure and the guard cells close. Changes in the rate of transpiration due to changes in temperature, wind velocity, and humidity result in the opening or closing of stomata. Plant hormones, such as **abscisic acid (ABA)**, CO_2 concentration, and light also affect the opening of the stomata. **CAM plants** can take in CO_2 at night when the stomata are open and decarboxylate organic compounds during the day to provide CO_2 for fixation when the stomata are closed.
- **Details**: Understand how guard cells regulate the

opening and closing of stomata. Know how ABA, CO_2 concentration, and temperature affect the opening of the stomata. Understand the mechanism by which CAM plants balance water loss and gas exchange.

38.5 Water-stress responses allow plants to survive in adverse conditions.

- **Overview**: Besides regulating the opening and closing of their stomata, plants can prevent water loss on a long-term scale by becoming dormant, or losing their leaves. Some plants have adapted to dry environments by having stomata only on the lower side of their leaves, having trichome-covered leaves, or having stomata that are located in pits reducing transpiration and the rate of water loss. Flood conditions can lead to oxygen deprivation and hormonal changes in plants. Plants can overcome these situations by forming larger lenticels, forming **aerenchyma**, or adventitious roots to allow gas exchange. Plants that grow in water that contains high concentrations of salt have **pneumatophores**, air-filled roots with large lenticels on the portions above water, and leaves that contain a large amount of water. Soil with a high salt concentration can stress plants for water. **Halophytes** are a unique type of plant that can grow in high salt soil.
- **Details**: Understand the mechanisms plants use to survive under drought and flood conditions, and the mechanisms that allow some plants to grow in high salt water or soil.

38.6 Phloem transports materials in all directions.

- **Overview**: Most of the organic molecules made by photosynthesis in the leaves and the stems of plants as well as sucrose are translocated to the other parts of the plant by the **phloem**. The **pressure-flow theory** describes carbohydrate transport through the phloem by active transport from a **source** to a **sink**. **Phloem loading** transports sucrose from mesophyll cells to sieve cells by active transport. As sugars are transported into the phloem at the source, the water potential drops and water moves into the phloem. Turgor pressure drives the sugars to the sink. Loading and unloading of carbohydrates are energy dependent and the direction of phloem can change because the sources and the sinks can change.
- **Details**: Understand how carbohydrates and plant hormones are transported.

CHALLENGING YOUR UNDERSTANDING

1. On the following diagram of cells, draw the three transport routes between the cells.

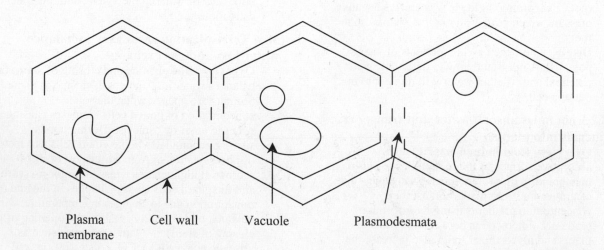

Plasma membrane   Cell wall   Vacuole   Plasmodesmata

2. The following diagram depicts the guard cells surrounding a stoma. In the first part, draw the events that lead to the stoma closing, and in the second part, draw the events that lead to their opening back up. Indicate the ions and molecules of importance. Below each diagram, describe what is happening. At the bottom, indicate whether the stomata would be opened or closed under the conditions listed.

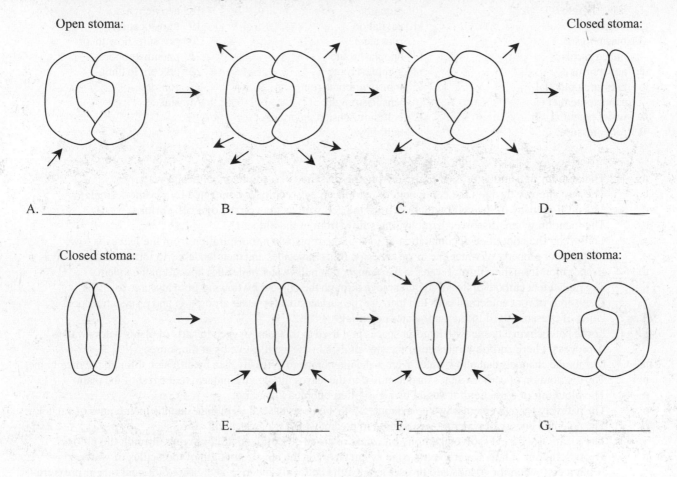

Open stoma:

Closed stoma:

A._____   B._____   C._____   D._____

Closed stoma:

Open stoma:

E._____   F._____   G._____

H._____ CO_2 levels high
I._____ Temperature high/water unfavorable
J._____ Blue light
K._____ CAM plants during the day
L._____ CAM plants at night

3. Distinguish between the transport of water and dissolved substances in the xylem and the transport of carbohydrates in the phloem.

KEY TERMS

Match the numbered term with the definition that fits it best. Put the corresponding number in front of the appropriate definition.

1. transpiration
2. turgid
3. plasmolysis
4. megapascals
5. aquaporins
6. pressure potential
7. solute potential
8. water potential
9. root pressure

10. guttation
11. cavitation
12. root hairs
13. apoplast route
14. symplast route
15. transmembrane route
16. tensile strength
17. cohesion-tension theory of bulk flow

18. aerenchyma
19. translocation
20. pressure-flow theory
21. pneumatophores
22. phloem loading
23. source
24. sink

a. ____ The amount of osmotic pressure arising from the presence of a solute or solutes in water.
b. ____ The passageway through the continuum of cytoplasm between cells connected by plasmodesmata.
c. ____ The pulling away of the cell membrane from the cell wall as the volume of a cell shrinks.
d. ____ The location where dissolved carbohydrates flow from in the phloem.
e. ____ Caused by the continued accumulation of ions in the roots when transpiration from the leaves is low.
f. ____ An inherent property of water due to the cohesion of its molecules and their tendency to form hydrogen bonds.
g. ____ Evaporation from thin films of water in the stomata that pulls water molecules upward in the xylem.
h. ____ The model that carbohydrates in solution move through the phloem by flowing from a source to a sink.
i. ____ Extensions of root epidermal cells that increase the surface area for water absorption and protein transport.
j. ____ Units of pressure used to measure water potential.
k. ____ Loose parenchymal tissue with large air spaces in it used to transport oxygen to parts of plants below water.
l. ____ A process where carbohydrates enter the sieve tubes in the smallest veins at the source.
m. ____ Membrane channels that allow water to cross the membrane more easily than by diffusion through the membrane.
n. ____ The distribution of carbohydrates manufactured in the leaves through the phloem to the rest of the plant.
o. ____ The blocking of a tracheid or vessel by a gas-filled bubble expanding.
p. ____ The pathway for movement of water and minerals that crosses the cell membrane and the membranes of vacuoles.
q. ____ The potential energy of water molecules used to predict which way water will move.
r. ____ The location where dissolved carbohydrates are released and utilized after moving through the phloem.
s. ____ The description of how water moves in the xylem based on the tensile strength of molecules of water.
t. ____ A plant cell when it expands and presses against the cell wall due to an increase in internal turgor pressure.
u. ____ A process in which water is forced up to the leaves and lost in a liquid form due to high root pressure.
v. ____ Long, spongy, air-filled roots that emerge above ground and have large lenticels to take in oxygen.
w. ____ The pathway for the movement of water and minerals that leads through cell walls and between cells.
x. ____ The turgor pressure resulting from pressure against the cell wall.

LEARNING BY EXPERIENCE

Find and list, in the spaces provided, six plant strategies for reducing water loss.

1.

2.

3.

4.

5.

6.

EXERCISING YOUR KNOWLEDGE

Briefly answer each of the following questions in the space provided.

1. What activity causes water to be "pulled" up a stem? Explain how this occurs.

2. In terms of water potential, which direction will water move?

3. What are the two components of water potential?

4. Why are root hairs almost always turgid?

5. In the absence of transpiration, what force moves water up a plant?

6. What mechanism, other than osmosis, moves water through the cell membranes?

7. What is the effect of water potential upon water transport in plants?

8. What factors stabilize the column of water in xylem tissues?

9. What maintains turgidity of guard cells?

10. Since carbohydrates flow from a source to a sink without the expenditure of energy, where does the ATP requirement occur?

Circle the letter of the one best answer in each of the following questions.

11. Most of the force on water that causes upward movement in plants comes from
    a. osmosis.
    b. evaporation.
    c. root absorption.
    d. active transport.
    e. Herkimer's forces.

12. Movement across a plant's cell wall requires
    a. solute pressure.
    b. auxin.
    c. osmotic pressure.
    d. pressure potential.
    e. physical pressure.

13. Water moves from the soil into the plant if the water potential of the root is _____
    a. less than that of the soil.
    b. continuously changing.
    c. greater than that of the soil.
    d. equal to the water potential of the soil.
    e. greater than that of the leaves.

14. The driving force for transpiration is the gradient of which of the following?
    a. solute concentration
    b. xylem
    c. vapor pressure
    d. turgor pressure
    e. none of the above

15. Root pressure
    a. results from active transport.
    b. moves water in the absence of transpiration.
    c. moves water up the xylem.
    d. is not affected by humidity.
    e. All of these are correct.

16. In plants, water rises beyond the point supported by atmospheric pressure mostly because of
    a. capillarity.
    b. gravity.
    c. evaporation.
    d. active transport.
    e. the proton pump.

17. Which of the following does NOT play a role in limiting water leakage out of the root?
    a. endodermis
    b. stomata
    c. epidermis
    d. cortex
    e. none of the above

18. Water potential is the
    a. combination of turgor pressure and pressure potential.
    b. difference between pressure potential and osmotic potential.
    c. combination of pressure potential and solute potential.
    d. product of pressure potential and osmotic potential.
    e. difference between pressure potential and solute potential.

19. In the absence of transpiration, water moves into and up xylem because of
    a. root pressure.
    b. turgor pressure.
    c. evaporation.
    d. high soil mineral concentration.
    e. guttation.

20. Specific ions are acquired by root hairs by the process of
    a. simple diffusion.
    b. osmosis.
    c. active transport.
    d. facilitated diffusion.
    e. reverse osmosis.

21. The tensile strength of water depends on which of the following?
    a. diameter of the column
    b. cohesion of water through hydrogen bonding
    c. adhesion of water to the sides of the vessel
    d. continuity of the water column
    e. all of the above

22. High root pressure can cause water to be lost by the leaves through the process of
    a. respiration.
    b. regurgitation.
    c. transpiration.
    d. guttation.
    e. translocation.

23. The reason that a column of water in a tall tree does not sink because of its weight is
    a. the formation of hydrogen bonds with the plant's vessels.
    b. bubbles form that are too large to be transported.
    c. the presence of strong ion concentrations near the top of the tree.
    d. the venturi effect of air flowing over the stomata.
    e. the tensile strength of a column of water.

24. About ____ % of the water taken in by roots is lost through transpiration.
    a. 100
    b. 90
    c. 80
    d. 60
    e. 50

25. The plant hormone ____ plays a role in the closing of stomata.
    a. auxin
    b. abscisic acid
    c. gibberellin
    d. cytochrome
    e. ethylene

26. Outward bulging of guard cells with increased turgor pressure occurs because of
    a. differences of wall thickness.
    b. wilting of the adjacent epidermal cells.
    c. contractions of the cytoskeleton.
    d. swelling of chloroplasts.
    e. accumulation of starch grains.

27. Loss of turgor pressure in guard cells causes an uptake of
    a. K^+.
    b. H^+.
    c. ATP.
    d. CO_2.
    e. Na^+.

28. When a plant is flooded, it often increases its
    a. cytokines.
    b. ethylene.
    c. gibberellins.
    d. all of these.
    e. none of these.

29. A common adaptation of plants to an aquatic existence is the formation of
    a. chlorenchyma.
    b. aerenchyma.
    c. collenchyma.
    d. sclerenchyma.
    e. hydrenchyma.

30. Scientists take advantage of _____ in studying translocation by phloem.
    a. ants
    b. aphids
    c. bees
    d. butterflies
    e. termites

ASSESSING YOUR KNOWLEDGE

Answers to the questions in this section test your ability to synthesize information gained from the chapter and to solve challenging problems on an exam or in everyday life.

Challenging Your Understanding—Answers

1.

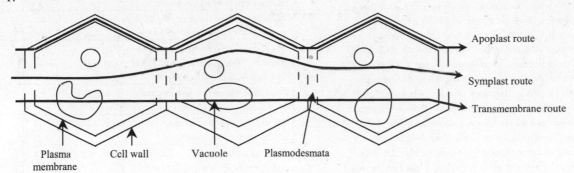

Apoplast route

Symplast route

Transmembrane route

Plasma membrane   Cell wall   Vacuole   Plasmodesmata

2.

Open stoma:

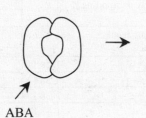

ABA

K^+ K^+

Cl^- Cl^-

Malate^{2-} Malate^{2-}

H_2O H_2O

H_2O H_2O

Closed stoma:

A. ABA binds receptor sites in the plasma membrane of the guard cells.

B. signaling pathway triggered by ABA opens K^+, Cl^-, malate ion channels.

C. water loss follows loss of ions.

D. Guard cells close.

Closed stoma:

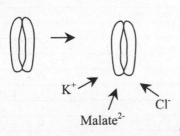

K^+

Malate^{2-} Cl^-

H_2O H_2O

H_2O H_2O

Open stoma:

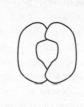

E. K+, Cl-, and malate are actively taken up by the guard cells.

F. Water potential decreases as the solute concentration increases. Water enters by osmosis.

G. Guard cells become turgid and open the stomata.

H. Closed – CO_2 levels high
I. Closed – Temperature high/water unfavorable
J. Open – Blue light
K. Closed – CAM plants during the day
L. Open – CAM plants at night

3. Transpiration is the main force for moving water and ionic solutes from the roots to the shoots. This transport is done through the vessels and tracheids in the xylem, which form hollow tubes from root to shoot. Water molecules connect in a continuous column within the xylem due to their tensile strength. Bulk water flow occurs only upward due to cohesion between water molecules and adhesion to the sides of the vessels and tracheids (cohesion-tension theory). In contrast, transport of carbohydrates and plant hormones in the phloem is bidirectional. Dissolved carbohydrates flow from a source and are released at a sink whose identities change through time depending on need. Carbohydrates enter the sieve tubes at the source in the energy-dependent manner. This loading causes a reduction in water potential. Water moving into the phloem causes an increase in turgor pressure, which drives the carbohydrates to the sink (pressure-flow theory). Water then diffuses back into the xylem. Unlike vessels and tracheids, sieve cells must be alive to participate in active transport at the source, which begins the transport process.

Key Terms—Answers

a. 7, b. 14, c. 3, d. 23, e. 9, f. 16, g. 1, h. 20, i. 12, j. 4, k. 18, l. 22, m. 5, n. 19, o. 11, p. 15, q. 8, r. 24, s. 17, t. 2, u. 10, v. 21, w. 13, x. 6.

Learning by Experience—Answers

1. Closing stomata
2. Shedding leaves
3. Developing thick leaves with few stomata
4. Covering leaf surfaces with trichomes
5. Recessing stomata in crypts or pits
6. Spending dry periods as dormant seeds

Exercising Your Knowledge—Answers

As you check your answers, put a mark in the review (Rvw.) column for the answers you missed. If you didn't miss any, congratulations—you have mastered the chapter! If you missed some, review the section (Sect.) in the text where this concept is discussed. In order to develop an efficient review strategy, it is important that you understand what types of questions you missed. The questions with asterisks test more for understanding of the **concepts**, whereas the others test more for **detail**. *See the preface for learning strategies for concepts and for detail.*

	Sect.	Rvw.
*1. The "pulling" is caused by transpiration. It occurs because water molecules are cohesive and adhesive. They stick to each other and to the walls of the tracheid or xylem vessel.	38.1	
*2. Water moves from an area of higher water potential to one of lower water potential.	38.1	
*3. The two components of water potential are physical forces, such as gravity, and solute concentration in each solution.	38.1	
*4. Active transport by proton pumps maintains a high solute concentration in the root hairs.	38.2	
*5. In the absence of transpiration, water is moved up the plant by root pressure.	38.3	
*6. Aquaporins are water channels that transport water across membranes.	38.1	
*7. Water travels down the water pressure gradient from soil to cell or from cell to cell, etc.	38.1	
*8. The cohesion of water molecules and the adhesion of water to the xylem walls result in a stable column of water.	38.3	
*9. Guard cells remain turgid because of the high solute potential created by actively transporting K^+ into the cells.	38.4	
*10. Phloem loading and unloading requires energy.	38.6	
11. a	38.1	
12. c	38.1	
13. a	38.1	
*14. c	38.1	
15. b	38.3	
16. c	38.1	
*17. b	38.2	
*18. c	38.1	
19. a	38.3	
20. c	38.2	
21. e	38.3	
22. d	38.3	
*23. e	38.3	
24. b	38.4	
25. b	38.4	
26. a	38.4	
*27. a	38.4	
28. b	38.5	
29. b	38.5	
30. b	38.6	

CHAPTER 39 PLANT NUTRITION AND SOILS

MASTERING KEY CONCEPTS

This chapter deals with the materials plants need and how they get them. The information has more than academic importance to anyone who wants to raise plants.

39.1 Soils contain the substrates that plants depend on for growth.

- **Overview**: **Soil** contains the minerals, organic matter, water, and air that plants require to grow. The roots of most plants are embedded in the **topsoil**, the top layer of the soil composed of differing amounts of sand, silt, and clay. Soil particles tend to be negatively charged so active transport is required to move positively charged ions into the cells of a root. Pores among soil particles are necessary to provide plants with water and air. Erosion caused by nature, poor farming practices, or poor landscaping can result in loss of topsoil, which has an adverse affect on crops due to the loss of nutrients and water. Most plants grow best in soils with a neutral pH and a low level of salt ions. At low pH, aluminum released from the rocks is toxic to plant growth. In soils with a high concentration of salt, there is a loss of turgor pressure in plants.
- **Details**: Know the composition of topsoil and how positive ions are moved into the root. Know the approaches that are being used to reduce soil loss and maintain nutrient levels in the soil. Understand why plants typically have difficulty growing in soils that are too acidic or contain a high salt concentration.

39.2 Plants require a variety of nutrients.

- **Overview**: In addition to the simple sugars produced by photosynthesis, plants require other nutrients, some in large quantities, **macronutrients**, and others in small quantities, **micronutrients**. The nutritional requirements of plants are determined by growing plants in hydroponic cultures lacking specific nutrients. Plants are analyzed for any detrimental effects that occur as a result of loss of specific nutrients. Plants can be genetically altered to increase their nutritional value.
- **Details**: Know the macronutrients and micronutrients required by plants. Understand how the nutritional requirements of a plant can be determined. Know what methods are being used to fortify foods and what effect these methods have on plants.

39.3 Some plants have novel strategies for obtaining nutrients.

- **Overview**: Symbiotic relationships between some plant groups and some bacteria have evolved because plants lack the ability to fix nitrogen. Bacteria live in close association with the roots of plants or are housed in **nodules** on the plant. Plants provide the bacteria, such as *Rhizobium*, with carbohydrates and oxygen, and the bacteria provide the plant with nitrogen compounds. Signaling between the plant and the bacteria identify the presence of the other, and determine whether there is a species match. Mycorrhizal fungi extend the absorptive surface area of plants and provide plants with phosphorus and some micronutrients. Carnivorous plants, such as pitcher plants, the Venus flytrap, sundews, and aquatic waterwheels, can obtain an adequate amount of nitrogen by capturing and digesting small insects through the release of digestive enzymes. Many other plants use special structures to tap into the nutrient resources of other plants (parasitic plants).
- **Details**: Know the different mechanisms that plants use to obtain nitrogen and phosphorus. Know how nodules are formed in legumes. Know how carnivorous plants trap and digest their prey.

39.4 Global change could alter the balance among photosynthesis, respiration, and use of nutrients acquired through the soil.

- **Overview**: Atmospheric CO_2 levels are increasing due to human-initiated causes. This increase in CO_2 may alter the carbon-nitrogen balance in plants, which is critical to plant growth and plant-eating organisms. As CO_2 levels increase, photosynthesis and plant growth are also increasing, but less nitrogen and other macronutrients are found in the leaves of these plants. As a result, herbivores have to eat more plants in order to obtain adequate amounts of protein. This could result in greater plant loss and could lead to devastating insect infestations and protein deficiencies in human diets. Global warming not only affects atmospheric CO_2 levels and photosynthesis, but may increase the rate of photorespiration as well. Respiration rates in plants are temperature sensitive on a short-term scale, but there is increasing evidence to suggest that the respiration rates may acclimate to temperature increases over long periods of time.
- **Details**: Understand how elevated CO_2 levels and elevated temperatures could affect plants, herbivores, and humans.

39.5 Plants can remove harmful chemicals from the soil by phytoremediation.

- **Overview**: Plants that can secrete a substance to breakdown contaminants in the soil, or take up heavy metals and toxins from the soil and either sequester them, or degrade and release them as nontoxic compounds into the atmosphere can be used for **phytoremediation**. TCE (trichloroethylene) is a volatile solvent that can be taken up from the soil and metabolized to CO_2 and chlorine by poplar trees, but some unmetabolized TCE can enter the atmosphere through the leaves. Some plants can also take up and degrade trinitrotoluene (TNT). Heavy metals, such as arsenic, cadmium, and lead, can also be taken up and sequestered in some plants.

This may occur by metal transporters in the root cell membrane that move the metals through the xylem to the leaves where they are sequestered in the vacuole or trichomes. One problem with this, however, is that animals might eat the plants sequestering the toxic heavy metals.

- **Details**: Know what harmful chemicals are found in the soil and how plants can remove them.

CHALLENGING YOUR UNDERSTANDING—Part I.

1. Fill in the blanks in the following flowchart to identify how the chapter concepts relate to each other.

MAINTENANCE OF PLANT NUTRITION

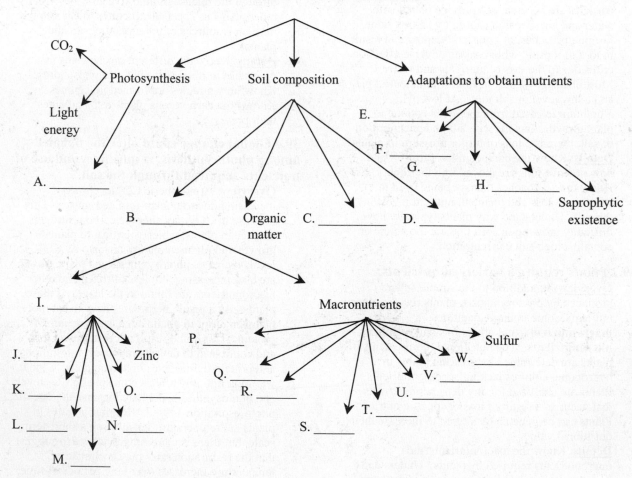

CHALLENGING YOUR UNDERSTANDING—Part II.

2. List four reasons why plants play such an important role in maintaining the world as we know it.

A.

B.

C.

D.

3. Describe three ways in which plants can be used to remove harmful substances from the soil.

A.

B,

C.

4. Describe the effects that elevated CO_2 levels and global warming may have on plant life.

5. Describe the properties of soil that determine whether nutrients are available for plants.

KEY TERMS
Match the numbered term with the definition that fits it best. Put the corresponding number in front of the appropriate definition.

1. soil
2. minerals
3. topsoil
4. humus
5. phytoremediation
6. nodules
7. macronutrients
8. micronutrients
9. phytodegradation
10. phytovolatilazation
11. phytoaccumulation

a. ____ The use of plants to concentrate or breakdown pollutants.
b. ____ Partly decayed organic material found in topsoil.
c. ____ The process by which toxins or heavy metals are taken up and sequestered by plants, but not degraded.
d. ____ Inorganic nutrients required by plants in trace amounts.
e. ____ The highly weathered outer layer of the Earth's crust composed of sand, rocks, clay, silt, humus, minerals.
f. ____ The process by which toxins are released as a gas through the stomata of plants.
g. ____ The uppermost layer in the soil containing organic matter, such as roots, small animals, humus, and minerals.
h. ____ Inorganic nutrients required by plants in relatively large quantities.
i. ____ The process by which toxins in the soil are taken up and degraded before being released into the atmosphere.
j. ____ Inorganic compounds in which most elements are found.
k. ____ Tissues the plant grows to house symbiotic bacteria.

LEARNING BY EXPERIENCE
List and give examples of plant adaptations involving interactions with other organisms, including plants, regarding nutrients.

1.

2.

3.

4.

5.

EXERCISING YOUR KNOWLEDGE

Briefly answer each of the following questions in the space provided.

1. The ground we grow plants in usually contains soil, minerals, and rocks. How do they differ in composition?

2. Describe how plants are being genetically modified to benefit human health.

3. Describe two ways in which plants benefit from associations with bacteria and fungi.

4. Describe the new approaches to cultivation that are aimed at reducing soil loss.

5. What nutrient does the carnivorous behavior provide plants that they can't get from their environment?

6. Why is iron, a micronutrient, required by plants?

7. What growth substrate is used to assess plant nutrient requirements?

8. What is the visible effect of chlorine deficiency in plants?

9. What is the composition of the soil where roots are found?

10. What soil water is readily available to plants?

Circle the letter of the one best answer in each of the following questions.

11. The element _____ is important as a component of ADP and ATP.
    a. phosphorus
    b. magnesium
    c. potassium
    d. chlorine
    e. manganese

12. An important function of the micronutrient _____ is chlorophyll synthesis.
    a. chlorine
    b. boron
    c. iron
    d. sulfur
    e. potassium

13. The micronutrient molybdenum is important
    a. in nitrogen fixation.
    b. as an enzyme activator.
    c. in carbohydrate transport.
    d. in chlorophyll synthesis.
    e. in osmotic and ionic balance.

14. Which of the following is used to move positively charged ions into root cells?
    a. facilitated diffusion
    b. selective permeability
    c. electrochemical gradient
    d. cavitation
    e. osmosis

15. The carnivorous habit of bog plants enables them to acquire ____, which is not otherwise available.
    a. water
    b. nitrogen
    c. oxygen
    d. phosphorus
    e. potassium

16. Soil salinity does which of the following?
    a. increases the turgor pressure in plants
    b. prevents the uptake of minerals
    c. causes significant water pollution
    d. decreases the water potential of the soil
    e. reduces the topsoil

17. 94% of the dry weight of plants is from
    a. nitrogen, potassium, and phosphorus.
    b. iron, magnesium, and calcium.
    c. manganese, phosphates, and zinc.
    d. carbon, hydrogen, and oxygen.
    e. chlorine, sodium, and potassium.

18. About half of the total soil volume is occupied by
    a. rock particles.
    b. humus.
    c. space.
    d. sand.
    e. clay.

19. Chlorosis in plants may be due to a deficiency in which of the following?
    a. calcium
    b. sulfur
    c. chlorine
    d. zinc
    e. molybdenum

20. A cultivation practice that allows for the rebuilding of a field's resources is
    a. plowing plant material under.
    b. pasturing sheep.
    c. letting it lie fallow.
    d. flooding the field.
    e. burning the vegetation.

21. One reason that plants cannot fix nitrogen is because they lack which of the following?
    a. oxygen
    b. nitrogenase
    c. N_2
    d. leghemoglobin
    e. more than one of the above.

22. Most elements in soil are in
    a. silt.
    b. clay.
    c. sand.
    d. humus.
    e. minerals.

23. Just below the topsoil lies the
    a. bedrock.
    b. gravel.
    c. water table.
    d. home of living organisms.
    e. subsoil.

24. The Calvin cycle of photosynthesis fixes atmospheric
    a. nitrogen.
    b. carbon dioxide.
    c. carbon monoxide.
    d. oxygen.
    e. hydrogen.

25. Assuming available soil nutrients remain the same, increased atmospheric carbon dioxide should result in fewer _____ in fast-growing plants.
    a. carbohydrates
    b. nitrogen compounds
    c. fats
    d. sulfur-containing compounds
    e. oxides

26. _____ growing in a European facility had a 40% higher photosynthetic rate in a concentrated carbon dioxide atmosphere.
    a. Potatoes
    b. Oak trees
    c. Potted plants
    d. Grass
    e. Wheat

27. Since 1750, atmospheric carbon dioxide has increased by
    a. about 30%.
    b. about 10%.
    c. about 100%.
    d. about 50%.
    e. very little.

28. With increased carbon dioxide levels in the atmosphere, cattle might have to eat more vegetation because of
    a. fewer plants available.
    b. less nutrition in plants.
    c. a corresponding increase in oxygen for respiration.
    d. a higher percent of indigestible plant fibers.
    e. declining levels of soil organisms.

29. Many responses of respiration rates to temperature are
    a. perpetual.
    b. short term.
    c. intermittent.
    d. long term.
    e. lethal.

30. Venus flytraps can open and close consecutively only a limited number of times because the mechanism is
    a. irreversible.
    b. growth-related.
    c. controlled by iron uptake.
    d. trophic.
    e. water dependent.

ASSESSING YOUR KNOWLEDGE

Answers to the questions in this section test your ability to synthesize information gained from the chapter and to solve challenging problems on an exam or in everyday life.

Challenging Your Understanding—Part I.—Answers

1. A. simple sugars; B. minerals; C-D. water, air; E-H. bacteria for N_2 fixation, mycorrhizal fungi for increased absorption and phosphorus, carnivorous habit, parasitism; I. micronutrients; J-O. chlorine, iron, manganese, boron, copper, molybdenum; P-W. carbon, oxygen, hydrogen, nitrogen, potassium, calcium, magnesium, phosphorus.

Challenging Your Understanding—Part II.—Answers

2. A. Herbivore nutrition; B. Photosynthesis; C. Phytoremediation; D. Medicinal purposes.

3A. Plants can secrete a substance from their roots that breaks down the contaminant.

B. Plants can take up a toxin from the soil and break down the contaminant into unharmful by-products that are released into the atmosphere.

C. Plants can take up toxins from the soil and sequester the toxins. The toxins can hyperaccumulate in the shoots of the plant, which can then be harvested.

4. Increased levels of CO_2 in the atmosphere will increase the rate of photosynthesis and the biomass of plants. With this increase, the ratio of carbohydrates and proteins in plants will change and herbivores will have to eat more plants to obtain adequate nutrients, particularly protein. This could lead to more devastating insect infestations, and protein deficiencies in the diets of humans.

5. Soil composition, water, pH, and salinity determine whether the nutrients in the soil are available to plants. Soil composition determines the amount of water and nutrient binding to soil particles. Only minerals dissolved in the water held in small pores in the soil are available for uptake by the roots of a plant. Therefore, water in the soil plays a critical role in determining whether nutrients in the soil are available to plants. The pH of the soil affects the release of minerals from rocks. Most plants grow best at a neutral pH. High salt soils cause a decrease

in the turgor pressure in plants due to a decrease in the water potential of the soil. Thus, water tends to move out of the plant, rather than moving in, limiting the nutrients that the plant receives from the soil. These conditions will limit plant growth.

Key Terms—Answers

a. 5, b. 4, c. 11, d. 8, e. 1, f. 10, g. 3, h. 7, i. 9, j. 2, k. 6.

Learning by Experience—Answers

1. Nitrogen fixation. Legumes form nodules containing symbiotic nitrogen-fixing bacteria.
2. Carnivorous habit. Pitcher plants and Venus flytraps capture insects and digest them. Bladderworts trap small aquatic animals and digest them.
3. Mycorrhizae. 90% of the vascular plants form a symbiotic relationship with fungi that enhances their nutrient uptake.
4. Saprophytic existence. Indian pipe lacks chlorophyll and uses decaying organic matter for nutrition.
5. Parasitism. Plants such as dodder parasitize other plants.

Exercising Your Knowledge—Answers

As you check your answers, put a mark in the review (Rvw.) column for the answers you missed. If you didn't miss any, congratulations—you have mastered the chapter! If you missed some, review the section (Sect.) in the text where this concept is discussed. In order to develop an efficient review strategy, it is important that you understand what types of questions you missed. The questions with asterisks test more for understanding of the **concepts**, whereas the others test more for **detail**. *See the preface for learning strategies for concepts and for detail.*

	Sect.	Rvw.
*1. Soil is a mixture of sand, clay, silt, humus, small rocks, assorted organic substances, and space. Rocks are made up of minerals.	39.1	
*2. Plants for human consumption are being genetically modified to increase their uptake of minerals and the storage of minerals in roots and shoots. Plants are being modified to secrete citrate to solubilize phosphate and increase its uptake, and at the same time limit the uptake of aluminum, which can be toxic. Genes encoding plasma membrane transporters for iron, manganese, and zinc are being genetically incorporated into crop plants to increase these nutrients in crops that are consumed by humans. Additional nutrients are being added to grains growing in fields.	39.2	

*3. Bacteria, such as *Rhizobium*, live in close association with the roots of plants, or are housed in nodules where they fix nitrogen for plants. Nitrogen fixation is an energy-expensive reaction that plants are not capable of doing themselves. Mycorrhizal fungi also live in close association with the roots of plants. They not only increase the surface area for water and mineral absorption, but also play a significant role in enhancing phosphorus transfer to the plant and in the uptake of micronutrients.	39.3	
*4. Approaches aimed at reducing soil loss include intercropping, mixing of crops in a field, conservation tillage including minimal till and no-till approaches, and not tilling fall crops.	39.1	
*5. From the insects, carnivorous plants get nitrogen that is not available in their environment.	39.3	
*6. Iron is essential to the production of chlorophyll, cytochromes, and nitrogenase.	39.2	
*7. Hydroponic cultures grown on a liquid medium are used to assess plant nutrients.	39.2	
*8. Chlorine-deficient plants show necrotic leaves with patches of dead tissue.	39.2	
*9. Roots are found in topsoil, which is composed of a mixture of mineral particles (mostly small), living organisms, and humus.	39.1	

*10. Water contained in small soil pores is readily available to plants.	39.1	
11. a	39.2	
12. c	39.2	
13. a	39.2	
*14. c	39.1	
15. b	39.3	
16. d	39.1	
*17. d	39.2	
*18. c	39.1	
19. d	39.2	
20. a	39.1	
*21. b	39.3	
22. e	39.1	
*23. e	39.1	
24. b	39.4	
25. b	39.4	
26. a	39.4	
*27. a	39.4	
28. b	39.4	
29. b	39.4	
30. b	39.3	

CHAPTER 40 PLANT DEFENSE RESPONSES

MASTERING KEY CONCEPTS

Plants can't get up and go. They can't swat bugs. They have to stand and take whatever comes their way. Under these circumstances, plants have developed some effective defense mechanisms.

40.1 Morphological and physiological features protect plants from invasion.

- **Overview**: Plants are threatened by weather, bacteria, viruses, fungi, animals, and other plants. Natural predators of some of these agents reduce the threat of these agents to plants, but some lack natural predators. Plants are protected by the epidermis, which secretes wax and is covered by cutin to protect the outer surfaces of the plant. Suberin, silica inclusions, trichomes, bark, and thorns are also protective substances or structures that prevent water loss and invasion. Plant predators can still invade plants through mechanical wounds created by the predator itself or created by another mechanism, or they can invade plants through stomatal openings. Soil bacteria and mycorrhizal fungi can also form mutualistic relationships with plant species in which the plant provides some nutrients to the bacteria or fungi, and the bacteria or fungi provides critical nutrients to the plant.
- **Details**: Know the agents that threaten plants. Know the external defenses of a plant, and the common ways in which invaders overcome these barriers. Know the steps of fungal invasion. Know examples of mutualistic relationships between plants and bacteria, or plants and fungi.

40.2 Some plant defenses act by poisoning the invader.

- **Overview**: Many plants produce **toxins** that can harm or even kill the organisms that feed on them. Plants produce chemicals called **secondary metabolites** as by-products of evolutionary adaptations. Some of these include nicotine, caffeine, cocaine, morphine, tannins, and plant oils that can be toxic in high concentrations. These toxins do not kill the plants that produce them because they are either sequestered in the plant in a membrane-bound structure, or the compound produced in the plant is only toxic if it is metabolized. Some plants can block the germination or growth of other plants nearby by secreting chemical toxins from their roots (**allelopathy**). Secondary metabolites produced by plants can be poisonous or beneficial to humans. **Cyanogenic glycosides**, hemlock extracts, and **ricin** are lethal to humans; but **taxol** (anticancer), **quinine** (antimalarial), **morphine** (pain killer), and **phytoestrogens** (anticancer) can have pharmaceutical value to humans.

- **Details**: Know how the production of secondary metabolites can protect plants. Understand why plant toxins do not kill the plant in which they are produced. Know why hemlock, ricin, and cyanogenic glycosides are lethal to humans. Know examples of secondary metabolites with pharmaceutical value to humans and the reasons why they are beneficial.

40.3 Some plants have coevolved with bodyguards.

- **Overview**: **Coevolution** of animal species and plant species can lead to a **mutualistic** relationship between the two. This is true of stinging ants that are sheltered by Acacia trees. These ants protect the Acacia tree by attacking other herbivores that may come to eat off of the tree. In exchange, the Acacia tree provides the ants with sugars and lipid food bodies. Similarly, parasitoid wasps are attracted to plants that release a volatile compound in response to caterpillars feeding on it. The wasps lay their fertilized eggs in the body of the caterpillar, which is killed by the larvae when the eggs hatch.
- **Details**: Know how coevolution can protect plants. Understand how ants and parasitoid wasps have coevolved with plants to have mutualistic relationships. Understand the benefits to each organism in those mutualistic relationships.

40.4 Systemic responses also protect plants from invaders.

- **Overview**: In addition to morphological defense systems, plants have inducible defense mechanisms that can be launched specifically when a plant is under attack. In response to **wounding**, plants produce proteinase inhibitors that bind digestive enzymes in the gut of the herbivore. Similarly, mechanical damage of a plant also leads to a wound response. Specific pathogens can trigger specific cellular responses within a plant. **Flor** proposed the **gene-for-gene hypothesis** stating that the product of a pathogen's **avirulence gene** (*avr*) could interact with the product of a plant's **resistance gene** (*R*). If the plant's R protein recognizes the avr protein, it mounts a defense triggering a **hypersensitive response** (HR) that isolates the pathogen by causing rapid cell death around the site of the invasion. If it does not recognize it, disease symptoms occur in the plant.
- **Details**: Know how proteinase inhibitors are produced throughout the tomato plant in response to a wound. Understand Flor's gene-for-gene hypothesis.

CHALLENGING YOUR UNDERSTANDING—Part I.

1. Fill in the blanks to identify how the chapter concepts relate to each other.

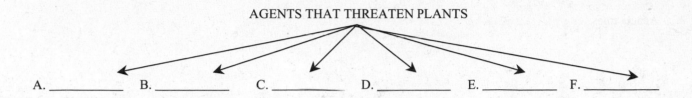

AGENTS THAT THREATEN PLANTS

A. _____   B. _____   C. _____   D. _____   E. _____   F. _____

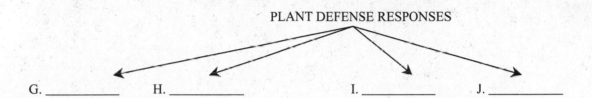

PLANT DEFENSE RESPONSES

G. _____   H. _____   I. _____   J. _____

2. For the following list of secondary metabolites that are produced by plants, indicate whether each is toxic or beneficial, and why.

A. Cyanogenic glycosides

B. Tannins

C. Oils from peppermint

D. Ricin

E. Taxol

F. Quinine

CHALLENGING YOUR UNDERSTANDING—Part II.

1. Describe how ants and Acacia trees, and parasitoid wasps and plants, both benefit from their relationships with each other.

Acacia trees:

Ants:

Parasitoid wasps:

Plants:

2. Describe the steps in a plant's response to an avirulent pathogen if (a) a defense response is initiated, or (b) a defense response cannot be initiated, according to the gene-for-gene hypothesis.

a.

b.

KEY TERMS

Match the numbered term with the definition that fits it best. Put the corresponding number in front of the appropriate definition.

1. allelopathy
2. phytoestrogens
3. hypersensitive response (HR)
4. systemic acquired resistance
5. coevolution
6. phytoalexins
7. avirulent pathogen
8. gene-for-gene hypothesis
9. systemin
10. jasmonic acid
11. salicylic acid
12. *R* gene
13. *avr* gene
14. wound response
15. taxol
16. quinine
17. ricin
18. secondary metabolites

a. ____ Several response pathways in plants that lead to broad-ranging resistance that lasts for a period of days.
b. ____ A chemical produced in the wound response that leads to the production of a proteinase inhibitor.
c. ____ A secondary metabolite found in the Pacific yew that is effective in fighting cancer.
d. ____ A plant invader that can utilize host resources for its own use without causing severe damage or death.
e. ____ Chemicals produced by plants that are not directly involved in their growth, development, or reproduction.
f. ____ Antimicrobial chemical defense agents.
g. ____ A systemic response to invaders or mechanical damage that leads to the rapid production of proteinase inhibitors.
h. ____ Compounds produced by soybean products that may prevent prostate cancer or minimize menopausal symptoms.
i. ____ An 18-amino-acid peptide signaling molecule that is produced by wounded leaves and moves through phloem.
j. ____ A gene carried by a pathogen whose product recognizes the product of the plant's resistance gene.
k. ____ Recognition of the pathogen by the R protein triggers this pathway leading to rapid cell death at the site of attack.
l. ____ The active ingredient in the bark of *Cinchona* trees that is still used today to treat malaria.
m. ____ The simultaneous development of adaptations in two or more species that act as a selective force on each other.
n. ____ A plant gene whose product interacts with the product of a pathogen's *avr* gene to signal the pathogen's presence.
o. ____ A chemical signal secreted by the roots of a plant that blocks germination or growth of a nearby plant.
p. ____ Another molecule involved in the wound response that is found in the bark of plants such as the white willow.
q. ____ An alkaloid found in castor beans that when metabolized is lethal because it can block the translation of proteins.
r. ____ Flor's proposal that plants produce a R protein that interacts with the product of a pathogen's *avr* gene.

LEARNING BY EXPERIENCE

1. List the hazards that plants are exposed to. For each hazard, list the plant's response.

a.

b.

c.

2. Describe how cells in distant parts of a plant are signaled to produce proteinase inhibitors in a wound response.

a.

b.

c.

d.

3. Describe why systemic plant responses are more energy efficient than static plant responses when plants are threatened.

EXERCISING YOUR KNOWLEDGE

Briefly answer each of the following questions in the space provided.

1. What is the plant's first line of defense?

2. What structures protect plants from being eaten?

3. Why is the nontoxic compound proricin toxic to humans?

4. What are two reasons why toxins produced by plants do not kill the plant itself?

5. What is the role of fatty acids in the plant's defense?

6. How does a nematode attack cause a plant tumor?

7. What leaf structure makes plants vulnerable to fungal invasion?

8. What event is required for a fungal germ tube to invade the plant?

9. What prevents a fungal spore that is blown onto the leaf from blowing off again?

10. What is the final location of the haustorium of a fungus that invades a plant?

Circle the letter of the one best answer in each of the following questions.

11. The natural predator of the alfalfa plant bug is a
    a. wasp.
    b. wolf spider.
    c. finch.
    d. praying mantis.
    e. none of these.

12. Plant structures below the ground are protected by
    a. cutin.
    b. lignin.
    c. suberin.
    d. auxin.
    e. a lipid.

13. Plants that suffer from grazing recover by the action of
    a. cambium.
    b. axillary bud.
    c. the Casparian strip.
    d. terminal buds.
    e. ground meristem.

14. Long-chain fatty acids are linked to form _____ to protect plants.
    a. chitin
    b. suberin
    c. cellulose
    d. cutin
    e. wax

15. Levels of _____ in tobacco plants are lethal to the tobacco hornworm.
    a. nicotine
    b. cyanide
    c. caffeine
    d. glycosides
    e. proteins

16. _____ becomes toxic inside the attacking animal when activated by its own enzymes.
    a. Opium
    b. Caffeine
    c. Tannin
    d. Morphine
    e. Cyanogenic glycoside

17. Very little vegetation will grow under a black walnut tree because of
    a. shade.
    b. symbiotic empathy.
    c. aboveground roots.
    d. allelopathy.
    e. symbiotic insects.

18. The protection by peppermint oil comes from
    a. its toxic effects on caterpillars.
    b. attracting insect-eating birds.
    c. sealing wounds.
    d. its fungicidal effect.
    e. repelling insects.

19. Taxol is a terpenoid that acts as
    a. an anticancer drug.
    b. a narcotic pain killer.
    c. a toxin to humans.
    d. an antibacterial drug.
    e. a sedative.

20. Genistein, an estrogen-mimicking drug, is produced by the
    a. oriental poppy.
    b. cassava.
    c. soybean.
    d. Pacific yew.
    e. water lily.

21. The antimalarial drug quinine is extracted from the plant's
    a. leaves.
    b. roots.
    c. bark.
    d. seeds.
    e. sap.

22. Chemically, morphine is
    a. protein.
    b. an alkaloid.
    c. a terpenoid.
    d. a polysaccharide.
    e. a fatty acid.

23. The plant known for its lethal product is the
    a. opium poppy.
    b. quinine tree.
    c. Pacific yew.
    d. soybean.
    e. cassava.

24. The toxin that killed Socrates came from the
    a. cassava.
    b. fig tree.
    c. walnut tree.
    d. olive leaves.
    e. hemlock.

25. The symbiotic relationship between the acacia tree and ants has a downside for the tree because it interferes with
    a. seed dispersal.
    b. nutrient flow.
    c. pollination.
    d. mycorrhizae.
    e. bud development.

26. A volatile substance released by the chewing of a caterpillar sometimes
    a. attracts a predatory wasp.
    b. causes ants to attack the caterpillar.
    c. attracts predatory birds.
    d. anesthetizes the caterpillar.
    e. repels the attacker.

27. Wounded tomato leaves produce the peptide _____ as a part of a defensive activity.
    a. auxin
    b. systemin
    c. phlonase
    d. salicylic acid
    e. methylene

28. The production of _____ leads to the production of proteinase inhibitors in tomato plants.
    a. gibberellic acid
    b. formic acid
    c. acetic acid
    d. jasminic acid
    e. propionic acid

29. The substance _____ leads to rapid cell death around the source of the animal invasion.
    a. RH
    b. RX
    c. HR
    d. SRS
    e. SAR

30. Systemic acquired resistance (SAR) is
    a. highly specific.
    b. able to recognize antigens.
    c. equivalent to the human immune system.
    d. long lasting.
    e. salicylic acid–induced.

ASSESSING YOUR KNOWLEDGE

Answers to the questions in this section test your ability to synthesize information gained from the chapter and to solve challenging problems on an exam or in everyday life.

Challenging Your Understanding—Part I, Answers

1. A-F. Weather, bacteria, viruses, fungi, animals, other plants; G-J. Dermal system, chemical, mutualistic relationships, systemic responses.

2. A. Cyanogenic glycosides: toxic; Cyanogenic glycosides break down into cyanide when ingested.
B. Tannins: toxic; Tannins bind to proteins and inactive them.
C. Oils from peppermint: toxic; At high concentrations, these oils are toxic if ingested, but the mechanism is not clear.
D. Ricin: toxic; Ricin A is released from proricin and binds to the 28s rRNA of the ribosome inhibiting translation of cellular mRNAs.
E. Taxol: beneficial; anticancer drug.
F. Quinine: beneficial; antimalarial drug.

Challenging Your Understanding—Part II, Answers

1. Acacia trees: Protection from other herbivores.
   Ants: Sugar in nectaries; lipid food bodies at the tips of the leaves.
   Parasitoid wasps: Wasps are attracted to a location where their larva will have something to feed on; wasps have a place to form cocoons and pupate.
   Plants: Protected from munching by herbivores such as caterpillars.

2. (a) Defense response is initiated:
   1. Pathogen enters the cell.
   2. Proteins are released by pathogen.
   3. The *avr* gene product interacts with *R* gene product.
   4. Avirulent pathogen is recognized.
   5. Hypersensitive response leads to local cell death at the site of attack.
   6. System acquired resistance provides long-term protection.
   (b) Defense response cannot be initiated:
   1. Pathogen enters the cell.
   2. Proteins are released by pathogen.
   3. The *avr* gene product cannot bind to the *R* gene product.
   4. Disease symptoms occur.

Key Terms—Answers

a. 4, b. 10, c. 15, d. 7, e. 18, f. 6, g. 14, h. 2, i. 9, j. 13, k. 3, l. 16, m. 5, n. 12, o. 1, p. 11, q. 17, r. 8.

Learning by Experience—Answers

1.a. Grazing organisms: Axillary buds and toxins.
b. Invasion by microorganisms: Structures such as thick cell walls, bark, etc.; protective deposits.
c. Wounding: Proteinase inhibitors.
2.a. Wounded leaves produce systemin, an 18-amino-acid peptide, from a large precursor molecule.
b. Systemin moves through the space between the cell walls of the wounded tissue into the nearby phloem.
c. All cells with a systemin receptor bind systemin leading to the production of jasmonic acid in other parts of the plant.
d. Jasmonic acid initiates a signaling pathway that activates gene expression to synthesize a proteinase inhibitor.
3. Systemic responses to invaders are more energy efficient because they are inducible and thus, only activated at the time when a threat has been recognized. Up until this time, resources can be conserved. Static plant responses, such as chemicals and the development of morphological structures such as thorns or trichomes, need to be maintained whether a plant is under attack or not and therefore, have an energetic downside.

Exercising Your Knowledge—Answers

As you check your answers, put a mark in the review (Rvw) column for the answers you missed. If you didn't miss any, congratulations—you have mastered the chapter! If you missed some, review the section (Sect.) in the text where this concept is discussed. In order to develop an efficient review strategy, it is important that you understand what types of questions you missed. The questions with asterisks test more for understanding of the **concepts**, whereas the others test more for **detail**. *See the preface for learning strategies for concepts and for details.*

	Sect.	Rvw.
*1. The first line of defense is thick cell walls.	40.1	
*2. Bark and trichomes protect the plant from being eaten.	40.1	
*3. Proricin is toxic to humans because the single disulfide bond is broken in the digestive system, creating a ricin A and a ricin B subunit. The ricin A subunit binds to the GAGA sequence of the 28s rRNA of the ribosome. This inactivates the ribosome and inhibits translation of cellular mRNAs.	40.2	
*4. Toxins produced by plants do not kill the plant itself because the plant either produces a compound that is not toxic unless it is metabolized in the intestine of an animal, or the toxins are sequestered in a membrane-bound structure so that it cannot disrupt the normal cellular metabolic processes.	40.2	
*5. Plants form protective substances such as cutin and suberin from fatty acids.	40.1	
*6. The wounding may trigger rapid cell growth, causing a tumor.	40.1	
*7. Plants are vulnerable to fungal invasion through stomata.	40.1	

*8. In order for invasion to proceed, host recognition must occur.	40.1	
*9. The germinated spore forms adhesion pads that stick it to the plant.	40.1	
*10. The haustorium ends up below the cell wall and surrounding the cell membrane.	40.1	
11. e	40.1	
12. c	40.1	
13. b	40.1	
14. d	40.1	
15. a	40.2	
16. e	40.2	
17. d	40.2	

18. e	40.2	
19. a	40.2	
20. c	40.2	
21. c	40.2	
22. b	40.2	
23. e	40.2	
24. e	40.2	
25. c	40.3	
26. a	40.3	
27. b	40.4	
28. d	40.4	
29. c	40.4	
30. e	40.4	

CHAPTER 41 SENSORY SYSTEMS IN PLANTS

MASTERING KEY CONCEPTS
This is about as close as you get to "plant psychology." Why do plants do what they do, and how do they do it? You are about to find out.

41.1 Plants respond to light.
- **Overview**: Light can trigger nondirectional development (**photomorphogenesis**) and directional growth responses (**phototropisms**) in plants. **Phytochrome** is a pigment containing protein consisting of a light-responsive **chromophore** and an **apoprotein** that initiates a signal transduction response. Phytochrome exists in two interconvertible forms, P_r and P_{fr}, and is present in all plants and in some green algae. Biological reactions dependent on phytochrome occur when P_{fr} is present. Red light, which converts P_r to its active form P_{fr}, stimulates events such as seed germination, the normal morphology of elongated shoots in an **etiolated** seedling, and signal plant spacing. Activated phytochrome (P_{fr}) is translocated from the cytoplasm to the nucleus where it can activate transcription of light-responsive genes by binding to transcription factors. P_{fr} can also autophosphorylate itself or another protein to initiate a signaling cascade that activates the transcription of light-responsive genes thereby initiating photomorphogenesis or phototropisms. P_{fr} is also regulated by ubiquitin-dependent proteasome degradation. Stems and some individual leaves, but typically not roots, grow toward sources of **blue light**. PHOT1 and PHOT2 are two blue-light receptor kinases. Absorption of blue light by PHOT1 leads to a conformational change in the protein resulting in its autophosphorylation and activation of a signal transduction cascade that leads to phototropic growth. Plants experience **circadian rhythms** that are daily cycles entrained through the action of phytochrome and blue-light photoreceptors.
- **Details**: Understand how phytochrome is regulated and how it initiates growth responses. Know how blue-light receptors can affect plant growth. Know the characteristics of a circadian cycle.

41.2 Plants respond to gravity.
- **Overview**: A plant's **gravitropic response** occurs in a series of four steps, the plant cell perceives gravity, a mechanical signal is transduced into a physiological signal in the cell perceiving gravity, this signal is transduced inside the cell and to other cells, and differential cell elongation occurs in the upward or downward direction in the roots and the shoots of a plant. Roots and shoots respond differently to gravity because the root grows down, while the shoot grows up. In roots, gravity is sensed by the cap, while in the shoots, it is perceived by the endodermal cells along the length of the stem. In both, **amyloplasts** sink toward the center of the gravitational field and **auxin** plays a critical role in transmitting the signal from the gravity-sensing cells to the site where growth occurs. Auxin concentrations govern which cells grow faster in the roots and the shoots. The upper side of roots grow more rapidly causing them to grow downward (**positive gravitropic response**), while the cells on the lower side of the stem grow more rapidly causing them to grow upward (**negative gravitropic response**). Mutations that affect auxin influx or efflux in the root eliminate the gravitropic response.
- **Details**: Understand the four steps required for a gravitropic response. Understand the difference between positive and negative gravitropic responses. Understand generally how each is thought to occur, and the role of auxin.

41.3 Plants respond to touch.
- **Overview**: Plants respond to touch and other mechanical stimuli by undergoing either short-term changes that result from reversible changes in turgor pressure in parts of the plant, or by undergoing permanent, irreversible changes in the form of the plant due to changes in growth (**thigmomorphogenesis**). Short-term changes in turgor pressure can result in leaf movement. In *Mimosa* leaves for example, the leaflets of the leaves "fold" as a result of ions moving to the outer side of the **pulvini** after the leaves are touched. Water follows the ions causing a drop in the interior turgor pressure of the leaves. After 15-30 minutes, water diffuses back into the cells that it had moved out of and the leaves are unfolded. Light can stimulate turgor movements allowing plants to track the movement of the Sun and maximize photosynthesis. Circadian rhythms also stimulate turgor movements that affect the orientation of the leaves of some plants over the course of a day. In contrast, directional growth that occurs as a result of contact (**thigmotropism**) is an irreversible response that changes the long-term form of the plant.
- **Details**: Know the two ways in which plants can respond to mechanical stimuli. Know an example of thigmotropism. Understand how reversible response to touch, light, or circadian rhythms occur within a plant.

41.4 Water availability and temperature elicit plant responses.
- **Overview**: Plants can survive harsh conditions by entering a **dormant stage** in which leaf **abscission** occurs in deciduous trees, buds, and

shrubs remain dormant, and apical meristems remain protected inside. Abscission occurs due to hormonal change in the **abscission zone** that cause chlorophyll pigments to break down, and cells in this region to differentiate into two layers, the **protective layer** and the **separation layer**. Pectins in the separation layer break down as a result of cooler temperatures, diminishing light, or other environmental changes, allowing the leaves to be easily shed by wind or rain. Seed dormancy allows new plants to prevent growth until favorable conditions in temperature, water, and light intensity exist. Plants can survive extreme temperature changes such as freezing or high temperatures. When **chilling** temperatures occur, plants convert saturated lipids in their membranes to unsaturated lipids lowering the temperature at which the membranes cannot properly function. The production of **antifreeze proteins** and preventing ice crystal formation allows some plants to survive extremely low temperatures. To resist temperature increases, plants produce **heat shock proteins** that prevent the denaturation of other cellular proteins. In addition, some plants may have acquired **thermotolerance**.

- **Details**: Know how leaf abscission occurs. Understand the mechanisms that plants use to survive extreme temperatures.

41.5 The hormones that guide growth sense environmental changes.

- **Overview**: Plant hormones, such as **auxin**, **cytokinins**, **gibberellins**, **brassinosteroids**, **oligosaccharins**, **ethylene**, and **abscisic acid**, are produced in tissues with other functions and then transported to other parts of the plant. Auxin is a plant hormone involved in stem elongation, softening of cell walls, and the activity of the vascular tissues. Auxin was discovered by experiments carried out by the **Charles and Francis Darwin, Boysen-Jensen, and Paal**, and **Frits Went** whose experiments demonstrated that differences in auxin concentrations on the two sides of a shoot cause a plant to bend toward the light. **Winslow**

Briggs demonstrated that auxin molecules migrate away from the light. Auxin regulates gene expression by binding to its receptor leading to the degradation of **Aux/IAA proteins** and allowing **ARF transcription factors** to be active. Cytokinins are a plant hormone produced in root apical meristems that induce lateral bud growth, inhibit the formation of lateral roots, act as antiaging compounds, and promote the synthesis or activation of proteins required for cytokinesis. Increased levels of cytokinins along with auxins can cause the formation of a **crown gall tumor**. Gibberellins are synthesized in the apical regions of stems and roots. These hormones affect stem elongation and hasten seed germination. Gibberellins activate a protein complex that degrades a repressor bound to GA-dependent transcription factors, allowing these factors to induce gene expression. Brassinosteroids are similar to animal steroid hormones and have overlapping functions with auxin and gibberellins. Brassinosteroids play a role in elongation, cell division, stem bending, reproductive and vascular tissue development, and membrane polarization. Oligosaccharins are cell wall components that have signaling functions, such as defense responses. Ethylene is a hormone that promotes fruit ripening, can accelerate the loss of damaged leaves or fruits, and may activate a plant's defense mechanisms. Abscisic acid (ABA) is produced in mature green leaves, fruits, and root caps. It suppresses growth and elongation of buds, and is necessary to induce dormancy.

- **Details**: Know the experiments of Charles and Francis Darwin, Boysen-Jensen and Paal, Frits Went, and Winslow Briggs and what each scientist was able to conclude. Know how light affects auxin. Understand the molecular basis of how auxin functions to regulate gene expression, and cell wall expansion. Know the uses of synthetic auxins. Know where the seven major plant hormones are produced and the role of each in the plant. Understand how ripening has been prevented in transgenic tomatoes, and how ripening can be induced.

CHALLENGING YOUR UNDERSTANDING

1. Fill in the following flowchart with the given names or events to depict two mechanisms by which phytochromes induce light-responsive genes (activation of transcription factors; gene expression; phosphorylation of phytochrome; binding to transcription factors; active; inactive; translocation to nucleus).

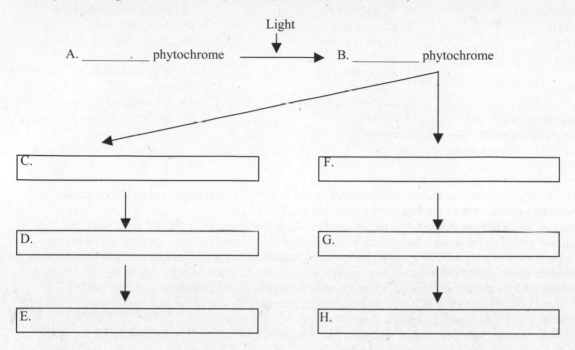

2. List 3 synthetic auxins and describe how each is used in society.

    A.

    B.

    C.

3. List the responses that plants have developed in order to endure each of the following environmental stresses.

Environmental stresses:	A. Drought	B. Cold	C. Heat
Plant responses:	1.	1.	1.
	2.	2.	2.
		3.	

KEY TERMS

Match the numbered term with the definition that fits it best. Put the corresponding number in front of the appropriate definition.

1. photomorphogenesis
2. phototropisms
3. phytochrome
4. chromophore
5. apoprotein
6. gravitropism
7. etiolation
8. negative gravitropic response
9. positive gravitropic response
10. thigmotropism
11. thigmonastic responses
12. turgor pressure
13. pulvini
14. abscission
15. supercooling
16. heat shock proteins
17. hormones
18. auxin
19. acid growth hypothesis
20. cytokinins
21. gibberellins
22. brassinosteroids
23. oligosaccharins
24. ethylene
25. abscisic acid
26. vivipary

a. ____ A model that links auxin to cell wall expansion.
b. ____ The ability of some plants to survive temperatures as low as -40°C by limiting ice crystal formation.
c. ____ The bending upward of the stem of a plant against the force of gravity.
d. ____ A plant pigment that is associated with the absorption of light; photoreceptor for red to far-red light.
e. ____ A hormone produced by green leaves, fruits, root caps, and seeds; involved in promoting seed dormancy.
f. ____ The larger portion of a phytochrome that initiates a signal transduction pathway leading to a biological response.
g. ____ The pressure inside a plant cell resulting from osmotic intake of water, that makes the cell rigid.
h. ____ A hormone produce by root and shoot tips that promotes stem elongation and hastens seed germination.
i. ____ In vascular plants, the shedding of leaves, flowers, fruits, or stems at the end of the growing season.
j. ____ Directional growth responses to light.
k. ____ Chemical substances produced in small quantities that bring about physiological or developmental responses.
l. ____ Cell wall components that have a hormonelike function and are released by enzymes secreted by pathogens.
m. ____ Two-sided multicellular swellings at the base of leaves that undergo turgor pressure changes in response to touch.
n. ____ The response of a plant to the gravitational field of the Earth.
o. ____ Proteins produced in plants when temperatures rise that stabilize other proteins to prevent their degradation.
p. ____ Precocious germination.
q. ____ Nondirectional, light-triggered development that can result in complex changes in the form of a plant.
r. ____ Roots grow downward because the upper sides of roots grow more rapidly than the lower sides.
s. ____ Plant hormone that promotes stem elongation, cell division, lateral bud dormancy, and inhibits leaf abscission.
t. ____ Growth response that occurs in the same direction regardless of the direction of the stimulus.
u. ____ A natural product of plant metabolism that promotes fruit ripening, and controls leaf, flower, and fruit abscission.
v. ____ The smaller part of a phytochrome that is light sensitive.
w. ____ The directional growth of a plant or plant part in response to contact with an object, animal, or another plant.
x. ____ Plant hormones that are similar to animal steroid hormones and affect elongation, cell division, and stem bending.
y. ____ Plant growth hormones that promote the synthesis or activation of proteins required for cytokinesis.
z. ____ An energy conservation strategy that help plants growing in the dark reach the light before they die.

LEARNING BY EXPERIENCE

Horticulturists use plant hormones as tools to regulate plant growth. List each of the plant hormones and cite at least one such use for each.

1.

2.

3.

4.

5.

6.

7.

EXERCISING YOUR KNOWLEDGE
Briefly answer each of the following questions in the space provided.

1. Distinguish between tropisms and nastic movements.

2. How does far-red light affect phytochrome activity?

3. How is etiolation a useful adaptation for plants?

4. How are amyloplasts thought to be related to gravitropism?

5. How do spring rains promote seed germination?

6. How is the prerequisite of a cold spell before seed germination a useful adaptation?

7. How does auxin promote stem elongation?

8. Describe how *Mimosa* leaves respond to being touched? Why?

9. Why was coconut "milk" important to tissue culture of plant cells?

10. How do gibberellins stimulate the growth of seedlings after germination?

Circle the letter of the one best answer in each of the following questions.

11. Light that passes through leaves of a tree inhibits seed germination because chlorophyll
    a. absorbs red and far-red light.
    b. passes both red and far-red light.
    c. absorbs far-red light but passes red light.
    d. passes only green light.
    e. absorbs red light but passes far-red light.

12. Which of the following is NOT a growth response that is linked to phytochrome action?
    a. entraining the circadian cycle
    b. shoot elongation
    c. thigmotropism
    d. signaling plant spacing
    e. seed germination

13. Cytokinins
    a. stimulate leaf drop.
    b. stimulate cell division only in the presence of auxin.
    c. inhibit the formation of lateral roots.
    d. inhibit cell division.
    e. promote lateral root development.

14. One of the most important uses of auxins is the _____ of abscission.
    a. initiation
    b. acceleration
    c. stimulation
    d. prevention
    e. reinforcing

15. Auxin increases the _____ of cell walls.
    a. plasticity
    b. thickness
    c. porosity
    d. layers
    e. rigidity

16. Auxin is synthesized in plants from
    a. adenine.
    b. praline.
    c. aspartame.
    d. phenylalanine.
    e. tryptophan.

17. Environmental signals influence the distribution of auxin in a plant by
    a. decreasing the cell's sensitivity to auxin.
    b. causing auxin to move to the lighted portion.
    c. destroying the auxin.
    d. causing auxin to move to the shaded portion.
    e. causing the plant to produce more auxin.

18. _____ in combination with auxin stimulate cell division in plants and determine the course of differentiation.
    a. Ethylene
    b. Indoleacetic acid
    c. Gibberellins
    d. Abscisic acid
    e. Cytokinins

19. Most cytokinins are produced in the _____ of vascular plants.
    a. roots
    b. shoots
    c. flowers
    d. leaves
    e. lateral branches

20. Which of the following is NOT a part of leaf abscission?
    a. Enzymes breakdown pectins in the middle lamellae of the separation cells.
    b. A protective and a separation layer differentiate.
    c. Green chlorophyll pigments breakdown.
    d. Hormones in the abscission zone change.
    e. Saturated lipids in the cell membranes are converted to unsaturated lipids.

21. _____ stimulates the production of hydrolytic enzymes.
    a. Ethylene
    b. Auxin
    c. Gibberellin
    d. Cytokinin
    e. Indoleacetic acid

22. Which of the following occurs in both roots and shoots in response to sensing gravity?
    a. Phytochrome concentration determines the direction of growth.
    b. Amyloplasts sink toward the center of the gravitational field.
    c. Gravity is sensed by the endodermal cells.
    d. Auxin concentrations in cells on the lower side cause those cells to grow more rapidly than those on the upper side.
    e. Cells experience a change in internal turgor pressure.

23. Stem elongation in grass seedlings and most herbs is promoted by
    a. abscisic acid.
    b. oligosaccharins.
    c. cytokinins.
    d. ethylene.
    e. gibberellins.

24. Vascular tissue development is one of the physiological effects of
    a. auxin.
    b. gibberellins.
    c. ethylene.
    d. abscisic acid.
    e. brassinosteroids.

25. Vivipary in ears of corn is prevented by
    a. ethylene.
    b. cytokinins.
    c. abscisic acid.
    d. ethylene.
    e. oligosaccharins.

26. Tomatoes may be shipped green and ripened by _____ at their destination.
    a. ethylene
    b. auxin
    c. abscisic acid
    d. gibberellins
    e. cytokinins

27. Plants can advantageously orient leaves by means of the reversible
    a. thigmotropism.
    b. turgor movements.
    c. phototropism.
    d. gravitropism.
    e. abscission.

28. Circadian rhythms are typified by the following characteristics except that they
    a. must be about 24 hours in duration.
    b. can be reset.
    c. run in the absence of external input.
    d. are interrupted by prolonged darkness.
    e. can compensate for temperature changes.

29. Which of the following does not occur as a result of turgor movements?
    a. tracking the Sun
    b. leaf folding in response to touch
    c. circadian rhythms in some leaves and flowers
    d. sleep movements of bean leaves
    e. snapping of the Venus flytrap

30. The hormone _____ may be critical to the survival of water stress in plants.
    a. auxin
    b. gibberellins
    c. ethylene
    d. abscisic acid
    e. brassinosteroids

ASSESSING YOUR KNOWLEDGE

Answers to the questions in this section test your ability to synthesize information gained from the chapter and to solve challenging problems on an exam or in everyday life.

Challenging Your Understanding—Answers

1. A. Inactive; B. Active; C. Phosphorylation of phytochrome; D. Activation of transcription factors; E. Gene expression; F. Translocation to the nucleus; G. Binding to transcription factors; H. Gene expression.

2. A. Napthalene acetic acid – prevention of fruit dropping or abscission in crops

    B. Indolebutyric acid – prevention of fruit dropping or abscission in crops

    C. 2,4,5 trichlorophenoxyacetic acid - herbicide

3. A1. Abscission; A2. Produce dormant seeds; B1. Induce desaturase enzyme; B2. Increase solute concentration; B3. Increase antifreeze proteins; C1. Produce heat-shock proteins.

Key Terms—Answers

a. 19, b. 15, c. 8, d. 3, e. 25, f. 5, g. 12, h. 21, i. 14, j. 2, k. 17, l. 23, m. 13, n. 6, o. 16, p. 26, q. 1, r. 9, s. 18, t. 11, u. 24, v. 4, w. 10, x. 22, y. 20, z. 7.

Learning by Experience—Answers

1. Auxin: Propagate plants by cuttings
           Prevent fruit drop
           Seedless fruit	

2. Cytokinins: Used with auxin for root and shoot development	
3. Gibberellins: Restore growth to dwarf mutants Increase grape size by elongating internodes	
4. Brassinosteroids: Delay senescence	
5. Oligosaccharins: Stimulate flower production in competent plants	
6. Ethylene: Ripen fruit	
7. Abscisic acid: Promote winter buds Prevent premature germination of seeds	

Exercising Your Knowledge—Answers

As you check your answers, put a mark in the review (Rvw.) column for the answers you missed. If you didn't miss any, congratulations—you have mastered the chapter! If you missed some, review the section (Sect.) in the text where this concept is discussed. In order to develop an efficient review strategy, it is important that you understand what types of questions you missed. The questions with asterisks test more for understanding of the **concepts**, whereas the others test more for **detail**. *See the preface for learning strategies for concepts and for detail.*

	Sect.	Rvw.
*1. Tropisms are responses to stimuli from only one direction, whereas nastic movements occur independent of direction.	41.3	
*2. Far-red light converts P_{fr}, the active form, to P_r the inactive form.	41.1	
*3. Etiolation enables a plant not receiving light to grow rapidly toward the sunlight.	41.1	
*4. One of the first steps in sensing gravity is the sinking of amyloplasts toward the gravitational field.	41.2	
*5. Rain causes leaching of inhibiting chemicals from the seed coat.	41.4	
*6. Seeds requiring a cold period before germination will not germinate until spring.	41.4	
*7. Auxin increases the plasticity of cell walls, allowing cells to elongate.	41.5	
*8. Touch generates an electrical signal that is translated into a chemical signal in the plant. As a result, potassium ions followed by water migrate from the cells in one half of the pulvinus to the intercellular spaces in the other half. The loss of turgor pressure in half of the pulvinus causes the leaf to fold.	41.3	
*9. Coconut milk contains cytokinins that promote cell differentiation.	41.5	
*10. Gibberellins enhance the DNA-binding proteins, allowing for the production of hydrolytic enzymes, which act on the aleurone layer.	41.5	
11. e	41.1	
12. c	41.1	
*13. b	41.5	
14. d	41.5	
15. a	41.5	
16. e	41.5	
17. d	41.5	
18. e	41.5	
19. a	41.5	
20. e	41.4	
21. c	41.5	
22. b	41.2	
23. e	41.5	
24. e	41.5	
25. c	41.5	
*26. a	41.5	
27. b	41.5	
*28. d	41.1	
*29. e	41.3	
*30. d	41.5	

CHAPTER 42 PLANT REPRODUCTION

MASTERING KEY CONCEPTS

Angiosperms are arguably the most successful plants on earth. This chapter describes their rise and the reasons for it. Lots of little things account for their success.

42.1 The environment influences reproduction.

- **Overview**: Plants become competent to reproduce through a series of developmental changes that lead to reproductive maturity. At this time, plants can undergo a **phase change** and flower in response to the appropriate internal and external signals. However, plants that are reproductively competent do not necessarily produce flowers, which is the mark of actual reproductive development. In *Arabidopsis*, the *EMF* **gene** suppresses flowering until the plant is mature. At this time, *EMF* expression decreases. Overexpression of the *Arabidopsis* *LEAFY* **gene** in an aspen induces the transition from juvenile to adult and promotes early flowering.

- **Details**: Know the factors involved in initiating flowering. Understand what is meant by a phase change. Know the characteristics of the *emf* mutant.

42.2 Flowers are highly evolved for reproduction.

- **Overview**: There are four known regulated pathways to flowering, **light-dependent**, **temperature-dependent**, **gibberellin-dependent**, and **autonomous pathways**. The environment can promote or repress flowering, or it can remain neutral. The light-dependent (**photoperiodic**) flowering pathway allows plants to respond to the length of the day (the amount of darkness). **Short-day plants** initiate flowering when the day length becomes shorter than a critical length, and **long-day plants** flower when the number of hours of daylight increase. **Day-neutral plants** flower when they reach maturity, independent of the length of the day, and still other plants require two photoperiods. The photoperiod is perceived by different forms of **phytochrome** and a **cryptochrome**, a blue-light sensitive molecule, whose conformational changes trigger a signal transduction cascade to initiate flowering. One gene that they affect is *CONSTANS* (*CO*), a transcription factor that activates *LFY* expression. In the temperature-dependent pathway, cold temperatures, or a period of chilling (**vernalization**), are necessary to accelerate or permit flowering. Gibberellins promote flowering by enhancing the expression of the *LFY* gene by binding directly to its promoter in the gibberellin-dependent pathway. The autonomous pathway allows plants to "count" and remember. Plants produce a uniform number of nodes before flowering, and become **determined to flower** at some point during the production of the nodes. Shoots know where they are due to floral promoting signals and inhibitory signals sent from the roots. All of the flowering pathways lead to an adult meristem becoming a **floral meristem** through the activation or repression of the inhibition of **floral meristem identity genes** that activate the **floral organ identity genes,** which specify the floral organs in the four floral whorls according to the **ABC model**. This model has been modified by the identification of class *D* (carpel formation), and class *E* genes (*SEP* genes), which are required for specifying floral organ identity.

- **Details**: Understand the four regulated pathways to flowering. Know the advantages of photoperiodic control of flowering. Understand the model for flowering, the ABC model for floral organ specification, and the modifications that have been made to this model.

42.3 The structure of flowers has evolved.

- **Overview**: Flowers contain the haploid generations that will produce gametes and are advantageous because they increase the probability that male and female gametes will find each other. Floral organs likely evolved from leaves. A complete flower consists of **four whorls**. The outermost whorl is the **calyx,** containing flattened **sepals** that protect the flower in the bud. Inside of the calyx is the **corolla** consisting of the **petals**. The **androecium** is the third whorl consisting of all of the **stamens,** which are the structures that bear the angiosperm microsporangia. The final whorl is the **gynoecium** consisting of the **carpel**, or the female parts of the flower. Flowering plants have evolved such that floral parts have been grouped or fused, or have been lost or reduced in some plants, and the flowers of some of the advanced groups are bilaterally symmetrical. The sexual reproductive cycle of a plant is characterized by an **alternation of generations** in which a haploid gametophyte generation is enclosed within the diploid sporophyte. The male gametophytes, or **pollen grains** (n), are produced from the **microspores** (n), which are generated by meiotic division of the **microspore mother cell** (2n) housed in the **anther**. The female gametophyte, or **embryo sac** containing eight nuclei is produced by meiotic division of the **megaspore mother cell** (2n).

- **Details**: Know the four distinct whorls of a flower and the structures that make up each.

Know the two evolutionary trends that led to the wide diversity of flowering plants. Understand how the reproductive organs of angiosperms are different from animals. Know how pollen grains and the eight-nucleate embryo sac are produced.

42.4 Flowers attract pollinators and allow fertilization of angiosperms.

- **Overview**: The first step in uniting the two sperm in a pollen grain with the egg cell and the polar nuclei is the placement of pollen on the stigma of the carpel. The pollen can come from either the same flower as the stigma (**self-pollination**) or from a different flower (**cross-pollination**). A **pollen tube** that penetrates the style grows down from a pollen grain until it reaches the **ovule** in the **ovary** allowing one sperm to fuse with the egg, and the second to fuse with the two polar nuclei (**double fertilization**), producing the zygote and the triploid endosperm nucleus, respectively. The zygote and the triploid endosperm nucleus divide to form the **embryo** and the **endosperm**. The seed develops inside the ripening fruit. Flower morphology has coevolved with **pollinators**, such as insects, birds, and other animals, which are responsible for transferring pollen between plants of the same species. Pollinators promote **outcrossing,** which is genetically important for diversity in plants. Like early seed plants, many angiosperms are still pollinated by the wind. The flowers of these plants are generally small, green, and odorless and the pollen-producing and ovule-bearing flowers may be separated to promote outcrossing. In general, outcrossing is promoted by separating stamens and pistils on different plants and by **self-incompatability**. Self-pollination among angiosperms also occurs primarily in temperate regions, which can be advantageous because these plants don't have to attract pollinators, and progeny identical to their parents can be well-adapted to particular habitats.
- **Details**: Know how bees, butterflies, birds, and other animals have coevolved with the flowers that they pollinate. Know how each group recognizes the flowers that they specialize on. Know the two basic reasons for the frequent occurrence of self-pollinated angiosperms. Understand the two strategies that plants use to promote outcrossing. Understand how self-incompatibility is controlled.

42.5 Many plants can clone themselves by asexual reproduction.

- **Overview**: **Asexual reproduction** produces individuals that are genetically identical to their parents. It is common in harsh environments where individuals that are highly adapted persist. **Vegetative reproduction** is an asexual method of reproduction by which new individuals are produced by cloning nonreproductive parts of adults. This can occur by **runners**, **rhizomes**, **suckers**, and **adventitious plantlets,** which act as important reproductive structures. Cultured leaf, stem, and root tissues can generate organsor, in some cases, give rise to whole plants in culture.
- **Details**: Know how asexual reproduction occurs and when it can be advantageous. Know the important reproductive structures in vegetative reproduction.

42.6 How long do plants and plant organs live?

- **Overview**: Plants have widely varied life spans. Woody plants that have secondary growth typically live longer than herbaceous plants that lack secondary growth. **Perennial plants** can be woody or herbaceous and continue to flower and produce seeds and fruit year after year. This is in contrast to **annual plants,** which grow, flower and produce seeds and fruits within one growing season and then die. **Biennial plants** store energy in the first year of their life cycle, and flower during the second year to complete the cycle.
- **Details**: Know how the life spans of perennial, annual, and biennial plants vary.

CHALLENGING YOUR UNDERSTANDING

1. There are five classes (A, B, C, D, and E) of genes whose expression promotes the development of specific floral organs. For each of the following floral organs, list the genes whose expression is required to produce them.

Sepals:

Petals:

Stamens:

Carpels:

2. What floral organs would you expect be missing from the flowers of a plant that contains mutations in the following genes?

B:
C:
D:
SEP1:
SEP3:

3. Fill in the flowchart below to show how four different stimuli (cold, autonomous signal, gibberellin, light) regulate flower development through the *LFY* and/or *AP1* genes. To the left of each stimulus, indicate whether it promotes or inhibits floral development.

Flower Repressing Genes	Flower Promoting Genes

LFY

Flower Development

AP1

4. List the characteristics of flowers that specialize them for pollination by the following animals.

Bees:

Butterflies:

Moths:

Birds:

KEY TERMS

Match the numbered term with the definition that fits it best. Put the corresponding number in front of the appropriate definition.

1. phase change
2. photoperiodic
3. short-day plants
4. long-day plants
5. day-neutral plants
6. vernalization
7. florally determined
8. floral organ identity genes
9. floral meristem identity genes
10. complete flower
11. pollinators
12. calyx

13. sepals
14. corolla
15. androecium
16. stamens
17. filaments
18. anther
19. gynoecium
20. carpel
21. ovule
22. ovary
23. style
24. stigma

25. pollen grains
26. embryo sac
27. pollination
28. dioecious
29. monoecious
30. dichogamous
31. self-incompatibility
32. double fertilization
33. pollen tube
34. annual plants
35. biennial plants
36. perennial plants

a. ____ Genes that establish the meristem as a flower meristem.
b. ____ Plants in which flowering is initiated when daylight becomes shorter than a critical length.
c. ____ The male gametophytes produced from mitotic division of the microspores in angiosperms.
d. ____ Plants having life cycles that take two years to complete.
e. ____ Slender, threadlike stalk part of the stamen.
f. ____ The outermost whorl in flowers consisting of flattened appendages that protect the flower in the bud.
g. ____ Plants that produce separate male and female flowers.
h. ____ Insects, birds, or other animals that transfer pollen between plants of the same species.
i. ____ Plants in which flowering begins when the number of hours of daylight becomes longer.
j. ____ Plants that grow, flower, produce seeds and fruits, and then typically die within one growing season.
k. ____ The slender column that arises from the top of the ovary through which the pollen tube grows.
l. ____ When the pollen and stigma recognize each other as being genetically related, and pollen tube growth is blocked.
m. ____ The requirement for a period of chilling of seeds or shoots for flowering to occur.
n. ____ Produced in the swollen lower portion of the carpel and develops into a seed.
o. ____ The tendency of some plants to respond to the duration and timing of day and night.
p. ____ A structure formed after germination of the pollen grain that carries the male gametes into the ovule.
q. ____ The whorl of a flower containing all of the female parts.
r. ____ The female gametophyte containing eight nuclei, which is produced by mitotic division of the megaspore.
s. ____ Flattened appendages that protect the flower in the bud.
t. ____ Plants that flower when they are mature regardless of day length as long as light for growth is sufficient.
u. ____ Genes that define the four concentric whorls, moving inward, as the sepal, petal, stamen, and carpel.
v. ____ Plants in which functional pistils and stamens are produced in each flower, but reach maturity at different times.
w. ____ Internal development changes that allow plants to respond to signals that trigger flower formation.
x. ____ The enlarged basal portion of a carpel that contains the ovule and matures to become the fruit.
y. ____ The whorl of a flower that is made up of the petals and is located just inside of the calyx.
z. ____ A certain point in the flowering process in which shoots become committed to making a flower.
aa. ____ The region of the carpel that serves as a receptive surface for pollen grains in the flowers of angiosperms.
bb. ____ Plants that produce only ovules or only pollen and must rely on outcrossing for fertilization.
cc. ____ A flower possessing all four whorls.
dd. ____ Plants that are able to flower and produce seeds and fruit for an indefinite number of growing seasons.
ee. ____ The whorl of a flower containing all of the male structures.
ff. ____ The process by which pollen is placed on the stigma of a flower.
gg. ____ The pollen-bearing portion of the stamen.
hh. ____ A leaflike organ in angiosperms that encloses one or more ovules.
ii. ____ The fusion of the egg and sperm and the simultaneous fusion of the second male gamete with the polar nuclei.
jj. ____ The organ of the flower that produces the pollen and consists of an anther and filament.

LEARNING BY EXPERIENCE

Color the four whorls on the upper flower diagram. Color the individual components on the lower diagram. Indicate your color code by coloring the circle to the right of each structure's name. Review the functions of the structures as you color.

Gynoecium ○

Androecium ○

Corolla ○

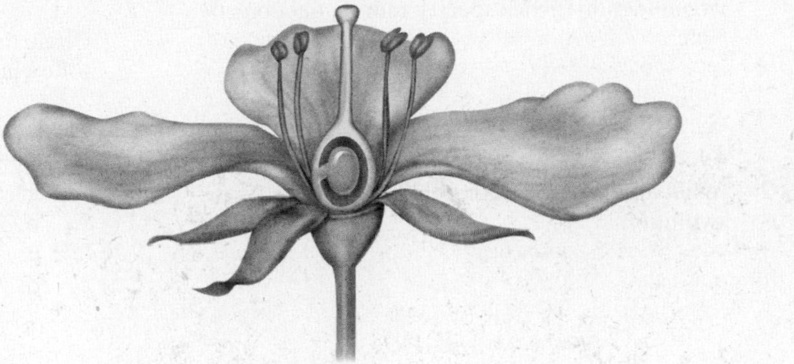

Calyx ○

Stigma ○

Style ○

Ovary ○

Ovule ○

Anther ○

Filament ○

Petals ○

Sepals ○

Receptacle ○

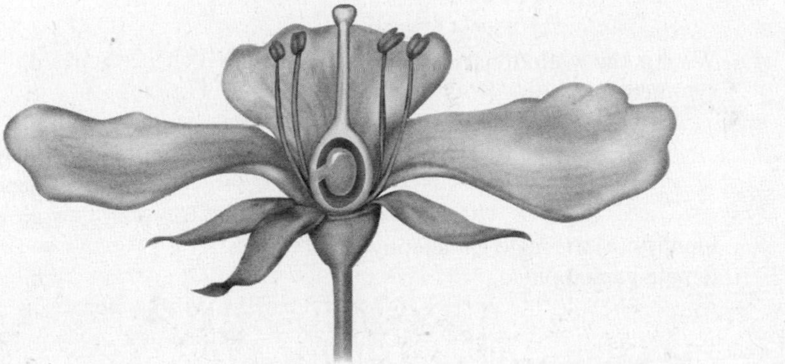

EXERCISING YOUR KNOWLEDGE

Briefly answer the following questions in the space provided.

1. Explain how five, not three, classes of floral organ identity genes specify four distinct organ types.

2. What are the two major trends in floral evolution?

3. Compare the effects of natural selection in plants to those of artificial selection (by humans).

4. What is the evolutionary trend in floral symmetry?

5. Identify (a) the male gametophyte and (b) the female gametophyte.

6. Discuss cell division in microspore formation.

7. Discuss cell division in embryo sac formation.

8. Why would producing too much nectar be disadvantageous to an insect-pollinated flower?

9. Under what circumstances might self-pollination be advantageous to flowering plants?

10. What advantage is the biennial mode of flowering?

Circle the letter of the one best answer in each of the following questions.

11. Branches of a tree that fail to lose their leaves in the winter are _____
    a. dead.
    b. juvenile branches.
    c. undergoing a phase change.
    d. mature.
    e. in the process of flowering.

12. The color called "bee's purple" is caused by reflection of
    a. a combination of yellow and ultraviolet light.
    b. ultraviolet light.
    c. a combination of red and blue light.
    d. a combination of red and ultraviolet light.
    e. red light.

13. Which of the following is NOT true of the light-dependent flowering pathway?
    a. Flowering occurs when pollinators are available.
    b. The photoperiod is perceived by several different forms of phytochrome and a cryptochrome.
    c. Flowering is regulated by the *CO* gene, a transcription factor that activates the expression of *LFY*.
    d. The amount of darkness determines whether a plant will flower.
    e. Vernalization can permit or accelerate flowering.

14. Which of the following is not characteristic of primitive flowers?
    a. numerous flowering parts
    b. tubular parts
    c. petals and sepals are similar
    d. unfused flower parts
    e. spirally arranged parts

15. Meiosis, followed by mitosis of the microspore mother cell, produces which of the following?
    a. pollen sac
    b. sporophytes
    c. synergids
    d. pollen tube
    e. microgametophytes

16. The surviving megaspore produced by meiotic division of the megaspore mother cell divides by mitosis to produce which of the following?
    a. an embryo sac
    b. an ovule
    c. synergids
    d. egg cell
    e. antipodal cell

17. Which of the following does not result from embryo sac formation?
    a. antipodals
    b. generative cell
    c. synergids
    d. polar nuclei
    e. egg

18. Which of the following is true of florally determined shoots when rooted in a pot?
    a. They flower immediately.
    b. They develop like a seedling and then flower.
    c. They will never flower.
    d. They produce the same number of nodes that they would have if they had grown on the plant and then flower.
    e. They delay flowering to form adventitious roots.

19. If a flower is to be pollinated by bees, it should be
    a. red.
    b. white.
    c. pink.
    d. green.
    e. yellow.

20. In nature, poinsettia pollen is dispersed by
    a. insects.
    b. mammals.
    c. wind.
    d. birds.
    e. water.

21. If a flower is to be pollinated by a moth, it should
    a. be heavily scented.
    b. be broad and flat.
    c. close at noon.
    d. be brightly colored.
    e. be dioecious.

22. Which of the following is a plant whose pollen is not dispersed by wind?
    a. phlox
    b. oak
    c. birch
    d. cottonwood
    e. grass

23. Which of the following is NOT part of the gynoecium?
    a. stigma
    b. pistils
    c. style
    d. anther
    e. ovule

24. Plants lacking A, B, and C gene function for floral organ specification actually have which of the following phenotypes, contrary to the ABC model?
    a. They lack stamens and carpels.
    b. They lack petals.
    c. They lack petals, stamens, and carpels.
    d. They lack petals and sepals.
    e. They lack petals, stamens, carpels, and sepals.

25. In sporophytic self-incompatibility, which of the following statements is NOT true?
    a. Self-pollination is blocked before pollen tube germination.
    b. If either S allele in the stigma matches the pollen's S allele, pollen tube growth stops.
    c. Both S alleles of the pollen parent are important.
    d. All of the above.
    e. None of the above.

26. Dichogamous plants
    a. require a stamen-bearing plant and a pistil-bearing plant to reproduce.
    b. have both an androecium and a gynoecium, but they may mature at different times.
    c. have staminate flowers on one plant and pistillate flowers on another.
    d. are self-pollinating.
    e. are self-incompatible.

27. Genetic self-incompatibility tends to increase
    a. pollen dispersal.
    b. inbreeding.
    c. pollination.
    d. isolation.
    e. outcrossing.

28. When planting potatoes, the seed pieces are parts of
    a. stolons.
    b. adventitious leaves.
    c. tubers.
    d. suckers.
    e. runners.

29. Perennial plants
    a. are woody.
    b. always persist above ground.
    c. are trees or shrubs.
    d. store most of their energy in stems.
    e. may be herbaceous.

30. Biennials
    a. flower every two years.
    b. flower for two years and die.
    c. flower in their second year and die.
    d. flower in their first year and die at the end of the second year.
    e. flower twice each year.

ASSESSING YOUR KNOWLEDGE

Answers to the questions in this section test your ability to synthesize information gained from the chapter and to solve challenging problems on an exam or in everyday life.

Challenging Your Understanding—Answers

1. Sepals: *A, SEP1*
   Petals: *A,B, SEP1, SEP3*
   Stamens: *B, C, SEP2, SEP3*
   Carpels: *C, D, SEP2, SEP3*

2. *B:* Petals and stamens
   C: Stamens and carpels
   D. Carpels
   SEP1: Sepals and petals
   SEP3: Stamens and carpels

3.

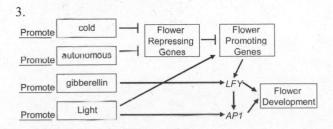

4. Bees: Yellow or blue flowers; often striped
   Butterflies: flat "landing pad" on flower
   Moths: heavily scented for night-locating
   Birds: Red flowers; large volumes of nectar

Key Terms—Answers

a. 9, b. 3, c. 25, d. 35, e. 17, f. 12, g. 29, h. 11, i. 4, j. 34, k. 23, l. 31, m. 6, n. 21, o. 2, p. 33, q. 19, r. 26, s. 13, t. 5, u. 8, v. 30, w. 1, x. 22, y. 14, z. 7, aa. 24, bb. 28, cc. 10, dd. 36, ee. 15, ff. 27, gg. 18, hh. 20, ii. 32, jj. 16.

Learning by Experience—Answers

Compare your work to textbook figure 42.14.

Exercising Your Knowledge—Answers

As you check your answers, put a mark in the review (Rvw.) column for the answers you missed. If you didn't miss any, congratulations—you have mastered the chapter! If you missed some, review the section (Sect.) in the text where this concept is discussed. In order to develop an efficient review strategy, it is important that you understand what types of questions you missed. The questions with asterisks test more for understanding of the **concepts**, whereas the others test more for **detail**. *See the preface for learning strategies for concepts and for detail.*

	Sect.	Rvw.
*1. It was originally thought that class A, B, and C genes specified four distinct organ types, where class A genes alone specified the sepals, class A and B genes together specified the petals, class B and class C genes together specified the stamens, and class C genes alone specify the carpels. However, the observation was made that plants lacking A, B, and C function produced four whorls of sepals, rather than four whorls of leaves. Class E genes (*SEP* genes) were discovered to be involved in sepal formation and to possibly affect the transcription of class A, B, and C genes. Additionally, class D genes have now been identified to play a role in carpel formation also.	42.2	
*2. The two major trends in floral evolution are grouping or fusing of floral parts and reduction of loss of parts.	42.3	
*3. Natural selection has adaptive advantage to the plant, whereas human selection has no adaptive advantage to the plant.	42.3	
*4. The evolutionary trend in floral symmetry is from radial to bilateral symmetry.	42.3	
*5. (a) The male gametophyte is the pollen grain. (b) the female gametophyte is the embryo sac.	42.3	
*6. The first cell division is the meiotic division of the microspore mother cell. The second division is the mitotic division of the meiotic product of the microspore mother cell.	42.3	
*7. First, the megaspore mother cell divides by meiosis to form four haploid megaspores. The one surviving megaspore divides repeatedly by mitosis until eight nuclei within seven cells are formed.	42.3	
*8. If an insect can get enough nectar from one flower, it has no incentive to carry pollen to another flower.	42.4	
*9. Plants in habitats where there are not enough pollinators would benefit from self-pollination. Well-adapted plants will avoid the risks of meiosis to their genome by self-pollination.	42.4	
*10. Biennial plants are able to store nutrients for the high energy demands of flowering and seed production.	42.6	
11. b	42.1	
12. a	42.4	
13. e	42.2	
*14. b	42.3	
*15. e	42.3	
*16. a	42.3	
17. b	42.3	
*18. d	42.2	
19. e	42.4	
20. a	42.4	
21. a	42.4	

22. a	42.4	
23. d	42.3	
24. c	42.2	
25. b	42.4	
26. b	42.4	
27. e	42.4	
28. c	42.5	
29. e	42.6	
30. c	42.6	

CHAPTER 43 THE ANIMAL BODY AND PRINCIPLES OF REGULATION

MASTERING KEY CONCEPTS

Each vertebrate body is made up of a variety of organs and organ systems that carry out different life processes, such as digestion, respiration, and reproduction. Organs are made up of groups of specialized cells that have similar structures and functions. These groups of cells are called tissues. Although there are between 50 and several hundred types of cells, and there are subdivisions within each tissue type, vertebrates have just four basic kinds of tissue: epithelium, connective, muscle, and nerve. Locomotion is a good example of how cells, tissues, organs, and organ systems work together. All animal locomotion follows the same basic principle: muscles contract and work against an internal or external skeleton, which results in movement.

43.1 The bodies of vertebrates are organized into functional systems.

- **Overview**: The bodies of vertebrates are organized into **cells**, **tissues**, **organs**, and **organ systems**. Tissues are groups of similar cells that operate together. There are three embryonic tissues (**germ layers**), **endoderm**, **mesoderm**, and **ectoderm**, and four **primary tissues** in adult vertebrates, **epithelial**, **connective**, **muscle**, and **nerve tissue**. Different types of tissues are organized into structural and functional units known as organs. These organs are arranged in organ systems, which are groups of organs that function together to carry out a similar function. All vertebrates have a digestive tract inside a body cavity that is surrounded by bones or cartilage and covered by skin (**tube within a tube**). The vertebrate body has both a **dorsal** and a **ventral body cavity**. The dorsal body cavity consists of the **cranial** and **vertebral cavities** containing the brain and spinal cord. The ventral body cavity is separated by the diaphragm into the **thoracic cavity** and the **abdominopelvic cavity**. The coelomic space in the abdominopelvic cavity is the **peritoneal cavity**, and the space within the mesodermal layers around the heart is the **pericardial cavity**.
- **Details**: Know the four levels of organization of the vertebrate body. Know the cavities that the vertebrate body is divided into, and how the coelom is subdivided.

43.2 Epithelial tissue forms membranes and glands.

- **Overview**: **Epithelial layers** originating from one of the three germ layers cover every surface of the vertebrate body and create selectively permeable barriers to substances outside (epidermis) and inside the body. The epithelium consists of a **basal surface** that is secured, and an **apical surface** that is free. Epithelium is extremely regenerative. Epithelial membranes are **simple** (one cell thick) or **stratified** (two to several cell layers thick), and are further categorized based on the shape of cells that they contain: **squamous**, **cuboidal**, or **columnar**. Glands form from invaginated epithelia. **Exocrine glands** remain as a duct and their secretions channel to the surface of the epithelial membrane; **endocrine glands** are ductless and their secretions enter the blood and circulate throughout the body.
- **Details**: Know the locations, functions, and characteristic cell types of epithelial membranes.

43.3 Connective tissues contain abundant extracellular material.

- **Overview**: **Connective tissue** arises from embryonic mesoderm and consists of **connective tissue proper** (loose and dense connective tissue) and **special connective tissue** (bones, cartilage, and blood). All connective tissue has abundant extracellular material, or **matrix** that is secreted by **fibroblasts** and consists of **ground substance** and protein fibers. **Loose connective tissue** consists of cells scattered within a matrix and a large amount of ground substance supported by a collagenous meshwork. It is typically located beneath the skin and between organs. **Adipose cells** are a type of loose connective tissue that store energy. **Dense connective tissue** consists of tightly packed collagen fibers that line up in parallel (**dense regular connective tissue**) like that found in tendons, or have many orientations (**dense irregular connective tissue**) like that found in the tough coverings around organs. **Cartilage**, **bone**, and **blood** are specialized connective tissues. Cartilage is made up of **chondrocytes** containing the glycoprotein **chondroitin**, and collagen fibers that make a firm structure that provides flexible support and shock absorption. In bone cells (**osteocytes**), the extracellular matrix is hardened by calcium phosphate. Bone makes up most of the skeleton and protects internal organs. Blood is a connective tissue that contains fluid **plasma** as the extracellular matrix and is the primary means of communication between organs.
- **Details**: Know the locations, functions, and characteristic cell types of connective tissue. Know the similarities among all of the connective tissues.

43.4 Muscle tissue provides for movement.

- **Overview**: Three general types of muscle are

found in the vertebrate body: **smooth**, **skeletal**, and **cardiac**. Muscles consist of actin and myosin filaments. Smooth muscle is found in the organs of the internal environment (**viscera**), such as in the walls of blood vessels and the digestive tract. It is arranged into sheets of long, spindle-shaped cells. Skeletal muscle and cardiac muscle are **striated muscles**. Skeletal muscles are attached to bones by tendons and are made up of **muscle fibers** containing **myofibrils** that control their contractions. Skeletal muscles are under voluntary control. Cardiac muscle consists of small, interconnected cells linked by gap junctions that allow the cells to function as a single unit, the heart.

- **Details**: Know the different types of muscle tissue and their locations and functions.

43.5 Nerve tissue provides for control.

- **Overview**: **Nerve tissue** consists of **neurons** and **neuroglia**. Neurons are made of a **cell body** containing a nucleus, **dendrites** that receive incoming stimulation and conduct electrical impulses, and an **axon** that conducts impulses away from the cell body. Neuroglia support and insulate the neurons and can form a **myelin sheath** around an axon. The nervous system consists of both the **central nervous system**, including the brain and spinal cord, and the **peripheral nervous system** consisting of the nerves and ganglia, which transmits signals to and from the central nervous system.
- **Details**: Know the types of nerve cells and the function of each. Know the components of the central and peripheral nervous systems and how each functions.

43.6 Vertebrate organ systems are grouped according to their functions.

- **Overview**: Vertebrate **organ systems** are defined based on functional groupings. The **nervous system**, **sensory system**, and **endocrine system** detect stimuli, integrate the message, and respond. The **musculoskeletal system** provides support and the ability to move. The **digestive**, **circulatory**, **respiratory**, and **urinary systems** maintain the body. The **integumentary** and **immune systems** defend the body from foreign invaders, and the **reproductive system** includes all of the organs necessary for fertilization and development of an embryo.
- **Details**: Know the organ systems, the critical organs in each, and the function that each provides to the body.

43.7 Homeostatic mechanisms help maintain stable internal conditions.

- **Overview**: The vertebrate body depends on the maintenance of **homeostasis** in the internal environment. A **negative feedback** system detects external and internal conditions and functions to maintain a **set point** in the body in terms of temperature, pH, glucose and oxygen concentrations, and so on. Deviations from this set point are detected by **sensors** that send a message to an **integrating center** leading to an increase or decrease in the activity of an **effector** that produces a response. Negative feedback to the sensor terminates the response. Many effectors have **antagonistic actions** such that increasing the activity of one is accompanied by decreasing the activity of another. **Positive feedback** mechanisms push a change farther in the same direction and do not help to maintain homeostasis.
- **Details**: Know how positive and negative feedback mechanisms work and how they affect homeostasis. Understand how sensors and effectors function in these two mechanisms.

CHALLENGING YOUR UNDERSTANDING—Part I.

1. List the primary tissue associated with each of the following cell types, or locations in the body.

a. Lining of the mouth _____

b. Osteocytes _____

c. Wall of the heart _____

d. Lining of the lungs _____

e. Joint tissue _____

f. Adipose cells _____

g. Brain _____

h. Walls of the intestine _____

i. Erythrocytes _____

j. Surface lining of the stomach _____

k. Formation of glands _____

l. Walls of the blood vessels _____

m. Tendons _____

n. Spinal cord _____

o. Outer layer of skin _____

p. Cells between organs _____

q. Cartilage _____

r. Pectoralis major _____

2. Identify whether each of the following is located in the dorsal body cavity, thoracic cavity, or abdominopelvic cavity.

a. Peritoneal cavity _____

b. Heart _____

c. Vertebrae _____

d. Kidneys _____

e. Pericardial cavity _____

f. Spinal cord _____

g. Lungs _____

h. Intestines _____

i. Pleural cavity _____

j. Spleen _____

CHALLENGING YOUR UNDERSTANDING—Part II.

1. List the steps in the negative feedback loop that is activated to maintain homeostasis in the body in response to each of the following stimuli. Your answer should include the sensors, integrating center, effectors involved, and the response.

a. Body temperature rises:

b. Body temperature drops:

2. List the steps in the positive feedback loop that is activated in response to the contractions of the uterus during childbirth. Your answer should again include the sensors, integrating center, effectors involved, and the response.

3. Indicate how this positive feedback cycle is stopped. Explain why it is advantageous to have a positive feedback loop rather than a negative feedback loop in this situation.

KEY TERMS

Match the numbered term with the definition that fits it best. Put the corresponding number in front of the appropriate definition.

1. peritoneal cavity
2. thoracic cavity
3. abdominopelvic cavity
4. tissues
5. endoderm
6. mesoderm
7. ectoderm
8. organs
9. organ system
10. epithelium
11. simple epithelial membrane
12. stratified epithelial membrane
13. exocrine glands
14. endocrine glands
15. connective tissue proper

16. special connective tissue
17. matrix
18. loose connective tissue
19. ground substance
20. adipose cells
21. dense connective tissue
22. chondrocytes
23. fibroblasts
24. cartilage
25. osteocytes
26. blood
27. smooth muscle
28. skeletal muscle
29. cardiac muscle
30. myofibrils

31. intercalated disks
32. neurons
33. neuroglia
34. central nervous system
35. peripheral nervous system
36. homeostasis
37. negative feedback
38. endocrine system
39. digestive system
39. circulatory system
40. respiratory system
41. reproductive system
42. positive feedback

a. ____ A gland that forms a duct with the epithelial membrane channeling its product to the surface.
b. ____ A homeostatic control mechanism that pushes or accentuates a change farther in the same direction.
c. ____ The interior region located posteriorly to the diaphragm in the divided ventral body cavity.
d. ____ The dynamic constancy of the internal environment in temperature, pH, glucose, and oxygen concentrations.
e. ____ The connective tissue that contains the abundant extracellular material, fluid plasma.
f. ____ The fluid material between cells and fibers containing an array of proteins and polysaccharides.
g. ____ The membranous tissue that covers every surface of the vertebrate body.
h. ____ Cells that support and insulate neurons and eliminate foreign materials in and around neurons.
i. ____ One of the three embryonic germ layers that gives rise to muscle, bone, and other connective tissue.
j. ____ Striated muscle cells in the walls of the heart that promote the rapid spread of signal initiating contraction.
k. ____ Epithelial membrane consisting of a single layer of cells found in the lining of the stomach and the lungs.
l. ____ Body structures composed of several different types of tissues that form a structural and functional unit.
m. ____ One type of connective tissue proper that contains tightly packed collagen fibers for flexible, strong connections.
n. ____ Substructures in each muscle fiber that contain highly ordered arrays of actin and myosin.
o. ____ One of the three embryonic germ layers that gives rise to the epithelium that lines internal structures.
p. ____ Regions between adjacent cells in cardiac muscle that are linked by gap junctions.
q. ____ The coelomic space in the abdominopelvic cavity.
r. ____ Specialized connective tissue that provides flexible support, shock absorption, and reduction of friction.
s. ____ The abundant extracellular material characteristic of all connective tissues.
t. ____ The division of the nervous system that includes the nerves and ganglia.
u. ____ Epithelial membranes that are two to several cell layers thick found in the outer layer of skin and the mouth lining.
v. ____ The system that issues chemical signals that regulate the chemical processes taking place in all organ systems.
w. ____ Fat cells that contain a droplet of triglycerides within a storage vesicle that can be hydrolyzed for energy.
x. ____ An organ system necessary to maintain the biological continuity of vertebrates.
y. ____ A major class of connective tissue that includes the loose and dense connective tissue.
z. ____ The earliest form of muscle to evolve occurring in the viscera to power involuntary contractions.
aa. ____ The part of the nervous system that includes the brain and spinal cord.
bb. ____ A type of connective tissue proper found beneath the skin or between organs to provide support and storage.
cc. ____ One of the three embryonic germ layers that gives rise to the outer epithelium of the body.
dd. ____ Cells that produce and secrete the extracellular matrix of connective tissue.
ee. ____ Consisting primarily of the trachea and lungs, this system is used to acquire oxygen and expel CO_2.
ff. ____ Cells that are specialized to produce and conduct electrochemical events or impulses.
gg. ____ The region located in front of the diaphragm in the ventral body cavity, containing the heart and lungs.
hh. ____ Ductless glands whose secretions enter the blood capillaries and circulate throughout the body.
ii. ____ Striated muscles that are attached to bones by tendons so that contraction causes the bones to move at their joints.
jj. ____ A group of organs that cooperate to perform the major activities of the body.

kk. _____ System including the esophagus, liver, stomach, and small and large intestine that absorbs nutrients into the body.

ll. _____ Bone cells that serve to protect internal organs and provide rigid support for muscle attachment.

mm. _____ A class of connective tissue that includes the cartilage, bone, and blood.

nn. _____ A homeostatic control mechanism in which an increase in a substance inhibits the process leading to the increase.

oo. _____ Organized groups of cells that are similar in structure and function.

pp. _____ Cells of the cartilage that live within spaces within the cartilage ground substance.

LEARNING BY EXPERIENCE

1. Fill in the following chart by listing the three types of fundamental tissues (germ layers) found in vertebrate embryos and the four types of primary tissues found in vertebrate adults.

Germ layers	Primary tissues
a.	d.
b.	e.
c.	f.
	g.

2. Name each of the types of cells or tissues illustrated below.

    a. _____

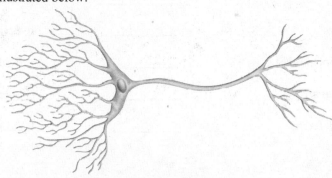

    b. _____

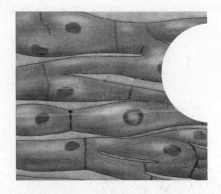

    c. _____

3. Identify which organ systems the following organs or glands belong to.

a. Salivary glands _____

b. Heart _____

c. Thyroid _____

d. Arteries _____

e. Lymph nodes _____

f. Liver _____

g. Lungs _____

h. Fallopian tubes _____

i. Bone marrow _____

j. Vas deferens _____

k. Veins _____

l. Brain _____

m. Kidney _____

n. Sternum _____

o. Trachea _____

p. Esophagus _____

q. Spinal cord _____

r. Bladder _____

s. Spleen _____

t. Stomach _____

4. Categorize the 11 vertebrate organ systems according to the main functions that each provides.

Communication:

Support:

Regulation:

Defense:

Reproduction:

EXERCISING YOUR KNOWLEDGE
Briefly answer each of the following questions in the space provided.

1. Why is the basic body plan of vertebrates referred to as "a tube suspended within a tube"?

2. Why does epithelium grow only to a limited thickness?

3. What structural feature is found in all connective tissue? What are the basic types of connective tissue?

4. What are the basic structural differences between cartilage and bone?

5. Why is bone marrow cancer so lethal? (Hint: Bone marrow produces blood cells.)

6. Describe the two major differences between exocrine and endocrine glands.

7. What characteristics do collagen fibers and hydroxyapatite crystals contribute to bone?

8. Describe how the structures of simple and stratified epithelial membranes are reflective of their functions in the body.

9. Compare and contrast skeletal and cardiac muscle.

10. Why are negative feedback systems in the body generally more advantageous than positive feedback mechanisms?

Circle the letter of the one best answer in each of the following questions.

11. The mesodermal germ layer gives rise to which of the following?
    a. the brain and spinal cord
    b. bone
    c. the inner surface of the digestive tract
    d. the outer portion of the skin
    e. none of the above

12. The thoracic and peritoneal cavities of mammals are separated by the
    a. coelom.
    b. diaphragm.
    c. matrix.
    d. pleural cavities.
    e. pericardial cavity.

13. Tissues are made up of
    a. germ layers.
    b. organs.
    c. organ systems.
    d. cells.
    e. all of these.

14. The water-resistant protein found in skin and calluses is called
    a. collagen.
    b. reticulin.
    c. heparin.
    d. cartilage.
    e. keratin.

15. Which of the following is a function of epithelial tissue?
    a. protection
    b. diffusion surface
    c. secretion
    d. all of these
    e. none of these

16. Which type of primary tissue has an extensive extracellular matrix?
    a. nerve tissue
    b. connective tissue
    c. epithelial tissue
    d. muscle
    e. They all do.

17. Which of the following is a type of loose connective tissue?
    a. blood
    b. tendons
    c. adipose tissue
    d. kidney capsules
    e. epidermis

18. Connective tissue is derived from
    a. endoderm.
    b. mesoderm.
    c. ectoderm.
    d. all of these.
    e. none of these

19. Which is the least flexible special connective tissue?
    a. tendons
    b. ligaments
    c. blood
    d. cartilage
    e. bone

20. Which type of muscle evolved first?
    a. striated muscle
    b. cardiac muscle
    c. skeletal muscle
    d. smooth muscle
    e. They all evolved at the same time.

21. The ectodermal germ layer gives rise to which of the following?
    a. the outer portion of the skin
    b. hair and nails
    c. the brain
    d. the spinal cord
    e. all of the above

22. Which of the following types of animals has an endoskeleton?
    a. echinoderms
    b. earthworms
    c. arthropods
    d. all of these
    e. none of these

23. Exocrine and endocrine glands form from which of the following?
    a. loose connective tissue
    b. epithelia
    c. fibroblasts
    d. smooth muscle
    e. dense connective tissue

24. Which of the following functions as the primary means of communication between organs?
    a. loose connective tissue
    b. epithelia
    c. neurons
    d. blood
    e. muscle fibers

25. Muscles are connected to bone by
    a. cross-bridges.
    b. sutures.
    c. ligaments.
    d. tendons.
    e. intervertebral disks.

26. Which of the following is NOT true of epithelial membranes?
    a. They are selectively permeable.
    b. Cells are bound tightly together with little space between them.
    c. The apical surface is attached to the underlying connective tissues.
    d. It is a useful surface tissue because it can be quickly renewed.
    e. Nutrients and oxygen must diffuse to epithelial cells from blood vessels.

27. Which of the following produces tough coverings that package the capsules of the kidneys?
   a. adipose tissue
   b. special connective tissue
   c. dense irregular connective tissue
   d. loose connective tissue
   e. dense regular connective tissue

28. Which of the following is NOT true of neuroglia cells?
   a. They produce impulses.
   b. They support neurons.
   c. They are present in both the central and the peripheral nervous systems.
   d. They eliminate foreign materials in neurons.
   e. They form a myelin sheath.

29. Osmoregulation is one of the major functions of which organ system?
   a. respiratory system
   b. circulatory system
   c. lymphatic system
   d. urinary system
   e. endocrine system

30. When a deviation in a set point occurs within the body, a message is sent to increase or decrease the activity of which of the following?
   a. integrating center
   b. effector
   c. comparator
   d. sensor
   e. motor neurons

ASSESSING YOUR KNOWLEDGE

Answers to the questions in this section test your ability to synthesize information gained from the chapter and to solve challenging problems on an exam or in everyday life.

Challenging Your Understanding—Part I. Answers

1a. Epithelial, b. Connective, c. Muscle, d. Epithelial, e. Connective, f. Connective, g. Nerve, h. Muscle, i. Connective, j. Epithelial, k. Epithelial, l. Muscle, m. Connective, n. Nerve, o. Epithelial, p. Connective, q. Connective, r. Muscle.

2a. Abdominopelvic, b. Thoracic, c. Dorsal, d. Abdominopelvic, e. Thoracic, f. Dorsal, g. Thoracic, h. Abdominopelvic, i. Thoracic, j. Abdominopelvic.

Challenging Your Understanding—Part II. Answers

1a. Body temperature rises:
Sensor: Neurons in the hypothalamus detect an increase in temperature.
Integrating Center: Neurons in the hypothalamus compare input from sensory neurons with set point.
Effector: Blood vessels to the skin dilate, glands release sweat.
Response: Body temperature drops.
Negative feedback: Neurons in the hypothalamus detect the drop in temperature.

1b. Body temperature drops:
Sensor: Neurons in the hypothalamus detect a decrease in temperature.
Integrating Center: Neurons in the hypothalamus compare input from sensory neurons with set point.
Effector: Blood vessels to the skin contract, muscles contract causing the body to shiver.
Response: Body temperature rises.
Negative feedback: Neurons in the hypothalamus detect the increase in temperature.

2a. Uterus contractions during childbirth:
Sensor: Receptors in the inferior uterus detect pushing of the fetus against the uterine opening.
Integrating Center: The brain receives information from the uterus that it is being stretched.
Effector: The pituitary gland is stimulated to increase the secretion of oxytocin.
Response: Oxytocin causes increased uterine contractions.
Positive feedback: Increased force against the uterine wall promotes the birth of the baby.

3. The birth of the baby reduces the contractions of the uterus stopping the positive feedback cycle. This positive feedback loop, rather than a negative feedback loop, is advantageous in this situation because it promotes the birth of the baby. A negative feedback loop would try to stop the stretching of the uterus and prevent the birth of the baby.

Key Terms—Answers

a. 13, b. 42, c. 3, d. 36, e. 26, f. 19, g. 10, h. 33, i. 6, j. 29, k. 11, l. 8, m. 21, n. 30, o. 5, p. 31, q. 1, r. 24, s. 17, t. 35, u. 12, v. 38, w. 20, x. 41, y. 15, z. 27, aa. 34, bb. 18, cc. 7, dd. 23, ee. 40, ff. 32, gg. 2, hh. 14, ii. 28, jj. 9, kk. 39, 11. 25, mm. 16, nn. 37, oo. 4, pp. 22.

Learning by Experience—Answers

1.	a. endoderm	
	b. mesoderm	
	c. ectoderm	
	d. epithelium	
	e. connective	
	f. muscle	
	g. nerve	
2.	a. motor neuron	
	b. cardiac muscle	
	c. bone	
3.	a. Digestive	k Circulatory
	b. Circulatory	l. Nervous
	c. Endocrine	m. Urinary
	d. Circulatory	n. Skeletal
	e. Immune	o. Respiratory
	f. Digestive	p. Digestive
	g. Respiratory	q. Nervous
	h. Reproductive	r. Urinary
	i. Immune	s. Immune
	j. Reproductive	t. Digestive

4. Communication: Nervous system, endocrine system
Support: Skeletal system, muscular system
Regulation: Respiratory system, digestive system, circulatory system, urinary system
Defense: Integumentary system, immune system
Reproduction: Reproductive system

Exercising Your Knowledge—Answers

As you check your answers, put a mark in the review (Rvw.) column for the answers you missed. If you didn't miss any, congratulations—you have mastered the chapter! If you missed some, review the section (Sect.) in the text where this concept is discussed. In order to develop an efficient review strategy, it is important that you understand what types of questions you missed. The questions with asterisks test more for understanding of the **concepts**, whereas the others test more for **detail**. *See the preface for learning strategies for concepts and for detail.*

43.1

*1. The first tube is the digestive tract, with the mouth at one end and the anus at the other. It is suspended in (runs through) another tube, the coelom or internal body cavity.

43.2

*2. Epithelial cells are packed together so tightly that there is very little extracellular space between them. There is no room for blood vessels between the epithelial cells, so the epithelium is kept alive just by diffusion of oxygen and nutrients from blood vessels in adjacent tissues. Thus, epithelium cannot be too thick or the cells farthest away from the blood vessels would not receive adequate supplies of oxygen and nutrients and would die and slough off. This is what constantly happens to the outer surface of your skin.

43.3

*3. All connective tissues have a lot of extracellular material called matrix, which has a different composition in different types of connective tissue. There are two major types of connective tissue: connective tissue proper (subdivided into loose and dense) and special connective tissue (subdivided into cartilage, bone, and blood).

43.3

*4. Cartilage is made up of chondrocytes within lacunae and a matrix that is not calcified. Cartilage has no blood vessels. Bone is made up of osteocytes in lacunae and a calcified matrix, and is vascularized.

43.3

*5. If bone marrow becomes cancerous and stops producing erythrocytes, the circulatory system loses its mechanism for transporting oxygen. If it stops producing leukocytes, the body's immune system cannot function properly.

43.2

*6. In exocrine glands, the connection between the gland and the epithelial membrane remains a duct, whereas endocrine glands are ductless and their connection with the epithelium has been lost during development. The secretions of exocrine glands are channeled to the surface of the epithelial membrane by the duct, while the secretions of endocrine glands are not channeled onto an epithelial membrane, but rather enter the blood capillaries and circulate in the body.

43.3

*7. Collagen fibers are flexible but weak; hydroxyapatite crystals are rigid but brittle. Having both in the matrix makes bones strong (from the crystals) but resistant to fracture (from the fibers).

43.2

*8. Simple epithelial membranes are one cell layer thick and line the lungs and blood capillaries where their delicate nature allows diffusion of gases. They also line some glands, kidney tubules, the stomach, and intestines, where their thin nature allows secretion and absorption. Stratified epithelial membranes are several cell layers thick. These membranes are present in the outer layer of skin and in the lining of the mouth where their toughness provides protection to the outer surface of the body and in the mouth.

43.4

*9. Skeletal and cardiac muscles are both striated muscles. Skeletal muscles are made up of numerous, long muscle cells with a single nucleus. Skeletal muscles are attached to the bones by tendons throughout the body and their connections are under voluntary control. In contrast, cardiac muscles are found only in the walls of the heart and their contractions are generally involuntary.

43.7

*10. Negative feedback mechanisms help maintain homeostasis in the body by increasing a substance or an activity in the body that controls a response, which in turn inhibits the process leading to its own increase. Negative feedback mechanisms often oppose each other allowing a finer degree of control. This is in contrast to positive feedback mechanisms in which the effector of the controlled variable drives the system farther away from the set point. Systems with positive feedback loops are highly unstable and do not help to maintain homeostasis. For these reasons, negative feedback loops are generally more advantageous for the body to use so that a point close to the set point is always maintained.

Question	Sect. Rvw.
*11. b	43.1
12. b	43.1
13. d	43.1
14. e	43.2
*15. d	43.2
16. b	43.3
17. c	43.3
18. b	43.3
*19. e	43.3
*20. d	43.4
*21. e	43.1
22. a	43.6
*23. b	43.2
*24. d	43.3
25. d	43.4
*26. c	43.2
27. c	43.3
28. a	43.5
29. d	43.6
*30. b	43.7

CHAPTER 44 THE NERVOUS SYSTEM

MASTERING KEY CONCEPTS

The nervous system of animals is a communication center that receives and sends rapid messages in the form of electrochemical signals. It receives information about the state of the external environment and about the animal's internal environment. It processes and integrates this information and sends signals that will initiate some response. The nervous system has a complex architecture in the higher vertebrates. Despite the complexity and elaborate functionings, though, remember that the central and peripheral nervous systems are built "merely" of neurons—billions and billions of them, to be sure—but each and every one of them operates the same basic way using action potentials and neurotransmitters.

44.1 The nervous system consists of neurons and supporting cells.

- **Overview**: Animals contain nervous systems with **sensory receptors** to detect stimuli and **motor effectors** to respond to stimuli. There are three types of neurons, (1) **sensory neurons** that carry information from sensory receptors to the central nervous system, (2) **motor neurons** that carry commands from the central nervous system to muscles and glands, and (3) **interneurons** in the brain and spinal cord that provide more complex functions, including learning and memory. Sensory and motor neurons are part of the **peripheral nervous system**. Neurons consist of a **cell body**, **dendrites**, and an **axon** and are supported functionally and structurally by **neuroglia**, such as **Schwann cells** and **oligodendrocytes** that encompass axons in a **myelin sheath**. Small interruptions in the sheath are called **nodes of Ranvier**. The motor pathway is subdivided into the **somatic nervous system**, which consists of motor neurons that stimulate skeletal muscles (voluntary), and the **autonomic nervous system, which** consists of motor neurons that regulate smooth and cardiac muscle, and glands (involuntary). The autonomic nervous system is further subdivided into the **sympathetic** (fight or flight) and **parasympathetic** (rest and repose) nervous systems.

- **Details**: Know the three types of neurons and the functions of each. Know the divisions of the vertebrate nervous system and the identity and functions of the supporting cells.

44.2 Nerve impulses are produced on the axon membrane.

- **Overview**: When a neuron is at rest, it maintains a **resting membrane potential** due to the fact that the inside of the neuron is electrically negative relative to the outside as a result of the **sodium-potassium pump,** which moves three Na^+ ions out of the cell for every two K^+ moved in, and **ion leakage channels** in which it is easier for K^+ to diffuse out of the cell than for Na^+ to diffuse in. Two types of sudden changes occur in response to stimuli that disrupt the resting membrane potential: **graded potentials** and **action potentials**. Graded potentials are small transient changes in the membrane potential caused by **gated ion channels** opening or closing as a result of signaling molecules binding to them. Permeability changes make the membrane potential more (**hyperpolarization**), or less negative (**depolarization**). Graded potentials can combine (**summation**) to amplify or reduce their effects. When a particular level of depolarization is reached, an action potential is generated as a result of **voltage-gated ion channels,** which open or close in response to changes in the membrane potential. During an action potential, the neuron depolarizes with an influx of Na^+, and then repolarizes as K^+ diffuses out of the cell. An action potential at one part of the neuron causes an action potential next to it, so the signal is passed along the neuron. The frequency of an action potential, not the amplitude, determines the intensity of a stimulus. The velocity of nerve impulses can be increased if the diameter of the axon is large or if the axon is myelinated.

- **Details**: Know the two factors that establish the resting membrane potential and the two major forces that act on ions in establishing it. Understand the **Nernst equation**. Know the two factors that can determine the size of a graded potential. Understand the movement of Na^+ and K^+ ions, and what is occurring during the **rising**, **falling**, and **undershoot phases** of an action potential. Know the two ways to increase the velocity of nerve impulses and why these two factors have that effect.

44.3 Neurons form junctions called synapses with other cells.

- **Overview**: Branches of an axon may form junctions with other neurons or with muscle or gland cells to form **synapses**. The **presynaptic cell** transmits an action potential to the synapse where it is received by the **postsynaptic cell**. Invertebrates have **electrical synapses** with direct cytoplasmic connections between neurons, while vertebrates have **chemical synapses** where neurons are separated by a **synaptic cleft**. When an action potential reaches the end of a presynaptic axon, there is an influx of Ca^{2+} ions that results in the release of a **neurotransmitter** into the synaptic cleft. Neurotransmitters bind to **chemical-** or **ligand-gated receptor proteins** in the membrane of the postsynaptic cell and can either promote a depolarization (**excitatory postsynaptic potential**) or a hyperpolarization (**inhibitory postsynaptic potential**). Axons may also release **neuropeptides** at synapses, such as **enkephalins**, **endorphins**, or **substance P**. Synaptic integration involves the integration of all the excitatory and inhibitory signals that determine whether a postsynaptic neuron fires. Drugs or chemicals, such as **cocaine** or **nicotine,** that affect the amount of neurotransmitter released, or how long it persists in the synaptic cleft, can alter the sensitivity and number of receptors in a neuron and have a major impact on how the nervous system functions.

- **Details**: Know the difference between electrical and chemical synapses. Know how neurotransmitters are released into and removed from the synaptic cleft. Know the difference between the effect of an excitatory and an inhibitory neurotransmitter. Know the effects caused by acetylcholine, glutamate, glycine, GABA, epinephrine, dopamine, and serotonin. Know the effects of substance P, enkephalins, endorphins, and nitric oxide. Understand the distinction between spatial summation and temporal summation. Know how addiction to cocaine is caused and the effects of nicotine on the nervous system.

44.4 The central nervous system consists of the brain and the spinal cord.

- **Overview**: The brains of all vertebrates have three major sections that are found in differing proportions: the **hindbrain, midbrain**, and **forebrain**. The hindbrain consists of the **medulla oblongata, pons**, and **cerebellum** and is primarily devoted to coordinating motor reflexes, with the cerebellum acting as a coordinating center. There has been an evolutionary trend toward increasing size and dominance of the forebrain. The forebrain of reptiles, amphibians, birds, and mammals consists of the **diencephalon** (containing the **thalamus** and **hypothalamus**) and the **telencephalon** also called the **cerebrum** in mammals. Mammals have brains that are particularly large relative to their body mass, in large part due to the size of the cerebrum. The cerebrum is separated into the **right** and **left hemispheres,** each of which receives sensory input form the opposite side of the body. Each region of the **cerebral cortex**, a layer of gray matter on the outer surface of the cerebrum, correlates with a specific function. The **spinal cord** is a cable of neurons extending from the brain down through the backbone, which relays information to and from the brain and functions in **reflexes** in which a sensory neuron passes information to a motor neuron in the spinal cord.

- **Details**: Recognize how nervous systems evolved to become more complex. Know the differences between the midbrain and forebrain of fishes and those of more recently evolved vertebrates. Know how the forebrains of the more recently evolved vertebrates are divided and the complex functions associated with each major region. Know the two hypotheses that have been proposed to explain the cause of **Alzheimer's disease**. Know the composition of the spinal cord and its role in relaying messages and in reflexes.

44.5 The peripheral nervous system consists of sensory and motor neurons.

- **Overview**: The **peripheral nervous system** consists of nerves and ganglia that receive stimuli from the environment and carry it to the **central nervous system**, and effectors, such as muscle cells. The peripheral nervous system is divided into the **sensory** and **motor pathways**. The motor pathway is further divided into the **somatic** and **autonomic systems**. The somatic system is involved in the voluntary control of skeletal muscles, while the autonomic system controls involuntary smooth muscles and internal organs through the **sympathetic** and **parasympathetic divisions,** which have antagonistic actions.

- **Details**: Know the divisions of the peripheral nervous system. Know the roles of the somatic system, the sympathetic system, and the parasympathetic system. Know the features shared by the sympathetic and parasympathetic divisions, and the differences that distinguish each division. Know how G proteins are involved in mediating cell responses to autonomic signals.

CHALLENGING YOUR UNDERSTANDING—Part I.

1. Fill in the following flowchart to complete an outline of the course of events that occur when a nerve impulse is produced.

I.   NERVE IMPULSE

          A. Resting membrane potential

          B. Incoming signal above threshold strength triggers an action potential.

          C. _____: Na^+ rushes into the neuron

          D. _____: K^+ moves out of the neuron

          E. Neuron returns to its resting membrane potential.

II.   F. Part I is repeated along the length of the axon.

III.   G. At the end of the axon, the action potential causes a _____ to be released into the _____ in vertebrates.

IV.   H. An excitatory _____ promotes a _____, or excitatory postsynaptic potential, while an inhibitory _____ promotes a _____, or inhibitory postsynaptic potential.

V.   I. Each postsynaptic neuron receives both excitatory and inhibitory synapses and undergoes a process known as _____.

VI.   J. As a result, the neuron is either _____ or _____.

CHALLENGING YOUR UNDERSTANDING—Part II.

1. In the graph of the action potential shown below, indicate what is happening in the cell in terms of Na^+ and K^+ ions at different parts of the curve.

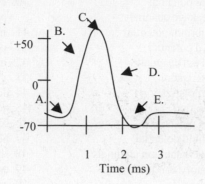

a.

b.

c.

d.

e.

2. List the two factors that contribute to the resting potential of a membrane.

a.

b.

3. Describe two ways to increase the velocity of nerve impulses and explain how each mechanism does so.

a.

b.

KEY TERMS

Match the numbered term with the definition that fits it best. Put the corresponding number in front of the appropriate definition.

1. sensory neurons
2. central nervous system
3. motor neurons
4. interneurons
5. peripheral nervous system
6. somatic motor neurons
7. autonomic motor neurons
8. sympathetic
9. parasympathetic
10. cell body
11. dendrites
12. axons
13. neuroglia
14. Schwann cells
15. oligodendrocytes
16. myelin sheaths
17. white matter
18. gray matter
19. nerves
20. nodes of Ranvier

21. resting potential
22. ion leakage channels
23. equilibrium potential
24. graded potential
25. gated ion channels
26. depolarization
27. hyperpolarization
28. summation
29. action potential
30. threshold potential
31. voltage-gated ion channels
32. salutatory conduction
33. synapses
34. synaptic cleft
35. synaptic vesicles
36. neurotransmitters
37. presynaptic cell
38. postsynaptic cell
39. acetylcholine

40. excitatory postsynaptic potential
41. inhibitory postsynaptic potential
42. glutamate
43. glycine
44. dopamine
45. norepinephrine
46. serotonin
47. neuropeptides
48. substance P
49. enkephalins
50. endorphins
51. nitric oxide
52. synaptic integration
53. dorsal root
54. ventral root
55. dorsal root ganglia

a. _____ A neurotransmitter that crosses the synapse between a motor neuron and a muscle fiber.
b. _____ A permeability change in a membrane that makes the membrane potential more negative.
c. _____ A process extending out from a neuron that conducts impulses away form the cell body.
d. _____ Small transient changes in membrane potential caused by the activation of gated ion channels.
e. _____ A depolarization of the postsynaptic membrane caused by the opening of ligand-gated ion channels.
f. _____ Efferent neurons that regulate the activity of the smooth muscles, cardiac muscle, and glands.
g. _____ A narrow space that separates presynaptic and postsynaptic cells.
h. _____ A type of neuroglia in vertebrates that produces myelin sheaths around the axons of neurons in the CNS.
i. _____ A neuropeptide released at synapses in the CNS by sensory neurons activated by painful stimuli.
j. _____ Efferent neurons that carry impulses from the CNS to effectors such as muscles and glands.
k. _____ A nerve impulse that is produced when a particular level of depolarization is reached.
l. _____ Intercellular junctions between the branches of an axon and the dendrites of other neurons, muscle, or gland cells.
m. _____ Myelinated axons in the central nervous system.
n. _____ An inhibitory neurotransmitter that causes the opening of ligand-gated ion channels for chloride ions.
o. _____ A subdivision of the autonomic nervous system whose nerve effects promote a rest and repose response.
p. _____ Chemical signals released by exocytosis when an action potential reaches the end of an axon.
q. _____ Small gaps that interrupt a myelin sheath at intervals of 1 to 2 μm.
r. _____ The division of the nervous system that includes the sensory and motor neurons.
s. _____ Membrane proteins that form pores through the membrane to allow the flow of specific ions in and out of the cell.
t. _____ An insulated covering surrounding many axons that consists of multiple layers of compacted membrane.
u. _____ Neuropeptides released by axons descending from the brain into the spinal cord that block the perception of pain.
v. _____ Part of the spinal nerve formed by motor axons leaving from the ventral surface of the spinal cord.
w. _____ The division of the nervous system that includes the brain and the spinal cord.
x. _____ The balance between the diffusional force and the electrical force.
y. _____ A neurotransmitter used in some areas of the brain controlling body movements and other functions.
z. _____ A type of neuroglia in vertebrates that produces myelin sheaths around the axons of neurons in the PNS.
aa. _____ A hyperpolarization of the postsynaptic membrane caused by opening of ligand-gated ion channels for Cl⁻.
bb. _____ Vesicles located at the swollen end of the presynaptic axon that release neurotransmitters.
cc. _____ Afferent neurons that carry impulses from sensory receptors to the CNS.
dd. _____ The neuron whose axon transmits action potentials to the synapse.
ee. _____ The grouping of the cell bodies of sensory neurons outside each level of the spinal cord.

ff. _____ A permeability change in a membrane that makes the membrane potential less negative.

gg. _____ Efferent neurons that stimulate skeletal muscles to contract.

hh. _____ A process extending from the cell body of a neuron that conducts impulses toward the cell body.

ii. _____ Channel proteins whose activation causes small transient changes in membrane potential.

jj. _____ Formed from the bundling of myelinataed axons in the peripheral nervous system.

kk. _____ The inside of a cell is more negatively charged than the outside due to the Na^+-K^+ pump and ion leakage.

ll. _____ The summed influence of excitatory and inhibitory synapses determining whether a postsynaptic cell will fire.

mm. _____ Association neurons found in the central nervous system providing a link between sensory and motor neurons.

nn. _____ Cells that support and insulate neurons and eliminate foreign materials but don't conduct electrical impulses.

oo. _____ A neurotransmitter involved in the regulation of sleep and implicated in various emotional states.

pp. _____ The level of depolarization needed to produce an action potential.

qq. _____ The unmyelinated dendrites and cell bodies in the CNS.

rr. _____ The cell that receives the signal on the other side of a synapse from the transmitting neuron.

ss. _____ Neuropeptides released by neurons in the brain stem that block the perception of pain.

tt. _____ Channels that open and close in response to changes in membrane potential and cause an action potential.

uu. _____ An enlarged region of a neuron containing the nucleus.

vv. _____ The major excitatory neurotransmitter in the vertebrate CNS that promotes depolarization.

ww. _____ A subdivision of the autonomic nervous system whose nerve effects promote a fight or flight response.

xx. _____ A gas that is released by some neurons in the PNS and acts as a regulatory molecule in the body.

yy. _____ The ability of graded potentials to combine, amplifying or reducing their effects.

zz. _____ Polypeptides released by axons at synapses that can act like neurotransmitters or may act more long term.

aaa. _____ The process by which one node depolarizes the next so that action potentials seem to jump from node to node.

bbb. _____ Part of the spinal nerve formed by the axons of sensory neurons entering the dorsal surface of the spinal cord.

ccc. _____ A neurotransmitter derived from tyrosine and released at synapses of neurons in the sympathetic nervous system.

LEARNING BY EXPERIENCE

1. Label the following parts of the neuron diagrammed here:

   axon
   cell body
   cell nucleus
   dendrite
   myelin sheath
   node of Ranvier

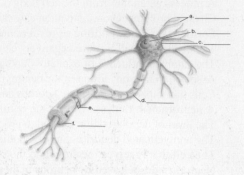

2. Label the following parts of the synapse diagrammed here:

   axon
   postsynaptic membrane
   presynaptic membrane
   synaptic cleft
   vesicle with neurotransmitter

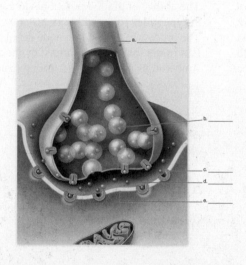

3. Provide the appropriate term to complete this outline of the organization of the vertebrate nervous system.

   I. _____

       A. Brain

       B. _____

   II. Peripheral Nervous System

       A. _____

       B. Motor pathways

           1. Somatic nervous system

           2. _____

              a. _____

b. Parasympathetic division

4. Color the following parts as indicated on the human brain diagrammed here:

cerebellum – red
cerebrum – yellow
medulla oblongata – blue
spinal cord – purple

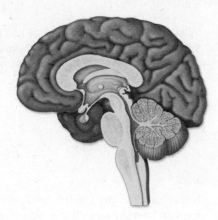

5. Match the region of the brain with the functions that they control.

_____ a. organization of motor output
_____ b. sleep and waking state
_____ c. sensory integration
_____ d. coordination of position
_____ e. language
_____ f. regulation of body temperature;
      hunger and thirst
_____ g. motor control
_____ h. emotion
_____ i. spatial reasoning; music
_____ j. higher mental activities

1. thalamus
2. hypothalamus
3. hippocampus (limbic system)
4. pons
5. left cerebral hemisphere
6. right cerebral hemisphere
7. basal ganglia
8. cerebral cortex
9. association cortex
10. cerebellum

6. Finish the table by indicating the responses activated by the sympathetic and parasympathetic divisions of the autonomic nervous system for each of the bodily functions or tissues listed.

	Sympathetic	Parasympathetic
A. Heart rate		
B. Breathing		
C. Blood vessels in the skin		
D. Salivation		
E. Pupils of the eye		
F. Urinary bladder muscles		
G. Glucose secretion from the liver		

EXERCISING YOUR KNOWLEDGE

Briefly answer each of the following questions in the space provided.

1. What are the three categories of neurons in the vertebrate body? Which of the three is most responsible for your ability to think about biology?

2. Nerve impulses are electrochemical in nature. Explain how the term "electrochemical" applies to the functioning of neurons.

3. What role do sodium-potassium pumps play in the functioning of the nervous system?

4. What would happen to the nervous system of a person who had a severe sodium deficiency?

5. If a nerve impulse is an all-or-none phenomenon, how can vertebrates show different levels or intensities of response to different stimuli?

6. Why is it advantageous to have inhibitory as well as excitatory neurotransmitters? Doesn't it get confusing?

7. Why are nerve gases lethal to humans? (Hint: Nerve gases inhibit acetylcholinesterase.)

8. Why does cocaine intensify pleasurable sensations?

9. Evolutionarily speaking, which part of the brain was dominant in the early, primitive vertebrates, and what was its major function? In modern, advanced vertebrates?

10. Explain the features that the sympathetic and parasympathetic divisions of the autonomic nervous system share and how they differ.

Circle the letter of the one best answer in each of the following questions.

11. Nerve impulses are normally carried toward a neuron cell body by the neuron's
    a. synaptic cleft.
    b. axon.
    c. myelin sheath.
    d. neurotransmitter.
    e. dendrites.

12. The spinal cord is part of the
    a. somatic nervous system.
    b. central nervous system.
    c. parasympathetic nervous system.
    d. sympathetic nervous system.
    e. all of these.

13. Which of the following would allow a neuron to receive more stimuli?
    a. more dendritic spines
    b. more myelin sheath material
    c. a larger cell body
    d. a longer axon
    e. more nodes of Ranvier

14. Which cells produce myelin in the peripheral nervous system?
    a. sensory neurons
    b. motor neurons
    c. oligodendrocytes
    d. Schwann cells
    e. none of these

15. In a neuron that is at rest but ready to fire,
    a. the inside and the outside of the neuron membrane have the same electrical charge.
    b. the outside of the neuron membrane is more negatively charged than the inside.
    c. the inside of the neuron membrane is more negatively charged than the outside.
    d. any of these can be true; it varies among individual neurons.

16. What process is most responsible for establishing the resting membrane potential of a neuron?
    a. active transport
    b. simple diffusion
    c. facilitated diffusion
    d. all of these
    e. none of these

17. During saltatory conduction, a nerve impulse jumps from one _____ to another.
    a. synapse
    b. dendrite
    c. axon
    d. node of Ranvier
    e. cell body

18. During depolarization of a neuron,
    a. Na^+ moves out of the neuron.
    b. K^+ moves into the neuron.
    c. organic ions move out of the neuron.
    d. All of these are correct.
    e. None of these are correct.

19. Which of the following should have the slowest conduction velocity?
    a. a myelinated, small-diameter axon
    b. a myelinated, large-diameter axon
    c. an unmyelinated, small-diameter axon
    d. an unmyelinated, large-diameter axon
    e. All neurons have the same conduction velocity.

20. Which of the following statements regarding the prolonged use of nicotine is NOT true?
    a. Removal can cause symptoms of withdrawal that diminish over time.
    b. It alters the release of acetylcholine, dopamine, and serotonin from neurons.
    c. The brain makes fewer receptor proteins to which nicotine can bind.
    d. It causes a change in the sensitivity of receptors to stimulation by neurotransmitters.
    e. None of the above.

21. Is a dendrite more likely to have a presynaptic membrane or a postsynaptic membrane?
    a. presynaptic
    b. postsynaptic
    c. Either is equally likely.
    d. Neither is likely.

22. Neurotransmitters are released from vesicles at the
    a. cell body.
    b. cell nucleus.
    c. dendrite.
    d. presynaptic membrane.
    e. postsynaptic membrane.

23. Which of the following is an inhibitory neurotransmitter?
    a. acetylcholine (ACh)
    b. glutamate
    c. GABA
    d. all of these
    e. none of these

24. Which neurotransmitter is involved in the regulation of sleep?
    a. serotonin
    b. glycine
    c. dopamine
    d. norepinephrine
    e. substance P

25. When you look at an intact human brain, what you see is mostly a large, highly convoluted outer surface. This is the
    a. medulla oblongata.
    b. thalamus.
    c. corpus callosum.
    d. cerebellum.
    e. cerebral cortex.

26. The midbrain of fish is primarily involved in processing what type of information?
    a. visual
    b. olfactory
    c. tactile
    d. auditory
    e. motor

27. The primary function of the thalamus is
    a. integrating visceral activities.
    b. integrating sensory information.
    c. coordinating motor reflexes.
    d. controlling consciousness and alertness.
    e. promoting memory and learning.

28. Most reflexes in vertebrates involve a single connecting interneuron between the sensory and the motor neurons. Where is this interneuron located?
    a. in the part of the body, such as the hand, receiving the stimulus
    b. in the brain
    c. in the spinal cord
    d. in the dorsal root of the spinal nerve
    e. in the ventral root of the spinal nerve

29. The sympathetic nervous system releases what neurotransmitter?
    a. acetylcholine
    b. serotonin
    c. G proteins
    d. epinephrine
    e. norepinephrine

30. If you are being a couch potato, just sitting there and about to fall asleep, which division of your nervous system is probably most active?
    a. the sensory pathways
    b. the somatic nervous system
    c. the sympathetic nervous system
    d. the parasympathetic nervous system
    e. They are all equally active.

ASSESSING YOUR KNOWLEDGE

Answers to the questions in this section test your ability to synthesize information gained from the chapter and to solve challenging problems on an exam or in everyday life.

Challenging Your Understanding—Part I. Answers

IC. Depolarization
ID. Repolarization
IIIG. Neurotransmitter; synaptic cleft
IVH. Neurotransmitter; depolarization
Neurotransmitter; hyperpolarization
VI. Synaptic integration
VIJ. Turned on; remains off

Challenging Your Understanding—Part II. Answers

1. a. Resting membrane potential, where voltage-gated ion channels are closed but there is some leakage of K^+ ions. In response to a stimulus, the cell depolarizes and an action potential is produced when the threshold level is reached.
   b. During the rising phase, rapid depolarization occurs because voltage-gated Na^+ channels open causing an influx of Na^+.
   c. At the top of the spike, Na^+ channel inactivation gates close, and voltage-gated K^+ channels that were previously closed, begin to open.
   d. K^+ diffusion out of the cell repolarizes the membrane in the falling phase.
   e. The K^+ channels remain open longer than necessary to restore the resting potential, resulting in a slight undershoot before the membrane returns to its original resting potential.

2. a. The sodium-potassium pump
   b. Differential permeability of the membrane to Na^+ and K^+ due to ion leakage channels

3. a. Increase the diameter of the axon: Larger diameter axons have less resistance to current flow. The positive charge of Na^+ is carried farther in an axon with a larger diameter, leading to a higher than threshold voltage farther from the origin of Na^+ influx.
   b. Myelinated axons: Action potentials in myelinated axons are produced only at nodes of Ranvier. Depolarization at one node spreads quickly beneath the insulating myelin to trigger the opening of voltage-gated ion channels at the next node. Impulses spread by saltatory conduction.

Key Terms—Answers

a. 39, b. 27, c. 12, d. 24, e. 40, f. 7, g. 34, h. 15, i. 48, j. 3, k. 29, l. 33, m. 17, n. 43, o. 9, p. 36, q. 20, r. 5, s. 22, t. 16, u. 49, v. 54, w. 2, x. 23, y. 44, z. 14, aa. 41, bb. 35, cc. 1, dd. 37, ee. 55, ff. 26, gg. 6, hh. 11, ii. 25, jj. 19, kk. 21, ll. 52, mm. 4, nn. 13, oo. 46, pp. 30, qq. 18, rr. 38, ss. 50, tt. 31, uu. 10, vv. 42, ww. 8, xx. 51, yy. 28, zz. 47, aaa. 32, bbb. 53, ccc. 45.

Learning by Experience—Answers

1.	a. dendrite
	b. cell nucleus
	c. cell body
	d. axon
	e. myelin sheath
	f. node of Ranvier
2.	a. axon
	b. vesicle with neurotransmitter
	c. presynaptic membrane
	d. synaptic cleft
	e. postsynaptic membrane
3.	I. Central Nervous System
	I.B. Spinal cord
	II.A. Sensory pathways
	II.B.2. Autonomic nervous system
	II.B.2.a. Sympathetic division
4. See figure 44.22, p. 886 in text.	
5. a. 8, b. 4, c. 1, d. 10, e. 5, f. 2, g. 7, h. 3, i. 6, j. 9.	

6.

	Sympathetic	Parasympathetic
A. Heart rate	Increased	Decreased
B. Breathing	Dilation of branchioles	Constriction of branchioles
C. Blood vessels in the skin	Constriction	None
D. Salivation	Vasoconstriction	Vasodilation
E. Pupils of the eye	Dilation	Constriction
F. Urinary bladder muscle	Relaxation	Contraction
G. Glucose sec. from the liver	Stimulated	Inhibited

Exercising Your Knowledge—Answers

As you check your answers, put a mark in the review (Rvw.) column for the answers you missed. If you didn't miss any, congratulations—you have mastered the chapter! If you missed some, review the section (Sect.) in the text where this concept is discussed. In order to develop an efficient review strategy, it is important that you understand what types of questions you missed. The questions with asterisks test more for understanding of the **concepts**, whereas the others test more for **detail**. *See the preface for learning strategies for concepts and for detail.*

	Sect.	Rvw.
*1. Sensory, motor, and association neurons. While sensory neurons allow you to hear the lecture and see the writing, and motor neurons allow you to turn the page and take notes, it is the association neurons in your brain that allow you to think about biology, study it, and learn it.	44.1	
*2. "Electro" because a nerve impulse is an electrical event due to the movement of electrically charge ions. "Chemical" because it is also a chemical event—the ions are chemicals, as are the neurotransmitters that are released and carry the signal to the next cell.	44.2	
*3. Sodium-potassium pumps do not cause the action potential, but they establish the polarity across the membrane of a resting neuron. Without this polarity, an action potential (depolarization) could not occur. Sodium-potassium pumps also reestablish polarity after an action potential has occurred, preparing the neuron for further firing.	44.2	
*4. Without sodium ions, neurons could not establish proper resting potentials, and therefore the nervous system could not function since depolarization could not occur.	44.2	
*5. Each individual neuron fires in an all-or-none response, but billions of neurons exist and interconnect in the vertebrate body. Integration of excitatory and inhibitory signals, and associative activities by neuron cell bodies and the central nervous system, plus the sheer number of neurons involved and the frequencies with which they fire result in different levels of response.	44.2, 44.3	
*6. Having antagonistic neurotransmitters allows for finer control and more complex responses to stimuli. It is not confusing to the nervous system since the different neurotransmitters are chemically distinct, are restricted to particular neurons, and bind to specific receptor proteins.	44.3	

	Sect.	Rvw.
*7. Acetylcholinesterase is an enzyme present in synaptic clefts. It removes the neurotransmitter acetylcholine from the cleft. If acetylcholinesterase is inhibited by nerve gas, acetylcholine remains in the synaptic cleft, and there is continuous stimulation of the postsynaptic membrane. This disrupts the normal functioning of the nervous system and can be lethal because many vital life processes, including breathing and blood circulation, require rhythmic muscular contraction, and muscles are stimulated to contract by acetylcholine released at neuromuscular junctions.	44.3	
*8. Cocaine binds to transporter proteins in synaptic clefts. These proteins normally remove the neurotransmitter dopamine from the cleft. In the presence of cocaine, dopamine stays in the cleft longer and continues to stimulate the postsynaptic cell, sending pleasure signals due to the part of the brain involved.	44.3	
*9. In early vertebrates, the hindbrain was dominant and controlled motor activity; in advanced vertebrates, the forebrain is dominant and is used for thought, learning, and processing of information.	44.4	
*10. The efferent motor pathway in both the sympathetic and parasympathetic divisions involves two neurons. The preganglionic neuron has its cell body in the central nervous system and sends an axon to an autonomic ganglion. The postganglionic neuron has its cell body in the autonomic ganglion and sends its axon to synapse with muscle or gland cells. Preganglionic neurons in the sympathetic division originate in the thoracic and lumbar regions of the spinal cord and synapse at an autonomic ganglion outside the spinal cord. In the parasympathetic division, preganglionic neurons exit the brain and facial region of the spinal cord and terminate in ganglia located near or within internal organs. The sympathetic division activates the body for a fight or flight response, while the parasympathetic division promotes rest and repose. The two divisions typically have antagonistic effects.	44.5	
11. e	44.1	
12. b	44.1	
*13. a	44.1	
14. d	44.1	
*15. c	44.2	
16. a	44.2	
17. d	44.2	
18. e	44.2	
*19. c	44.2	
20. e	44.3	
*21. b	44.3	

22. d	44.3	
23. c	44.3	
24. a	44.3	
25. e	44.4	
26. a	44.4	
27. b	44.4	
28. c	44.4	
29. e	44.5	
*30. d	44.5	

CHAPTER 45 SENSORY SYSTEMS

MASTERING KEY CONCEPTS

The central nervous system is the information-processing center and the command post for sending out responsive orders. But sensory systems provide the information to the brain in the first place. Sensory receptors monitor both the internal and external environments of the animal, and fire when they are stimulated by particular signals. Sensory neurons then relay this information to the brain. The brain builds a complete picture of the internal and external environments by monitoring which sensory neurons are active and how frequently they fire.

45.1 Animals employ a wide variety of sensory receptors.

- **Overview**: **Sensory receptors** sense environmental stimuli (**exteroceptors**) and internal stimuli (**interoceptors**). Receptors are grouped based on the type of stimulus that they respond to. There are three general classes: **mechanoreceptors**, **chemoreceptors**, and **energy-detecting receptors**. Sensory stimuli are conveyed to the central nervous system by being transformed into a receptor potential (**transduction**) and transmitted along an afferent nerve pathway (**transmission**) to the brain, which can **interpret** the stimulus. Stimuli cause **stimulus-gated ion channels** in the membranes of sensory cells to open or close. The greater the stimulus, the higher the frequency of action potentials.
- **Details**: Know how sensory receptors are grouped and how sensory information is conveyed to the central nervous system.

45.2 Mechanical receptors sense touch and pressure.

- **Overview**: **Nociceptors** transmit impulses perceived as pain and consist of free nerve endings located throughout the body. **Mechanoreceptors** in the skin contain sensory cells that have ion channels that open in response to mechanical distortion of the membrane. **Phasic receptors**, such as **hair follicle receptors** and **Meissner corpuscles**, and **tonic receptors**, such as **Ruffini corpuscles** and **Merkel disks,** are morphologically specialized receptors in the human skin that respond to fine touch. **Pacinian corpuscles** are pressure-sensitive receptors in the subcutaneous tissue that detect the application and removal of pressure. **Proprioceptors**, located in muscle spindles, tendons, and joints, provide information about the position and movement of an organism's body. **Baroreceptors** monitor the blood pressure in the **carotid sinus** and **aortic arch**.
- **Details**: Know how extreme temperature can result in a sensation of pain. Know the different receptors in the skin, whether each is phasic or tonic, where it is located, and how it functions. Know the role of proprioceptors and baroreceptors. Know how baroreceptors and the nervous system respond to increases or decreases in blood pressure.

45.3 Auditory receptors detect pressure waves in the air.

- **Overview**: The **lateral line system** consisting of hair cells located within a canal in the skin of a fish allows them to hear and sense objects that reflect pressure waves and lower frequency vibrations. **Mechanosensory cells**, similar to those in the lateral line system, allow pressure waves to be transduced into nerve impulses in the ear. In fish, **otoliths** in the ear vibrate against hair cells to produce action potentials. In the ears of terrestrial vertebrates, vibrations in the air are channeled to the **tympanic membrane** causing movement of the small bones in the **middle ear**, the **malleus**, **incus**, and **stapes**. Vibration of the **oval window** by movement of the stapes produces pressure waves of fluid in the **vestibular canal** of the **cochlea** in the **inner ear**. Pressure waves travel down the **tympanic canal** to the **round window** membrane that transmits pressure back into the middle ear causing the **cochlear duct** to vibrate. Cilia of the **hair cells in the cochlea** bend in response to the movement of the **basilar membrane** relative to the **tectorial membrane** causing depolarization of the hair cells, which stimulate the production of action potentials in sensory neurons that project into the brain. Bats, shrews, whales, and dolphins use **echolocation** to perceive the presence and distance of objects by emitting sounds and determining how long it takes to come back to them. The **vestibular apparatus** in the **labyrinth** of the human ear allows the brain to maintain balance and equilibrium. It consists of two chambers, the **utricle** (horizontal acceleration) and the **saccule** (vertical acceleration) whose membranes are continuous with three fluid-containing **semicircular canals** allowing acceleration in any direction to be detected.
- **Details**: Know how the lateral line system in fish allows sensory neurons to be activated or inhibited. Know the structure of the human ear. Know the advantages and disadvantages of using hearing to monitor the environment.

45.4 Chemoreceptors detect taste, smell, and pH.

- **Overview**: Vertebrates use **chemoreceptors** to sense taste and smell. **Taste buds** are chemosensitive epithelial cells located on the tongue and in the oval cavity of vertebrates. Chemicals that produce **salty** or **sour** taste in a taste bud act directly through ion channels, while detection of **sweet**, **bitter**, and **umami** occur indirectly through G protein-coupled receptors that lead to release of a neurotransmitter from receptor cells. The sense of smell involves chemoreceptors located in the nasal passages. The axons of neurons in the nasal passage transmit information directly into the cerebral cortex. **Peripheral chemoreceptors** and **central chemoreceptors** detect the plasma pH and the pH of the cerebrospinal fluid respectively.

- **Details**: Know the structure of a taste bud and how different tastes are sense. Understand how smells are sensed, and why more smells than tastes can be discerned. Understand how chemoreceptors regulate breathing rate.

45.5 Optic receptors detect light over a broad range of wavelengths.

- **Overview**: The first step in visualizing something is the capture of light energy by **photoreceptors**. Eyespots in the flatworm detect the direction of a light source and turn away from it, but cannot form a visual image. Only four different phyla of animals have **image-forming eyes**, annelids, mollusks, arthropods, and chordates. The eyes of all of these phyla have evolved independently. All image-forming eyes have one or more **lenses** for focusing the light and a **retina** where the actual receptors are located. The photoreceptor cells in the retina are **rods** (black and white vision) and **cones** (sharpness; color vision). **Photopigments** located on the membranes of the disks in rods (**rhodopsin**) and cones (**photopsins**) contain *cis-*

retinal, which undergoes chemical changes when exposed to light causing activation of the **bipolar cells** and then the **ganglion cells,** which transmit impulses to the brain through the **optic nerve**. A one-to-one connection between each cone in the **fovea** with a bipolar cell, and each bipolar cell with one ganglion cell allows high **visual acuity**. The slight displacement of images due to slightly different views in animals having two eyes facing forward permits **binocular vision,** which allows depth perception.

- **Details**: Know the structure of the vertebrate eye. Understand how light enters the eye and a visual image is formed. Understand the defects in **near-sighted** and **far-sighted** people and how these defects are corrected. Understand the structure of rods and cones. Know how light affects photoreceptors and the signal transduction cascade that is activated. Know how visual acuity and depth perception are achieved.

45.6 Some vertebrates use heat, electricity, or magnetism for orientation.

- **Overview**: Pit vipers can sense infrared radiation using exteroceptors known as **pit organs** that transmit information to the brain in a region that is similar to the visual center in other vertebrates. Electrical fields generated from the contraction of muscles in aquatic animals can be detected by electroreceptors (**ampullae of Lorenzini**) found in sharks, rays, skates, and duck-billed platypuses. **Magnetic receptors** in birds may contribute to their migratory patterns.
- **Details**: Know how heat and electricity are detected by some organisms.

CHALLENGING YOUR UNDERSTANDING

1. List the four steps required for impulses to be perceived by the central nervous system. Then describe the action that occurs during each of these steps.

   a.

   b.

   c.

   d.

2. Place the following events involved in the detection of sound waves in order of occurrence.

   _____ a. The brain interprets the sound.
   _____ b. Hair cells stimulate the production of action potentials in sensory neurons that project to the brain.
   _____ c. The round window membrane is pushed by pressure waves in the tympanic canal.
   _____ d. Vibrations channel through the ear canal to the tympanic membrane.
   _____ e. The cochlea duct vibrates.
   _____ f. The middle ear ossicles move.
   _____ g. Cilia of the hair cells bend in response to movement of the basilar membrane.
   _____ h. Pressure waves of fluid are generated in the cochlea.

3. Place the following in the order to indicate the path of light after it enters the eye and how it forms a visual image.

   _____ a. retina ganglion cell
   _____ b. pupil
   _____ c. rods/cones
   _____ d. optic nerve
   _____ e. brain
   _____ f. bipolar cell
   _____ g. stimulation of ganglion cells
   _____ h. lens
   _____ i. cornea
   _____ j. stimulation of bipolar cells

4. List the types of rods and cones and the wavelength of maximum light absorption of each. How are these rods and cones different in people with color blindness? Why is this trait more common in men than in women?

5. Place the following actions in order to show how light affects a photo receptor cell.

   _____ a. activation of G protein
   _____ b. conversion of cGMP to GMP
   _____ c. prevention of the release of inhibitory neurotransmitter
   _____ d. activation of phosphodiesterase
   _____ e. closing of Na^+ and Ca^{2+} channels
   _____ f. conversion of 11-*cis*-retinal to all-trans-retinal

KEY TERMS

Match the numbered term with the definition that fits it best. Put the corresponding number in front of the appropriate definition.

1. mechanoreceptors
2. chemoreceptors
3. energy-detecting receptors
4. exteroceptors
5. interoceptors
6. receptor potential
7. cutaneous receptors
8. nociceptors
9. thermoreceptors
10. proprioceptors
11. baroreceptors
12. lateral line system
13. cochlea
14. middle ear ossicles
15. organ of Corti
16. echolocation
17. statocyst
18. vestibular apparatus
19. peripheral chemoreceptors
20. central chemoreceptors
21. rods
22. cones
23. rhodopsin
24. photopsin
25. retina
26. color blindness
27. binocular vision

a. _____ A process analagous to sonar where animals orient themselves by emitting sound and monitoring its return.
b. _____ A bony structure in the inner ear that transmits pressure waves to the round window.
c. _____ A sensory structure in the inner ear that senses movement of the head to help the body maintain balance.
d. _____ A sensory system on fish that detects distant movement in the water by sensing pressure waves.
e. _____ Depolarization of a sensory receptor following a stimulus.
f. _____ The light-capturing photopigment found in cones.
g. _____ The light-capturing photopigment found in rods.
h. _____ Sensory receptors that transmit impulses perceived as pain.
i. _____ Sensory receptors in the arteries responsible for monitoring plasma pH.
j. _____ Sensory receptors in the brain that are responsible for monitoring spinal fluid pH.
k. _____ Receptors that sense stimuli in the external environment.
l. _____ Receptors that sense stimuli inside the body.
m. _____ The three small bones of the inner ear.
n. _____ A sensory structure used by invertebrates to orient themselves with respect to gravity.
o. _____ Afferent neurons that detect tension in artery walls to help the body monitor blood pressure.
p. _____ A condition in which some colors cannot be distinguished from one another due to the loss of one type of cone.
q. _____ Sensory receptors found in the skin of animals.
r. _____ The process of using two eyes to visualize one object in order to determine 3D shape and distance.
s. _____ Sensory receptors in muscle spindles that provide information about the position or movement of body parts.
t. _____ Sensory apparatus on the bottom of the cochlear duct.
u. _____ Receptors that sense chemicals or chemical changes such as those involved in smelling.
v. _____ Receptors that sense physical stimuli such as those involved in touch, hearing, and balance.
w. _____ Receptors that sense electromagnetic or thermal energy such as those involved in vision.
x. _____ Dendritic endings found in the skin that are sensitive to temperature changes.
y. _____ Specialized cells in the eye that sense color.
z. _____ Specialized cells in the eye that are responsible for black-and-white vision in low light.
aa. _____ The inside surface of the eye upon which the rods and cones are found.

LEARNING BY EXPERIENCE

1. Complete the following chart by listing each of these stimuli in its proper category: electricity, gravity, heat, humidity, inertia, light, magnetism, pressure, smell, sound, taste, touch, vibration.

Mechanical forces	Chemicals	Electromagnetic energy

2. Match the following stimuli with the sensory receptor that detects them.

_____ a. pain	i.	Merkel cells
_____ b. levels of CO_2 in the blood	ii.	baroreceptors
_____ c. blood pressure	iii.	ampullae of Lorenzini
_____ d. fine touch in surface areas without hair	iv.	Meissner's corpuscles
_____ e. duration and extent of touch (pressure)	v.	Pacinian corpuscles
_____ f. limb position, muscle length	vi.	nociceptors
_____ g. changes in electrical currents	vii.	pit organs
_____ h. vibration	viii.	proprioceptors
_____ i. heat	ix.	statocysts
_____ j. gravity	x.	peripheral and central chemoreceptors

3. Label the following parts on the eye diagram at right.

ciliary muscle
cornea
fovea
iris
lens
optic nerve
pupil
retina
sclera
suspensory ligament

Where are the actual receptor cells located?

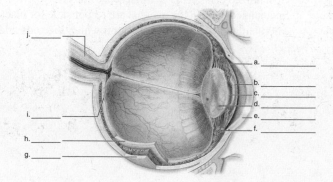

EXERCISING YOUR KNOWLEDGE

Briefly answer each of the following questions in the space provided.

1. If the nerve impulse of any neuron is identical to any other neuron in terms of its depolarization and action potential, how can we perceive the vast array of sensory sensations that we do?

2. Many people claim to have a "sixth sense" that they call ESP, extrasensory perception. How would you design a sensory system for ESP? What would be its components and how would they function? (Hint: What are the basic components of all sensory systems?)

3. Where are the taste buds of a fish located? Why is this advantageous?

4. Which is the more sensitive sensory system in humans, taste or smell?

5. How is the electrical sensory system of electric fish analogous to the sonar system of some mammals? Is it similar to the lateral line system of fishes?

6. What are the advantages and disadvantages of auditory stimuli as a way of monitoring terrestrial environments?

7. Why can dogs hear dog whistles that people can't hear?

8. Do all animals with image-forming eyes have the same type of color vision? Why or why not?

9. Athletes such as boxers, football players, and rugby players often suffer a detached retina when a sharp blow to the head causes a piece of the retina to detach or break loose from the back of the eye. How would this affect their vision? Why?

10. Why don't fish have pit organs like snakes have to help them locate prey?

Circle the letter of the one best answer in each of the following questions.

11. Which of the following is a true statement regarding baroreceptors?
    a. When blood pressure decreases, the frequency of impulses produced by baroreceptors increases.
    b. A rise in blood pressure reduces sympathetic activity.
    c. Baroreceptors monitor blood pressure in the pulmonary artery and left ventricle.
    d. As blood pressure increases, the CNS stimulates an increase in vasoconstriction.
    e. Baroreceptors are motor neurons that cause the heart to contract.

12. The simplest sensory receptors in a nervous system are
    a. found only in invertebrates.
    b. auditory receptors.
    c. mechanical receptors that employ a lever device.
    d. free nerve endings that depolarize in response to direct physical stimulation.
    e. responsible for both monitoring and interpreting internal body conditions.

13. Which of the following is *not* a mechanical stimulus?
    a. gravity
    b. sound
    c. humidity
    d. touch
    e. vibration

14. The greater the intensity of a sensory stimulus,
    a. the stronger the resulting action potential sent to the brain.
    b. the greater the frequency of action potentials sent to the brain.
    c. Both of these are correct.
    d. None of these are correct.

15. Which of the following is *not* one of the four basic taste categories that human taste buds respond to?
    a. bitter
    b. salty
    c. sweet
    d. sour
    e. spicy

16. A proprioceptor detects
    a. taste.
    b. pain.
    c. gravity.
    d. color.
    e. temperature.

17. The most sensitive vertebrate chemoreceptors known are the
    a. organs of Corti of bats.
    b. organs of Corti of humans.
    c. rods and cones of mammals.
    d. olfactory receptors of mammals.
    e. taste receptors of fishes.

18. Which of the following statements is true?
    a. Blood pressure is monitored by chemoreceptors.
    b. The lateral line system of fishes helps them maintain an upright position by monitoring gravity.
    c. If a person suffers from motion sickness, it is probably due to sensory signals originating in the cochlea.
    d. Flies have taste receptors on their feet.
    e. All of these are true.

19. In humans, the receptors cells for hearing are located in the
    a. tympanic membrane.
    b. cochlea.
    c. semicircular canals.
    d. Eustachian tube.
    e. oval window.

20. The membrane that separates the outer ear from the middle ear of mammals is called the
    a. tympanic membrane.
    b. basilar membrane.
    c. tectorial membrane.
    d. oval window.
    e. round window.

21. Which of the following animals use echolocation?
    a. bats
    b. shrews
    c. whales and dolphins
    d. all of these
    e. none of these

22. Which sensory system provides the most detailed information about the distance and direction of an object?
    a. hearing
    b. vision
    c. smell
    d. touch
    e. taste

23. The amount of light entering a mammal's eye is determined primarily by the size of the
    a. retina.
    b. fovea.
    c. optic nerve.
    d. lens.
    e. pupil.

24. Action potentials are carried from the eyes to the brain by the
    a. bipolar cells.
    b. rod and cone cells.
    c. optic nerves.
    d. fovea.
    e. sclera.

25. Which of the following statements is true?
    a. All image-forming eyes have at least one lens.
    b. All animals have image-forming eyes.
    c. All animals have binocular vision.
    d. All of these are true.
    e. None of these are true.

26. Color is detected by
    a. cone cells.
    b. rod cells.
    c. bipolar cells.
    d. cupula cells.
    e. utricle cells.

27. The bleaching reaction in photopigments occurs when
    a. a person is color blind.
    b. no light is reaching the photopigment.
    c. the photopigment absorbs light.
    d. the dark current is flowing.
    e. a person has too many cone cells and not enough rod cells.

28. Which of the following substances is *not* involved in the electromagnetic and chemical events of vision?
    a. rhodopsin
    b. G proteins
    c. phosphodiesterase
    d. All of these are involved.
    e. None of these are involved.

29. Information transmitted by the pit organ of a snake is processed by the
    a. auditory center of the snake's brain.
    b. visual center of the snake's brain.
    c. taste center of the snake's brain.
    d. ampullae of Lorenzini.
    e. muscle spindles.

30. Which of the following stimuli is detected and used by both aquatic and terrestrial organisms?
    a. infrared radiation
    b. electricity
    c. magnetism
    d. all of these
    e. none of these

ASSESSING YOUR KNOWLEDGE

Answers to the questions in this section test your ability to synthesize information gained from the chapter and to solve challenging problems on an exam or in everyday life.

Challenging Your Understanding—Answers

1. a. Stimulation: a physical stimulus impinges on a sensory neuron or associated sensory receptor.
   b. Transduction: graded potentials are created in the dendrites of the sensory neuron.
   c. Transmission: action potentials are passed along an afferent pathway to the CNS.
   d. Interpretation: the brain creates a perception of the electrochemical events.

2. a:8; b:7; c:4; d:1; e:5; f:2; g:6; h:3.

3. a:4; b:2; c:6; d:9; e:10; f:5; g:8; h:3; i:1; j:7.

4. Blue cones: 420 nm; Green cones: 530 nm; Red cones: 560 nm; Rods: 500 nm. Individuals with color blindness lack one of the three types of cones. This trait is observed more frequently in men because the genes for the cones are located on the X chromosome and males only have one X chromosome.

5. a:2; b:4; c:6; d:3; e:5; f:1.

Key Terms—Answers

a. 16, b. 13, c. 18, d. 12, e. 6, f. 24, g. 23, h. 8, i. 19, j. 20, k. 4, l. 5, m. 14, n. 17, o. 11, p. 26, q. 7, r. 27, s. 10, t. 15, u. 2, v. 1, w. 3, x. 9, y. 22, z. 21, aa. 25.

Learning by Experience—Answers

1. Mechanical forces	Chemicals	Electromagnetic energy
gravity	humidity	electricity
inertia	smell	heat
pressure	taste	light
sound		magnetism
vibration		
touch		

*2. a. vi, b. x, c. ii, d. iv, e. I, f. viii, g. iii, h. v, i. vii, j. ix
3. a. suspensory ligament
b. iris
c. pupil
d. lens
e. cornea
f. ciliary muscle
g. sclera
h. retina

i. fovea
j. optic nerve
Receptor cells (rods and cones) are located in the retina.

Exercising Your Knowledge—Answers

As you check your answers, put a mark in the review (Rvw.) column for the answers you missed. If you didn't miss any, congratulations—you have mastered the chapter! If you missed some, review the section (Sect.) in the text where this concept is discussed. In order to develop an efficient review strategy, it is important that you understand what types of questions you missed. The questions with asterisks test more for understanding of the **concepts**, whereas the others test more for **detail**. *See the preface for learning strategies for concepts and for detail.*

	Sect.	Rvw.
*1. The brain perceives the difference between different senses (for example, between pain and vision and taste) and between different intensities strictly on the basis of which part of the brain receives the signal and the frequency with which the signal is received, respectively. An impulse arriving in the auditory region of the cerebral cortex, for example, is perceived as a sound, not a temperature or a smell or a touch. All of the sensations we experience are the result of the integration and processing of nerve impulses by our brains, not any character inherent in the nerve impulse itself.	45.1	
*2. There would have to be a sensory receptor of some sort to perceive the stimulus, whatever its form. The receptors would have to connect to sensory neurons that would conduct impulses to a specific region of the brain, where the information would be processed and integrated, and be interpreted by the brain as ESP. The details are up to you – for example, to what category do the stimuli belong? Are there structural adaptations for amplifying the signal? Have fun!	45.1	
*3. Fish taste buds are scattered over the surface of the body. This allows a fish to taste the surrounding water, not just what it puts in its mouth. It is advantageous especially for fish that live and feed in dark or murky water because they can find food even when can't see well.	45.4	
*4. Smell; humans can detect only four basic categories of taste (salty, sour, bitter, and sweet), but thousands of different smells. Humans can respond to extremely low levels of scent. Smell also impacts taste—for example, food doesn't taste as good or isn't as flavorful when you have a cold and can't smell properly.	45.4	

*5. Electrical fish discharge electricity and then monitor disturbances in the electrical field that are caused by environmental objects. In sonar, mammals use sound waves to establish a three-dimensional picture of their environment. They emit sound waves and monitor the pattern in which they return after bouncing off objects in the environment. Both processes involve the animal putting out a signal and then monitoring how the environment changes it. Fishes do not emit anything with their lateral line systems, but instead monitor changes in water pressure or movement as they or other objects move through the water.	45.3, 45.6
*6. Hearing works better in water than air because water transmits pressure waves more efficiently. Auditory stimuli travel faster and farther than chemical ones and provide better directional information. Auditory stimuli do not provide accurate information about distance.	45.3
*7. A dog's auditory receptors are more sensitive to high-pitched sounds than are a human's auditory receptors. The ability to hear a particular pitch depends on the flexibility of the basilar membrane in the cochlea; the less flexible it is, the less the animal will hear. Children can hear high-pitched sounds up to 20,000 cycles per second, but this ability declines with age as the basilar membrane becomes less flexible and the ear becomes less efficient at amplifying sound waves. Dogs can hear frequencies as high as 40,000 cycles per second because of the greater sensitivity (flexibility) of their basilar membranes.	45.3
*8. Not all animals with image-forming eyes have color vision, and those that do don't all see color the same way. Different types of animals have different numbers of types of cone cells (for example, 2, 3, 4, or 5 different types), resulting in different perceptual abilities (what colors can and can't be perceived).	45.5

*9. Depending on how much of the retina was detached, the person would lose part or all vision in the affected eye. If the retina is detached, necessary connections between rod cells, cone cells, bipolar cells, ganglion cells, and the optic nerve may be destroyed, and nerve impulses could not be transmitted from the eye to the brain.	45.5	
*10. Pit organs detect heat, and water is not good at conducting heat – it absorbs it instead.	45.6	
11. b	45.2	
*12. d	45.1	
13. c	45.1	
*14. b	45.1	
15. e	45.4	
16. c	45.2	
17. e	45.4	
*18. d	45.4	
19. b	45.3	
20. a	45.3	
21. d	45.3	
22. b	45.5	
23. e	45.5	
24. c	45.5	
*25. a	45.5	
26. a	45.5	
*27. c	45.5	
28. d	45.5	
29. b	45.6	
30. c	45.6	

CHAPTER 46 THE ENDOCRINE SYSTEM

MASTERING KEY CONCEPTS

The central nervous system processes incoming information from the sensory system and sends out response commands. Some of these orders given by the central nervous system are carried out by hormones produced by endocrine glands. These activities help regulate body activities and unite a diverse collection of cells, tissues, and organs into a smoothly functioning single organism that can maintain the homeostasis necessary for life. Not all hormones, however, are under the control of the nervous system, and the nervous system itself is influenced by hormones.

46.1 Regulation is often accomplished by chemical messengers.

- **Overview**: Specific cells in the body secrete chemical messengers such as neurotransmitters, **hormones**, and **paracrine regulators**. Hormones are produced by **endocrine glands** and circulate throughout the body in the blood to target cells that have a specific receptor to which the hormone will bind. Hormonal secretion is controlled primarily by the brain, but can also be affected by other factors such as blood glucose levels, or the amount of Ca^{2+} in the blood. Hormones must be sufficiently complex and relatively stable to be able to convey information to cells in different parts of the body. Three types of molecules serve as hormones: **peptides or proteins**, **amino acid derivatives**, and **steroids**. Steroids and thyroid hormone are **lipophilic** (lipid-soluble); all other hormones are **hydrophilic** (water-soluble). The lipophilic hormones are carried in the blood by transport proteins that make them soluble. They cross the plasma membrane and bind to intracellular receptors in target cells where they are active for a period of time before they are destroyed or inactivated. Hydrophilic hormones bind to membrane receptors and activate intracellular signaling cascades. Hydrophilic hormones are rapidly inactivated. Paracrine regulators, including growth factors such as **cytokines**, **neurotropins**, as well as **prostaglandins** and **nitric oxide gas**, are secreted and transmitted among the cells of a particular organ to regulate one another.
- **Details**: Know the distinct characteristics of lipophilic and hydrophilic hormones. Know the effects of paracrine regulators, such as growth factors, prostaglandins, and nitric oxide gas. Understand how **nonsteroidal anti-inflammatory drugs**, such as aspirin, work.

46.2 Lipophilic and hydrophilic hormones regulate their target cells by different means.

- **Overview**: **Lipophilic hormones** circulate in the blood attached to transport proteins increasing their stability and allowing them to act over prolonged periods. Lipophilic hormones dissociate from their transport proteins, pass through the plasma membrane, and bind to their receptors in the cytoplasm or in the nucleus. The hormone-receptor complex binds to **hormone response elements** found in the promoters of some genes to activate or inhibit gene expression. **Hydrophilic hormones** cannot enter cells, but instead bind to receptor proteins located on the outer surface of the plasma membrane. These receptors act as kinases themselves, or act through **G proteins** to produce a **second messenger**, such as **cAMP**, that activates a protein kinase leading to the phosphorylation of target proteins that initiate a cellular response. Importantly, a single hormone can have different effects in two different cell types by the hormone receptors being linked to two different G proteins. Hydrophilic hormones dissociate from their receptors shortly after binding, or are rapidly deactivated, along with second messengers and protein kinases leading to attenuation of the hormone-initiated response.
- **Details**: Know where the receptors for lipophilic and hydrophilic hormones are located and how each produces an intracellular response. Understand how the cellular response is attenuated.

46.3 The hypothalamus controls the secretions of the pituitary gland.

- **Overview**: The **pituitary gland** is attached to the hypothalamus at the base of the brain. It consists of a glandular region, the **anterior pituitary** (**adenohypophysis**), and a fibrous region, the **posterior pituitary** (**neurohypophysis**), both of which are conserved in all vertebrates. The posterior pituitary gland forms from growth of the brain and receives an axon tract from the hypothalamus. It is involved in the storage and secretion of **antidiuretic hormone** (**ADH**), which stimulates water reabsorption by the kidneys. The posterior pituitary also secretes **oxytocin,** which stimulates milk ejection reflexes, uterine contractions during childbirth, and pair-bonding. Both of these hormones are secreted by neuron cell bodies in the hypothalamus and stored in the posterior pituitary. The **anterior pituitary** forms from epithelial tissue and produces **peptide hormones** including **ACTH** and **MSH**, **protein hormones** including **GH** and **prolactin**, and glycoprotein hormones including **TSH**, **LH**, and **FSH**. **Releasing hormones** or **inhibiting hormones** secreted by the hypothalamus enter the **hypothalamohypophysial portal system** and regulate the secretion of **tropic hormones** from the anterior pituitary glands. These hormones have several targets and a variety of effects in cells. Both the hypothalamus and the anterior pituitary are regulated by the hormones that they promote the secretion of in a **negative feedback loop**.

- **Details**: Know what types of hormones are secreted by the anterior and posterior pituitary glands, the composition of each hormone, and the functions carried out by each. Know the hypothalamus releasing and inhibiting hormones, and the hormones that they affect secretion of, from the anterior pituitary. Know how negative feedback inhibits the secretion of hormones from the hypothalamus and anterior pituitary. Understand the effects of lack of iodine in a diet and how a **goiter** is formed. Know the effects of removal of the pituitary gland, and excessive secretion or deficiency of growth hormone (GH). Know the targets of prolactin, TSH, ACTH, FSH, LH, and MSH.

46.4 The major peripheral endocrine glands are located in the thyroid, kidneys, and pancreas.

- **Overview**: Other than the pituitary gland, there are several endocrine glands in the body, including the **thyroid** and **parathyroid glands**, **adrenal glands**, and pancreatic **islets of Langerhans**, which produce hormones that regulate a variety of processes in the body. The thyroid gland, found in the neck, secretes three hormones, **thyroxine, triiodothyronine**, and **calcitonin,** which bind to nuclear receptors and affect the production and activity of cellular proteins. These hormones regulate metabolic rate, growth and development, and calcium levels in the blood. The parathyroid gland produces **parathyroid hormone,** which stimulates the release of Ca^{2+} into the blood by the dissolution of bone, the reabsorption of Ca^{2+} from the urine by the kidneys, and the production of the active form of vitamin D stimulating the intestinal absorption of Ca^{2+}. The adrenal glands are composed of the **adrenal medulla** and the **adrenal cortex**. The adrenal medulla secretes **epinephrine** and **norepinephrine,** which trigger alarm responses, while the adrenal cortex secretes **corticosteroids**

to regulate glucose, sodium, and potassium levels in the blood. The islets of Langerhans in the pancreas produce the antagonistic hormones, **insulin** and **glucagon,** which regulate blood glucose levels.

- **Details**: Know what hormones the thyroid, parathyroid, and adrenal glands secrete and the functions of each. Understand how calcitonin and parathyroid hormone regulate the levels of Ca^{2+} in the blood. Know how insulin and glucagon act antagonistically to control blood glucose levels and the defect in individuals with **type I** and **type II diabetes**.

46.5 Other endocrine glands secrete hormones that regulate numerous other body functions.

- **Overview**: **Ovaries** and **testes** are endocrine glands that secrete the **sex steroid hormones** such as **estrogen, progesterone**, and **testosterone**. These hormones play a critical role in the development of male sex organs, maintaining the reproductive cycle in females, and sexual maturation. The **pineal gland** in the brain secretes the hormone **melatonin**, whose daily cycling regulates sleeping/waking and temperature cycles. The **thymus** secretes hormones involved in the regulation of the immune system; the heart secretes **atrial natriuretic hormone,** which stimulates the kidneys to excrete salt and water; and the kidneys secrete **erythropoietin,** which stimulates bone marrow to produce red blood cells. **Molting** and **metamorphic changes** in insects are both controlled by hormones. Hormone are linked to **cancer** in that malfunctions in hormonal production can be caused by tumors in the endocrine glands, or mutations in hormone receptors can cause a loss of hormone sensitivity that results in excessive cell divisions and tumor formation.

- **Details**: Know the effects of the sex hormones, melatonin, and the hormones secreted by the thymus, heart, and kidneys. Understand the role that hormones play in molting and metamorphosis in insects. Know how hormone production could either be a cause of, or be detrimentally affected by, tumor formation.

CHALLENGING YOUR UNDERSTANDING

1. For the following hormones, list the endocrine gland that produces it.

a. testosterone

b. follicle-stimulating hormone

c. inhibiting hormones

d. estradiol

e. parathyroid hormone

f. adrenaline

g. glucocorticoids

h. growth hormone

i. thyroid stimulating hormone

j. glucagon

k. progesterone

l. melatonin

m. releasing hormones

n. melanocyte stimulating hormone

o. prolactin

2. Classify the following hormones as a peptides, proteins, amino acid derivatives, or steroids: insulin, testosterone, growth hormone, parthyroid hormone, oxytocin, prolactin, progesterone, glucagon, estradiol, inhibiting hormones, adrenaline, antidiuretic hormone, glucocorticoids, melatonin, releasing hormones.

Peptides

Proteins

Amino acid derivatives

Steroids

3. Draw a map that shows the hormones, tissues, and pathways by which the hypothalamus promotes bone growth.

KEY TERMS

Match the numbered term with the definition that fits it best. Put the corresponding number in front of the appropriate definition.

1. hormone
2. endocrine glands
3. neurohormones
4. paracrine regulators
5. endocrine system
6. exocrine glands
7. pheromones
8. glycoprotein hormones
9. protein hormones
10. peptide hormones
11. sex steroids
12. corticosteroids
13. catecholamines
14. lipophilic hormones
15. cytokines
16. growth factors
17. neurotropins
18. prostaglandins
19. nonsteroidal anti-inflammatory drugs
20. hormone response elements
21. cyclic AMP
22. adenyl cyclase
23. pituitary gland
24. releasing hormones
25. inhibiting hormones
26. adrenal glands
27. parathyroid glands
28. hypothyroidism
29. hyperthyroidism
30. anterior pituitary
31. posterior pituitary
32. antidiuretic hormone (ADH)
33. oxytocin
34. thyroxine
35. insulin-like growth factors
36. ecdysone
37. juvenile hormone
38. pineal gland
39. insulin
40. glucagon
41. calcitonin
42. parathyroid hormone
43. hypothalamohypophysial portal system

a. _____ Growth factors that regulate the nervous system.
b. _____ A hormone secreted by the α cells of the islets of Langerhans; promotes the hydrolysis of stored glycogen.
c. _____ Hormones, such as estrogen, progesterone, and testosterone, that are produced in the ovaries and testes.
d. _____ A hormone produced by the posterior pituitary gland that stimulates water reabsorption by the kidneys.
e. _____ A disorder in which adults have a low metabolism due to the underproduction of thyroxine.
f. _____ Organs that are specialized to produce hormones.
g. _____ A hormone secreted by the thyroid gland that plays a role in maintaining proper levels of Ca^{2+} in the blood.
h. _____ Hormones such as epinephrine and norepinephrine secreted by the adrenal medulla to trigger alarm responses.
i. _____ A hormone produced by the prothoracic gland in insects to bring about the necessary changes for molting.
j. _____ Peptide neurohormones secreted by neurons in the hypothalamus to stimulate the release of other hormones.
k. _____ Chemicals released into the environment to communicate among individuals of a single species.
l. _____ An enzyme activated by a G protein in response to epinephrine, which catalyzes the formation of cAMP.
m. _____ A major endocrine gland located in the roof of the third ventricle of the brain that secretes the hormone melatonin.
n. _____ A class of drugs including aspirin that inhibit cyclooxygenase-1 and 2 and reduce the effects of prostaglandins.
o. _____ The organs and tissues that produce hormones.
p. _____ Four small glands attached to the thyroid that synthesize and release a peptide when blood Ca^{2+} levels are low.
q. _____ Proteins produced in the liver and bone in response to growth hormone stimulation that promote bone elongation.
r. _____ Structurally similar hormones secreted by the anterior pituitary that consist of a chain of 200 amino acids.
s. _____ The glandular portion of the pituitary gland that produces seven peptide, protein, and glycoprotein hormones.
t. _____ Steroids secreted by the adrenal cortex that regulate glucose, sodium, and potassium levels in the blood.
u. _____ A hormone secreted by the β cells of islets of Langerhans that promotes the cellular uptake of glucose.
v. _____ A regulatory chemical that is secreted into the extracellular fluid and carried by the blood to target cells.
w. _____ A gland that hangs by a stalk from the hypothalamus at the base of the brain and produces many hormones.
x. _____ Structurally similar hormones secreted by the anterior pituitary that are cleaved from a precursor protein.
y. _____ A system of capillaries and veins that run from the hypothalamus to the pituitary stalk to the anterior pituitary.
z. _____ Peptide neurohormones secreted by neurons in the hypothalamus to inhibit the release of other hormones.
aa. _____ Glands that secrete their products into a duct for transport to the outside.
bb. _____ A diverse group of fatty acids that act as paracrine regulators and are involved in the inflammatory response.
cc. _____ A peptide neurohormone that is secreted by the posterior pituitary and stimulates milk ejection and pair-bonding.
dd. _____ A hormone produced by the parathyroid gland that is released in response to falling levels of Ca^{2+}.
ee. _____ Growth factors specialized to control cell division and differentiation in the immune system.
ff. _____ A hormone produce by the corpora allata in insects whose levels are regulated to allow metamorphosis.
gg. _____ Chemicals secreted by neurons and carried in the blood.
hh. _____ A disorder in which adults have an overactive metabolism due to the overproduction of thyroxine.
ii. _____ Fat-soluble hormones that can cross cell membranes and bind to intracellular receptors.
jj. _____ A hormone containing iodine that is produced by the thyroid gland and stimulates metabolic rate.

kk. _____ A second messenger molecule that is produced from ATP by adenyl cyclase.
ll. _____ Structurally similar family of hormones containing α and β subunits and around 100 amino acids in size.
mm. _____ Glands located just above the kidney that are composed of the adrenal medulla and the adrenal cortex.
nn. _____ DNA sequence found in promoters that bind hormone-receptor complexes to activate or inhibit gene expression.
oo. _____ Proteins that act as paracrine regulators to promote growth and cell division in specific organs.
pp. _____ The fibrous portion of the pituitary gland that stores and releases antidiuretic hormone and oxytocin.
qq. _____ Chemical molecules that are released and act within an organ as local regulators.

LEARNING BY EXPERIENCE

1. Hormones that have opposite effects are called antagonistic. Arrange the following six hormones into their proper antagonistic pairs and indicate what physiological parameter the pair regulates: calcitonin, aldosterone, glucagon, parathyroid hormone, insulin, atrial natriuretic hormone.

Pairs	Regulates
a.	
b.	
c.	

2. Complete the following table about the endocrine system by filling in the blanks with the appropriate term.

Hormone	Where Produced	Function
Thyroxine	a. _____	Increase metabolic rate
ACTH	b. _____	c. _____
d. _____	e. _____	Stimulate uterine contractions, milk ejection
Insulin	f. _____	g. _____

3. Diagram the hormonal chain of command by using the following terms to fill in the blanks below. Each blank should contain the name of the organ and the hormone it produces. Terms: anterior pituitary, hypothalamus, luteinizing hormone (LH), ovary, progesterone, gonadotropin-releasing hormone (GnRH).

Chain of command:

a. _____ → b. _____ → c. _____

EXERCISING YOUR KNOWLEDGE

Briefly answer each of the following questions in the space provided.

1. Compare and contrast neurotransmitters and hormones in terms of where they are produced and how they function.

2. Compare and contrast paracrine regulators and pheromones in terms of how they function.

3. Why can't water-soluble hormones enter cells?

4. In the two-messenger system of hormone action, where are the two messengers located, and what are their basic functions?

5. Why does epinephrine have such diverse effects on different tissues of the body?

6. What do the anterior and posterior pituitary have in common? What is different about them?

7. Many of the symptoms of a hangover are caused by dehydration. Why?

8. Why is negative feedback, rather than positive feedback, used to control the hypothalamus and anterior pituitary?

9. People with diabetes have high levels of glucose in their blood. People with hypoglycemia have the opposite problem – low blood glucose levels. Besides fasting, what else might cause hypoglycemia, and why can it be a serious problem?

10. Why can some hormones be taken orally (for example, female sex hormones in contraceptive pills), but other hormones must be injected (for example, insulin) to be effective?

Circle the letter of the one best answer in each of the following questions.

11. Insulin and ADH are examples of
    a. steroid hormones.
    b. amine hormones.
    c. polypeptide hormones.
    d. glycoproteins.
    e. pheromones.

12. Norepinephrine is a
    a. neurotransmitter.
    b. hormone.
    c. both of these
    d. neither of these

13. Which of the following statements about prostaglandins is true?
    a. Aspirin promotes the production of prostaglandins.
    b. Prostaglandins are produced only by endocrine glands.
    c. Prostaglandins travel in the circulatory system to reach their target cells.
    d. All of these are true.
    e. None of these are true.

14. Cytokines
    a. regulate different cells of the immune system.
    b. promote growth and cell division in specific organs.
    c. help maintain proper mineral balance in the body.
    d. help maintain proper water balance in the body.
    e. regulate reproductive cycles.

15. Which of the following types of hormones enter their target cells?
    a. polypeptide hormones
    b. steroid hormones
    c. glycoprotein hormones
    d. all of these
    e. none of these

16. Lipophilic hormones
    a. are able to enter their target cells.
    b. are lipid soluble.
    c. attach to protein receptors and DNA.
    d. All of these are correct.
    e. None of these are correct.

17. In the two-messenger system of hormone activity, what is the first messenger?
    a. the endocrine gland
    b. the hormone
    c. DNA
    d. a receptor protein on the target cell's plasma membrane
    e. cyclic AMP

18. Which endocrine gland develops from an outgrowth of the epithelium lining the roof of the mouth?
    a. anterior pituitary
    b. posterior pituitary
    c. pineal gland
    d. hypothalamus
    e. thymus

19. Releasing hormones are produced by
    a. various endocrine glands.
    b. the anterior pituitary.
    c. the posterior pituitary.
    d. the pineal gland.
    e. the hypothalamus.

20. Releasing hormones directly affect
    a. various target organs.
    b. the anterior pituitary.
    c. the posterior pituitary.
    d. the pineal gland.
    e. the hypothalamus.

21. Which of the following hormones has no known function in mammals?
    a. GnRH
    b. PRL
    c. MSH
    d. calcitonin
    e. oxytocin

22. ADH and oxytocin are produced by the
    a. hypothalamus.
    b. posterior pituitary.
    c. anterior pituitary.
    d. adrenal cortex.
    e. adrenal medulla.

23. If your ADH levels are really high, your urine will be
    a. very dilute.
    b. very concentrated.
    c. alcoholic.

24. Robert Wadlow grew to a gigantic size because of a tumor in his
    a. thyroid gland.
    b. adrenal cortex.
    c. adrenal medulla.
    d. anterior pituitary.
    e. posterior pituitary.

25. The target organ(s) for luteinizing hormone is(are) the
    a. liver.
    b. kidneys.
    c. bones.
    d. Pancreas.
    e. gonads.

26. A portal system connects the
    a. anterior and posterior pituitary glands.
    b. anterior pituitary and the hypothalamus.
    c. posterior pituitary and the hypothalamus.
    d. thyroid and parathyroid glands.
    e. adrenal cortex and the adrenal medulla.

27. According to the text, which two hormones are most essential for your survival?
    a. estrogen and testosterone
    b. calcitonin and insulin
    c. parathyroid hormone and aldosterone
    d. somatotropin and cortisol
    e. ADH and thyroxine

28. Type I diabetes is caused by a deficiency of
    a. exercise.
    b. glucagon.
    c. glucose.
    d. glycogen.
    e. insulin.

29. In an insect that is about to undergo metamorphosis, what levels of juvenile hormone and ecdysone would you expect to find?
    a. low juvenile, low ecdysone
    b. high juvenile, high ecdysone
    c. high juvenile, low ecdysone
    d. low juvenile, high ecdysone
    e. You would not find any hormones in an insect.

30. Which of the following pairs is properly matched?
    a. insulin – produced by the beta cells of the islets of Langerhans in the pancreas
    b. aldosterone – produced by the adrenal medulla
    c. parathyroid hormone – regulates Na^+ and K^+ levels in the blood
    d. calcitonin – stimulates oxidative respiration
    e. melatonin – produced by the thymus

ASSESSING YOUR KNOWLEDGE

Answers to the questions in this section test your ability to synthesize information gained from the chapter and to solve challenging problems on an exam or in everyday life.

Challenging Your Understanding—Answers

1. a. testis, b. adenohypophysis, c. hypothalamus, d. ovary, e. parathyroid gland, f. adrenal medulla, g. adrenal cortex, h. adenohypophysis, i. thyroid gland, j. pancreas, k. ovary, l. pineal gland, m. hypothalamus, n. adenohypophysis, o. adenohypophysis.

2.
Peptides	Proteins	Amino acid derivatives	Steroids
insulin	growth hormone	adrenaline	testosterone
parathyroid hormone	prolactin	melatonin	progesterone
oxytocin			estradiol
glucagon			glucocorticoids
inhibiting hormones			
antidiuretic hormone			
releasing hormones			

3.

Hypothalamus $\longrightarrow$ Adenohypophysis $\longrightarrow$ Blood vessels $\longrightarrow$ Bone tissue $\longrightarrow$ Bone Growth
  (Releasing hormone)   (Growth Hormone)   (Growth Hormone)

Key Terms—Answers

a. 17, b. 40, c. 11, d. 32, e. 28, f. 2, g. 41, h. 13, i. 36, j. 24, k. 7, l. 22, m. 38, n. 19, o. 5, p. 27, q. 35, r. 9, s. 30, t. 12, u. 39, v. 1, w. 23, x. 10, y. 43, z. 25, aa. 6, bb. 18, cc. 33, dd. 42, ee. 15, ff. 37, gg. 3, hh. 29, ii. 14, jj. 34, kk. 21, ll. 8, mm. 26, nn. 20, oo. 16, pp. 31, qq. 4.

Learning by Experience—Answers

1. **Pairs**	**Regulates**
a. calcitonin and parathyroid hormone	calcium levels in blood
b. aldosterone and atrial natriuretic hormone	retention of salt and water
c. glucagon and insulin	glucose levels in blood.

2. a. thyroid gland
   b. anterior pituitary
   c. stimulate production of adrenal cortex hormones
   d. oxytocin
   e. hypothalamus
   f. beta cells in islets of Langerhans in pancreas
   g. decrease blood glucose levels

3. a. hypothalamus, GnRH
   b. anterior pituitary, LH
   c. ovary, progesterone.

Exercising Your Knowledge—Answers

As you check your answers, put a mark in the review (Rvw.) column for the answers you missed. If you didn't miss any, congratulations—you have mastered the chapter! If you missed some, review the section (Sect.) in the text where this concept is discussed. In order to develop an efficient review strategy, it is important that you understand what types of questions you missed. The questions with asterisks test more for understanding of the **concepts**, whereas the others test more for **detail**. *See the preface for learning strategies for concepts and for detail.*

	Sect.	Rvw.
*1. Both are chemical messengers that regulate body activities, but hormones are produced by endocrine glands, transported all around the body in the circulatory system, and have their impact when they reach their specific target cells. Neurotransmitters are released at the ends of axons, diffuse across the tiny synaptic cleft, and have an impact on the next cell.	46.1	
*2. Both are chemical messengers, but paracrines have their impact within the organ that produces them, while pheromones have their impact outside the organism's body—that is, the target of the message is another organism.	46.1	
*3. A cell membrane with its double layer of phospholipid molecules prevents hydrophilic, polar molecules from passing through.	46.1	

*4. The first messenger is on the outer surface of the target cell membrane. When the hormone binds to it, the second messenger is activated. The second messenger is inside the cell membrane and causes a chain reaction of chemical events, which results in the final action of the hormone (for example, converting glycogen to glucose).	46.2	
*5. Epinephrine can bind to two different categories of first messenger receptors, and in different target cells, different cellular proteins are involved in the chain reaction of chemical events initiated by the second messenger.	46.2	
*6. The anterior and posterior pituitary share a common location below the hypothalamus and are connected to each other. Both are endocrine glands, but they have different embryological origins, secrete different hormones, and are regulated by different control systems.	46.3	
*7. Alcohol inhibits the secretion of ADH. With less ADH being produced, less water is reabsorbed in the kidneys, and much more dilute urine is produced. The person becomes dehydrated due to loss of so much water in the urine.	46.3	
*8. Negative feedback allows the body to maintain homeostasis (relatively constant internal conditions). Positive feedback would accentuate changes; negative feedback works so that if a change occurs in one direction (for example, concentration of some substance in the blood increases), something else happens to cause a change in the opposite direction (for example, to decrease the concentration) so that the concentration stays relatively constant. With positive feedback, a change in one direction (for example, increased concentration) would cause further change in the same direction (for example, even more increase in concentration).	46.3	
*9. Hypoglycemia can be caused when overactive beta cells in the islets of Langerhans in the pancreas secrete too much insulin, which decreases glucose levels. It could also be caused by underactive alpha cells in the islets of Langerhans secreting too little glucagon, which increases glucose levels. Hypoglycemia can be serious because glucose is the main fuel source for cells—that is, the oxidation of glucose provides the ATP necessary to keep cells running.	46.4	
*10. Only the nonpolar, lipophilic hormones (i.e., thyroxine and steroid hormones) can be taken orally. They can pass through the plasma membrane of cells lining the digestive tract and get into the circulatory system before being digested. The hydrophilic hormones cannot pass through plasma membranes, and so are digested.	46.2	

11. c	46.3	
12. c	46.1	
*13. e	46.1	
14. a	46.1	
*15. b	46.2	
*16. d	46.2	
17. b	46.2	
18. a	46.3	
19. e	46.3	
20. b	46.3	
21. c	46.3	
22. a	46.3	
*23. b	46.3	
24. d	46.3	
25. e	46.3	
26. b	46.3	
27. c	46.4	
28. e	46.4	
*29. d	46.5	
30. a	46.4	

CHAPTER 47 THE MUSCULOSKELETAL SYSTEM

MASTERING KEY CONCEPTS

Locomotion is a good example of how cells, tissues, organs, and organ systems work together. All animal locomotion follows the same basic principle: muscles contract and work against an internal or external skeleton, which results in movement. The microscopic anatomy and physiology of vertebrate skeletal muscles results in contractions that can generate significant force.

47.1 Muscles push against the skeletal systems of animals to allow movement.

- **Overview**: **Hydrostatic skeletons**, **exoskeletons**, and **endoskeletons** are the three types of skeletal systems found in animals. Hydrostatic skeletons are primarily found in soft-bodied invertebrates, such as the earthworm, jellyfish, squid, and octupus. The body of an earthworm contains a fluid-filled central cavity surrounded by walls containing circular and longitudinal muscles. Opposing actions of the circular muscles pushing on the fluid-filled cavity and the longitudinal muscles allow an earthworm to contract and then stretch resulting in movement. Jellyfish "jet" through the production of pulsations in the contractile fibers of their bells that press out some of the water beneath it. Squids take in fluid from the environment and use muscle contractions to force it back out, propelling the animal through the water. This type of locomotion is called jet-swimming. Arthropods have muscles attached to exoskeletons that are composed of **chitin**. Vertebrates and echinoderms have endoskeletons that like hydrostatic skeletons and exoskeletons provide protection for organs, body support, and surfaces for muscle attachment. Vertebrate endoskeletons are divided into **axial** and **appendicular regions**, and are composed of bone, cartilage, and dense connective tissue.
- **Details**: Know how earthworms, jellyfish, and squid move. Know the disadvantages of an exoskeleton. Know the composition of a vertebrate endoskeleton. Understand what structures make up the axial and appendicular skeletons.

47.2 Bone is a hard, resilient tissue unique to vertebrate animals.

- **Overview**: **Bones** develop either by **intramembranous development** in which they form within a layer of connective tissue, or by **endochondral development,** which involves adding bone to the outside of a cartilaginous model and then replacing the interior with bone. Bone is made by **osteoblasts** that secrete alkaline phosphatase to form **hydroxyapatite**, but it consists of equal volumes of hydroxyapatite and collagen. As bone grows, it is remodeled by **osteoclasts** that breakdown the bone matrix. In mammals, endochondral bones retain blood vessels (**vascular bone**) and can contain **osteocytes**, but in fishes and birds, bones are **avascular** and metabolically inactive. In vertebrates, **bone marrow** is contained in the central cavity (**medullary cavity**) of endochondral bones, but in birds, this cavity remains empty allowing their bones to be light weight. Frequent outside force can cause bone **remodeling** to occur resulting in thickening, changes in surface features, or changes in the direction of bone struts.
- **Details**: Know the cells involved in bone development, how bone is made, and how it can change shape. Understand how bone thickness and the bone length are increased. Know the three categories of bones based on density and texture.

47.3 Bones meet each other at joints that respond to muscular action to allow movement.

- **Overview**: There are three main types of joints: **immovable**, **slightly movable**, and **freely movable** that are used to respond to muscular action and allow movement. The four basic joint movement patterns are **ball-and-socket**, **hinge**, **gliding**, and a **combination,** which determine the range of motion of different parts of the body. Muscle fibers are attached to bones either directly by the fibrous bone covering (**periosteum**), or as a dense connective tissue cord attached to the periosteum (**tendon**). When a muscle contracts, one end remains stationary (**the origin**), while the other end (**the insertion**) is attached to a bone that moves. Muscles are arranged in mutually **antagonistic** groups such that any movement produced by one can be reversed by another.
- **Details**: Know the three types of joints and an example of each. Understand the four basic joint movement patterns. Recognize why muscles are mutually antagonistic and how they allow joints to move.

47.4 Muscle contraction involves the sliding of action of myosin and actin filaments.

- **Overview**: Muscle fibers are made up of **myofibrils** that are composed of **myofilaments**. A **sarcomere** is the smallest subunit of a muscle contraction that consists of a repeating structure of myofibrils in between two **Z lines**. When a muscle contracts, the myofilaments slide relative to one another. The thin filaments, consisting of globular **actin**, slide deeper into the **A bands**, and the **H** and **I bands** become narrower (**sliding** filament mechanism). The thick filaments are composed of **myosin** and have a filament and a head region. The heads on the two ends of the thick filaments form **cross-bridges** that extend from the thick to the thin filaments and are oriented in opposite directions. When a muscle contracts, cross-bridges pull the thin filaments toward the center causing the filaments to slide against each other. In the relaxed state, the myosin heads are blocked from binding to actin by **tropomyosin**. Tropomyosin is displaced by Ca^{2+} binding to **troponin**, exposing the myosin-binding sites on actin. This allows cross-bridges between the thick and the thin filaments to form and contraction to occur. Muscles are stimulated to contract by somatic motor neurons whose axons branch to make synapses with muscle fibers (neuromuscular junctions). These neurons release acetylcholine causing an influx of Na^+ in muscle cells and depolarization. This impulse is carried down and into the muscle fibers, stimulating the release of Ca^{2+} and displacing tropomyosin. Skeletal muscles can be either slow or fast twitch. **Slow-twitch** fibers can sustain action for long periods of time; **fast-twitch** fibers can rapidly generate power but can not sustain it.

- **Details**: Know the structures of sarcomeres in relaxed and contracted muscle. Recognize the A bands, I bands, H bands, and Z lines in each. Know what the thick and thin filaments are composed of, how they interact, and what happens when a muscle contracts. Know what causes **rigor mortis**. Understand why Ca^{2+} is so important to muscles and how Ca^{2+} is released from the **sarcoplasmic reticulum**. Know how a somatic motor neuron stimulates muscle contraction. Know the difference between slow-, and fast-twitching muscle fibers, and the factors that can cause **muscle fatigue**.

47.5 Muscle contraction powers animal locomotion.

- **Overview**: Active locomotion in animals is produced either by appendages that oscillate (**appendicular locomotion**), or bodies that undulate, pulse, or undergo peristaltic waves (**axial locomotion**). Aquatic invertebrates move along the bottom of water-covered surfaces using the same methods employed by terrestrial invertebrates or by hydraulic propulsion, whereas aquatic vertebrates swim. Mollusks move by secreting mucus that they glide along using a muscular foot to push themselves. Arthropods and vertebrates have jointed appendages and legs for support and locomotion. An increased number of legs in arthropods makes them more stable but slower moving than vertebrates who are tetrapods. Flying organisms create lift due to lower pressure on top of the wing than on the bottom of the wing as a result of air moving faster over the top surface.

- **Details**: Know the different mechanisms of locomotion in aquatic and terrestrial animals. Understand the similarities and differences in locomotion among arthropods and vertebrates. Understand how some organisms can fly.

CHALLENGING YOUR UNDERSTANDING

1. Draw a flowchart that depicts how a somatic motor neuron stimulates a muscle fiber to contract.

2. Classify each of the following organisms by which type of skeleton it possesses:

   earthworm, human, jellyfish, cat, grasshopper, beetle, squid, slug, octopus, fish, starfish, lobster, eagle.

   <u>Hydrostatic skeleton</u>　　　　　　　<u>Exoskeleton</u>　　　　　　　<u>Endoskeleton</u>

3. Indicate how the following exercise regimens affect fast-twitch muscle fibers.

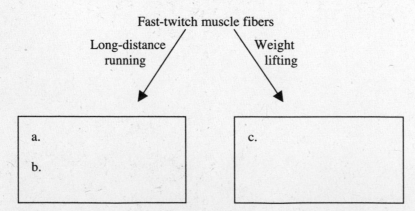

KEY TERMS

Match the numbered term with the definition that fits it best. Put the corresponding number in front of the appropriate definition.

1. hydrostatic skeleton
2. exoskeleton
3. endoskeleton
4. origin
5. agonist
6. antagonist
7. isotonic contraction
8. isometric contraction
9. axial skeleton
10. appendicular skeleton
11. osteoblasts
12. osteocytes
13. osteoclasts
14. periosteum
15. vascular bone
16. medullary cavity

17. intramembranous development
18. endochondral development
19. muscle fibers
20. myofibrils
21. myofilaments
22. sarcomere
23. sliding filament mechanism
24. cross-bridges
25. myosin
26. actin
27. cross-bridge cycle
28. tropomyosin
29. troponin
30. transverse tubules

31. excitation-contraction coupling
32. motor unit
33. tetanus
34. slow-twitch fibers
35. fast-twitch fibers
36. summation
37. myoglobin
38. muscle fatigue
39. hypertrophy
40. A bands
41. H bands
42. I bands
43. Z lines

a. _____ The repeating structure of a myofibril from Z line to Z line that is the smallest subunit of muscle contraction.

b. _____ The attachment of a muscle that remains relatively stationary during a contraction.

c. _____ Invaginations of the cell membrane of muscle fibers whose depolarization causes Ca^{2+} to be released.

d. _____ The thick and thin filaments that compose each myofibril.

e. _____ A protein that blocks the myosin-binding sites on the actin molecule in the relaxed state.

f. _____ A muscle contraction in which the length of the muscle does not change as force is exerted.

g. _____ A type of development where bones form within a layer of connective tissue.

h. _____ Growth by increased cell size, rather than by an increased number of cells.

i. _____ A mature osteoblast formed by cells undergoing dramatic changes in shape and function.

j. _____ Muscle fibers that are adapted to respire anaerobically for the rapid generation of power, but lack endurance.

k. _____ A set of limb bones and their associated pectoral girdle or pelvic girdle.

l. _____ A muscle group in action.

m. _____ The muscles that counter a muscle group in action.

n. _____ Structures that extend from the thick to the thin filaments in muscle fibers.

o. _____ A regulatory protein complex that holds tropomyosin and actin together.

p. _____ The use-dependent decrease in the ability of a muscle to generate force.

q. _____ A skeleton that surrounds the body as a rigid, hard case.

r. _____ The set of muscle fibers innervated by all the axonal branches of a motor neuron and the motor neuron itself.

s. _____ A bundle of 4 to 20 elongated structures that are enclosed in a muscle fiber.

t. _____ A muscle contraction in which the force remains relatively constant throughout the shortening process.

u. _____ A cummulative response in which a second twitch may partially "ride piggyback" on the first twitch.

v. _____ The release of Ca^{2+} that links excitation of a muscle fiber by a motor neuron to contraction of the muscle.

w. _____ A central cavity in bones that houses the bone marrow in vertebrates but is empty in light-boned birds.

x. _____ A series of events that convert the chemical energy in ATP into mechanical energy by motor proteins.

y. _____ A sustained contraction with no visible relaxation between successive twitches in a stimulated muscle.

z. _____ Rigid internal skeletons that form the body's framework in vertebrates and echinoderms.

aa. _____ Specialized cells that secrete the enzyme alkaline phosphatase causing hydroxyapatite to form in bone.

bb. _____ Disks of protein that divide each I band in a myofibril in half and are located on both sides of a sarcomere.

cc. _____ Dark bands in a myofibril formed by thick myofilaments stacked together.

dd. _____ The center of an A band that is ligher than the areas on each side.

ee. _____ The thin filaments alone found in light bands in a myofibril.

ff. _____ Bones that form the axis of the body including the skull and tail, the vertebrae, ribs, and sternum.

gg. _____ Bones that retain internal blood vessels.

hh. _____ The skeleton of most soft-bodied invertebrates based on the incompressibility of an internal fluid-filled cavity.

ii. _____ A type of bone development in which bone is added to the outside of a cartilaginous model.

jj. _____ Contraction in which the thin filaments slide deeper into the A bands, making the H and I bands narrower.

kk. _____ Muscle fibers that can sustain action for a long period of time without fatigue.

ll. _____ The fibrous bone covering.

mm. _____ One of two major proteins that make up vertebrate muscle; this protein makes up the thin filaments of myofibrils.

nn. _____ A long, cylindrical, multinucleated cell containing numerous myofibrils, capable of contraction when stimulated.

oo. _____ A red pigment with a high affinity for oxygen that improves the delivery of oxygen to the slow-twitch fibers.

pp. _____ One of two major proteins that make up vertebrate muscle; a protein that makes up myofibril thick filaments.

qq. _____ Cells formed by the fusion of monocytes whose function is to break down the bone matrix.

LEARNING BY EXPERIENCE

1. There are many levels of organization in a skeletal muscle. Arrange the following terms in proper order, going from largest structure to smallest.

Terms	Order
actin filament	
muscle fibers (cells)	
myofibrils	
myofilaments	
myosin filament	
sarcomeres	
skeletal muscle	

2. Label the actin filament, myosin filament, myosin head, and Z line on the sarcomere below.

a. _____

b. _____

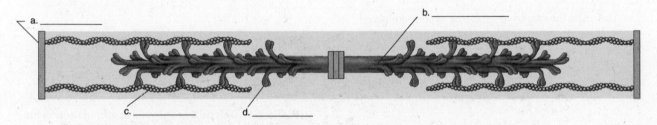

c. _____

d. _____

3. The sarcomere illustrated in the previous question is at rest. Sketch what it would look like if it were contracted.

4. Label the A band, H band, I band, and Z line on the sarcomere below.

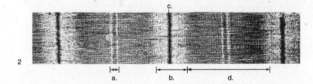

c.

a. b. d.

EXERCISING YOUR KNOWLEDGE

Briefly answer each of the following questions in the space provided.

1. Compare and contrast "jetting" in jellyfish with jet-swimming in the squid.

2. What are the advantages and disadvantages of an exoskeleton?

3. Describe the negative feedback system involved in bone remodeling due to large compressive forces.

4. (a) How do endochondral bones thicken?
   (b) How do endochondral bones increase in length?

5. Identify the four joint movement patterns, describe the movement that each allows, and give an example of each.

6. Describe two ways that skeletal muscles are attached to bone.

7. Describe the series of events that occur in the cross-bridge cycle.

8. Describe the major differences between slow-twitch and fast-twitch muscle fibers.

9. What causes rigor mortis?

10. Each muscle fiber responds to stimulation in an all-or-none fashion. How, then, can you control the strength of a muscle contraction (for example, when picking up a pencil versus picking up a 6-lb book)?

Circle the letter of the one best answer in each of the following questions.

11. Chitin is the primary material in
    a. hydrostatic skeletons.
    b. exoskeletons.
    c. endoskeletons.
    d. appendicular skeletons.
    e. axial skeletons.

12. Which of the following is NOT part of the appendicular skeleton?
    a. scapula
    b. pelvic girdle
    c. rib cage
    d. humerus
    e. none of the above

13. Fibroblasts produce which of the following?
    a. collagen
    b. osteocytes
    c. epithelium
    d. chondrocytes
    e. osteoclasts

14. Osteoblasts are found in which of the following?
    a. lacunae
    b. periosteum
    c. medullary cavity
    d. Haversian lamellae
    e. canaliculi

15. Which of the following contribute to a bone's strength?
    a. medullary and compact bone
    b. compact bone alone
    c. compact and spongy bone
    d. medullary bone alone
    e. medullary and spongy bone

16. Movement of the leg quadriceps muscle is countered by which of the following?
    a. an extensor muscle
    b. a flexor muscle
    c. a tendon
    d. a ligament
    e. a smooth muscle

17. Which of the following is NOT a true statement about isotonic or isometric contractions?
    a. Isotonic contractions are important for supporting objects in a fixed position.
    b. Both isotonic and isometric contractions expend energy.
    c. If the force produced by a muscle is greater than the force of gravity on an object, an isotonic contraction is produced.
    d. Most movement involves both isotonic and isometric contractions.
    e. The maintenance of posture depends on isometric contractions.

18. When a skeletal muscle contracts, which bone moves?
    a. the bone attached to the insertion end of the muscle
    b. the bone attached to the origin end of the muscle
    c. any bone attached anywhere to the muscle
    d. none; muscles can't move bones

19. Freely movable joints are also called
    a. sutures.
    b. cartilaginous joints.
    c. synovial joints.
    d. cross-bridges.
    e. sarcomeres.

20. During a muscle contraction, which of the following shortens?
    a. sarcomeres
    b. A bands
    c. actin and myosin filaments
    d. all of these
    e. none of these

21. Cross-bridges are made of
    a. troponin.
    b. tropomyosin.
    c. myoglobin.
    d. myosin.
    e. actin.

22. During muscle contractions, calcium ions bind to
    a. myosin.
    b. actin.
    c. troponin.
    d. tropomyosin.
    e. acetylcholine.

23. Which of the following is a requirement for coordinated movements?
    a. a short relaxation time between successive muscle twitches
    b. the division of muscle into motor units
    c. slow- and fast-twitch fibers
    d. summation of muscle twitches
    e. none of the above

24. Skeletal muscles at rest obtain most of their energy from which of the following?
    a. anaerobic respiration
    b. lactic acid fermentation
    c. aerobic respiration of fatty acids
    d. stores of glucose delivered by the blood
    e. none of the above

25. When a somatic motor neuron delivers electrochemical impulses to stimulate the contraction of muscle fibers, it releases which of the following?
    a. norepinephrine
    b. dopamine
    c. glumate
    d. acetylcholine
    e. endorphins

26. Muscle fibers store Ca^{2+} in which of the following?
    a. transverse tubules
    b. sarcolemma
    c. muscle cell membranes
    d. canaliculi
    e. sarcoplasmic reticulum

27. In longer-term, lower intensity exertion, fatigue appears to result from which of the following?
    a. buildup of inorganic phosphate
    b. aerobic capacity
    c. buildup of lactic acid
    d. depletion of muscle glycogen
    e. none of the above

28. Which of the following does NOT change in size when muscle fibers contract?
    a. the distance between Z lines
    b. the I bands
    c. the H bands
    d. the A bands
    e. more than one of the above

29. A stronger muscle contraction is produced by which of the following?
    a. neurons with fewer muscle fibers
    b. action potentials with greater amplitudes
    c. a cumulative increase in the size and number of motor units
    d. slow- and fast-twitch muscle fibers working together
    e. none of the above

30. Because they have more legs than vertebrates, arthropods
    a. are incapable of walking.
    b. have less stability and greater speed during locomotion.
    c. have less stability and slower speed during locomotion.
    d. have more stability and greater speed during locomotion.
    e. have more stability and slower speed during locomotion.

ASSESSING YOUR KNOWLEDGE

Answers to the questions in this section test your ability to synthesize information gained from the chapter and to solve challenging problems on an exam or in everyday life.

Challenging Your Understanding—Answers

1. motor neuron release of ACh

    ▼

    opening of Na$^+$ channels in muscle

    ▼

    depolarization of muscle cell

    ▼

    depolarization spreads through T tubules

    ▼

    Ca^{+2} is released from sarcoplasmic reticulum

    ▼

    Ca^{+2} removes Troponin from actin filaments

    ▼

    actin and myosin filaments interact and slide

2. Hydrostatic skeleton
    earthworm, jellyfish, squid, slug, octopus
    Exoskeleton
    grasshopper, beetle, starfish, lobster
    Endoskeleton
    human, cat, fish, eagle

3. a. Increased number of fibers with high oxidative
    capacity
    b. Increased vascularization
    c. Increased size of muscle cells due to
    hypertrophic growth

Key Terms—Answers

a. 22, b. 4, c. 30, d. 21, e. 28, f. 8, g. 17, h. 39, i. 12,
j. 35, k. 10, l. 5, m. 6, n. 24, o. 29, p. 38, q. 2, r. 32,
s. 20, t. 7, u. 36, v. 31, w. 16, x. 27, y. 33, z. 3,
aa. 11, bb. 43, cc. 40, dd. 41, ee. 42, ff. 9, gg. 15,
hh. 1, ii. 18, jj. 23, kk. 34, ll. 14, mm. 26, nn. 19,
oo. 37, pp. 25, qq. 13.

Learning by Experience—Answers

1.	skeletal muscle → muscle fibers (cells) → myofibrils → sarcomeres → myofilaments → myosin → actin
2.	a. Z line b. myosin filament c. actin filament d. myosin head

3.

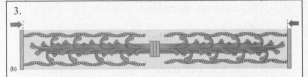

Note: The overall length of the sarcomere has decreased so that the unattached ends of the actin filaments are closer to each other, and the ends of the myosin filament are closer to the Z line, but the length of the actin and myosin filaments has not changed.

4. a. II band
    b. I band
    c. Z line
    d. A band

Exercising Your Knowledge—Answers

As you check your answers, put a mark in the review (Rvw.) column for the answers you missed. If you didn't miss any, congratulations—you have mastered the chapter! If you missed some, review the section (Sect.) in the text where this concept is discussed. In order to develop an efficient review strategy, it is important that you understand what types of questions you missed. The questions with asterisks test more for understanding of the **concepts**, whereas the others test more for **detail**. *See the preface for learning strategies for concepts and for detail.*

	Sect.	Rvw.
*1. In jellyfish "jetting," contractile fibers at the edge of the bell pulsate, squeezing together the mesoglea and expelling water out from under the bell, to propel the jellyfish gently forward. Squids also use fluid from the environment in jet-swimming. Seawater fills the mantle cavity and is expelled forcibly out through the siphon by the contraction of circular muscles in the mantle walls. The propulsion produced is much stronger than the jetting action of the jellyfish and the squid is propelled backward.	47.1	
*2. Advantages: Strong and stiff, good protection for internal organs and against predators. Disadvantages: Animal must molt in order to grow; vulnerable while molting; exoskeleton also limits overall size of animal — would need to have very thick, heavy exoskeleton to be strong enough for a large-sized animal; would be so thick and heavy, animal wouldn't be able to move.	47.1	
*3. Under a large compressive force, a bone will bend because it is not thick enough to withstand the pressure. This stress stimulates osteoblasts in the bent section of the bone to produce additional bone. As the bone becomes thicker, the degree of bending is reduced. More bone is added until significant bending is entirely prevented. At this time, the production of new osteoblasts stops due to negative feedback that indicates that the bone is not bending anymore.	47.2	

*4. (a) Growth in bone thickness of endochondral bones occurs by the addition of bone layers just beneath the periosteum and the medullary cavity is hollowed out by osteoclasts. (b) To increase in length, cartilage of the epiphyseal growth plates actively grows lengthwise to increase the thickness of the plate. This pushes the widened ends of the bone (epiphysis) farther away from the shaft and increases the length of the bone. Cartilage calcification from the side of the shaft creeps in on the cartilaginous growth plate so the bony portion of the shaft elongates. As long as the rate of cartilaginous expansion is greater than the rate of encroaching calcification, the bone continues to grow in length.	47.2	
*5. The four joint movement patterns are ball-and-socket, hinge, gliding, and combination. Ball-and-socket joints permit universal movements in all directions and twisting of the ball in the socket. An example is the hip joint. Hinge joints allow movement in only one plane, either forward and backward rotation, or rotation side-to-side, but not both. An example is the knee joint. Gliding joints permit sliding of one surface on another. An example is the lateral vertebral projections. Combination joints allow movements characteristic of more than one joint type, such as rotation and side-to-side movement. An example is the mammalian jaw joint.	47.3	
*6. Muscle fibers can be connected directly to the periosteum or outer covering of bones, or connective tissue sheets within skeletal muscle may join together to form a tendon that connects the aggregation of muscle fibers to a bone's periosteum.	47.3	
*7. In the cross-bridge cycle of muscle contraction, myosin converts the chemical energy in ATP into mechanical energy. To do so, the myosin heads hydrolyze ATP to ADP + P_i and undergo a conformational change that moves them into an energized state. With ADP and P_i bound to the myosin head, it is kept in an activated conformation. In this conformation, the myosin heads can bind to actin to form cross-bridges. Actin binding releases ADP and P_i and causes another conformational change in myosin that pulls the thin actin filament toward the center of the sarcomere in a power stroke. ATP then binds to the myosin heads again, breaking the cross-bridge and releasing actin. If the muscle is still stimulated to contract, the cycle repeats.	47.4	

*8. Slow-twitch fibers have a rich capillary supply, numerous mitochondria, aerobic respiratory enzymes, and a high concentration of myoglobin. These fibers can sustain action for long periods of time without fatigue. Fast-twitch fibers are just the opposite. They have fewer capillaries, mitochondria, and myoglobin and are adapted to respire anaerobically. These fibers are used for the rapid generation of power, but lack the endurance characteristics of slow-twitch fibers.	47.4	
*9. When an organism dies, the cells no longer produce ATP. Without ATP, the myosin head cross-bridges cannot let go of the actin filament, and the muscle can't relax.	47.4	
*10. Muscle fibers are arranged in motor units. All the fibers in one unit are innervated by one motor neuron. Different motor units have different numbers of fibers in them. The strength of a contraction is determined by the size and number of motor units involved.	47.4	
11. b	47.1	
12. c	47.1	
*13. a	47.2	
14. b	47.2	
*15. c	47.2	
*16. b	47.3	
*17. a	47.3	
*18. a	47.3	
19. c	47.3	
*20. a	47.4	
21. d	47.4	
22. c	47.4	
*23. b	47.4	
*24. c	47.4	
*25. d	47.4	
*26. e	47.4	
*27. d	47.4	
*28. d	47.4	
*29. c	47.4	
30. e	47.5	

CHAPTER 48 THE DIGESTIVE SYSTEM

MASTERING KEY CONCEPTS

All organisms require energy to live and carry out their life functions. Heterotrophs must obtain their energy by eating other organisms. Vertebrates have evolved highly efficient digestive systems to process their food. Our digestive systems process food (fuel) and make it available to be utilized by our cells. In processing food, the digestive system also provides the necessary raw materials for making new macromolecules, cells, and tissues.

48.1 Digestive systems can consist of a simple gastrovascular cavity or be more specialized.

- **Overview**: Heterotrophs are divided into **herbivores** (plant eaters), **carnivores** (meat eaters), or **omnivores** (plant and meat eaters). Food must be broken down mechanically and chemically before it can be used by an animal. Single-celled organisms and sponges digest food intracellularly, but most animals digest their food extracellularly in a digestive tract. This tract can have one opening to the outside like that found in cnidarians and flatworms, or two openings, a **mouth** and an **anus**, in organisms with specialized digestive tracts, such as nematodes, earthworms, and vertebrates. Specialized tracts allow ingestion, storage, mechanical fragmentation, chemical digestion, and absorption to occur in different regions. Molecules that cannot be absorbed are excreted through the anus. In the human digestive system, food passes from the mouth to the **pharynx**, to the **esophagus**, and into the **stomach** and the **small intestine**, where digestion occurs. What can not be absorbed through the epithelial lining of the gut, passes to the **large intestine** where material is separated for secretion. The **liver**, **gallbladder**, and **pancreas** play accessory roles in digestion by secreting **bile**, storing bile, or producing pancreatic juice, respectively.
- **Details**: Know the path that food follows in the digestive tract in humans. Know the tissues of the digestive tract. Recognize the differences between the digestive tracts of herbivores and carnivores.

48.2 The mouth and teeth are required for capturing food and bulk processing.

- **Overview**: The digestive systems of different organisms are specialized for different modes of digestion. Some organisms mechanically fragment their food using **teeth**, while birds store their food in a **crop** and then grind and churn it in a muscular **gizzard** to break it down. The shape of teeth located in different parts of the mouth varies depending on whether the animal is a herbivore, carnivore, or omnivore. The **salivary glands** in the mouth of humans secrete **saliva** at a constant rate when food is not present, and at an increased rate when food can be seen, smelled, or is being talked about. **Swallowing** is initiated voluntarily by moving food to the back of the mouth, but pressure against the pharynx triggers the **swallowing reflex,** which is involuntary, to move food into the esophagus.
- **Details**: Know how the digestive organs of birds differ from those found in other vertebrates. Know how the patterns of dentition vary in herbivores, carnivores, and omnivores. Understand how swallowing occurs.

48.3 Digestion begins as food travels from the esophagus to the stomach.

- **Overview**: Swallowed food enters the esophagus, which undergoes **peristaltic** waves of muscular contraction to move it into the stomach. Food is mixed with **gastric juice** containing **HCl** and **pepsinogen,** which is cleaved to yield the active protease **pepsin** in the **stomach**. In adult humans, only partial digestion of proteins and some absorption of water and substances, like aspirin and alcohol, take place in the stomach. Digestion of carbohydrates, lipids, and terminal digestion of proteins occurs in the **small intestine** where amino acids and glucose are absorbed into the blood.
- **Details**: Know how food travels from the esophagus to the stomach and into the intestine, and how it is broken down. Know the two kinds of **secretory cells** in the stomach: the chemicals, enzymes, or factors that they secrete; and how those molecules function. Understand what the environment is like in the stomach and the cause of peptic ulcers.

48.4 The small intestine is where most food is broken down and absorbed.

- **Overview**: **Chyme** moves from the stomach to the small intestine through the **pyloric sphincter**. The small intestine consists of the **duodenum, jejunum,** and **ileum**. In addition to chyme from the stomach, the small intestine also receives digestive enzymes, such as **trypsin, chymotrypsin, pancreatic amylase**, and **lipase,** as well as **bicarbonate** from the **pancreas** by way of the **pancreatic duct**, and **bile** from the **liver** and **gallbladder,** which travels through the **common bile duct** and into the duodenum. Bile salts aid in the digestion of fats. The epithelial wall of the small intestine is covered with **villi** that are themselves covered with **microvilli,** which increase its surface area for absorption. Broken down proteins and carbohydrates are absorbed as amino acids and monosaccharides, respectively, into the blood capillaries. They are transported through the blood to the **hepatic portal vein** in the liver. Fatty acids and monoglycerides absorbed through intestinal cells are converted to triglycerides and moved into the lymphatic capillaries as **chylomicrons**.

- **Details**: Know the structures and the three distinct regions of the small intestine. Understand what substances move into the small intestine and where they originate. Know how these substances are activated and how they function. Understand the importance of the pancreas, liver, and gallbladder in digestion. Understand how the products of digestion are absorbed.

48.5 The large intestine separates waste material.

- **Overview**: The **large intestine, or colon,** has a larger diameter than the small intestine but is shorter in length. Two vestigial structures, the **cecum** and the **appendix,** mark the opening of the large intestine from the small intestine. The large intestine absorbs water, remaining electrolytes, and the products of bacterial metabolism. The large intestine also separates waste material, and processes food with high fiber content. Compacted waste material moves from the large intestine to the **rectum** by peristaltic contractions, and exits the body through the **anus,** which is controlled by two **sphincter muscles**, one that is involuntary and the second that is voluntary.
- **Details**: Know how the small and large intestines differ. Know the structures of the large intestine, its critical functions, and the pathway that digested food follows to exit the body.

48.6 The digestive tracts of some animals contain microorganisms to allow digestion of cellulose.

- **Overview**: The digestive tracts of some animals contain microorganisms, such as bacteria or protists, that allow the digestion of **cellulose,** wax, and the synthesis of vitamin K. **Ruminants** contain a four-chambered stomach. Food enters the stomach and is partially digested in the **rumen,** which contains bacteria that digests cellulose. Food can be regurgitated and rechewed in the rumen, or can be passed to the **reticulum**, then to the **omasum**, and finally to the true stomach, the **abomasum,** which secretes gastric juice. In other animals, digestion of cellulose takes place in the **cecum**. Rodents and lagomorphs capture nutrients from cellulose by eating the feces (**coprophagy**).
- **Details**: Understand why bacteria in the digestive tracts of animals are essential. Know how digestion in ruminants takes place.

48.7 The digestive system is regulated by neural and hormonal control.

- **Overview**: Both the endocrine system and the nervous system regulate the activities of the digestive system. The nervous system stimulates salivary and gastric secretions in the mouth and the stomach, respectively. **Enterogastrones** secreted by the duodenum and a neural reflex inhibit the passage of chyme from the stomach to the duodenum until the previous chyme has been processed. Enterogastrones also inhibit gastric functions, and stimulate increased pancreatic secretion of digestive enzymes and gallbladder contraction.
- **Details**: Know the hormones secreted by the stomach and by the duodenum. Know how the production of each hormone is stimulated and the functions of each.

48.8 The liver and the pancreas provide functions other than the secretion of digestive enzymes.

- **Overview**: The liver can chemically modify substances sent to it from the gastrointestinal tract before they reach the rest of the body. In this way, the liver plays a critical role in the conversion and removal of toxins. It is also involved in the regulation of the levels of different compounds produced in the body, and the production of the proteins found in the blood plasma. Hormones produced in the pancreas regulate blood glucose levels. **Insulin** stimulates the removal of glucose from the blood and promotes the formation of glycogen, while **glucagon** stimulates the breakdown of glycogen in the liver and fat in adipose tissue.
- **Details**: Know how the liver and the pancreas play key roles in the maintenance of homeostasis and blood glucose levels.

48.9 The ingestion of food provides energy and essential nutrients.

- **Overview**: Food provides a source of energy and raw materials. **Essential minerals** and **essential nutrients**, such as vitamins, some amino acids, and long-chain unsaturated fatty acids, are substances that an animal can not make itself, but are required for health and must be obtained from its diet. The **basal metabolic rate (BMR)** of an organism is the minimum rate of energy consumption under resting conditions. When the amount of **kilocalories** that are ingested is greater than the amount of energy expended, excess energy is stored as glycogen and fat. Brain neurons in the hypothalamus express the leptin receptor, which binds to the hormone **leptin,** which is produced by adipose tissue in response to feeding. This is believed to be the main sensor of food intake and energy expenditure. **Insulin** and **gut hormones** also send inhibitory signals to the brain in response to food intake to reduce appetite. High levels of leptin and insulin increase levels of α-**MSH** and decrease **NPY** to suppress feeding activity and increase energy expenditure.

- **Details**: Understand the model for energy

balance and feeding behavior. Know the roles of leptin, insulin, and the gut hormones in this model. Know the major vitamins and other essential nutrients and minerals required by humans.

CHALLENGING YOUR UNDERSTANDING—Part I

1. In the following flowchart, fill in the blanks to indicate the four functions carried out in different regions of a specialized digestive system. At the bottom, indicate the two primary resources that the ingestion of food provides.

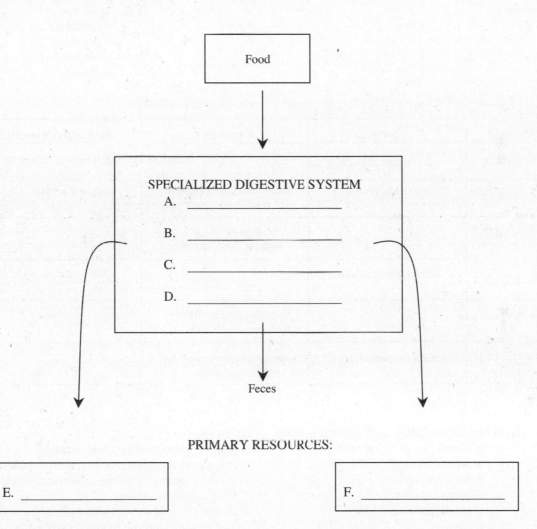

CHALLENGING YOUR UNDERSTANDING—Part II

1. Using the following list of digestive parts, describe the components that make up the digestive systems of the following organisms in the order in which food would pass through them.

Organisms	**Digestive parts:**
A. nematode	a. mouth
	b. anus
B. cnidarian	c. gastrovascular cavity
	d. intestine/small intestine
C. bird	e. esophagus
	f. stomach
D. earthworm	g. large intestine
	h. pharynx
E. fox	i. crop
	j. gizzard
F. cow	k. rumen
	l. reticulum
	m. omasum
	n. abomasums
	o. cecum

2. Complete the following table about the major vitamins required by humans.

Vitamin	Source	Function	Deficiency symptom
Vitamin A	green vegetables, milk		
	green vegetables	coenzymes in amino acid and nucleic acid metabolism	anemia, diarrhea
Vitamin D		absorption of Ca^{2+}; promote bone formation	
	green leafy vegetables		severe bleeding
Vitamin C		forming collagen; fighting infections; cement of bone, teeth	
	red meat; dairy products	coenzyme in the production of nucleic acids	

3. Match each of the following functions with the organs that perform them.

_____ a. liver	1. prepare waste material to be expelled
_____ b. stomach	2. churn pebbles together with food by muscular action
_____ c. large intestine	3. collect products of the reproductive, urinary, digestive tract
_____ d. pancreas	4. store compacted feces
_____ e. small intestine	5. chemically modify substances absorbed in digestive tract
_____ f. cloaca	6. digestion of cellulose by microorganisms
_____ g. pharynx	7. secrete hormones that regulate blood glucose levels
_____ h. gizzard	8. pressure against this trigger the swallowing reflex
_____ i. crop	9. food storage
_____ j. cecum	10. churning and mixing food with gastric juice
_____ k. esophagus	11. store and concentrate bile
_____ l. rectum	12. Absorption of glucose and amino acids from food
_____ m. gallbladder	13. saliva is used to moisten and lubricate food
_____ n. mouth	14. peristalsis moves a processed lump of food to the stomach

KEY TERMS

Match the numbered term with the definition that fits it best. Put the corresponding number in front of the appropriate definition.

1. herbivores
2. carnivores
3. omnivores
4. cecum
5. duodenum
6. villi
7. ruminants
8. saliva
9. salivary amylase
10. swallowing reflex

11. peristalsis
12. gastric juice
13. pepsin
14. intrinsic factor
15. chyme
16. pancreas
17. liver
18. hepatic portal vein
19. chylomicrons
20. coprophagy

21. enterogastrones
22. basal metabolic rate (BMR)
23. body mass index (BMI)
24. leptin
25. obesity
26. gizzard
27. pyloric sphincter
28. brush border

a. ____ The hydrolytic enzyme contained in saliva that initiates the breakdown of starch into maltose.
b. ____ A chamber in the stomach of birds where small pebbles are churned together with food by muscular action.
c. ____ The mixture of partially digested food and gastric juice produced in the stomach.
d. ____ The minimum rate of energy consumption under defined resting conditions.
e. ____ A pouch between the small and large intestine that contains cellulose-digesting bacteria in some herbivores.
f. ____ The canal that carries blood containing the first products of digestion from the intestine to the liver.
g. ____ Another name for the epithelial wall of the small intestine, due to the microvilli resembling the bristles of a brush.
h. ____ Animals that exclusively eat other animals, such as crabs, squid, many insects, eagles, trout, and frogs.
i. ____ The hormone that acts as the main signaling molecule for energy sensing, food intake, and energy expenditure.
j. ____ An acidic secretion of the tubular exocrine glands in the mucosa of the stomach.
k. ____ A polypeptide needed for the intestinal absorption of vitamin B_{12}, secreted by the parietal cells of the stomach.
l. ____ Mammals that consume grass who have several prestomach chambers where bacteria digest cellulose.
m. ____ An automatic, involuntary response triggered by pressure against the pharynx.
n. ____ Animals that eat both plants and other animals, such as humans, pigs, bears, and cows.
o. ____ A ring of smooth muscle that controls the entrance into the duodenum.
p. ____ Small, fingerlike projections found on the epithelial wall of the small intestine that increase its surface area.
q. ____ Small particles formed by triglycerides and proteins that are too bulky to enter the intestinal blood capillaries.
r. ____ Animals that eat plants exclusively, such as sap-sucking insects, cattle, horses, rabbits, and sparrows.
s. ____ A condition in which a person accumulates an amount of fat that is deleterious to health.
t. ____ Duodenal hormones secreted into the blood that inhibit the contractions of the stomach.
u. ____ The largest internal organ of the body that secretes bile and plays a key role in the removal of toxins.
v. ____ A mucous solution in the mouth that moistens and lubricates food so that it is easier to swallow.
w. ____ A practice of rodents and lagomorphs in which they eat their feces to capture nutrients from cellulose.
x. ____ Rhythmic waves of muscular contraction produced in various parts of the digestive tract to move substances.
y. ____ A ratio of height and weight that is intended to estimate body fat without directly measuring it.
z. ____ A large gland that secretes digestive enzymes into the duodenum, and hormones to regulate blood glucose levels.
aa. ____ An active protease produced by cleavage of a precursor molecule secreted by chief cells in the stomach.
bb. ____ The beginning of the small intestine that receives chyme from the stomach, bile from the liver, and digestive enzymes and bicarbonate from the pancreas.

LEARNING BY EXPERIENCE

1. List the following terms in their proper sequence to trace the pathway food follows through the human digestive tract.

Terms	Proper sequence
anus	
colon	
duodenum	
esophagus	
mouth	
pharynx	
rectum	
rest of small intestine	
stomach	

2. Complete the following chart by listing whether each substance is a hormone or an enzyme and where it is produced.

Substance	Hormone or enzyme	Where produced
a. cholecystokinin (CCK)		
b. chymotrypsin		
c. gastrin		
d. glucagon		
e. insulin		
f. lactase		
g. pepsinogen		
h. salivary amylase		
i. secretin		

3. Which of these two digestive tracts is from an herbivore and which is from a carnivore? How can you tell? Is the herbivore a ruminant or a nonruminant?

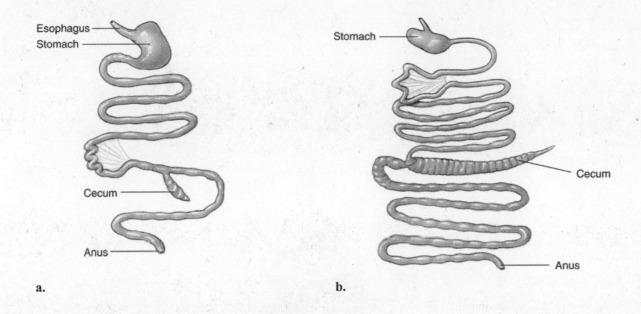

a.

b.

4. Use the following terms to label the three layers of the small intestine shown here. Also label the fingerlike projections. Terms: submucosa, muscularis, villi, mucosa.

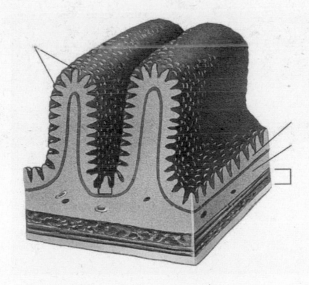

5. Use the following terms to label the major parts of the human digestive system and its accessory organs on the figure below: anus, appendix, cecum, colon, esophagus, gallbladder, liver, pancreas, pharynx, rectum, salivary gland (used twice), small intestine, stomach.

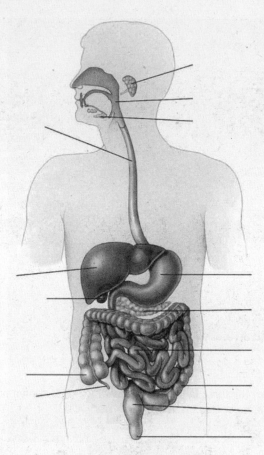

EXERCISING YOUR KNOWLEDGE

Briefly answer each of the following questions in the space provided.

1. Why don't plants have digestive systems?

2. What is the significance of a digestive tract with one-way flow of materials compared to a gastrovascular cavity?

3. Explain the statement "humans are carnivores in the front of their mouth and herbivores in the back."

4. Carnivores have stomachs that can distend and hold much more food than our stomachs can. Why is this advantageous?

5. Commercials on TV commonly advertise products that will cure acid stomach. Is acid stomach good or bad? Why?

6. During the digestive process, the duodenum receives material from several other organs. Describe in general terms what it receives and where it comes from.

7. Bacteria living in the digestive tracts of animals are examples of a symbiotic relationship that is mutually beneficial. The animals benefit by having the bacteria digest cellulose or wax and synthesize compounds such as vitamin K for them. How do the bacteria benefit?

8. What is the significance of the hepatic portal vein with regard to maintaining homeostasis?

9. What are the two primary reasons animals ingest food (what does it accomplish)?

10. Kwashiorkor is a disease caused by protein deficiency and is common in malnourished people. There has been an increase of kwashiorkor in the United States, not just among poor people but among college students as well. Can you think of an explanation?

Circle the letter of the one best answer in each of the following questions.

11. Which of the following is required to prepare fats for subsequent enzymatic digestion?
    a. hydrochloric acid
    b. pepsin
    c. pancreatic juice
    d. bile salts
    e. bicarbonate

12. Which of the following empties into the cloaca of vertebrates?
    a. the digestive tract
    b. the reproductive tract
    c. the urinary tract
    d. all of these
    e. none of these

13. Which of the following animals has a gizzard?
    a. nematode
    b. earthworm
    c. hydra
    d. all of these
    e. none of these

14. In vertebrates, the innermost layer of the digestive tract is the
    a. mucosa.
    b. submucosa.
    c. lumen.
    d. muscularis.
    e. serosa.

15. Which of the following occurs in the mouth?
    a. initiation of starch breakdown
    b. digestion of proteins
    c. absorption of carbohydrates
    d. all of these
    e. none of these

16. When a mammal swallows, the nasal cavity is closed off by the
    a. glottis.
    b. epiglottis.
    c. soft palate.
    d. larynx.
    e. esophagus.

17. Which of the following would you be least likely to find in a herbivore?
    a. a rumen
    b. a cecum
    c. pointed molars
    d. a large intestine
    e. bacteria in the gut

18. The body of a tooth is made up of
    a. enamel.
    b. dentin.
    c. central pulp.
    d. plexus.
    e. chyme.

19. Which of the following statements about the stomach is true?
    a. Parietal cells in the lining of the stomach secrete hydrochloric acid.
    b. The pH of the stomach is normally about 6.2.
    c. Digestion of carbohydrates is completed in the stomach.
    d. Gastric ulcers in the lining of the stomach are the most common type of ulcers.
    e. No substances can be absorbed through the wall of the stomach.

20. Villi and microvilli are found in the
    a. stomach.
    b. esophagus.
    c. large intestine.
    d. small intestine.
    e. all of these.

21. The hepatic portal vein carries blood from the _____ to the _____.
    a. small intestines, liver
    b. liver, small intestines
    c. stomach, small intestines
    d. stomach, liver
    e. liver, heart

22. Which of the following is embedded in the brush border of the small intestines?
    a. chylomicrons
    b. digestive enzymes
    c. sphincters
    d. islets of Langerhans
    e. chief cells

23. Which of the following statements is true?
    a. The primary function of the large intestine is to digest proteins.
    b. The middle section of the small intestine is called the ileum.
    c. Approximately 9 liters of fluid pass through the small intestine every day, but most of it is absorbed.
    d. All mammals rely on intestinal bacteria to synthesize vitamin D.
    e. High levels of dietary fiber are associated with increased risk of colon cancer.

24. In ruminants, which chamber of the stomach has the same function as the human stomach?
    a. reticulum
    b. rumen
    c. omasum
    d. abomasum
    e. all of these

25. The pancreas produces digestive enzymes and releases them into the
    a. blood capillaries.
    b. colon.
    c. stomach.
    d. liver.
    e. duodenum.

26. Which of the following is *not* a function of the liver?
    a. converts glucose to glycogen
    b. converts glycogen to glucose
    c. detoxifies poisonous substances
    d. produces blood plasma proteins
    e. All of these *are* functions of the liver.

27. Which of the following stimulates the gallbladder to contract?
    a. secretin
    b. gastrin
    c. cholecystokinin
    d. gastric inhibitory peptide
    e. glucagon

28. Bicarbonate is produced by the
    a. duodenum.
    b. liver.
    c. stomach.
    d. pancreas.
    e. salivary glands.

29. Improper functioning of leptin is associated with
    a. diabetes.
    b. obesity.
    c. anorexia nervosa and bulimia.
    d. jaundice.
    e. pernicious anemia.

30. Essential nutrients
    a. cannot be synthesized so must be obtained in the diet.
    b. are needed in large quantities.
    c. are only found in vegetables.
    d. all belong to the category of nutrients known as vitamins.
    e. All of these are correct.

ASSESSING YOUR KNOWLEDGE

Answers to the questions in this section test your ability to synthesize information gained from the chapter and to solve challenging problems on an exam or in everyday life.

Challenging Your Understanding—Part I, Answers

1A–D. Storage, Mechanical fragmentation, Chemical digestion, Absorption.

1E–F. Energy, Raw materials.

Challenging Your Understanding—Part II, Answers

1A. nematode: a, h, d, b.

1B. cnidarian: a, c.

1C. bird: a, e, i, f, j, d, b.

1D. earthworm: a, h, i, j, d, b.

1E. fox: a, e, f, d, o, g, b.

1F: cattle: a, e, k, l, m, n, d, o, g, b.

2.

Vitamin	Source	Function	Deficiency Symptom
Vitamin A	milk; green veg.	visual pigment epithelial maint.	Night blindness
Folic acid	green veg.	Coenzymes	anemia, diarrhea
Vitamin D	dairy prod.; cod liver oil	Ca^{2+} absorptn.; bone formation	rickets; bone deformities
Vitamin K	green leafy veg.	essential to blood clotting	severe bleeding
Vitamin C	fruit; green leafy veg.	form collagen; fight inf.,cement	scurvy, breakdown of skin, blood vess.
Vitamin B_{12}	red meat; dairy prod.	Coenzymes in nucleic acid prd.	pernicious anemia

3. a. 5, b. 10, c. 1, d. 7, e. 12, f. 3, g. 8, h. 2, i. 9, j. 6 k. 14, l. 4, m. 11, n. 13.

Key Terms—Answers

a. 9, b. 26, c. 15, d. 22, e. 4, f. 18, g. 28, h. 2, i. 24,

j. 12, k. 14, l. 7, m. 10, n. 3, o. 27, p. 6, q. 19, r. 1,

s. 25, t. 21, u. 17, v. 8, w. 20, x. 11, y. 23, z. 16,

aa. 13, bb. 5.

Learning by Experience—Answers

1. Proper sequence: mouth, pharynx, esophagus, stomach, duodenum, rest of small intestine, colon, rectum, anus

2. a. hormone, duodenum

    b. enzyme, pancreas

    c. hormone, stomach

    d. hormone, pancreas

    e. hormone, pancreas

    f. enzyme, small intestine

    g. enzyme, stomach

    h. enzyme, salivary gland

    i. hormone, duodenum

3. (a) carnivore, (b) nonruminant herbivore. (a) has a relatively short intestine and small cecum, typical of the easily digested protein diet of a carnivore. (b) has a much longer intestine and larger cecum, needed to deal with the hard-to-digest cellulose in the diet of an herbivore. It is a nonruminant since the stomach is simple, single chambered, and relatively small. Bacteria that can digest cellulose probably live in the large cecum.

4.

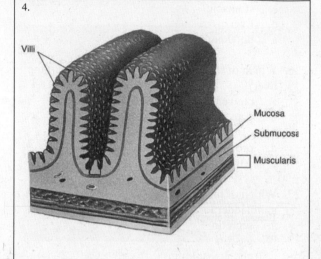

5.

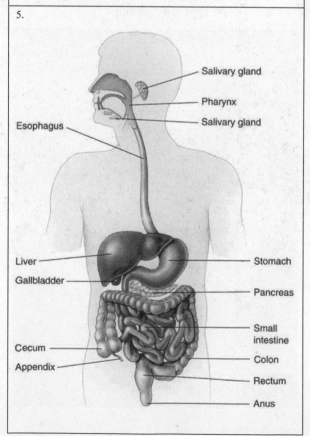

Exercising Your Knowledge—Answers

As you check your answers, put a mark in the review (Rvw.) column for the answers you missed. If you didn't miss any, congratulations—you have mastered the chapter! If you missed some, review the section (Sect.) in the text where this concept is discussed. In order to develop an efficient review strategy, it is important that you understand what types of questions you missed. The questions with asterisks test more for understanding of the **concepts**, whereas the others test more for **detail**. *See the preface for learning strategies for concepts and for detail.*

	Sect.	Rvw.
*1. Plants are autotrophs and make their food from inorganic materials. They do not ingest food and therefore do not need a digestive tract.	Intro.	
*2. A one-way digestive tract with a mouth at one end and an anus at the other allows for specialization of different regions with different functions along the way. It also allows more efficient processing of food compared to a gastrovascular cavity, which has only one opening that must function as both a mouth and an anus and allows no specialization.	48.1	
*3. Humans are omnivores, eating both meat and plants. The incisors and canine teeth at the front of the mouth are designed for processing meat; the premolars and molars at the back of the mouth are designed for processing plant material.	48.2	
*4. Finding and catching other animals for food is more difficult and less reliable than finding and eating plants. By being able to gorge and take in large amounts of food at one time, carnivores are able to take advantage of a successful kill and abundant food source before it can get away, spoil, or be eaten by competitors.	48.3	
*5. A low pH in the stomach is normal and good. It allows pepsin to function and digest protein, helps physically break apart food, and kills harmful bacteria. Problems arise when the stomach secretes too much acid or when not enough bicarbonate is produced by the pancreas to neutralize the acid when it reaches the duodenum. If the lining of the digestive tract is exposed to too much acid, ulcers can form.	48.3	

	Sect.	Rvw.
*6. Chyme (partially digested food and gastric juice) comes from the stomach. Digestive enzymes and bicarbonate come from the pancreas. Bile comes from the liver via the gallbladder.	48.4	
*7. The intestines provide a protected, relatively stable environment in which the bacteria are literally surrounded and bathed by their food.	48.6	
*8. The hepatic portal vein carries blood from the small intestines directly to the liver. The nutrients and other materials that have been absorbed from the digestive tract have a chance to be processed by the liver before being circulated throughout the body. Toxins and other harmful substances can be metabolized and broken down, and the levels of nutrients such as glucose can be regulated, preventing great fluctuations right after meals, and thus helping maintain homeostasis.	48.4	
*9. Food is a source of energy (used to make ATP during cellular respiration) and a source of raw materials needed as building blocks for making macromolecules and cells needed by the animal.	48.9	
*10. There has been an increase in vegetarianism, and it is more difficult to obtain a balanced, complete diet with all the necessary essential amino acids from plants alone. Eating disorders such as anorexia nervosa and bulimia also contribute significantly to malnutrition.	48.9	
11. d	48.4	
12. d	48.5	
13. b	48.2	
14. a	48.3	
*15. a	48.2	
16. c	48.2	
*17. c	48.2	
18. b	48.2	
*19. a	48.3	
20. d	48.4	
21. a	48.4	
22. b	48.4	
*23. c	48.4	
24. d	48.6	
25. e	48.4	
26. e	48.8	
27. c	48.7	
28. d	48.4	
29. b	48.9	
*30. a	48.9	

CHAPTER 49 THE CIRCULATORY AND RESPIRATORY SYSTEMS

MASTERING KEY CONCEPTS

Complex, three-dimensional multicellular animals could not exist without circulatory and respiratory systems. The circulatory system transports vital materials such as oxygen and nutrients to cells throughout the body and at the same time removes waste materials from them. The circulatory system travels close to every living cell in the body and helps integrate all the different parts into one functional whole. Blood transports not only oxygen, nutrients, and wastes, but also hormones and cells of the immune system; it also distributes heat. The respiratory systems of vertebrates, whether gills or lungs, are mechanical devices that ensure an adequate exchange of gas between the circulatory system and the external environment. The anatomy and functioning of the circulatory and respiratory systems are the products of adaptation and evolutionary change.

49.1 The circulatory systems of invertebrates are related to their size and complexity.

- **Overview**: The circulatory systems of sponges consist of the circulation of water from the environment through a series of channels in their bodies. Similarly, most cnidarians pass water from the environment through their **gastrovascular cavity,** which serves as both a digestive and a circulatory system. Pseudocoelomate invertebrates use fluids from their body cavities for circulation. Mollusks and arthropods have **open circulatory systems,** which pump **hemolymph** from a tubular heart into body cavities. Cephalopod mollusks, annelids, and all vertebrates have **closed circulatory systems** in which **blood**, enclosed in vessels, is circulated through the body by a central pump, the **heart**.
- **Details**: Understand the general organization of the circulatory systems of sponges, cnidarians, nematodes, arthropods, annelids, and vertebrates.

49.2 The circulatory and respiratory systems evolved together in vertebrates.

- **Overview**: The circulatory and respiratory systems of vertebrates are linked allowing vertebrates to grow larger and to be mobile on land. The fish heart evolved to become a **two-chambered heart** where blood passes through four structures: the **sinus venosus, atrium, ventricle**, and **conus arteriosus**. From the heart, blood moves to the **gills**, becomes oxygenated, travels to the rest of the body by a network of arteries, and then back to the heart. Organisms with **lungs** have **double circulation** in which blood is pumped by the heart to the lungs, returned to the heart, and then pumped to other tissues. This system is more efficient and

allowed the evolution of endothermy in mammals and birds. Amphibians have a **three-chambered heart** with two atria and one ventricle. Two atria and channels in the ventricle help to prevent mixing of oxygenated and deoxygenated blood. **Cutaneous respiration** also allows oxygen to be obtained through the skin. Reptiles have a septum that subdivides the ventricle, and the **conus arteriosus** has been incorporated into the arteries leaving the heart. Mammals, birds, and crocodiles have **four-chambered hearts** that completely prevent mixing of oxygenated and deoxygenated blood.

- **Details**: Know how blood circulates in fish and the limitation in its circulation. Know the structural differences in the hearts of amphibians, reptiles, mammals, and birds. Know the path of blood through the four-chambered heart, and the advantages of having two separate atria and ventricles.

49.3 Mammals, birds, and crocodiles have four-chambered hearts.

- **Overview**: The **cardiac cycle** is made up of two contractions, one to send blood from the atria to the ventricles, and the other to send blood from the ventricles to the lungs, or to the rest of the body, with a resting period in between. The **atrioventricular valves**, the **tricuspid valve** (right), and the **bicuspid valve** (left) prevent blood from flowing back into the atria from the ventricles; the **semilunar valves**, the **pulmonary valve** (right), and the **aortic valve** (left) ensure that blood can flow only from the ventricles to the arterial systems. Veins that empty into the left and right atria return blood to the heart. The **pulmonary arteries** deliver oxygen-depleted blood from the **right ventricle** to the **lungs**, and the **pulmonary veins** deliver oxygenated blood from the lungs to the **left atrium**. The **aorta** and the systemic arteries deliver oxygen-rich blood from the **left ventricle** to the body. Blood from the organs returns to the heart through systemic veins that empty into the **superior** and the **inferior vena cava**. Autorhythmic fibers in the heart, such as the **sinoatrial node**, allow action potentials to be initiated periodically without neural activation. Each depolarization is transmitted to the left atrium and the **atrioventricular node** (**AV**) in the right atrium. From the AV node, it is transmitted to both ventricles by the **bundle of His** and then to the **Purkinje fibers** stimulating ventricular contraction.
- **Details**: Know the functions and locations of the four valves in the heart. Know which arteries and veins blood travels through to enter and exit the heart. Understand how **blood pressure** is

measured, and the definition of high blood pressure. Understand how contraction is initiated and controlled in cardiac muscle. Know the path of electrical excitation in the heart.

49.4 Blood vessels transport oxygenated and deoxygenated blood to and from organs.

- **Overview**: **Arteries,** which branch into smaller **arterioles** and **capillaries,** carry oxygenated blood from the heart to the body, while **veins** branch into smaller **venules** and carry deoxygenated blood back to the heart. All of these blood vessels, except the capillaries, have the same tissue layers--an endothelium on the inside, an elastic layer covering the endothelium, a smooth muscle layer on top of the elastic layer, and connective tissue as the outermost covering. Veins and venules have a thinner layer of smooth muscle than arteries. Capillaries consist of a single layer of endothelial cells allowing the exchange of gases and metabolites. Skeletal muscles and venous valves help move blood from the organs of the body back to the heart. Contraction or relaxation of the smooth muscle layer controls the rate of blood flow to an organ and regulates heat loss. **Interstitial fluid**, filtered out of the capillaries, bathes the tissues of the body. Some of this fluid returns to the capillaries by osmosis, the rest (**lymph**) is returned by the **lymphatic system**. **Cardiovascular diseases**, such as heart attacks, strokes, atherosclerosis, and arteriosclerosis, are a result of restrictions in blood flow.
- **Details**: Know the structures of the blood vessels. Know the components of the lymphatic system, and how fluid is moved through it back to the cardiovascular system. Know the causes of each of the cardiovascular diseases discussed.

49.5 Blood flow and blood pressure are regulated in the body.

- **Overview**: Two neuronal centers in the medulla oblongata (hindbrain): the **cardioacceleratory center** and the **cardioinhibitory center**, control the heart rate by signaling the secretion of norepinephrine or acetylcholine to increase or decrease heart rate, respectively. **Cardiac output**, or the volume of blood pumped by each ventricle per minute, increases during exertion due to an increase in **heart rate** and **stroke volume**. **Arterial blood pressure** increases as a result of either of these increases or because of vasoconstriction. An increase or decrease in blood pressure is detected by baroreceptors in the arch of the aorta and in the carotid arteries that are sensitive to the expansion and the contraction of the arteries. Therefore, blood pressure depends on blood volume, which is regulated by antidiuretic hormone, aldosterone, atrial natriuretic hormone, and nitric oxide gas.
- **Details**: Understand how heart rate and blood pressure are controlled. Know how ADH, aldosterone, atrial natriuretic hormone, and nitric oxide regulate blood volume.

49.6 Blood consists of plasma, red and white blood cells, and platelets.

- **Overview**: Blood is responsible for the transportation of oxygen, nutrient molecules, and metabolic wastes. It is also required to transport regulatory hormones, regulate temperature, and protect against injury and foreign invaders. Blood consists of **plasma**—containing water, ions, proteins, nutrients, wastes, hormones, and other solutes— and **formed elements**, including **red blood cells (erythrocytes)**, **platelets**, and **white blood cells (leukocytes)**. The erythrocytes of vertebrates contain **hemoglobin** for the transport of oxygen. Leukocytes, including **neutrophils**, **eosinophils**, and **basophils** (granular) and **monocytes** and **lymphocytes** (nongranular), play an important role in defending against invaders and foreign substances. Platelets are cell fragments that release **clotting factors** into the blood after an injury. All of the formed elements develop from **pluripotent stem cells**. **Hematopoiesis** generates **lymphoid stem cells,** which give rise to lymphocytes, and **myeloid stem cells,** which give rise to the rest of the blood cells.
- **Details**: Know the composition and primary functions of circulating blood. Know the components of plasma. Know the functions of the other components of the blood. Know how the formed elements in the blood are produced from stem cells. Understand how blood clotting occurs.

49.7 Gas exchange occurs across respiratory surfaces.

- **Overview**: One of the primary functions of the circulatory system is the exchange of oxygen and carbon dioxide in respiratory organs. Whether organisms possess gills, skin, or lungs for respiration, gas exchange always occurs in an aqueous environment. In invertebrates, gases diffuse into the aqueous layer covering the cells that line respiratory organs. Animals have developed methods to enhance gas exchange, such as creating water currents over respiratory surfaces or increasing the surface area available for diffusion.
- **Details**: Know the different gas exchange systems that animals possess. Understand **Fick's law of diffusion**, and how the rate of diffusion can be optimized.

49.8 Gills, cutaneous respiration, and tracheal systems allow respiration in a number of organisms.

- **Overview**: Fish larvae and amphibians have external gills that must be constantly moved and are easily damaged. Other aquatic animals have **branchial chambers** that protect the gills and provide a means of pumping water across them. The gills of bony fish use two sets of cavities to pump water into and out of the fish and have gills covered by an **operculum**. Some bony fish also use **ram ventilation** to force water over the gills. The gills of fish use **countercurrent flow** to maximize oxygenation of the blood and respiration efficiency. Cutaneous respiration in some vertebrates exchanges oxygen and carbon dioxide across the skin. Terrestrial arthropods have **spiracles** that pass air through the exoskeleton into **trachea** that branch into **tracheoles,** which are in direct contact with cells to allow oxygen to diffuse directly across their plasma membranes.

- **Details**: Know the disadvantages of external gills. Understand how countercurrent flow works and know the advantages of this system. Know the respiratory structures in arthropods.

49.9 Terrestrial animals replaced gills with lungs.

- **Overview**: Terrestrial vertebrates could not use gills because air is less supportive than water and gills would collapse outside of water. Gills also would provide an enormous surface area for water evaporation. Tracheal systems and lungs minimize evaporation. Lungs permit gas exchange across a thin, wet membrane in a two-way flow system. Amphibians have lungs that exist as pouches on the side of their guts. They force air into these lungs by **positive pressure breathing**, and also use cutaneous respiration. Reptiles use **negative pressure breathing** to pull air into their lungs by expanding their rib cages. Mammals and birds have more efficient respiratory systems. **Alveoli** in the lungs of mammals increase the surface area available for gas exchange, and the distance that gas must diffuse into the blood capillaries is small. The lungs of birds channel air unidirectionally through **parabronchi,** which take in only fresh air, while old air is moved out by another route preventing mixing of old and fresh air. Birds also have a **cross-current flow** of blood through the lungs that gives them a greater capacity to extract oxygen from the air.
- **Details**: Understand the relationship between air pressure and altitude above sea level and how this affects respiration. Understand how amphibians, reptiles, birds, and mammals breathe.

49.10 Mammalian breathing is a dynamic process.

- **Overview**: Neurons in the respiratory control center in the medulla oblongata initiate **inhalation** that occurs by contraction of the diaphragm and intercostal muscles producing **negative pressure ventilation**. **Exhalation** occurs when these neurons stop producing impulses, the diaphragm and rib cage relax, and the rib cage and lungs undergo elastic recoil. Neurons in the **respiratory control center** are sensitive to changes in blood P_{CO2} and P_{O2}. A rise in P_{CO2}, lowers the pH of the blood, stimulating peripheral chemoreceptors in the aortic and carotid bodies, which stimulates the respiratory control center in the brain to increase breathing. **Asthma**, **chronic bronchitis**, and **emphysema** are **chronic obstructive pulmonary diseases** that obstruct air flow on a long-term basis. **Lung cancer** can result from, or occur in conjunction with, chronic obstructive pulmonary diseases.

- **Details**: Know how inspiration and expiration occur. Understand how an increase in blood P_{CO2} can stimulate an increase in breathing. Know the causes and effects of the chronic obstructive pulmonary diseases discussed.

49.11 Gases are transported in the blood and hemolymph.

- **Overview**: Most of the oxygen in the blood is bound to the protein **hemoglobin** inside of red blood cells. Hemoglobin consists of four **heme groups** with an **iron atom** at the center of each and four polypeptide chains. Each iron atom can bind one molecule of oxygen. Hemoglobin provides an oxygen reserve that allows it to supply the body with oxygen during exertion, as well as when it is at rest, and also allows the blood to contain enough oxygen to sustain life for four to five minutes if breathing is interrupted. Lowering the blood pH, or increasing the temperature or CO_2 binding to hemoglobin, decreases hemoglobin's affinity for oxygen. Carbon monoxide and nitric oxide can also bind to hemoglobin. **Hemocyanin** is another oxygen carrier found in some invertebrates. It contains copper, rather than iron, and circulates freely in the **hemolymph**. Carbon dioxide is primarily transported as bicarbonate produced from CO_2 and water by **carbonic anhydrase** in the red blood cells.

- **Details**: Know the basic structure of hemoglobin. Understand the **oxyhemoglobin dissociation curve** and the effects of pH and temperature on this curve. Know how CO_2 is transported in the blood and why carbonic anhydrase is an important enzyme.

CHALLENGING YOUR UNDERSTANDING—Part I

1. Describe the three primary functions of circulating blood and explain why these functions are important.

2. Describe how breathing occurs in the following organisms.

Amphibian:

Terrestrial reptile:

Bird:

Mammal:

Fish:

3. Which of the organisms listed above has the most efficient respiratory organs? Explain why.

CHALLENGING YOUR UNDERSTANDING—Part II

1. List the steps in the negative feedback loop that are activated to maintain homeostasis in the body in response to each of the following stimuli. Your answer should include the sensors, integrating center, effectors involved, and the response.

a. High blood pressure

b. Increased levels of blood CO_2 concentration

2. Complete the following table for the cardiovascular and respiratory diseases listed.

Disease	Cardiovascular or respiratory	Problems that lead to the disease
Heart attack		
Emphysema		Alveolar walls break down, lungs become fibrotic and less elastic
		Interference with the blood supply to the brain.
Atherosclerosis		
	Respiratory	An allergen triggers the release of histamine, other inflammatory chemical causing constriction of the bronchi.
Arteriosclerosis		

KEY TERMS

Match the numbered term with the definition that fits it best. Put the corresponding number in front of the appropriate definition.

1. hemolymph
2. interstitial fluid
3. plasma
4. serum
5. erythrocytes
6. granular leukocytes
7. nongranular leukocytes
8. platelets
9. vasoconstriction
10. vasodilation
11. venous pump
12. venous valves
13. lymphatic system
14. lymph
15. atrium
16. ventricle
17. pulmonary circulation
18. systemic circulation

19. cutaneous respiration
20. atrioventricular valves
21. sinoatrial node (SA)
22. atrioventricular node (AV)
23. semilunar valves
24. autorhythmic fibers
25. formed elements
26. cardiac cycle
27. pulmonary arteries
28. pulmonary veins
29. aorta
30. coronary arteries
31. superior vena cava
32. inferior vena cava
33. systolic pressure
34. diastolic pressure
35. bundle of His
36. Purkinje fibers

37. cardiac output
38. Fick's law of diffusion
39. operculum
40. gill arches
41. countercurrent flow
42. bronchi
43. alveoli
44. cross-current flow
45. visceral pleural membrane
46. parietal pleural membrane
47. pleural cavity
48. tidal volume
49. vital capacity
50. hemoglobin
51. positive pressure breathing
52. negative pressure breathing
53. systemic arteries
54. systemic veins

a. ____ The relationship between pressure, area, and distance that governs the rate of diffusion of a dissolved gas.
b. ____ White blood cells, including monocytes and lymphocytes.
c. ____ Excess fluid in the tissues that drains into blind-ended lymph capillaries with highly permeable walls.
d. ____ The first branches of the aorta that supply oxygenated blood to the heart muscle itself.
e. ____ Contraction of the smooth muscle layer of the arterioles that greatly increases resistance and decreases flow.
f. ____ "Self-excitable" muscle cells, which can initiate periodic action potentials without neural activation.
g. ____ The space between the visceral pleural membrane and parietal pleural membrane.
h. ____ Vessels that carry partially deoxygenated blood from the organs of the body back to the heart.
i. ____ A group including red blood cells, white blood cells, and platelets that develop from pluripotent stem cells.
j. ____ Part of the double circulatory system in which blood is moved between the heart and the rest of the body.
k. ____ Tiny sacs in the lungs of mammals that provide each lung with an enormous surface area for gas exchange.
l. ____ Forcing air into the lungs by taking in air, closing the mouth and nostrils, and elevating the floor of the oral cavity.
m. ____ A network of fibers that conduct a wave of depolarization over both ventricles when received from the AV node.
n. ____ A pair of valves that ensure the one-way flow of blood out of the ventricles to the arterial systems.
o. ____ In the measurement of blood pressure, the minimum pressure between heartbeats when the ventricles relax.
p. ____ A flat, bony, external protective covering over the gill chamber in fish.
q. ____ In mammals, a fragment of white blood cell that circulates in the blood to form blood clots at the site of injury.
r. ____ The circulating and extracellular fluid of the body tissues in organsims with an open circulatory system.
s. ____ A mechanism in which skeletal muscles surrounding the veins can contract to move blood by squeezing the veins.
t. ____ A process in the gills of fish in which blood and water flow in opposite directions to maximize oxygenation.
u. ____ Part of the double circulatory system in which blood is moved between the heart and the lungs.
v. ____ A structure in the wall of the right atrium that acts as a pacemaker for the rest of the heart.
w. ____ The volume of blood pumped by each ventricle per minute.
x. ____ A thin membrane covering the outside of each lung in mammals.
y. ____ Red blood cells, or doughnut-shaped disks in the blood that contain an oxygen-binding pigment.
z. ____ A pair of valves that ensure the one-way flow of blood between the atria and the ventricles.
aa. ____ A thin-walled chamber in the heart that receives venous blood and passes it on to the ventricle.
bb. ____ A thin membrane that lines the inner wall of the thoracic cavity.
cc. ____ Vessels that deliver oxygen-depleted blood from the right ventricle to the right and left lungs.
dd. ____ Ventilation that pulls air into the lungs due to lower pressure in the lungs compared with the atmosphere.
ee. ____ The amount of air moved into and out of the lungs with each breath.
ff. ____ The process of exchanging oxygen and carbon dioxide across the skin.
gg. ____ The flow of blood through the avian lung that runs at a 90° angle to the air flow.

hh. ____ In the measurement of blood pressure, the peak pressure at which ventricles are contracting.
ii. ____ The atrial and ventricular contractions plus the resting period between them, which encompass the heartbeat.
jj. ____ A fluid matrix in which blood cells and platelets are suspended containing water, proteins, ions, nutrients, etc.
kk. ____ Air passages that branch off from the mammalian trachea and enter each lung.
ll. ____ A muscular chamber of the heart that receives blood from an atrium and pumps it to the lungs or body tissues.
mm. ____ The major vertebrate systemic artery that carries oxygenated blood away from the left ventricle to the body.
nn. ____ Blood plasma with the fibrinogen removed.
oo. ____ Valves that help blood move back through the veins to the heart in one direction.
pp. ____ One of the major veins that drains deoxygenated blood from the lower body into the right atrium of the heart.
qq. ____ The maximum amount of air that can be expired after a forceful, maximum inspiration.
rr. ____ White blood cells, including neutrophils, eosinophils, and basophils.
ss. ____ Vessels that return oxygenated blood from the lungs to the left atrium of the heart.
tt. ____ The aorta and all of its branches that carry oxygen-rich blood from the heart to all of the tissues of the body.
uu. ____ Water and solutes in the blood plasma that filter through the walls of the capillaries and bathes tissues.
vv. ____ Located on the side of a fish's head; two rows of gill filaments with lamellae that project out into the water flow.
ww. ____ Fibers that directly stimulate the myocardial cells of the left and right ventricles causing their contraction.
xx. ____ An open circulatory system that returns fluid filtered out of the capillaries to the cardiovascular system.
yy. ____ A slender connection of cardiac muscle cells that receives the heartbeat impulse from the sinoatrial node.
zz. ____ Relaxation of the smooth muscle layer of the arterioles that decreases resistance and increases blood flow.
aaa. ____ A major vein that drains deoxygenated blood from the upper body into the right atrium of the heart.
bbb. ____ A globular protein in vertebrate red blood cells and in the plasma of many invertebrates that carries oxygen.

LEARNING BY EXPERIENCE

1. Using the following list of "heart parts," describe the components that make up the hearts of the animals listed below.

Heart parts:
a. conus arteriosus without septum
b. conus arteriosus with septum
c. left atrium
d. left ventricle
e. right atrium
f. right ventricle
g. single atrium
h. single ventricle without septum
i. single ventricle with partial septum
j. sinus venosus

Animal	**Heart components**
fish	
frog	
lizard	
bird	
mammal	

2. Trace the pathway of blood through the human circulatory system by arranging the following terms in their proper sequence, beginning with the right atrium and returning to the right atrium.

Terms
aorta
aortic valve
bicuspid valve
left atrium
left ventricle
lungs
pulmonary arteries
pulmonary valve
pulmonary veins
right atrium (start)
right atrium (finish)
right ventricle
systemic circulation
tricuspid (mitral) valve

Pathway
right atrium →

right atrium

3. This is a schematic diagram of a fish's circulatory system. Label the four chambers of the heart (A = atrium, CA = conus arteriosus, SV = sinus venosus, V = ventricle). Color red the part of the circulatory system that carries oxygenated blood, and color blue the part with deoxygenated blood.

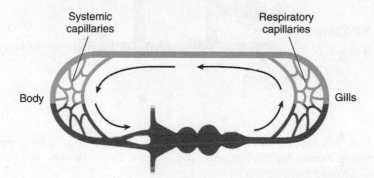

4. Label and color on this cut-away view of the human heart the tissues involved with the electrical excitation of the heart that leads to contraction. Label terms: AV node, bundle of His, Purkinje fibers, SA node.

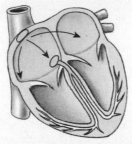

5. Match each of the following types of animal with the type of respiratory organ or structure it has. Note: One of the animals has two answers.

_____ a. amoeba	i. papulae
_____ b. frog	ii. gills
_____ c. echinoderm	iii. lungs
_____ d. insect	iv. cell membrane
_____ e. fish	v. tracheae
_____ f. bird	vi. skin

469

6. Arrange the following terms in their proper sequence to show the pathway air follows when a human inhales through the nose.

Terms
alveoli
bronchi
bronchioles
glottis
larynx
nostrils
pharynx
trachea

Inhalation pathway

7. This is a schematic diagram of a bird's respiratory system. Trace the pathway air follows during respiration by numbering the anterior air sacs, the parabronchi, and the posterior air sacs (1–3) to indicate the proper sequence of air movement in the lungs.

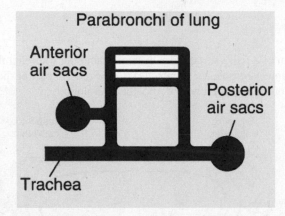

8. This figure shows the effect of pH on the oxyhemoglobin dissociation curve. If there were curves for human maternal hemoglobin and human fetal hemoglobin, which curve do you think would be farther to the left – the maternal or the fetal? Explain your answer.

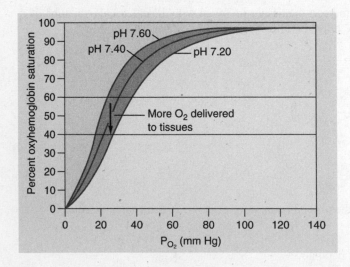

EXERCISING YOUR KNOWLEDGE

Briefly answer each of the following questions in the space provided.

1. You have been asked by a science fiction fan club to design a large, multicellular animal with no circulatory system. Describe the animal you design. What is its shape? Where does it live? How active is it? Is it endothermic? Explain your answer.

2. Why does exchange of materials between the blood and the surrounding tissues occur in the capillaries, but not in the arteries and veins?

3. Both elephantiasis and radical mastectomies interfere with the lymphatic system. In elephantiasis, parasitic worms called filaria get into the lymph vessels and block them. When a woman has a radical mastectomy, the lymph glands and vessels are commonly removed from the chest, armpit, and upper arm on the side from which the cancerous breast is removed. What symptoms would you expect to see in people who have elephantiasis or have had a radical mastectomy?

4. Compared to the fish circulatory system, what are the efficiencies and inefficiencies of the amphibian circulatory system?

5. Why is the circulatory system of birds and mammals referred to as a double circulatory system with a two-cycle pump? Why is this system advantageous?

6. Some fish drown or suffocate if they don't keep swimming, and almost all fish suffocate if taken out of the water and exposed to air, even though air has 20 to 40 times as much oxygen as water does. Why is this?

7. Describe two ways amphibian respiration is different from that of other terrestrial vertebrates.

8. Why can birds be active at much higher altitudes than mammals can?

9. What happens physiologically when a person hyperventilates?

10. Can you think of a reason it might be advantageous for mammals to not have nuclei in their mature erythrocytes? (Hint: Think about the primary function of red blood cells.) Are there disadvantages?

Circle the letter of the one best answer in each of the following questions.

11. Which of the following is a function of the vertebrate circulatory system?
    a. regulating body temperature
    b. transporting metabolic wastes
    c. providing immunological defense
    d. transporting oxygen and carbon dioxide
    e. all of these

12. Hemolymph is found in
    a. hydra and planaria.
    b. insects.
    c. earthworms.
    d. all of these.
    e. none of these.

13. Which of the following is NOT true regarding the circulatory systems in vertebrates?
    a. Blood pressure in fish drops significantly in passing through the capillaries in the gills.
    b. Reptiles have a septum that partially subdivides the ventricle.
    c. The amphibian heart has a single ventricle.
    d. Blood leaving the gills in fish travels back to the heart to be pumped to the rest of the body.
    e. There is no mixing of oxygenated and deoxygenated blood in the mammalian heart.

14. Interstitial fluid is derived from fluid that is forced out of the
    a. arteries.
    b. veins.
    c. arteriole end of capillaries.
    d. venule end of capillaries.
    e. lymph vessels.

15. Platelets are formed from the cytoplasm of
    a. erythrocytes.
    b. granular leukocytes.
    c. nongranular leukocytes.
    d. megakaryocytes.
    e. heart muscle cells.

16. The lymphatic system of all vertebrates
    a. is a closed circulatory system.
    b. has lymph hearts to help move the lymph along.
    c. returns fluid directly to the aorta.
    d. All of these are correct.
    e. None of these are correct.

17. The sinoatrial (SA) node is derived from the more primitive
    a. ventricle.
    b. bundle of His.
    c. conus arteriosus.
    d. tricuspid valve.
    e. sinus venosus.

18. Which of the following contains oxygenated blood in an adult human?
    a. right atrium
    b. pulmonary artery
    c. pulmonary vein
    d. all of these
    e. none of these

19. The first vessels to branch off the aorta are the
    a. coronary arteries.
    b. pulmonary arteries.
    c. pulmonary veins.
    d. superior and inferior venae cavae.
    e. No vessels branch off the aorta.

20. What causes the "dub" part of the "lub-dub" you hear when you listen with a stethoscope to a beating human heart?
    a. the semilunar valves opening
    b. the semilunar valves closing
    c. the AV valves opening
    d. the AV valves closing

21. Diffusion alone cannot meet metabolic demands for oxygen if the diffusion distance is greater than approximately
    a. 0.5 mm.
    b. 5.0 mm.
    c. 0.5 cm.
    d. 5.0 cm.
    e. 0.5 m.

22. Which of the following is *not* a way to increase the efficiency of a respiratory system?
    a. increase the surface area available for diffusion of gases
    b. decrease the distance over which the gases must diffuse
    c. increase the concentration gradient of the gases on the two sides of the diffusion surface
    d. dry the system out so the gases do not have to diffuse through water
    e. All of these *will* increase respiratory efficiency.

23. Which of the following respiratory systems is the most efficient at obtaining oxygen from the surrounding environment?
    a. mammal lungs
    b. reptile lungs
    c. amphibian lungs
    d. bird lungs
    e. fish gills

24. Which of the following animals have tracheae as their respiratory system?
    a. grasshoppers
    b. earthworms
    c. echinoderms
    d. mollusks
    e. none of these

25. Which of the following is NOT true of the molecule hemoglobin?
    a. Hemoglobin loads up with oxygen in the alveolar capillaries.
    b. Approximately 97% of hemoglobin in red blood cells is in the form of oxyhemoglobin.
    c. Hemoglobin has a lower affinity for oxygen at higher temperatures.
    d. Each molecule of hemoglobin can carry one molecule of oxygen.
    e. Roughly one-fifth of the oxygen carried by hemoglobin is unloaded to the tissues.

26. Which of the following statements is true?
    a. When a bird breathes, air moves from the lungs into the posterior air sacs.
    b. The hemolymph of insects binds and transports oxygen.
    c. Cutaneous respiration has been demonstrated in fish, amphibians, and terrestrial reptiles.
    d. In the average adult human, the surface area of the lungs is more than 400 times greater than the surface area of the body.
    e. The only place where gas exchange occurs in mammalian respiratory systems is in the alveoli.

27. The respiratory control center of humans is located in the
    a. diaphragm.
    b. alveoli.
    c. medulla oblongata of the brain stem.
    d. hypothalamus of the brain.
    e. larynx.

28. When do the external intercostals and the diaphragm contract?
    a. during inhalation
    b. during exhalation
    c. during both inhalation and exhalation
    d. during neither inhalation and exhalation
    e. The external intercostals contract during inhalation; the diaphragm contracts during exhalation.

29. The Bohr effect explains why
    a. diffusion occurs so slowly over long distances.
    b. oxygen is present in the atmosphere in relatively low concentrations.
    c. hemoglobin unloads its oxygen when it encounters low pH levels.
    d. the visceral pleural membrane and the parietal pleural membrane are attracted to each other.
    e. some introductory biology students do not like their instructor.

30. Hemoglobin can bind
    a. oxygen.
    b. carbon dioxide.
    c. nitric oxide.
    d. all of these.
    e. none of these.

ASSESSING YOUR KNOWLEDGE

Answers to the questions in this section test your ability to synthesize information gained from the chapter and to solve challenging problems on an exam or in everyday life.

Challenging Your Understanding—Part I, Answers

1. Transportation: Blood carries oxygen, nutrient molecules, and metabolic wastes through the body. Regulation: Blood carries regulatory hormones throughout the body and is involved in temperature regulation, and in contraction or dilation of the blood vessels to regulate heat conservation and loss. Protection: White blood cells contained in the blood protect the body against foreign substances, such as bacteria and viruses. Blood clotting helps protect the body from blood loss when injury occurs.

2. Amphibians use positive pressure breathing to force air into their lungs. They fill their mouths with air, close their mouths and nostrils, and elevate the floor of their mouths to push the air down into the lungs. They also use cutaneous respiration to exchange gases through their skin.

Terrestrial reptiles use negative pressure breathing to pull air into their lungs by expanding their rib cages using muscular contraction, which creates a lower pressure inside the lungs compared to the atmosphere.

Birds breathe in two cycles, in the first, they inhale air that is drawn into the posterior air sacs and exhaled into the lungs. In the second cycle, air from the lungs is moved into the anterior air sacs and exhaled through the trachea. This system prevents mixing of "old" oxygen-depleted air with freshly inhaled air, producing respiratory efficiency. This is further increased by the flow of blood in the lung of the bird that runs at a 90° angle to the air flow allowing a greater capacity to extract oxygen from the air.

Mammals have lungs with alveoli that create an enormous area for gas exchange. Each alveoli is only one cell thick and is surrounded by blood capillaries with walls that are also only one cell thick. This creates a very small distance that gas must diffuse. Air is taken in, moves into the windpipe, into the bronchi and then the bronchioles, which deliver air to the alveoli.

Fish breathe by drawing water into the buccal cavity while the opercular cavity is closed. The oral valve is then closed and the operculum is opened, drawing water through the gills. Fish use countercurrent flow in which blood flows opposite to the direction of water movement to maximize the oxygenation of blood. This system ensures that an oxygen concentration gradient remains between blood and water throughout the length of the gill lamellae.

3. As a result of the countercurrent exchange of gases, fish gills are the most efficient respiratory organ. Blood and water flowing in opposite directions increase the concentration gradient of oxygen along the pathway for diffusion, such that blood leaving the gills has nearly as high an oxygen concentration as the water entering the gills.

Challenging Your Understanding—Part II, Answers

1a. High blood pressure:
Sensor: Baroreceptor senses expansion of blood vessels.
Integrating Center: Cardiac center of the medulla increases the frequency of impulses.
Effector: Parasympathetic nerves that innervate the heart increase in activity, while sympathetic nerves decrease in activity.
Response: Decreased heart rate and stroke volume, vasodilation lowers the blood pressure.
Negative feedback: Baroreceptors sense that blood pressure has returned to normal.

1b. Increased levels of blood CO_2 concentration:
Sensor: Changes in the pH of the cerebrospinal fluid are detected by H^+ ion chemoreceptors in the brain. Changes in the pH of the blood are detected by peripheral chemoreceptors in the aortic and carotid bodies.
Integrating Center: The brain process information sent from the chemoreceptors that the levels of CO_2 are too high.
Effector: Impulses sent to the respiratory control center in the medulla oblongata, which stimulates increased breathing.
Response: Diaphragm stimulated to increase breathing.
Negative feedback: As levels of blood CO_2 drop, chemoreceptors and peripheral receptors are no longer stimulated.

2.

Disease	Cardio/Respiratory	Problems leading to
Heart attack	Cardiovascular	Insufficient supply of blood to one or more parts of the heart
Emphysema	Respiratory	Alveolar walls break down; lungs become fibrotic, less elastic
Strokes	Cardiovascular	Interference with the supply to the brain
Atherosclerosis	Cardiovascular	Accumulation of fatty material in the arteries
Asthma	Respiratory	An allergen triggers release of histamine
Arteriosclerosis	Cardiovascular	Artery hardening due to calcium deposits in the arterial walls.

Key Terms—Answers

a. 38, b. 7, c. 14, d. 30, e. 9, f. 24, g. 47, h. 54, i. 25, j. 18, k. 43, l. 51, m. 35, n. 23, o. 34, p. 39, q. 8, r. 1, s. 11, t. 41, u. 17, v. 21, w. 37, x. 45, y. 5, z. 20, aa. 15, bb. 46, cc. 27, dd. 52, ee. 48, ff. 19, gg. 44, hh. 33, ii. 26, jj. 3, kk. 42, ll. 16, mm. 29, nn. 4, oo. 12, pp. 32, qq. 49, rr. 6, ss. 28, tt. 53, uu. 2, vv. 40, ww. 36, xx. 13, yy. 22, zz. 10, aaa. 31, bbb. 50.

Learning by Experience—Answers

1.

Animal	Heart components
fish	j, g, h, a
frog	j, e, h, c, b
lizard	j, e, i, c
bird	e, f, c, d
mammal	e, f, c, d

2. right atrium → tricuspid valve → right ventricle → pulmonary valve → pulmonary arteries → lungs → pulmonary veins → left atrium → bicuspid (mitral) valve → left ventricle → aortic valve → aorta → systemic circulation → right atrium

3.

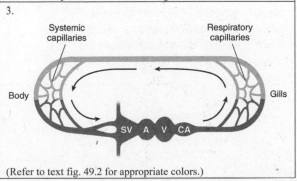

(Refer to text fig. 49.2 for appropriate colors.)

4.

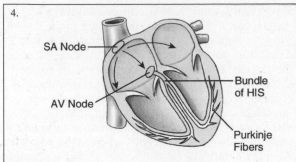

5.   a. iv
    b. iii, vi
    c. i
    d. v
    e. ii
    f. iii

6. nostrils → pharynx → glottis → larynx → trachea → bronchi → bronchioles → alveoli

7. posterior air sacs = 1; parabronchi = 2; anterior air sacs = 3

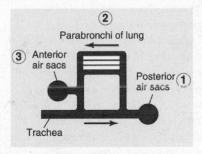

8. The fetal curve should be to the left, meaning the hemoglobin is more saturated with oxygen or hangs on to it more. This is necessary if the fetus is to get oxygen since the only source of oxygen for the fetus is the mother's blood, across the placenta. The fetal hemoglobin must be able to outcompete the maternal hemoglobin.

Exercising Your Knowledge—Answers

As you check your answers, put a mark in the review (Rvw.) column for the answers you missed. If you didn't miss any, congratulations—you have mastered the chapter! If you missed some, review the section (Sect.) in the text where this concept is discussed. In order to develop an efficient review strategy, it is important that you understand what types of questions you missed. The questions with asterisks test more for understanding of the **concepts**, whereas the others test more for **detail**. *See the preface for learning strategies for concepts and for detail.*

	Sect.	Rvw.
*1. To be large and multicellular and have no circulatory system, the animal would have to be aquatic and essentially flat and only one or two cells thick (analogous to a giant kelp seaweed). This way, each cell could be in direct contact with the environment, and exchange of materials could take place by direct diffusion. Being aquatic would avoid desiccation problems and allow direct diffusion. Because diffusion is a fairly slow process, the animal would have to be fairly inactive – it could not meet the energy demands of an active lifestyle. The animal most likely would not be endothermic – because of its flat, thin shape it would have an extremely large surface area-to-volume ratio, and it would be almost impossible for the animal to maintain a body temperature much different from that of the surrounding environment without huge energy expenditures.	49.1 49.2	
*2. Arteries and veins have too many tissue layers making up the vessel wall. Capillaries have only a single cell layer of endothelium, which is relatively easy for substances to diffuse or move across.	49.4	
*3. With the lymph vessels blocked or removed, fluid that diffuses out of the blood plasma and is normally picked up by the lymph capillaries cannot be returned to the bloodstream; instead, it will accumulate in the tissue, causing edema. The affected area will appear bloated.	49.4	
*4. Amphibians have lungs instead of gills for oxygenating their blood. Blood returns to the heart from the lungs and then is pumped to the rest of the body rather than going directly from the lungs to the body. This is more efficient than the fish pathway in that the systemic circulation is not as sluggish since the blood is being pumped directly from the heart to the body. But since amphibians only have one ventricle in their heart, there is an inefficient partial mixing of oxygenated (from the lungs) and deoxygenated (from the body) blood in the ventricle.	49.2	
*5. Birds and mammals have a four-chambered heart. The right side pumps blood to the lungs where it is oxygenated and returns to the left side of the heart where it is pumped to the rest of the body. There is double circulation – pulmonary (to and from the lungs) and systemic (to and from the body). It is a two-cycle pump in that the two atria contract simultaneously to fill the ventricles, and then the ventricles contract simultaneously to send blood to the lungs and body. The increased efficiency of complete separation of pulmonary and systemic circulation (no mixing of oxygenated and deoxygenated blood, no sluggish blood flow) allows for an extremely active lifestyle and endothermy, both of which require a high metabolic rate, which in turn requires an efficient circulatory system to support it.	49.2	
*6. Some fish (such as tuna and some sharks) cannot pump water across their gills, so must swim continually with their mouths open to move water across their gills. If they cannot swim, the water around their gills is not replaced and becomes depleted of oxygen, and the fish dies from lack of oxygen. When a fish is exposed to the air, the gill filaments and lamellae collapse into a big lump instead of staying supported and separated by the water. This greatly decreases the surface area available for diffusion, and the fish cannot get enough oxygen to keep it alive.	49.9	
*7. Amphibians fill their lungs by positive pressure breathing instead of negative pressure breathing. Many amphibians can supplement their lung respiration with cutaneous respiration through the skin.	49.9	
*8. Because of the unidirectional air flow through their lungs and the cross-current blood flow, the lungs of birds are much more efficient than mammal lungs and can extract more oxygen from the air.	49.9	
*9. The excessive breathing during hyperventilation lowers the level of carbon dioxide in the blood as CO_2 is "blown off" with each exhalation. This decreases the urge to breathe since the urge to breathe is triggered more by high CO_2 levels than by low O_2 levels in the blood. Hyperventilation also causes dizziness due to constriction of cerebral blood vessels.	49.10	

*10. With no nucleus taking up space in the red blood cell, there is more room to pack in more hemoglobin molecules, and thus each erythrocyte can transport more oxygen. Without a nucleus, however, the cell does not have the genetic instructions for repairing damage to itself and has a relatively short life span. It also cannot undergo mitosis. New erythrocytes must be made constantly from other precursor cells to replace the worn-out red blood cells.	49.6 49.11	
11. e	49.6	
12. b	49.1	
*13. d	49.2	
14. c	49.4	
15. d	49.6	
*16. e	49.4	

17. e	49.2	
18. c	49.3	
19. a	49.3	
20. b	49.3	
21. a	49.7	
*22. d	49.7	
23. c	49.9	
24. a	49.8	
25. d	49.11	
*26. e	49.9	
27. c	49.10	
28. a	49.10	
*29. c	49.11	
30. d	49.11	

CHAPTER 50 TEMPERATURE, OSMOTIC REGULATION, AND THE URINARY SYSTEM

MASTERING KEY CONCEPTS

To remain alive and functioning properly, organisms and cells need to maintain homeostasis. Unless they are isotonic with their surrounding environment, all organisms tend to gain water and lose salts, or lose water and gain salts, depending on the relative osmolality of the organism and the environment. Such gains and losses can be lethal if they are too extreme. Organisms also need to dispose of nitrogenous wastes. In vertebrates, osmoregulation and nitrogenous waste excretion are carried out by the kidney, regulated by the central nervous system and hormones.

50.1 Body temperature is regulated by internal and external factors.

- **Overview**: External factors and the overall metabolic rate affect an organism's body temperature. **Body heat** is equal to the sum of the heat produced and the heat transferred, where **radiation**, **conduction**, **convection**, **evaporation**, and the factors influencing these physical processes all determine the amount of heat transferred. **Endothermic** animals use metabolism to generate body heat and maintain their internal temperatures above the ambient temperature, while **ectotherms** have a body temperature that conforms to the ambient temperature due to behavioral regulation. Typically, ectotherms have low metabolic rates, and a low intake of energy, while endotherms have high metabolic rates requiring a high energy intake. Sharks, tuna, and large fish use a **countercurrent heat exchange** system in which the cooler blood in the veins is warmed by the blood in the nearby arteries by radiation, allowing these organisms to limit heat loss in cool waters. Reptiles maintain their body temperatures by behavioral means, and also by regulating their heart rates and controlling the dilation or contraction of blood vessels. Endotherms regulate their temperatures by controlling the blood flow to the surface, and use evaporative cooling, such as sweating or panting, to dissipate heat. Control centers in the hypothalamus detect changes in the core temperature of an organism. Endotherms undergo increases in their body temperatures to inhibit infections (**fever**), or can reduce their body temperatures and their metabolic rates to produce a state of dormancy (**torpor**).
- **Details**: Know the factors that affect body heat. Understand the difference between ectotherms and endotherms. Know how insects, large fish, and reptiles maintain their body temperatures. Know the relationship between body mass and metabolic rates in mammals, and the difference between **shivering** and **nonshivering thermogenesis**.

50.2 Osmolarity and osmotic balance depend on exchange with the external environment.

- **Overview**: The amount of water and solutes that enter and leave the body of an organism must be balanced to maintain homeostasis. **Osmotic balance** in an organism relies on the ability to take in water from the environment and to excrete excess water and ions to the environment. This exchange with the environment occurs in the extracellular fluids of the body by transport of water and solutes, filtered out of the blood by the **kidneys**, across specialized epithelial cells. **Osmoconformers**, such as marine invertebrates, are in osmotic equilibrium with their environments, while **osmoregulators**, including most vertebrates, maintain a relatively constant blood **osmolarity** although the concentration in the surrounding environment is different. They do this by continuous regulation of water and ion levels.
- **Details**: Know how the body interacts with the environment to control water and solute levels. Understand the difference between osmoconformers and osmoregulators. Know what will happen to an animal cell in a **hypertonic**, **hypotonic**, or an **isotonic** solution.

50.3 Animals contain osmoregulatory organs.

- **Overview**: In most animals, removal of excess water and salts from the body is coupled with the removal of metabolic wastes through the **excretory system**. Protists and sponges use contractile vacuoles to remove wastes. In flatworms, cilia in the **flame cells** draw in fluids from the body to the **protonephridia**, a network of tubules. Substances are excreted through pores to the outside. Earthworms have **nephridia** that obtain fluid from the body cavity that is filtered through **nephrostomes**. Insects secrete waste products and potassium ions into **Malpighian tubules** by active transport. In vertebrates, the **kidneys** filter the blood to produce a filtrate that enters the tubules. In all of these organisms, water and ions are reabsorbed, and waste products are removed by excretion to the outside.
- **Details**: Know the osmoregulatory organs used by different organisms, what substances are reabsorbed, and how substances are excreted.

50.4 Organisms have solved osmotic problems by adapting to their environments.

- **Overview**: Freshwater teleosts are hypertonic to their environments and tend to take in water and lose ions. To overcome this problem, freshwater fish don't drink water, excrete a large volume of dilute urine, reabsorb ions across their nephron tubules, and transport ions from the environment across their gill surfaces. In contrast, marine bony fish are hypotonic to their environments and tend to drink large amounts of seawater, eliminate excess ions by active transport across their gill surfaces, and excrete concentrated urine. Sharks and rays reabsorb urea from their nephron tubules and maintain an extremely high concentration of blood urea to solve the osmotic problem caused by seawater. Amphibians, like freshwater teleosts, produce dilute urine, and actively transport Na^+ across their skin. Reptiles living in freshwater and marine habitats have kidneys similar to freshwater fish. Marine reptiles overcome the osmotic problem by drinking seawater, excreting isotonic water, and eliminating excess salt through salt glands. Terrestrial reptiles reabsorb salt and water in their nephron tubules and empty urine into a **cloaca** where water can be reabsorbed. Mammals and birds excrete urine that is more concentrated than their body fluids due to the presence of the loop of Henle in their nephrons.
- **Details**: Know the problems of freshwater and marine teleosts and how they overcome these problems. Know how reptiles cope with excess salt. Know what evolutionary advancement allows mammals and birds to produce urine with an osmotic concentration higher than their body fluids.

50.5 Nitrogenous wastes must be eliminated from the body.

- **Overview**: **Nitrogenous wastes**, such as **ammonia**, **urea**, and **uric acid** are produced by the metabolic breakdown of amino acids and nucleic acids. Bony fish and tadpoles excrete ammonia which is toxic to cells in a large volume. Other organisms convert ammonia to urea, or uric acid which are both less toxic.
- **Details**: Know how nitrogenous wastes are produced and the different forms that are excreted by different organisms. Understand why bony fish and tadpoles don't have a problem excreting ammonia.

50.6 Kidneys are critical for maintaining homeostasis in mammals.

- **Overview**: Kidneys maintain homeostasis in the body through the excretion of nitrogenous waste products. The outside of the mammalian kidney

is the **cortex**, and the inside is the **medulla**. Blood is carried to each kidney by the **renal artery**. Urine produced in the kidney, drains into the **ureter**, is carried to the **urinary bladder,** and moves out of the body through the **urethra**. The three basic functions of the kidney include **filtration**, **reabsorption**, and **secretion**. Blood is filtered in the **glomerulus** of each **nephron** in the kidney. The filtrate enters the **Bowman's capsule**, moves into the **proximal convoluted tubule**, into the **loop of Henle**, and then into the **distal convoluted tubule**. The fluid drains to a **collecting duct,** which moves urine into the **renal pelvis**. Fluid flows in opposite directions in the ascending and the descending limbs of the loop of Henle forming a **countercurrent multiplier system** in which a gradient of increasing osmolarity is established from the cortex to the medulla by NaCl being actively pumped out of the ascending loop, allowing the reabsorption of water in the descending loop.
- **Details**: Know the structure and the functions of the kidney. Know how urine is excreted out of the body. Understand the function of the ascending and the descending limbs in the loop of Henle and how water is reabsorbed.

50.7 Hormones control the osmoregulatory functions of the kidneys.

- **Overview**: The volume of blood, blood pressure, and osmolarity of the blood plasma are all maintained by hormonal regulation of the kidneys. **Antidiuretic hormone** increases the reabsorption of water from the filtrate making the walls of the distal convoluted tubule and the collecting ducts more permeable to water. **Aldosterone** stimulates the reabsorption of Na^+ from the distal convoluted tubules and collecting ducts. Reabsorption of Cl^- and water follows, promoting the retention of salt and water. In this way, aldosterone maintains blood volume, osmolarity, and pressure. **Atrial natriuretic hormone** antagonizes the action of aldosterone. Its release is triggered by an increase in blood volume. Atrial natriuretic hormone promotes the excretion of salt and water to lower the blood volume.
- **Details**: Know how antidiuretic hormone, aldosterone, and atrial natriuretic hormone affect kidney function.

CHALLENGING YOUR UNDERSTANDING—Part I

1. Describe the three primary functions of the mammalian kidney.

2. For the following ions or molecules listed below, indicate all of the locations where they are reabsorbed in the mammalian kidney. The figure shown in the Learning by Experience section, question 2, may be a useful reference. Indicate the region in the kidney that has the highest and the lowest total solute concentration.

   Na^+:

   Cl^-:

   H_2O:

   Glucose:

   Amino acids:

   Divalent ions:

   Highest solute concentration:

   Lowest solute concentration:

3. Indicate the effects of the following hormones in terms of what molecules they stimulate the reabsorption of, and where this reabsorption occurs in the mammalian kidney.

   Antidiuretic hormone (ADH):

   Aldosterone:

CHALLENGING YOUR UNDERSTANDING—Part II

1. Complete the following flowchart to trace the path of blood, filtrate or blood cells and plasma proteins, and urine to, through, and out of the mammalian kidney, and then out of the body. The terms listed at the left will assist you.

you.

glomerulus
descending loop of Henle
efferent arteriole
collecting duct
ureter
renal artery
Bowman's capsule
renal vein
distal convoluted tubule
vasa recta
urethra
afferent arteriole
proximal convoluted tubule
renal pelvis
peritubular capillaries
urinary bladder
ascending loop of Henle

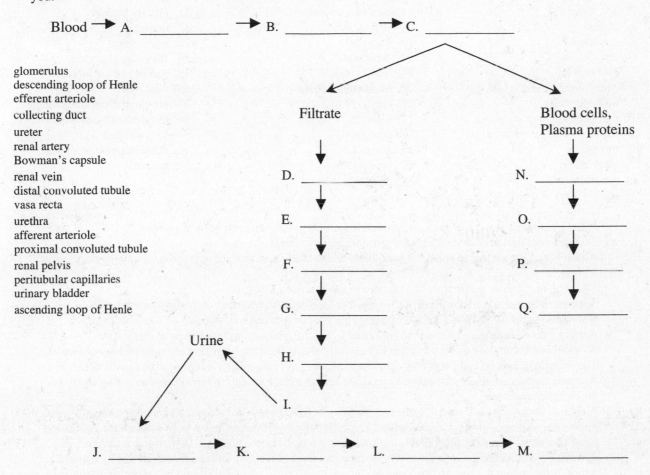

2. List the steps in the negative feedback loop that is activated to maintain homeostasis in the body in response to each of the following stimuli. Your answer should include the sensors, integrating center, effectors involved, and the response.

a. Increased plasma osmolarity

b. Low blood flow

KEY TERMS

Match the numbered term with the definition that fits it best. Put the corresponding number in front of the appropriate definition.

1. endotherms
2. ectotherms
3. heterotherms
4. radiation
5. conduction
6. convection
7. evaporation
8. countercurrent heat exchange
9. thermogenesis
10. pyrogens
11. fever
12. torpor
13. hibernation
14. osmolarity

15. tonicity
16. osmoconformers
17. osmoregulators
18. protonephridia
19. flame cells
20. nephridia
21. reabsorption
22. Malpighian tubules
23. secretion
24. kidneys
25. nephrons
26. ammonia
27. urea
28. uric acid

29. allantoin
30. ureter
31. urinary bladder
32. urethra
33. glomerulus
34. Bowman's capsule
35. peritubular capillaries
36. vasa recta
37. proximal convoluted tubule
38. distal convoluted tubule
39. loop of Henle
40. countercurrent multiplier system

a. _____ An extreme state in which deep torpor lasts for several weeks or even several months.
b. _____ Transport out of the tubule and into the surrounding body fluids.
c. _____ A portion of the kidney in mammals and birds where water and salt are reabsorbed from the glomerular filtrate.
d. _____ The tube that carries urine from the bladder to the exterior of mammals.
e. _____ Specialized cells in the tubules of flatworms that assist in water regulation and waste excretion.
f. _____ A measure of the ability of a solution to change the volume of a cell by osmosis.
g. _____ A more soluble derivative of uric acid converted by uricase, an enzyme found in most mammals.
h. _____ A vessel in the cortex of the mammalian kidney that collects fluid after it passes through the loop of Henle.
i. _____ The transfer of heat brought about by the movement of a gas or liquid caused by wind or density differences.
j. _____ Animals that do not use metabolism to produce heat and have a body temperature that conforms to the ambient temperature.
k. _____ A state of dormancy produced in some endotherms when the metabolic rate and body temperature are reduced.
l. _____ Functional, repeating units of the vertebrate kidney involved in filtration and selective reabsorption of blood.
m. _____ Fluid flowing in opposite directions in the limbs of the loop of Henle creating a hypertonic renal medulla.
n. _____ A water-soluble, organic molecule that is the principal form of disposal of nitrogenous wastes by mammals.
o. _____ Animals that maintain a relatively constant blood osmolarity despite different concentration in the environment.
p. _____ Substances that cause a rise in temperature.
q. _____ The transfer of heat from hotter to colder bodies by electromagnetic radiation that does not require direct contact.
r. _____ A bulbous unit of the nephron, which surrounds the glomerulus in the vertebrate kidney.
s. _____ In flatworms, a branching system of tubules, flame cells, and excretory pores that expel substances from the body.
t. _____ The use of normal energy metabolism to produce heat.
u. _____ Extensions of the peritubular capillaries that carry blood components that didn't enter the glomerular filtrate.
v. _____ Blind tubules opening into the hindgut of terrestrial arthropods that function as excretory organs.
w. _____ The vessel through which urine drains from each mammalian kidney into the urinary bladder.
x. _____ An adaptation allowing cooler blood in the veins to be warmed through radiation by blood in the arteries.
y. _____ A tuft of capillaries in the renal cortex of the mammalian kidney that filters the blood.
z. _____ A state that results from the resetting of the body's normal set point to a higher temperature.
aa. _____ The direct transfer of heat from hotter objects to colder ones.
bb. _____ In vertebrates, an organ that filters the blood to remove nitrogenous wastes and regulates blood plasma concentration.
cc. _____ A vessel in the cortex of the mammalian kidney that carries filtrate to the loop of Henle.
dd. _____ Animals that use metabolism to generate body heat and maintain their temperatures above ambient temperatures.
ee. _____ Organisms that are in osmotic equilibrium with their environments.
ff. _____ The change of a substance from a liquid to a gas phase.
gg. _____ The immediate by-product of the metabolism of amino acids and nucleic acids that is toxic to cells.

hh. ____ The transport of ions or molecules from the body fluids into the tubule; the opposite of reabsorption.

ii. ____ Capillaries that receive blood components that did not enter the glomerular filtrate from the peritubular capillaries.

jj. ____ Animals that fall in between endotherms and ectotherms.

kk. ____ A measurement of the number of osmotically active moles of solute per liter of solution.

ll. ____ In earthworms, tubules that obtain fluid from the body cavity by filtration through nephrostomes.

mm. ____ The slightly water-soluble form of nitrogenous wastes excreted by reptiles, birds, and insects.

nn. ____ An organ that collects urine from the ureter and passes it to the urethra for excretion.

LEARNING BY EXPERIENCE

1. Complete the following chart by answering each question for both freshwater fishes and marine bony fishes (not sharks or other elasmobranchs).

Questions	Freshwater fishes	Marine bony fishes
a. Are they hyperosmotic or hypoosmotic relative to their environment?		
b. Do they drink a lot or very little?		
c. Do they produce a lot of dilute urine or less urine that is isotonic?		
d. Do their gills pump ions into or out of the blood?		

2. Use the following terms to label the parts of the nephron diagrammed below: ascending limb, Bowman's capsule, collecting duct, descending limb, distal convoluted tubule, glomerulus, loop of Henle, proximal convoluted tubule, urine.

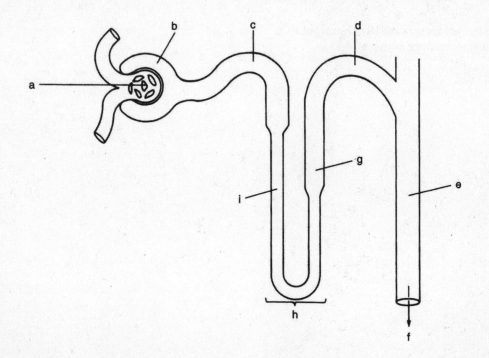

3. Match the following types of organisms with their type of osmoregulatory organ.

_____ a. insects
_____ b. flatworms
_____ c. annelids
_____ d. mammals

i. protonephridia
ii. kidneys
iii. Malpighian tubules
iv. nephridia

EXERCISING YOUR KNOWLEDGE

Briefly answer each of the following questions in the space provided.

1. Explain why moderate fevers should potentially not be medically treated.

2. (a) Describe the relationship between body mass and metabolic rate in mammals.
   (b) What are the major problems that small and large organisms face?

3. What are the advantages and disadvantages of being an osmoregulator as opposed to an osmoconformer?

4. Insects and vertebrates filter their blood to remove nitrogenous wastes and other substances. Explain what is meant by the statement that insects pull their blood through the filter while vertebrates push theirs through. How is this related to the type of circulatory system each has?

5. What are the advantages and disadvantages of the vertebrate kidney filtering almost everything out of the blood plasma and then putting a lot of it back into the blood?

6. Most aquatic organisms can survive in just salt water or just fresh water. Why do you think this is so; why can't they survive in both?

7. If urine is formed by filtering blood, why isn't urine normally red in color like blood?

8. Why does penicillin have to be given in high doses and several times a day to be effective in fighting infections? (Hint: It has to do with kidney function.)

9. How would blood pressure disorders (for example, high pressure or low pressure) affect the functioning of the kidneys?

10. If humans cannot produce aldosterone, they will die if they don't receive treatment. Why is this?

Circle the letter of the one best answer in each of the following questions.

11. Which of the following factors does NOT influence the overall rate of heat transfer?
    a. surface area
    b. temperature difference
    c. specific heat conduction
    d. all of the above
    e. none of the above

12. In a negative feedback loop, the system operates to elicit responses that are detected by the_____ to inhibit further action.
    a. effectors
    b. integrating centers
    c. sensors
    d. set point
    e. stimuli

13. In the countercurrent heat exchange system found in some vertebrate circulatory systems,
    a. both the arteries and veins carry blood away from the heart.
    b. both the arteries and veins carry blood toward the heart.
    c. heat is retained in the core of the animal because the arteries and veins run in opposite directions right next to each other.
    d. heat is readily lost from the core of the animal because the arteries and veins run in opposite directions next to each other.
    e. the heart occasionally reverses the direction in which the blood flows through it.

14. Which of the following animals have loops of Henle?
    a. insects
    b. fish
    c. birds
    d. all of these
    e. none of these

15. Aquatic organisms that are hypoosmotic relative to the surrounding water tend to
    a. gain water from the environment.
    b. gain salt from the environment.
    c. Both of these are correct.
    d. None of these are correct.

16. Which of the following is an osmoconformer?
    a. an earthworm
    b. a human
    c. a freshwater fish
    d. a bird
    e. a shark

17. The osmoregulatory organs of insects are called
    a. flame cells.
    b. contractile vacuoles.
    c. nephrostomes.
    d. collecting ducts.
    e. Malpighian tubules.

18. Marine reptiles and marine birds eliminate excess salt through
    a. salt glands in their heads.
    b. their kidneys.
    c. their general body surface.
    d. their flippers and feet.
    e. None of these; marine reptiles and marine birds don't eliminate excess salt.

19. The major cation in the extracellular fluids of vertebrates is
    a. Cl^-
    b. K^+
    c. Na^+
    d. Mg^{++}
    e. Ca^{++}

20. The more concentrated the urine an animal can produce, the longer are its
    a. ureters.
    b. proximal convoluted tubules.
    c. distal convoluted tubules.
    d. loops of Henle.
    e. glomeruli.

21. How many nephrons does a typical human have?
    a. 2
    b. 20
    c. about 200
    d. about 20,000
    e. about 2 million

22. The part of the nephron that is least permeable to water is the wall of the
    a. ascending limb.
    b. descending limb.
    c. collecting duct.
    d. proximal convoluted tubule.
    e. distal convoluted tubule.

23. Which of the following would be *least* likely to be found in the filtrate in the nephrons?
    a. plasma proteins
    b. glucose and amino acids
    c. water
    d. urea
    e. All of these are likely to be found in the filtrate.

24. The greatest amount of filtrate gets reabsorbed from what part of the nephron?
    a. the loop of Henle
    b. the distal convoluted tubule
    c. the proximal convoluted tubule
    d. the glomerulus
    e. the collecting duct

25. Freshwater fish excrete
    a. urea.
    b. ammonia.
    c. uric acid.
    d. none of these.

26. Urea is formed in the
    a. loop of Henle.
    b. glomerulus.
    c. collecting duct.
    d. liver.
    e. urinary bladder.

27. Filtrate moves into the proximal convoluted tubule from the
    a. collecting duct.
    b. Bowman's capsule.
    c. distal convoluted tubule.
    d. glomerulus.
    e. loop of Henle.

28. The osmolality of the kidney tissue is highest
    a. at the top of the renal cortex.
    b. at the bottom of the renal cortex.
    c. at the top of the renal medulla.
    d. at the bottom of the renal medulla.
    e. It is the same throughout the kidney.

29. ADH increases the permeability of the
    a. loop of Henle to water.
    b. loop of Henle to salt.
    c. collecting duct to water.
    d. collecting duct to salt.

30. Which of the following statements about the human kidney is true?
    a. More than one hormone influences the functioning of the kidney.
    b. When a lot of salt and water are reabsorbed from the filtrate, blood volume and pressure tend to go up.
    c. Some substances are actively secreted from the blood into the capillaries.
    d. The proximal and distal convoluted tubules are located primarily in the renal cortex.
    e. All of these are true.

ASSESSING YOUR KNOWLEDGE

Answers to the questions in this section test your ability to synthesize information gained from the chapter and to solve challenging problems on an exam or in everyday life.

Challenging Your Understanding—Part I, Answers

1. Filtration: Fluid in the blood is filtered into the tubule system, leaving large proteins and cells in the blood. A filtrate composed of water and all of the solutes in the blood is passed through the nephrons in the kidney. Some water, ions, and solutes are reabsorbed, the rest is excreted as urine.

Reabsorption: The selective movement of important solutes out of the filtrate in the tubule into the extracellular fluid and then back into the blood by way of the peritubular capillaries.

Secretion: The movement of substances from the blood into the extracellular fluid, and then into the filtrate in the tubules. These substances will be eliminated from the body. Secretion can be used to remove toxins from the body.

2. Na^+: Proximal convoluted tubule, ascending limb of the loop of Henle.
Cl^-: Proximal convoluted tubule, ascending limb of the loop of Henle.
H_2O: Proximal convoluted tubule, descending limb of the loop of Henle, walls of the collecting duct.
Glucose: Proximal convoluted tubule.
Amino acids: Proximal convoluted tubule.
Divalent ions: Proximal convoluted tubule.
Highest solute concentration: Inner medulla
Lowest solute concentration: Cortex

3. Antidiuretic hormone (ADH): stimulates reabsorption of H_2O in the distal convoluted tubule, and the collecting duct.
Aldosterone: stimulates reabsorption of Na^+, followed by Cl^- and H_2O in the distal convoluted tubule and the collecting duct.

Challenging Your Understanding—Part II, Answers

1A. Renal artery, B. Afferent arteriole, C. Glomerulus,
D. Bowman's capsule, E. Proximal convoluted tubule,
F. Descending loop of Henle, G. Ascending loop of Henle,
H. Distal convoluted tubule, I. Collecting duct, J. Renal pelvis,
K. Ureter, L. Urinary bladder, M. Urethra,
N. Efferent arteriole, O. Peritubular capillaries,
P. Vasarecta, Q. Renal vein.

2a. Increased plasma osmolarity:
Sensor: Osmoreceptors in the hypothalamus sense the increase in plasma osmolarity and send increased action potentials to the integration center.
Integrating Center: The hypothalamus receives the increased action potentials from the osmoreceptors, triggering a feeling of thirst.
Effector: The posterior pituitary gland is stimulated to increase ADH secretion.
Response: ADH stimulates increased reabsorption of water by kidneys, and the feeling of thirst stimulates increased water intake.
Negative feedback: Plasma osmolarity decreases with the reabsorption of additional water from the kidney and the intake of water, this is sensed by osmoreceptors in the hypothalamus.

2b. Low blood flow:
Sensor: When blood flow is reduced, it is sensed by the juxtaglomerular apparatus in the nephrons of the kidney.
Integrating Center: The kidney acts as the integrating center by releasing rennin into the blood.
Effector: Renin catalyzes the production of angiotensin I from angiotensinogen. Angiotensin I is converted to angiotensin II, which stimulates blood vessel constriction and the release of aldosterone from the adrenal cortex, leading to increased Na^+ reabsorption in the distal convoluted tubules.
Response: Angiotensin II stimulates blood vessel constriction, while aldosterone stimulates increased Na^+ reabsorption, followed by Cl^- and H_2O reabsorbtion, which all lead to increased blood volume.
Negative feedback: As the blood volume increases, this change is sensed by the juxtaglomerular apparatus in the nephrons of the kidneys.

Key Terms—Answers

a. 13, b. 21, c. 39, d. 32, e. 19, f. 15, g. 29, h. 38, i. 6, j. 2, k. 12, l. 25, m. 40, n. 27, o. 17, p. 10, q. 4, r. 34, s. 18, t. 9, u. 36, v. 22, w. 30, x. 8, y. 33, z. 11, aa. 5, bb. 24, cc. 37, dd. 1, ee. 16, ff. 7, gg. 26, hh. 23, ii. 35, jj. 3, kk. 14, ll. 20, mm. 28, nn. 31.

Learning by Experience—Answers

1 Freshwater fishes	Marine bony fishes
a. hyperosmotic	hypoosmotic
b. drink very little	drink a lot
c. a lot of dilute urine	less urine, isotonic
d. into blood	out of blood

2. a. glomerulus, b. Bowman's capsule, c. proximal convoluted tubule, d. distal convoluted tubule, e. collecting duct, f. urine, g. ascending limb, h. loop of Henle, i. descending limb.

3. a. iii, b. i, c. iv, d. ii.

Exercising Your Knowledge—Answers

As you check your answers, put a mark in the review (Rvw.) column for the answers you missed. If you didn't miss any, congratulations—you have mastered the chapter! If you missed some, review the section (Sect.) in the text where this concept is discussed. In order to develop an efficient review strategy, it is important that you understand what types of questions you missed. The questions with asterisks test more for understanding of the **concepts**, whereas the others test more for **detail**. *See the preface for learning strategies for concepts and for detail.*

	Sect.	Rvw.
*1. Fevers reset the body's normal set point to a higher temperature. This seems to be a natural defense mechanism to inhibit the growth of bacteria and therefore should potentially not be medically reduced by treatment.	50.1	
*2. (a) Smaller animals have a much higher metabolic rate per unit body mass relative to larger animals. (b) In cold environments, small animals with high metabolic rates cannot produce enough internal heat to balance conductive loss through their large surface areas, and thus require insulation in order to maintain their body temperatures. In hot environments, large animals produce a large amount of heat and have less relative surface area to dissipate it. For this reason, large animals have to use behaviors to increase heat loss.	50.1	
*3. Advantage: Maintaining a constant internal solute concentration has permitted vertebrates to evolve complex patterns of internal metabolism and live in harsh environments. Disadvantage: Osmoregulators must constantly spend energy to continually regulate the osmolality and try to maintain it at relatively constant levels.	50.2	
*4. In insects, potassium ions are secreted into the Malpighian tubules. This establishes a high osmotic concentration in the tubules, and water is pulled into the tubules by osmosis. The walls of the Malpighian tubules act as the filter, letting some substances in, but not others. In the glomerulus of the vertebrate kidney, water and dissolved substances are forced (pushed) out of the blood into the Bowman's capsule by the blood pressure. The capillary walls act as the filter, letting some substances through into the nephron and retaining others. The difference in these two systems is related to the insect's open circulatory system, with its more sluggish flow, versus the vertebrate's closed circulatory system, with significant pressure and flow.	50.3 50.6	
*5. It takes time and energy to filter and then reabsorb, but it allows great flexibility in processing the filtrate. This system essentially customizes the process for the particular habitat and the substances likely to be found in the blood and needed to be retained or eliminated.	50.3	
*6. Freshwater and saltwater environments present totally opposite osmoregulation problems in terms of gaining or losing water or ions. Most kidneys and other osmoregulatory systems are specialized for handling one set of problems, not both.	50.4	
*7. Blood is red because of the hemoglobin in the red blood cells. Red blood cells are too large to be filtered out of the glomerulus—they stay in the circulatory system and do not become part of the filtrate.	50.6	
*8. Penicillin is actively secreted from the blood capillaries in the kidneys into the filtrate in the nephron tubules. A high volume of blood passes through the kidneys rapidly, so high levels of penicillin need to be administered frequently to make sure it's not all eliminated by the kidneys before it can have its effect.	50.6	
*9. Blood pressure is the driving force for pushing substances out of the glomerular capillaries to form the filtrate in the nephrons. High blood pressure would tend to force out more filtrate; low blood pressure would result in less filtrate. Changes in blood pressure would also probably affect what was in the filtrate, not just volume. High pressure would force out bigger and more molecules; low pressure would force out fewer and only the smaller molecules.	50.6	

*10. Aldosterone causes Na^+ to be reabsorbed into the blood from the filtrate; Cl^- and water follow the Na^+. It also causes K^+ to be secreted into the filtrate. Without aldosterone, a person would die from their osmoregulation being totally out of whack—losing too much salt and water and having too much K^+ in the blood.	50.7	
11. d	50.1	
12. c	50.1	
*13. c	50.1	
14. c	50.4	
*15. b	50.4	
16. e	50.2	
17. e	50.3	

18. a	50.4	
19. c	50.2	
*20. d	50.4	
21. e	50.6	
22. a	50.6	
*23. a	50.6	
24. c	50.6	
25. b	50.5	
26. d	50.5	
27. b	50.6	
28. d	50.6	
29. c	50.7	
*30. e	50.6	

CHAPTER 51 THE IMMUNE SYSTEM

MASTERING KEY CONCEPTS

Every organism's body is constantly attacked and invaded by viruses, bacteria, protists, fungi, and/or multicellular parasites. Organisms have evolved myriad defensive mechanisms to protect themselves from the invaders. Vertebrates have an extremely sophisticated defense system based on several types of highly specialized white blood cells, which search out and destroy foreign materials that have entered the host's body. Some of the cells even provide long-term, future protection against reinvasion by a previously defeated attacker. A disease such as AIDS, which destroys the immune system, makes us realize with brutal clarity the importance of the immune system. Without it, we cannot live—we succumb to the hordes of invaders.

51.1 The integumentary system provides the body's first line of defense against foreign invaders.

- **Overview**: Vertebrate animals have several lines of defense against foreign invaders. The first line of defense against pathogens includes the **skin**, sweat, oil, and mucous membranes. The skin provides an impenetrable barrier, has normal flora that prevent colonization by pathogenic bacteria, produces sweat that makes the body surface acidic, and contains **lysozyme** that digests bacterial cell walls. Microorganisms and viruses can also enter the body through openings to the outside in the digestive, respiratory, or urogenital tracts. All of these are lined with epithelial cells that are continuously replaced, and have specialized cells that secrete mucus interspersed among them. Microbes in food are frequently killed by normal flora, or by the acidic environment in the gastrointestinal tract. Microorganisms inhaled in the air are trapped by mucus in the bronchi before they reach the lungs, and are swept out by cilia. Vaginal secretions and acidic urine also help prevent against foreign invaders.
- **Details**: Understand the ways in which the skin provides a barrier to infection. Know the layers of the epidermis, the layers of tissue below the epidermis, and the functions of each. Understand how the body prevents microorganisms and viruses from entering the digestive, respiratory, and urogenital tracts.

51.2 The nonspecific immune system provides the second line of defense.

- **Overview**: If the first line of defense is broken, the **innate immune system** mounts a response by producing white blood cells and proteins that destroy invading microbes. This second line of defense includes the production of **leukocytes**, such as **macrophages**, **neutrophils**, and **natural**

killer cells that circulate through the body and nonspecifically attack pathogens in tissues. Macrophages engulf and digest or degrade microorganisms, viruses, and cellular debris with lysosomal enzymes, and free radicals. Neutrophils move between the capillary endothelial cells, enter infected tissues, and ingest pathogens by phagocytosis. Natural killer cells attack cells in the body that are infected with viruses, and induce apoptosis of these cells to produce membrane-bound vesicles that are ingested by macrophages. Redness, warmth, swelling, pain, and potential loss of function are **hallmarks of inflammation** caused by the release of histamines, prostaglandins, and bradykinins causing blood vessels to dilate promoting increased blood flow and allowing the accumulation of phagocytic cells. The inflammatory response is accompanied by an **acute phase response**. Activation of **complement proteins** and **interferons** attract phagocytes, promote the destruction of pathogens, and protect normal cells from becoming infected.
- **Details**: Know how macrophages, neutrophils, and natural killer cells work to protect the body. Know the hallmark signs of inflammation and why these signs are produced. Know the role of complement proteins and interferons in the elimination of pathogens.

51.3 The specific immune response provides the body's third line of defense.

- **Overview**: The experiments of **Edward Jenner** and **Louis Pasteur** first indicated that exposure to an infectious agent can confer resistance. The **specific immune response** is activated in response to **antigens,** which have different parts known as **epitopes**. Receptor proteins on the surfaces of **lymphocytes** specifically recognize these epitopes on an antigen to direct an immune response. Rarely do any two lymphocytes have identical specificities. **B cells** produce antibodies in response to specific antigens; **T cells** directly attack cells carrying specific antigens. The specific immune system can recognize many antigens, specifically. It can respond more rapidly to antigens it has encountered previously, and can distinguish **self antigens from nonself**. **Active immunity** is acquired by infection with a pathogen, or by immunization with a portion or less virulent form of a pathogen. **Passive immunity** is acquired by obtaining antibodies from another individual. Cells of the immune system are all derived from **hematopoietic stem cells** in the bone marrow. Lymphocytes acquire their specific receptors, and self-reactive cells are eliminated in the bone marrow and thymus (**primary lymphoid organs**). Those that are not eliminated circulate in the blood and lymph to **secondary lymphoid organs** and become activated when they encounter an antigen. Antigens that pass through mucosal surfaces are immediately confronted by lymphocytes in the **mucosal-associated lymphoid tissues** (**MALT**).

- **Details**: Know what occurs when a lymphocyte encounters a new antigen. Know the functions of the cells in the immune system and how these cells originate. Know how active and passive immunity are acquired. Understand how B and T lymphocytes mature. Know the two forms of adaptive immunity that have evolved.

51.4 Cytotoxic T cells induce apoptosis, and helper T cells secrete cytokines.

- **Overview**: T cells distinguish an individual's own cells from foreign cells by recognition of **MHC proteins** on tissue cells of the body. **Cytotoxic T cells** (T_C) respond to peptides bound to **class I MHC proteins**, while **helper T cells** (T_H) respond to peptides bound to **class II MHC proteins**. Every nucleated cell has MHC class I proteins, but only **antigen-presenting cells** have MHC class II proteins. Activated cytotoxic T cells respond to unusual peptides bound to self MHC class I proteins to induce apoptosis of all target host cells expressing this unusual peptide. Activated helper T cells secrete **cytokines** that bind to membrane receptors to activate signaling cascades that promote their activation or differentiation. Cytokines released by T_H cells determine whether a **humoral** or a **cell-mediated immune response** is initiated. Both T_C and T_H produce **effector** and **memory cells**. T_C cells and T_H cells can be distinguished based on their cell surface markers, T_C cells have **CD8 protein**, and T_H cells have **CD4 protein**.
- **Details**: Understand the differences between T_H cells and T_C cells and why it is important that T cells undergo selection in the thymus. Know how T_H and T_C cells are activated and the result of this activation. Know the differences between a humoral and a cell-mediated immune response. Understand why the immune system can reject transplanted tissues.

51.5 B cells produce antibodies and are involved in the humoral immune response.

- **Overview**: **Immunoglobulin** molecules on a B cell bind to specific epitopes on an antigen and activate the B cell in the presence of additional signals leading to their proliferation into plasma cells and memory cells. Each plasma B cell produces antibodies with the same specificity as the membrane-bound antibodies in the parent B cell. These antibodies circulate in the lymph, blood, and extracellular fluid, and bind to epitopes of the antigen. Each immunoglobulin consists of two **light-chain** and two **heavy-chain**

molecules held together by disulfide bonds and arranged in a Y-shaped structure. The **variable region** located at the amino terminal ends of the arms (**Fab region**) contains the specificity for binding to antigen epitopes (**antigen-binding site**), which is determined by the size and the shape of the cleft in the Y-shaped structure. The rest of the sequence is relatively constant from one immunoglobulin to the next (**constant region**). The classes of antibodies, **IgH, IgD, IgG, IgA**, and **IgE,** are based on the structures of the constant regions of their heavy chains. Vertebrates generate diversity in antigen recognition by random **DNA rearrangements** of two (light-chain) or three (heavy-chain) separate DNA sequences (**VDJ segments**), which are joined to form each chain of the variable region. T-cell receptors also have variable and constant regions on two chains joined by a disulfide bond. The variable region at the amino terminal end of each chain binds to an MHC-peptide complex and is determined by the arrangement of V, D, J or V, J DNA segments. **Active immunity** develops during a primary response because of the production of memory cells that are activated more rapidly than naïve lymphocytes during a secondary response. This is the basis of vaccinations.

- **Details**: Know how B cells become activated and the result of this activation. Know the structure of an immunoglobulin molecule. Know the five classes of immunoglobulins and the functions of each. Understand how vertebrates generate antibody diversity. Recognize the similarities between the immunoglobulins of B cells and T-cell receptors. Understand how vaccines work.

51.6 Autoimmunity and hypersensitivity are examples of inappropriate or heightened immune responses.

- **Overview**: **Autoimmune diseases** are the result of the activation of auto-reactive T and B cells caused by a number of mechanisms. These diseases require suppression of the immune system to alleviate the symptoms. **Allergens** can provoke immediate **hypersensitivity** that results in excessive IgE production, which binds to mast cells. When exposed to the same allergen again, it binds to the exposed regions of IgE molecules in mast cells, triggering the release of histamines and prostaglandins. If the allergic reaction is severe, it can cause a rapid inflammatory response that can lead to **anaphylactic shock**. **Delayed hypersensitivity** requires that an antigen travel to a secondary lymphoid organ where T_H cells are then activated to release cytokines and activate macrophages.
- **Details**: Understand how an allergic response occurs. Understand how autoimmune diseases and delayed hypersensitivity occur.

51.7 Antibodies can be used in medical treatment and diagnosis.

- **Overview**: **Blood type** is determined by the antigens present on the surface of red blood cells. Depending on the allele present at a specific gene locus, I^A, I^B, or i, a specific sugar molecule is, or is not, added to a protein in the membrane of red blood cells. This protein-sugar complex acts as an antigen. The immune system makes antibodies that bind to red blood cells that are different from its own causing clumping and lysis of foreign red blood cells. The **Rh factor** is another antigen that is either present or absent on the surface of red blood cells. These antigens determine a person's blood type. **Polyclonal antibodies** to an antigen can be produced by purification and injection of a specific antigen into a laboratory animal, followed by subsequent serum isolation. **Monoclonal antibodies** are secreted from a B-cell/myeloma hybridoma produced by the isolation of B lymphocytes from an animal injected with an antigen that are then fused to cancerous multiple myeloma cells. Antibody production has a number of beneficial applications in medical research and in the treatment of cancer.
- **Details**: Understand how an individual's blood type is determined. Understand how polyclonal and monoclonal antibodies can be produced and the difference between the two. Know how monoclonal antibodies can be used to monitor the progression of AIDS and to eliminate tumors.

51.8 Some pathogens can evade the immune system.

- **Overview**: Pathogens, such as the **influenza virus**, can evade the immune system by altering the structures of their surface antigens. **Antigenic drift** caused by point mutations in the **hemagglutinin** and **neuraminidase** genes, and **antigenic shift** caused by the appearance of new viral subtypes allow the influenza virus to avoid immune system recognition. Bacteria can evade the immune system by altering flagellar proteins, inhibiting the fusion of a phagosome with lysosomes inside macrophages, or by secreting proteases that degrade antibodies that protect mucosal surfaces. **HIV** attacks the immune system itself by binding to CD4-expressing cells, such as T_H cells and monocytes, and either killing them, altering them so they are killed by T_C cells, or integrating into their genomes.
- **Details**: Understand how the influenza virus, some bacteria, and the virus that causes AIDS can evade the immune system.

CHALLENGING YOUR UNDERSTANDING—Part I

1. Fill in the following outline to indicate the components of each line of defense the body uses to protect itself from pathogens.

THE BODY'S DEFENSES AGAINST PATHOGENS

I. First Line of Defense: Prevent Entry

      A._____
      B._____
      C._____
      D._____

↓

II. Second Line of Defense: Nonspecific

      E._____
      F._____
      G._____
      H._____
      I._____

↓

III. Third Line of Defense: Specific and Long-Term

      J._____
      K._____

2. In the diagram of the immunoglobulin molecule below, label the light and heavy chains, the constant region, the variable region, the Fab regions, and the Fc region.

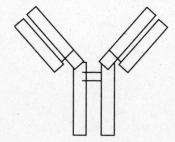

494

CHALLENGING YOUR UNDERSTANDING—Part II

1. Arrange the following lists of events in their proper sequence to show how each of the processes listed below occurs.

A. Formation of an immunoglobulin protein:
a. ____ Transcription through constant region exons.
b. ____ Heavy chain polypeptides are joined with light chains in the rough endoplasmic reticulum.
c. ____ DJ segments are joined to a V segment.
d. ____ Immunoglobulin protein is transported to the cell surface.
e. ____ Transcription of the VDJ segment.
f. ____ Transcripts are translated to produce heavy chain polypeptides.
g. ____ D segment joined to a J segment.
h. ____ Pre-mRNA splicing removes extra downstream J regions, and joins the variable region to either a μ, or a δ constant region.

B. Local inflammation:
a. ____ Blood flow causes swelling and promotes the accumulation of phagocytic cells.
b. ____ Histamines and prostaglandins are released from damaged cells.
c. ____ Invading pathogens penetrate the epithelial surface.
d. ____ Nearby blood vessels dilate and increase in permeability.
e. ____ Neutrophils and macrophages attack and engulf the invading pathogen.

C. Natural killer cells kill cells of the body infected with a virus:
a. ____ Apoptosis is induced.
b. ____ Vesicles in the natural killer cell containing perforin and granzymes move to the plasma membrane.
c. ____ Granzymes move into the target cell.
d. ____ The natural killer cell binds to the target cell.
e. ____ The target cell is broken down into membrane-enclosed vesicles.
f. ____ Caspase enzymes are activated in the target cell.
g. ____ Natural killer cell releases perforin and granzyme-containing vesicles by exocytosis.
h. ____ Perforins insert into the plasma membrane of the target cell and form a pore.
i. ____ Macrophages ingest the vesicles preventing the release of their contents into the tissues.

D. Production of a monoclonal antibody:
a. ____ Hybridoma cells are produced.
b. ____ A mouse is immunized several times with the antigen.
c. ____ Selected clones are regrown, and antibody specificity is checked again.
d. ____ The mouse is killed.
e. ____ A portion of the selected hybridoma culture is frozen for future use.
f. ____ The antibody produced by each hybridoma is tested.
g. ____ B lymphocytes are fused with myeloma cells.
h. ____ The selected hybridoma of interest is grown in mass culture for antibody production.
i. ____ Individual hybridoma cells are grown.
j. ____ An antigen is purified.
k. ____ B lymphocytes are collected from the mouse's spleen.

E. Action of a cytotoxic T cell against altered "self" cells:
a. ____ Naïve cytotoxic T cell undergoes clonal expansion.
b. ____ T_c cells destroy the altered cells by apoptosis.
c. ____ Naïve cytotoxic T cells are activated by TCR recognition of a foreign peptide on self-MHC class I proteins on dendritic cells; T_c cell binds to the dendritic cell.
d. ____ Activated progeny of the T_c cells recognize cells with the same self-MHC class I-peptide combination.
e. ____ Memory T_c cells persist in the cell.
f. ____ Many activated T_c cells and memory T_c cells are produced.

495

KEY TERMS

Match the numbered term with the definition that fits it best. Put the corresponding number in front of the appropriate definition.

1. skin
2. specific immune system
3. innate immune system
4. lysozyme
5. macrophages
6. neutrophils
7. natural killer cells
8. vaccination
9. antigen
10. antigenic determinants
11. antibodies
12. humoral immune response
13. cell-mediated immune response
14. active immunity
15. passive immunity

16. eosinophils
17. monocytes
18. basophils
19. MHC proteins
20. human leukocyte antigens
21. self-vs-nonself recognition
22. antigen-presenting cells
23. cytokines
24. immune surveillance
25. primary immune response
26. secondary immune response
27. immunoglobulins
28. light chains
29. heavy chains
30. DNA rearrangement

31. immunological tolerance
32. clonal selection
33. agglutinate
34. Rh factor
35. monoclonal antibodies
36. antigen shift
37. immediate hypersensitivity
38. delayed hypersensitivity
39. anaphylactic shock
40. polyclonal antibodies
41. antigen-binding site
42. constant region
43. variable region
44. mast cell

a. _____ The sudden appearance of a new influenza virus in which the HA or NA proteins are completely different.
b. _____ A type of leukocyte that becomes a phagocytic cell after moving into tissues; the precursor to macrophages.
c. _____ The ability of an individual's immune system to distinguish its own cells from foreign cells.
d. _____ An immune response carried out by T cells in which abnormal or virus-infected body cells are killed.
e. _____ Cells located under mucosal surfaces that release mediators such as histamine that promote inflammation.
f. _____ A phagocytic cell that is able to engulf and digest cellular debris and invading bacteria; an antigen-presenting cell.
g. _____ Integral membrane proteins in the plasma membrane of B-cells that act as receptors for antigens.
h. _____ A life-threatening state resulting from a rapid inflammatory response and the release of chemical mediators.
i. _____ The acceptance of one's own cells; an animal's immune system does not respond to the animal's own tissue.
j. _____ Two identical short polypeptides in an immunoglobulin molecule.
k. _____ An enzyme contained in sweat that digests bacterial cell walls.
l. _____ Immunity gained by obtaining antibodies from another individual.
m. _____ Circulating cells that secrete mediators such as histamine that promote inflammation.
n. _____ A cleft formed by the folding of the variable regions of the immunoglobulin heavy and light chains.
o. _____ The weak immune response that is mounted the first time a pathogen invades the body.
p. _____ Glycoproteins on the surfaces of most vertebrate cells that serve as self markers to the immune system.
q. _____ The outermost layer of the vertebrate body that represents the first barrier to penetration by microbes.
r. _____ The most abundant circulating leukocyte that ingests bacteria, or releases chemicals that kill bacteria.
s. _____ Abnormal B cells' response to an allergen due to excessive IgE production that occurs within seconds or minutes.
t. _____ The joining together of different segments of DNA to form the variable region of an immunoglobulin.
u. _____ Immunoglobulin proteins that are produced by lymphocytes and released in response to a foreign substance.
v. _____ A leukocyte that is important to the elimination of parasites and involved in chronic inflammatory diseases.
w. _____ Proteins secreted by activated T_H cells that initiate signaling cascades to promote activation of other cells.
x. _____ The second line of defense in which leukocytes nonspecifically attack pathogens within tissues.
y. _____ A group of antigens on red blood cells that an individual has (positive) or does not have (negative).
z. _____ Cells that take in and partially digest foreign particles, process antigens and move them to the membrane surface.
aa. _____ Cells that kill cells of the body that have been infected with viruses by inducing apoptosis.
bb. _____ Immunity acquired by infection with a pathogen, or by immunization with a portion or less-virulent form.
cc. _____ Antibodies that exhibit specificity for one antigenic determinant only.
dd. _____ Proteins encoded by the MHC complex in humans.
ee. _____ The third line of defense used to specifically identify and remove any foreign invading pathogens.
ff. _____ The detection and attack of tumor cells by natural killer cells often before they have had a chance to divide.
gg. _____ The amino terminal half of each Fab region in an immunoglobulin molecule.
hh. _____ Division of a naïve lymphocyte after it binds a foreign antigen to produce cells with identical antigen specificity.
ii. _____ Two identical longer polypeptides in an immunoglobulin molecule.

jj. _____ Injection of a harmless agent to confer resistance to a dangerous one.

kk. _____ An effective immune response elicited by the body once upon the second or subsequent exposure to an antigen.

ll. _____ B cells recognize antigens and divide resulting in large amount of circulating antibodies.

mm. _____ Abnormal immune response mediated by T_H cells and macrophages; symptoms occur 48 hours after the second exposure.

nn. _____ The region of an immunoglobulin molecule that does not change from one immunoglobulin to the next.

oo. _____ Different parts of a large antigen that can stimulate a distinct immune response; also known as epitopes.

pp. _____ Antibodies secreted by B-cell clones with many different specificities.

qq. _____ A molecule, such as a protein or a component of a microorganism, that provokes a specific immune response.

rr. _____ A clumping of red blood cells that occurs when one type of blood is mixed with serum from a person with a different blood type.

LEARNING BY EXPERIENCE

1. The cells of the immune system have different types of cell surface proteins that are crucial in the functioning of the immune system. Some of these proteins are immune receptors, and some are MHC (major histocompatibility complex) proteins. Complete the following chart by using a "+" sign or a "−" sign to indicate which type of cell has which type of surface protein.

Cell Type	T Receptor	B Receptor	MHC-1	MHC-2
B cells				
CD4$^+$ T cells (inducer and helper)				
CD8$^+$ T cells (cytotoxic and suppressor)				
Macrophages				

2. Match each of the following types of cells with its proper function in the immune system.

_____ a. B cells	i. lyse infected body cells
_____ b. cytotoxic T cells	ii. initiate the inflammatory response
_____ c. helper T cells	iii. decrease or terminate the immune response
_____ d. inducer T cells	iv. precursors of plasma cells and memory cells
_____ e. macrophages	v. phagocytize cells and present antigens
_____ f. neutrophils	vi. secrete antibodies
_____ g. plasma cells	vii. mediate maturation of T cells
_____ h. suppressor T cells	viii. initiate immune response

EXERCISING YOUR KNOWLEDGE

Briefly answer each of the following questions in the space provided.

1. Why is the skin an effective first line of defense against pathogens?

2. Compare and contrast the complement system to natural killer cells in terms of what they do.

3. Are fevers harmful or beneficial?

4. (a) Explain why blood is typed before transfusions. (b) How is this done? (c) Explain why type O blood is the international donor.

5. Why are T cells called T cells?

6. Why are helper T cells called the commanders of the immune system?

7. Why does a person's body try to reject transplanted organs? Why is the drug cyclosporine given to transplant patients?

8. What part of the immune system is responsible for long-term defense and explains why you only get childhood diseases such as chicken pox and measles once?

9. Are vertebrates the only animals that have an immune system?

10. Why is antigen shifting good for the pathogen and bad for the host?

Circle the letter of the one best answer in each of the following questions.

11. Which of the following cells participate in nonspecific defense responses when your body is invaded by microbes?
    a. natural killer cells
    b. macrophages
    c. neutrophils
    d. all of these
    e. none of these

12. The cells you see when you look at your skin were produced in the
    a. dermis.
    b. psoriasis layer.
    c. stratum basale.
    d. stratum corneum.
    e. subcutaneous tissue.

13. Monocytes are precursors of which of the following type of cells?
    a. macrophages
    b. plasma cells
    c. T cells
    d. mast cells
    e. complement

14. Interferons are produced by
    a. macrophages.
    b. memory cells.
    c. plasma cells.
    d. foreign cells that have invaded a host.
    e. host cells that have been invaded by a virus.

15. What is the first type of cells to appear at the site of tissue damage or infection?
    a. natural killer cells
    b. neutrophils
    c. monocytes
    d. macrophages
    e. lymphocytes

16. Which type of surface marker is present on every nucleated cell in your body?
    a. B receptor
    b. T receptor
    c. MHC-I
    d. MHC-II
    e. all of these

17. Which of the following is NOT a secondary lymphoid organ?
    a. appendix
    b. lymph nodes
    c. follicles in the connective tissue under the mucosal surfaces
    d. spleen
    e. none of the above

18. While T cells mature in the _____, B cells mature in the _____.
    a. spleen; thymus
    b. lymph nodes; bone marrow
    c. thymus; lymph nodes
    d. thymus; bone marrow
    e. bone marrow; spleen

19. If a T cell binds too strongly to self-MHC proteins with bound self-peptides in the thymus, which of the following occurs?
    a. It is transported out of the thymus to the blood.
    b. It undergoes apoptosis.
    c. It is altered in the spleen.
    d. It enters a lymph node
    e. It is ingested, and phagocytosed.

20. Which of the following is NOT true of the structures of both an immunoglobulin molecule and a T cell receptor?
    a. Both consist of four chains wound around each other.
    b. Both have a membrane-proximal constant region.
    c. Both have amino terminal variable regions on each chain.
    d. Both variable region gene segments are joined in a similar fashion.
    e. Disulfide bonds hold the chains of both molecules together.

21. Memory cells
    a. are produced by macrophages.
    b. are responsible for passive immunity.
    c. prevent an animal from encountering certain pathogens.
    d. are responsible for determining what MHC receptors a cell will have.
    e. provide an accelerated secondary immune response.

22. A person with anti-A and anti-B antibodies in the blood has what blood type?
    a. type A
    b. type B
    c. type AB
    d. type O

23. Your body has millions of different antibodies for detecting millions of different antigens because
    a. your body has millions of different antibody genes.
    b. antibody genes undergo antigen shifting.
    c. antibody genes undergo somatic rearrangement and somatic mutation.
    d. your body has millions of different T cells.
    e. Nobody knows why.

24. Which antibody is responsible for allergic responses?
    a. IgA
    b. IgD
    c. IgE
    d. IgG
    e. IgM

25. To be activated, T cells must do which of the following?
    a. recognize the antibodies secreted by B cells
    b. be infected by a pathogen
    c. recognize peptide fragments bound to self-MHC proteins
    d. have the CD8 protein on their cell surface
    e. bind to an epitope of an intact antigen that is or is not a protein

26. Evidence of a two-part immune system with cell-mediated and humoral responses is first seen in what group of animals, evolutionarily speaking?
    a. insects
    b. sea star
    c. sponges
    d. earthworms
    e. fish

27. Which of the following is an example of a mechanism by which an autoimmune disease may result?
    a. A protein that is normally hidden from the immune system becomes exposed in a certain tissue.
    b. Cells become infected with a pathogen.
    c. T cells become tolerant.
    d. B cells become permanently active against any protein.
    e. All of the above.

28. How are autoimmune diseases usually treated?
    a. blood transfusion
    b. surgery to remove the auto-reactive tissue
    c. suppression of the immune system with drugs
    d. bone marrow transplant
    e. administration of nonreactive antibodies

29. How are antibodies being used to treat cancer?
    a. Antibodies that activate macrophages are administered.
    b. Antibodies are fused to tumor suppressor proteins and reintroduced into the body.
    c. Antibodies to oncogenic proteins are raised and injected into cancer patients.
    d. A toxin is attached to antibodies that bind to cancer cells.
    e. None of the above.

30. Why can humans maintain immunity to some pathogens for several decades, but they cannot maintain immunity to others such as the influenza virus?
    a. Some pathogens fail to activate the immune system, but are eradicated by other means.
    b. The antigens of some pathogens change very frequently.
    c. The antigens of some pathogens induce autoimmune reactions.
    d. Some pathogens kill memory cells.
    e. Some pathogens actively prevent the maturation and differentiation of naïve lymphocytes.

ASSESSING YOUR KNOWLEDGE

Answers to the questions in this section test your ability to synthesize information gained from the chapter and to solve challenging problems on an exam or in everyday life.

Challenging Your Understanding—Part I, Answers

1. IA-D. Skin, Mucous membranes, Acidic sweat containing lysozyme, Normal flora

   IIE-I. Macrophages, Neutrophils, Natural killer cells, Complement system, Interferons

   IIIJ-K. Cell-mediated response by T cells, Humoral immune response by B cells

2.

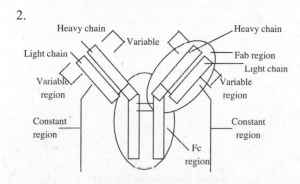

Challenging Your Understanding—Part II, Answers

1A. Formation of an immunoglobulin protein:
a. 4, b. 7, c. 2, d. 8, e. 3, f. 6, g. 1, h. 5.

1B. Local inflammation:
a. 4, b. 2, c. 1, d. 3, e. 5.

1C. Natural killer cells kill cells of the body infected with a virus:
a. 7, b. 2, c. 5, d. 1, e. 8, f. 6, g. 3, h. 4, i. 9.

1D. Production of a monoclonal antibody:
a. 6, b. 2, c. 9, d. 3, e. 11, f. 8, g. 5, h. 10, i. 7, j. 1, k. 4.

1E. Action of a cytotoxic T cell against altered "self" cells:
a. 2, b. 5, c. 1, d. 4, e. 6, f. 3.

Key Terms—Answers

a. 36, b. 17, c. 21, d. 13, e. 44, f. 5, g. 27, h. 39, i. 31, j. 28, k. 4, l. 15, m. 18, n. 41, o. 25, p. 19, q. 1, r. 6, s. 37, t. 30, u. 11, v. 16, w. 23, x. 3, y. 34, z. 22, aa. 7, bb. 14, cc. 35, dd. 20, ee. 2, ff. 24, gg. 43, hh. 32, ii. 29, jj. 8, kk. 26, ll. 12, mm. 38, nn. 42, oo. 10, pp. 40, qq. 9, rr. 33.

Learning by Experience—Answers

1.

Cell Type	T Receptor	B Receptor	MHC-1	MHC-2
B cells	-	+	+	+
CD4$^+$ T cells (inducer and helper)	+	-	+	+
CD8$^+$ T cells (cytotoxic and suppressor)	+	-	+	-
Macrophages	-	-	+	+

2. a. iv
   b. i
   c. viii
   d. vii
   e. v
   f. ii
   g. vi
   h. iii

Exercising Your Knowledge—Answers

As you check your answers, put a mark in the review (Rvw.) column for the answers you missed. If you didn't miss any, congratulations—you have mastered the chapter! If you missed some, review the section (Sect.) in the text where this concept is discussed. In order to develop an efficient review strategy, it is important that you understand what types of questions you missed. The questions with asterisks test more for understanding of the **concepts**, whereas the others test more for **detail**. *See the preface for learning strategies for concepts and for detail.*

	Sect.	Rvw.
*1. Skin is a physical barrier that is hard to penetrate. It has low pH due to oil and sweat, which inhibits growth of microorganisms. Sweat contains lysozyme that digests bacterial cell walls. The surface layer of cells continually sloughs off and is replaced so pathogens don't get well established.	51.1	
*2. The complement system is just proteins, not cells, but both attack and destroy invading pathogens as part of the nonspecific second line of defense. Both systems have a similar mechanism: create a hole in the plasma membrane so that the cell lyses (ruptures). Natural killer cells attack virus-infected host cells. Complement proteins attack invading bacterial and fungal cells.	51.2	
*3. Fevers are beneficial as long as they don't get too high. Elevated temperature stimulates phagocytosis and removes iron from the blood (bacteria need iron). High fevers are dangerous since high temperatures can denature proteins and thus shut down enzyme activity.	51.2	

*4. (a) Blood has to be typed before a blood transfusion because the immune system is tolerant to its own red blood cell antigens, but makes antibodies that bind to those that differ, causing clumping and lysis of foreign red blood cells. Therefore, if the wrong blood type is used in a transfusion this will occur. After lysis of the red blood cells, hemoglobin is released and converted to bilirubin, which is toxic to cells and can cause severe organ damage. (b) Blood is typed by mixing it with serum from a person with type A, B, AB, or O blood. If the blood in question is type A, the anti-A antibodies in the serum from the person with type B or type O blood cause the type A red blood cells to agglutinate. This does not happen when the type A blood is mixed with serum from a person with type A or type AB blood. (c) Type O blood does not express either A or B antigens, so it is impossible for any other individual of a different blood type to produce antibodies that will agglutinate it. — 51.7

*5. Although they originate in the bone marrow, T cells migrate to the thymus gland, where they mature and become functional. T is for thymus. — 51.3

*6. Helper T cells participate in and help facilitate every aspect of the immune response. They activate inducer T cells and suppressor T cells, stimulate B cells and cytotoxic T cells to multiply, and stimulate macrophages to congregate at sites of infection. — 51.2, 51.3, 51.4

*7. The transplanted organ has MHC proteins that are different from self and therefore are attacked by the immune system. Cyclosporine inactivates cytotoxic T cells, which would normally attack and destroy the foreign cells. — 51.4

*8. Memory cells; when B cells are activated in response to an antigen, they divide rapidly and produce both plasma cells and memory cells. The memory cells confer long-term immunity, immediately recognizing and attacking the pathogen if it ever invades again. The memory cells allow a quick enough response that the pathogen cannot get established. — 51.5

*9. No; vertebrates have the most sophisticated immune system, with B cells and T cells, but all animals have physical defenses against pathogens, can recognize self versus nonself cells, and have phagocytic cells. — 51.3

*10. Antigen shifting makes it difficult, if not impossible, for the host's immune system to mount a successful attack and defense against the pathogen. If a pathogen invades your body with antigen #1 on its surface, your immune system will produce antibodies against antigen #1 and seek out and destroy all cells with antigen #1 on them. But if the pathogen has shifted antigens and now has antigen #2 on its surface, it will not be attacked by the antibodies and other defenses directed against antigen #1. By the time your body musters its defenses against antigen #2, the pathogen may have shifted antigens again. Antigen shifting not only evades your body's immune response, but also makes it difficult to develop a successful vaccine against the pathogen. — 51.8

11. d	51.2
12. c	51.1
13. a	51.2
14. e	51.2
15. b	51.2
16. c	51.4
17. e	51.3
*18. d	51.3
*19. b	51.3
*20. a	51.5
*21. e	51.5
*22. d	51.7
*23. c	51.5
24. c	51.5
*25. c	51.5
*26. e	51.3
27. a	51.6
28. c	51.6
29. d	51.7
*30. b	51.8

CHAPTER 52 THE REPRODUCTIVE SYSTEM

MASTERING KEY CONCEPTS

Sexual reproduction is a very old phenomenon. It evolved in the sea, long before the vertebrates, and ensures high levels of genetic diversity in the offspring. Almost all vertebrates reproduce sexually, and sex is one of the most powerful of all drives. Sexual reproduction on land has desiccation constraints not found with aquatic sex, and terrestrial vertebrates have evolved various ways to protect their eggs and developing embryos. The anatomy and physiology of human reproduction provide a good example for understanding vertebrate sexual reproduction.

52.1 Animals employ both sexual and asexual reproductive strategies.

- **Overview**: Bacteria, protists, archaea, cnidarians, and tunicates undergo **asexual reproduction** to produce genetically identical cells from a single parent cell by mitosis. Single-celled organisms divide by the asexual process of **fission** to become separate, identical organisms. Cnidarians reproduce asexually by **budding,** in which part of the body separates to become a new individual. Some female arthropods produce offspring from unfertilized eggs by the asexual process of **parthenogenesis**. Other organisms, such as tapeworms, can produce both sperm and eggs (**hermaphrodites**) and can undergo **self-fertilization**. Some other hermaphrodites, such as earthworms, still require another individual to reproduce. Some hermaphroditic fish act as male or female and can change their sex apparently according to social contact (**sequential hermaphroditism**). Most animals reproduce **sexually** through the fusion of two haploid gametes produced by two different parents. This fusion produces a zygote that undergoes mitosis to form an embryo. The sex of an embryo is determined by the presence or absence of the *SRY* **gene** on the **Y chromosome**. If an embryo has the *SRY* gene, it becomes a male, but if it lacks the *SRY* gene, it becomes a female.
- **Details**: Know the different types of reproductive methods that organisms undergo. Understand how sex is determined in mammalian embryos.

52.2 The evolution of reproduction among the vertebrates has led to internalization of fertilization and development.

- **Overview**: Marine bony fish and most amphibians undergo **external fertilization,** where females release eggs, and males release sperm into the water. Union of these gametes depends on a synchronized release that may be governed by the lunar cycle. **Internal**

fertilization in terrestrial vertebrates evolved under selective pressure for gametes to be kept in moist environments. Offspring produced by internal fertilization develop outside the mother's body in eggs (**oviparity**), or develop inside of the mother obtaining nourishment from the egg yolk (**ovoviviparity**), or develop inside of the mother obtaining nourishment from the mother's blood (**viviparity**). Most reptiles and birds are oviparous. They undergo internal fertilization and lay **amniotic eggs** with a series of **extraembryonic membranes**. Reptiles typically abandon their eggs, while birds incubate their eggs, and nurture their young until they reach maturity. Some mammals, such as the duck-billed platypus (**monotremes**), are oviparous, but most are viviparous. **Marsupials** give birth to underdeveloped fetuses that complete their development in a pouch, while **placental mammals** have longer periods of gestation nourishing their young internally through a **placenta**. Most female mammals undergo an **estrous cycle** during which they ovulate and are sexually receptive. Humans and apes have **menstrual cycles**, while rabbits and cats are induced ovulators.
- **Details**: Know which organisms undergo external and internal fertilization. Know the three strategies for vertebrate development. Understand the similarities and the differences between reptile eggs and the eggs of birds. Understand how reptile and bird eggs differ from the eggs of fish and amphibians. Know how different mammals reproduce and how their fetuses develop.

52.3 The male reproductive system is specialized to produce and deliver large quantities of sperm cells to the female.

- **Overview**: **Testosterone** secretion by the **Leydig cells** during embryonic development leads to the formation of the **scrotum** and the **penis**. The scrotum is a sac that holds the **testes,** which contain **seminiferous tubules** containing **spermatogonia** (2n), which will undergo mitosis. One of these cells, the **primary spermatocyte**, will then undergo meiosis to produce four haploid cells that become **sperm cells**. From the seminiferous tubules, sperm cells are passed into the **epididymis** and then to the **vas deferens**. Sperm cells are mixed with fluids produced by the **seminal vesicles, prostate gland**, and **bulbourethral gland** that make up the **semen,** which is carried out of the body through the **urethra**. Hormones secreted by the anterior pituitary gland stimulate sperm development by the **Sertoli cells (follicle-stimulating hormone**), and the secretion of testosterone by the Leydig cells (**luteinizing hormone**).

- **Details**: Know the structures of the human male reproductive system. Understand how sperm cells are produced and the main components of these cells. Know where sperm cells are produced and the path they follow to move out of the body. Understand the importance of follicle-stimulating hormone, luteinizing hormone, and testosterone to male development and sperm production.

52.4 The female reproductive system provides a site for fertilization to take place and is specialized for development of the embryo.

- **Overview**: In the absence of testosterone, an embryo develops a **clitoris** and **labia majora** and develops as a female. The **ovary** consists of many ovarian follicles, each containing a **primary oocyte**. During the menstrual cycle, some of the follicles containing primary oocytes are stimulated to develop by **follicle-stimulating hormone (FSH)**, but only one reaches maturity by ovulation, the **Graafian follicle**. The primary oocyte in the Graafian follicle completes the first meiotic division to produce a **polar body** and a **secondary oocyte,** which is released at ovulation into the **Fallopian tube** by the secretion of **luteinizing hormone (LH)**. This secondary oocyte only completes the second meiotic division if it becomes fertilized. At this same time, **estradiol** is stimulating the growth of the **endometrial lining** of the uterus. During the **luteal phase** of the cycle, which occurs after ovulation, the Graafian follicle develops into a **corpus luteum** by LH stimulation. The corpus luteum secretes estradiol and **progesterone,** which inhibits the secretion of FSH and LH by the anterior pituitary gland, and causes the endometrium to become more vascular preparing it for embryo implantation. At the end of the luteal phase, the corpus luteum degenerates and estradiol and progesterone levels decline causing the endometrium to be sloughed off accompanied by bleeding during the **menstrual phase**. Mammals with estrous cycles do not undergo menstruation. If the oocyte is fertilized by a sperm cell that travels up to the Fallopian tubes through the **vagina**, the embryo secretes a LH-like hormone, **human chorionic gonadotropin**, which maintains the corpus luteum, keeping estradiol and progesterone levels high and preventing menstruation. The zygote undergoes several mitotic divisions in the Fallopian tube and then reaches the **uterus**, where it is implanted in the endometrial wall.

- **Details**: Know the structures of the human female reproductive system. Understand how and when the primary and secondary oocytes and the egg cell are produced. Understand the roles of FSH, LH, estradiol, progesterone, and human chorionic gonadotropin in the menstrual cycle. Know when these hormones are produced, how their levels are regulated, and what events correlate with changes in their levels during the menstrual cycle.

52.5 Many methods of birth control exist that differ in their effectiveness, permanence, and side effects.

- **Overview**: **Contraception** is used to prevent pregnancy by acting prior to the implantation of an embryo in the uterine wall. **Abstinence** is the most reliable method of birth control. Male contraceptive devices, such as **condoms**, and female contraceptive devices, such as **cervical caps**, **diaphragms**, or **chemical spermicides**, prevent the delivery of sperm to the egg, but have differing rates of effectiveness. **Birth control pills** prevent follicle development and ovulation, and cause a buildup of the endometrium due to the presence of hormone analogues in the pills. Hormone-containing capsules can also be implanted beneath the skin. **Intrauterine devices** are placed in the uterus to prevent implantation of the embryo in the uterine wall. Surgical procedures can be performed to promote sterility. **Sterilization** in males involves a vasectomy, which prevents sperm from entering the semen, while in females it involves tubal ligation, which prevents an ovulated oocyte from reaching the uterus. **Infertility** in females can result from blockage of the Fallopian tubes, premature ovarian failure, or disruption of the normal hormonal control of ovulation, or of the thickening of the uterine wall. Male infertility results from a reduction in the number of sperm, viability, or motility. Hormonal treatments, **artificial insemination**, *in vitro* **fertilization**, and **intracytoplasmic sperm injection** are all techniques being used to treat infertility and promote reproduction.

- **Details**: Know the different methods of birth control, how they work, and how effective they are. Understand the disadvantages of each. Know how males and females are surgically sterilized, and the methods being used to treat infertility.

CHALLENGING YOUR UNDERSTANDING—Part I

1. Indicate the hormones responsible for each of the male reproductive events listed below.

a. ----------------------------- Stimulates Leydig cells to secrete testosterone.

b. ----------------------------- Stimulates Sertoli cells to facilitate sperm development.

c. ----------------------------- Stimulates the anterior pituitary gland to secrete LH and FSH.

d. ----------------------------- Causes Sertoli cells to release inhibin, which inhibits FSH secretion.

e. ----------------------------- Development of the beard, deeper voice, and body hair.

2. Fill in the following flowchart using the information above to indicate the hormonal interactions that stimulate sperm production and maintain male secondary structures. Identify the negative feedback inhibition that controls hormone production.

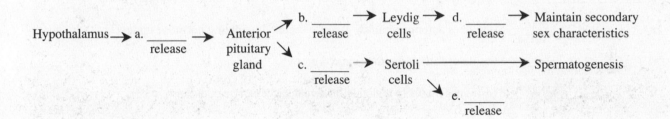

3. Fill in the blanks in the following flowcharts to indicate how spermatogenesis and oogenesis occur.

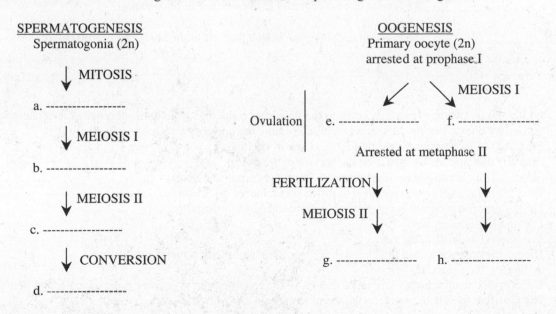

CHALLENGING YOUR UNDERSTANDING—Part II

1. Indicate the hormones responsible for each of the events in the female reproductive cycle listed below. Note: Each event listed may be stimulated by more than one hormone. In those cases, indicate both hormones involved.

a. _____ Development of the Graafian follicle into the corpus luteum.

b. _____ Stimulates the endometrium to grow.

c. _____ Triggers the onset of menstrual cycling.

d. _____ Hormones secreted by the corpus luteum.

e. _____ Hormones that stimulate the endometrium to become more vascular and glandular.

f. _____ Maintenance of the corpus luteum, keeping estradiol and progesterone levels high, if fertilization occurs.

g. _____ Graafian follicle bursts releasing its secondary oocyte.

h. _____ Hormones that inhibit FSH and LH secretion by the anterior pituitary gland.

i. _____ Stimulates anterior pituitary gland to secrete luteinizing hormone midcycle.

j. _____ Stimulates follicles in the ovary to grow.

k. _____ Hormones that help maintain the female accessory sex organs.

2. Indicate the hormones whose levels decline to bring about each of the events in the female reproductive cycle listed below. Note: Each event listed is caused by a decrease in the levels of more than one hormone.

a. _____ The corpus luteum degrades in the absence of fertilization.

b. _____ The built-up endometrium is sloughed off in the absence of fertilization.

3. Put in order the following events that occur in the female reproductive cycle in the absence of fertilization.
a. ____ Secondary oocyte begins the second meiotic division, but becomes arrested at metaphase II.
b. ____ Estradiol and progesterone levels in the blood rapidly decline.
c. ____ Graafian follicle forms a blister on the surface of the ovary.
d. ____ Graafian follicle completes development to form the corpus luteum.
e. ____ Follicles in the ovary are stimulated to grow; one achieves full maturity.
f. ____ The built-up endometrium is sloughed off accompanied by bleeding.
g. ____ The oocyte disentegrates.
h. ____ The corpus luteum disintegrates.
i. ____ The primary oocyte within the Graafian follicle completes the first meiotic division producing the secondary oocyte.
j. ____ The corpus luteum secretes hormones that cause the endometrium to become more vascular and glandular.
k. ____ The Graafian follicle bursts releasing the potential egg cell from the ovary.

KEY TERMS

Match the numbered term with the definition that fits it best. Put the corresponding number in front of the appropriate definition.

1. oviparity	16. internal fertilization	31. sterilization
2. ovoviviparity	17. estrus	32. oral contraceptives
3. viviparity	18. estrous cycle	33. contraception
4. gametes	19. monotremes	34. seminiferous tubules
5. sperm	20. marsupials	35. Fallopian tubes
6. egg	21. placental mammals	36. uterus
7. zygote	22. acrosome	37. epididymis
8. fission	23. luteal phase	38. vas deferens
9. budding	24. follicular phase	39. seminal vesicles
10. parthenogenesis	25. Graafian follicle	40. prostate gland
11. hermaphroditism	26. proliferative phase	41. Sertoli cells
12. protogyny	27. secretory phase	42. endometrium
13. protandry	28. menstrual phase	
14. *SRY* gene	29. infertility	
15. external fertilization	30. intrauterine device	

a. _____ Oviparous mammals that incubate their eggs in a nest or pouch; young feed by licking their mother's skin.

b. _____ The birth control pill taken by some women, which contains hormones to prevent ovulation.

c. _____ A simple, columnar epitherlial membrane lining the uterus.

d. _____ A highly conserved gene on the Y chromosome in vertebrates; determines if an embryo develops as a male.

e. _____ Reproduction in which eggs develop within the mother's body and young are born free-living.

f. _____ The phase following ovulation in the uterine cycle in which estradiol and progesterone maintain the endometrium.

g. _____ A small plastic or metal device placed in the uterus that prevents implantation of an embryo.

h. _____ A reproductive strategy in which one individual has both testes and ovaries and can produce sperm and eggs.

i. _____ A vesicle that caps the head of spermatozoa and contains enzymes that aid in the penetration of the egg layers.

j. _____ Asexual reproduction in which an organism divides and each part becomes a separate, identical organism.

k. _____ In male mammals, glandular tissue at the base of the urethra that contributes up to 30% of the bulk of the semen.

l. _____ A period of time around the time of ovulation in which female mammals are sexually receptive to males.

m. _____ Highly convoluted tubules in the testes of the human male in which spermatogenesis takes place.

n. _____ The male gamete required for fertilization by sexual reproduction.

o. _____ A phase in the ovarian cycle when ovarian follicles are stimulated to grow, producing the Graafian follicle.

p. _____ A form of asexual reproduction in which females produce offspring from unfertilized eggs.

q. _____ Mammals that nourish their fetuses by a structure derived from the chorion and the mother's uterine lining.

r. _____ The portion of the uterine cycle where the built-up endometrium is sloughed off, accompanied by bleeding.

s. _____ The diploid fertilized egg formed as a result of fusion of two gametes during fertilization.

t. _____ Reproduction where the eggs, fertilized internally, are deposited outside of the mother's body to develop.

u. _____ The introduction of male gametes directly into the female reproductive tract.

v. _____ A phase in the ovarian cycle following ovulation when the Graafian follicle develops into the corpus luteum.

w. _____ A long tube that sperm enters from the epididymis that then passes it into the abdominal cavity.

x. _____ Sequential hermaphroditism in which an organism undergoes a sex change from a male to a female.

y. _____ The surgical removal of portions of the tubes that transport gametes from the gonads, preventing reproduction.

z. _____ The inability to conceive after 12 months of contraception-free sexual intercourse.

aa. _____ Nongerminal cells in the seminiferous tubules that secrete products required for spermatogenesis.

bb. _____ Fertilized eggs complete development inside of the mother, but obtain nourishment from the yolk.

cc. _____ The female gamete required for fertilization by sexual reproduction.

dd. _____ Another name for the reproductive cycle in most mammals.

ee. _____ The uterine tubes, or oviducts, that transport ova from the ovaries to the uterus.

ff. _____ One follicle in the ovaries that achieves full maturity by ovulation and contains the primary oocyte.

gg. _____ Sequential hermaphroditism in which an organism undergoes a sex change from a female to a male.

hh. _____ A pair of glands in the human male that produces a fructose-rich fluid; joins with the vas deferens.

ii. _____ A group of mammals that give birth to fetuses that are incompletely developed; complete development in a pouch.

jj. _____ A phase in the uterine cycle in which estradiol causes growth of the endometrium.

kk. ____ An organ found in female mammals in which a developing embryo is contained and nurtured during pregnancy.

ll. ____ Reproduction in which an outgrowth of an organism's body becomes separated to form a new individual.

mm. ____ Methods of birth control that act prior to the implantation of an embryo.

nn. ____ Haploid reproductive cells.

oo. ____ The union of free gametes outside of the body.

pp. ____ A long tube in the human male that receives sperm from the seminiferous tubules and passes it to the vas deferens.

LEARNING BY EXPERIENCE

1. Complete the following chart by writing in the specific part of the male or female body where each of the events takes place in humans.

Event	Location
a. fertilization of egg cell	
b. production of FSH and LH	
c. production of GnRH	
d. production of progesterone	
e. production of testosterone	
f. release of sperm into female during normal intercourse	
g. sperm cells become motile	
h. spermatogenesis	

2. Trace the pathway of a human male gamete from its site of production to its release from the body by arranging the following terms in their proper sequence.

Terms	Sequence
epididymis	
seminiferous tubules	
urethra	
vas deferens	

3. Trace the pathway of a human female gamete from its site of production to its release from the body (either as a developed baby or an unfertilized egg) by arranging the following terms in their proper sequence.

Terms	Sequence
cervix	
fallopian tube	
follicle	
uterus	
vagina	

EXERCISING YOUR KNOWLEDGE

Briefly answer each of the following questions in the space provided.

1. What are the advantages and disadvantages of being a self-fertilizing hermaphrodite?

2. In mammals, females are the "default" sex when it comes to sex determination. Explain what this means.

3. Evolutionarily, which developed first in vertebrates, internal or external fertilization? Why?

4. How do amphibians get around the problem of not putting huge amounts of costly yolk in their eggs, but having long development times required for their offspring to become adults?

5. Both birds and reptiles are oviparous, but birds incubate their eggs and reptiles don't. Why?

6. There has been an evolutionary trend among the vertebrates toward increasing protection of the developing embryo, going from the "naked" eggs of bony fish and amphibians, to the amniotic eggs of reptiles and birds, to the increasingly long retention of the fetus inside the mother's womb in mammals. What are some of the advantages and disadvantages of such increasing protection for the mothers as well as for their offspring? Do you think there is a limit to how far this trend can or will proceed?

7. A typical single ejaculation by a man contains about 300 million sperm cells. Why so many—isn't this wasteful?

8. If an ovulated egg is successfully fertilized by a sperm cell, what causes the woman's reproductive system to shift into pregnancy mode with the uterus receptive to the embryo, rather than continuing the menstrual cycle and having the lining of the uterus slough off?

9. The older a woman is when she becomes a mother, the greater the chance that her child will suffer a genetic defect. Do you think the same relationship holds true regarding the age of the father? Why or why not?

10. In addition to the forms of contraception discussed in the text, some couples use the so-called "rhythm method," abstaining from sex for a few days each month of the woman's cycle. What is the physiological basis behind this method of contraception?

Circle the letter of the one best answer in each of the following questions.

11. Cnidaria commonly reproduce by
    a. budding.
    b. fission.
    c. parthenogenesis.
    d. hermaphroditism.
    e. metamorphosis.

12. Which of the following is NOT a true statement regarding reproduction in reptiles and birds?
    a. Birds incubate their eggs, while most reptiles abandon their eggs.
    b. Both reptiles and birds practice internal fertilization.
    c. Bird eggs have hard, calcerous shells, while reptile eggs do not.
    d. Bird eggs have several extraembryonic membranes, while reptile eggs have only a yolk sac.
    e. None of the above.

13. For how long are the embryonic gonads of mammals sexually "indifferent"?
    a. about 4 days
    b. about 40 days
    c. about 4 months
    d. about 4 years
    e. until puberty

14. The first vertebrates to engage in sexual reproduction were
    a. primitive terrestrial vertebrates.
    b. advanced terrestrial vertebrates.
    c. primitive marine vertebrates.
    d. advanced marine vertebrates.

15. Internal fertilization evolved in terrestrial vertebrates due to strong selective pressure for which of the following?
    a. gametes to be released close to each other
    b. fetuses to be kept warm, moist, nourished, and protected inside the mother
    c. the simultaneous release of gametes
    d. gametes to be kept in a nondesiccating environment
    e. fetuses to be fully developed before birth

16. Which of the following animals obtain milk from their mother by licking her skin?
    a. a dog
    b. a duck-billed platypus
    c. a kangaroo
    d. a frog
    e. none of these

17. Compared with fish, most amphibians have
    a. internal fertilization rather than external.
    b. a much shorter development time.
    c. just one offspring in each reproductive cycle.
    d. all of these.
    e. none of these.

18. Which mammals are oviparous?
    a. marsupials
    b. placental mammals
    c. monotremes
    d. All mammals are oviparous.
    e. No mammals are oviparous.

19. The placenta is derived from both the mother's uterine lining and the embryo's
    a. chorion.
    b. yolk sac.
    c. amnion.
    d. allantois.
    e. cloaca.

20. How many chromosomes does a normal, mature human sperm cell have?
    a. 1
    b. 2
    c. 23
    d. 46
    e. millions

21. During sexual intercourse, what makes the human penis enlarge and become rigid?
    a. blood
    b. semen
    c. bone
    d. muscular contractions
    e. None of the above.

22. The majority of the volume of the semen is produced by the
    a. seminal vesicles.
    b. prostate gland.
    c. bulbourethral glands.
    d. seminiferous tubules.
    e. They all contribute equal amounts.

23. What is the function of the acrosome?
    a. provide swimming mechanism for sperm cells
    b. help keep the testes at an appropriate temperature
    c. provide a storage place for sperm
    d. make the penis rigid during sexual arousal
    e. help the sperm cell penetrate the egg cell during fertilization

24. Which of the following is the largest in size?
    a. a mature sperm cell
    b. a mature egg cell
    c. a polar body
    d. They are all approximately the same size.

25. Ovulation is caused by a surge of
    a. estradiol.
    b. progesterone.
    c. FSH.
    d. LH.
    e. hCG.

26. How long does it take a fertilized egg cell (zygote) to reach the uterus?
    a. a few hours
    b. about one day
    c. about three days
    d. about a week
    e. about a month

27. During each menstrual cycle, a woman's uterine lining builds up and becomes vascularized in preparation for possible pregnancy. This proliferative phase of the endometrium is caused primarily by which hormones?
    a. estradiol and progesterone
    b. FSH and LH
    c. GnRH and hCG
    d. estradiol and FSH
    e. progesterone and LH

28. Which of the following does NOT contribute to infertility in females?
    a. decreased levels of GnRH in the follicular phase
    b. reduction in the thickening of the uterine wall
    c. premature ovarian failure
    d. blockage of the Fallopian tubes
    e. inadequate levels of FSH in the luteal phase

29. Which of the following forms of birth control does *not* prevent conception?
    a. a condom
    b. a diaphragm
    c. birth control pills
    d. a vasectomy
    e. an IUD

30. Which of the following statements is true?
    a. A vasectomy or tubal ligation makes the person sterile and unable to produce sex hormones.
    b. In a vasectomy, the urethra is cut and tied off.
    c. The failure rate of birth control pills is higher than that of diaphragms.
    d. "Morning-after pills" contain 50 times more estrogen than birth control pills do.
    e. Birth control pills and IUDs are considered virtually risk free.

ASSESSING YOUR KNOWLEDGE

Answers to the questions in this section test your ability to synthesize information gained from the chapter and to solve challenging problems on an exam or in everyday life.

Challenging Your Understanding—Part I, Answers

1a. Luteinizing hormone
 b. Follicle-stimulating hormone
 c. Gonadotropin-releasing hormone
 d. Follicle-stimulating hormone
 e. Testosterone

2.

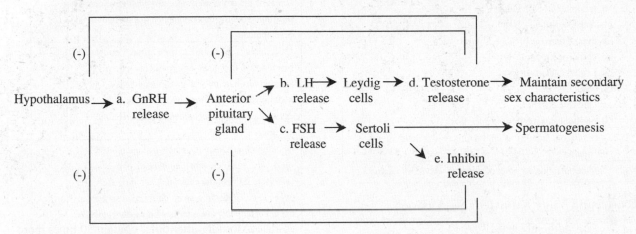

3a. Primary spermatocyte (2n)
 b. Secondary spermatocytes (n)
 c. Spermatids (n)
 d. Spermatozoa (n)
 e. Polar body
 f. Secondary oocyte (n)
 g. Second polar body
 h. Ovum (n)
(Answers for 3e and 3f may be exchanged, but the answers for 3g and 3h must also be exchanged in that situation.)

Challenging Your Understanding—Part II, Answers

1a. Luteinizing hormone
 b. Estradiol
 c. Estradiol
 d. Estradiol, progesterone
 e. Estradiol, progesterone
 f. Human chorionic gonadotropin
 g. Luteinizing hormone
 h. Estradiol, progesterone
 i. Estradiol
 j. Follicle-stimulating hormone
 k. Estradiol, progesterone

2a. Luteinizing hormone, Follicle-stimulating hormone
 b. Estradiol, progesterone

3. a. 4, b. 10, c. 2, d. 7, e. 1, f. 11, g. 6, h. 9, i. 3, j. 8, k. 5.

Key Terms—Answers

a. 19, b. 32, c. 42, d. 14, e. 3, f. 27, g. 30, h. 11, i. 22,
j. 8, k. 40, l. 17, m. 34, n. 5, o. 24, p. 10, q. 21, r. 28,
s. 7, t. 1, u. 16, v. 23, w. 38, x. 13, y. 31, z. 29, aa. 41,
bb. 2, cc. 6, dd. 18, ee. 35, ff. 25, gg. 12, hh. 39,
ii. 20, jj. 26, kk. 36, ll. 9, mm. 33, nn. 4, oo. 15,
pp. 37.

Learning by Experience—Answers

1.	a. fallopian tube (oviduct)
	b. anterior pituitary gland
	c. hypothalamus
	d. corpus luteum in ovary
	e. Leydig cells in testes
	f. vagina
	g. epididymis
	h. seminiferous tubules in testes
2.	seminiferous tubules → epididymis → vas deferens → urethra
3.	follicle → fallopian tube → uterus → cervix → vagina

Exercising Your Knowledge—Answers

As you check your answers, put a mark in the review (Rvw.) column for the answers you missed. If you didn't miss any, congratulations—you have mastered the chapter! If you missed some, review the section (Sect.) in the text where this concept is discussed. In order to develop an efficient review strategy, it is important that you understand what types of questions you missed. The questions with asterisks test more for understanding of the **concepts**, whereas the others test more for **detail**. *See the preface for learning strategies for concepts and for detail.*

	Sect.	Rvw.
*1. Advantage: The organism can reproduce even when the chances of finding a mate are extremely low. Disadvantage: While genetic recombination can occur in the offspring, no new genes will be brought in, so there will be no increase in overall genetic diversity. Self-fertilization is more like asexual reproduction than sexual.	52.1	
*2. In mammals, sex is determined by the sex chromosomes, but at the beginning of development, tissues are "indifferent" and have the potential to develop as either male or female organs. The embryo will develop as a male only if there is a functioning *SRY* gene on the Y chromosome. The *SRY* gene converts the indifferent gonad tissue into testes, which then produce testosterone that leads to development of male genitalia and accessory sex organs. If there is no functioning *SRY* gene, none of this happens, and the embryo develops as a female. Female is the default sex since it is what develops if something specific doesn't happen to alter that development.	52.1	
*3. External fertilization evolved first. Vertebrates first evolved in aquatic environments where external fertilization was possible and easy. Only with movement onto land with its drying environments did internal fertilization become necessary.	52.2	
*4. Amphibians keep the embryo stage relatively short, so a relatively small amount of yolk is enough to nourish the embryo. Then they shift over to a separate, free-swimming larval stage (for example, tadpole) that can feed on its own and take a long time growing and developing before metamorphosing into the adult form.	52.2	
*5. Birds are homeothermic (warm blooded) and must incubate their eggs to keep the developing embryo warm enough for proper development and survival. Reptiles are poikilothermic (cold blooded) and don't have to incubate their eggs.	52.2	
*6. Advantages: Greater protection means greater chance of survival, good not only for offspring but also for the mother in terms of successfully passing her genes on to future generations; offspring is more developed, better able to care for itself when finally hatched or born. Disadvantages: Higher energy costs for mother to make an amniotic egg rather than a naked egg; energetically costly for mother to carry around developing embryo inside her and provide it with nutrients; limits clutch or litter size; pregnant female may be more vulnerable to predation because not as agile or quick; if pregnant mother is killed, offspring will die too. Limits: Mammalian mother cannot retain fetus too long or it will impose too large an energetic drain and physical impediment; offspring might also become too large to pass through birth canal.	52.2	

*7. It is not wasteful: A huge number of sperm are needed because the odds of any one sperm cell actually making its way to the egg cell to fertilize it is incredibly low. Also, it is a very long, difficult journey for the sperm. Finally, sperm cells are relatively "inexpensive" to make; they are much smaller in size and content than egg cells, and a single primary spermatocyte gives rise to four functional sperm cells, whereas a single primary oocyte only gives rise to one functional egg cell.	52.3	
*8. The developing embryo, even at the earliest stages, secretes human chorionic gonadotropin hormone (hCG), which maintains the corpus luteum. The corpus luteum continues to produce high levels of estradiol and progesterone, which prevent menstruation.	52.4	
*9. The same relationship probably does not hold for men. A man's gametes are made continuously after puberty and are either ejaculated or reabsorbed relatively soon after production. They do not hang around for years, potentially accumulating damaging mutations. A woman's gametes, on the other hand, are formed while the woman herself is an embryo, so they have been around a long time and may have accumulated significant mutations or damage by the time they are finally used.	52.3, 52.4	
*10. Women can become pregnant only when an ovulated egg cell is available to be fertilized. Ovulation occurs only once in each cycle, and the egg cell is only viable for about a day. Sperm cells can live for several days in the female reproductive tract, so presumably pregnancy can be avoided by abstaining from intercourse for a day or two on either side of the actual ovulation day. The difficulty is in the timing: a woman does not ovulate on the exact same day each cycle, and it is hard to tell in advance when ovulation is going to occur.	52.4	

11. a	52.1	
12. d	52.2	
13. b	52.3	
*14. c	52.2	
15. d	52.2	
16. b	52.2	
*17. e	52.2	
18. c	52.2	
19. a	52.2	
20. c	52.3	
21. a	52.3	
22. b	52.3	
*23. e	52.3	
*24. b	52.4	
25. d	52.4	
26. c	52.4	
27. a	52.4	
28. e	52.5	
*29. e	52.5	
*30. d	52.5	

CHAPTER 53 VERTEBRATE DEVELOPMENT

MASTERING KEY CONCEPTS

Embryonic development converts a single-celled zygote into a complex, multicellular vertebrate with specialized tissues and organs. Whether this development takes place rapidly or slowly, and whether in a naked egg, an amniotic egg, or within the mother's body, the process involves a sequence of similar steps in all vertebrates. This chapter explains how vertebrates wind up with their particular tissues, organs, and body parts arranged the way they are.

53.1 Fertilization is the initial event in development.

- **Overview**: **Fertilization** is the union of male and female gametes that results in the formation of a zygote. It consists of three major events, sperm penetration and membrane fusion, egg activation, and the fusion of the egg and sperm nuclei. Embryonic development begins when the plasma membranes of the egg and the sperm fuse together. For this to occur, the sperm must penetrate a layer of protective cells on the outside of the membrane of the egg through the release of digestive enzymes from the acrosome. Fusion of the plasma membranes results in egg activation and a block to polyspermy. It also results in movement of the cytoplasm in the egg, and an increase in protein synthesis and metabolic activity, and can result in the completion of meiosis in some animals. The nuclei of the egg and the sperm fuse by migration toward each other along a microtubule-based aster to form the diploid nucleus of a zygote.

- **Details**: Know the three events of fertilization, and how these events occur. Know the mechanisms that different organisms use to prevent multiple sperm from entering an egg. Know the other events that result from sperm penetration of an egg. Understand how the nuclei of the egg and the sperm fuse.

53.2 Cell cleavage and the formation of a blastula set the stage for later development.

- **Overview**: Fertilization is followed by a series of rapid cell divisions in which the size of the embryo changes very little, but the number of cells rapidly increases (**cleavage**) forming a tightly packed mass of cells, each known as a **blastomere**. These blastomeres do not appear to be committed as they are in some organisms due to **cytoplasmic determinants**. In mammals, blastomeres become polarized resulting in asymmetrical cell divisions, and body form is primarily determined by cell-cell interactions. Cleavage patterns differ in different organisms, but largely depend on the amount of nutritive yolk that is present, and its distribution.

Organisms with little yolk, such as mollusks, annelids, echinoderms, amphibians, and mammals, undergo **holoblastic cleavage** (complete), while organisms with a large amount of yolk, such as reptiles, birds, and some fishes, undergo **meroblastic cleavage** (incomplete) where cleavage is restricted to the **blastodisc**. Cleavage leads to the formation of a hollow ball of cells called the **blastula**. The blastula in mammals consists of an outer layer of cells, the **trophoblast**, surrounding a fluid-filled cavity, the **blastocoel**, with an **inner cell mass** at one pole that forms the developing embryo.

- **Details**: Know the major cleavage patterns in animal embryos. Know the similarities between the embryos of mammals, birds, and reptiles.

53.3 Gastrulation forms the three germ layers of the embryo.

- **Overview**: **Gastrulation** converts the blastula into a bilaterally symmetrical embryo with three germ layers: the **endoderm**, **mesoderm**, and ectoderm that establish the basic body plan of the embryo. The endoderm gives rise to cells that line the internal structures and the digestive and respiratory tract. The ectoderm gives rise to the epidermis and to nervous tissue; cells in the mesoderm layer give rise to muscle, bones, connective tissue, blood vessels, and internal organs. During gastrulation, cells move by **lamellipodia**, **filopodia**, or **ingression**, or cell sheets move by **invagination**, **involution**, or **delamination**. In sea urchins, cells of the blastula form a **vegetal plate**. Some of these cells ingress in the **blastocoel cavity** (**primary mesenchyme cells**). Remaining cells invaginate into the blastocoel cavity forming the endoderm. This inward moving tube of cells forms the **archenteron**. An opening at the end of the archenteron that contacts the opposite side of the gastrula forms the mouth, and the original opening or **blastopore** forms the anus. In birds, the blastoderm is divided into two layers by delamination, where the upper layer gives rise to all of the cells of the embryo. Some cells ingress into the blastocoel cavity forming the **primitive streak**. Cells migrating through the primitive streak form the endoderm and the mesoderm. Similarly, in mammals, the embryo forms from the inner cell mass and a primitive streak is formed, giving rise to the three germ layers. The embryos of reptiles, birds, and mammals develop within an **amniotic membrane** suspending the embryo in amniotic fluid. The amniotic membrane is surrounded by the **chorion**, **yolk sac**, and **allantois**. The yolk sac nourishes the embryo in reptiles and birds, and the chorio-allantois membrane is involved in gas exchange.

- **Details**: Know the three primary germ layers and the cells that they give rise to. Know how cells move during gastrulation. Know how gastrulation occurs in sea urchins, frogs, birds, and mammals. Recognize the similarities between gastrulation in mammals and birds.

53.4 Organogenesis establishes organs in their proper locations in a developing embryo.

- **Overview**: Interactions within and between the three primary germ layers lead to the formation of organs in their proper locations. A cell's fate can become determined by **cytoplasmic determinants**, or by interactions between cells (**induction**). Induction results from paracrine signaling between one cell and neighboring cells that changes the pattern of expression in target cells. Organogenesis in vertebrates begins with the formation of the **notochord** from the mesoderm and the **dorsal nerve cord** (**neurulation**) from the ectoderm. In vertebrates, the notochord is replaced by the vertebral column later in development. Ectodermal cells, above the notochord form the **neural plate**, whose cells change shape to form the **neural groove,** which closes to form the **neural tube**. The neural tube pinches off from the ectoderm to end up beneath the surface of the embryo's back and will form the brain and spinal cord. In vertebrates, the **neural crest** is formed just before the neural tube is formed. Cells of the neural crest migrate to form many structures found in the vertebrate body. **Cranial neural crest cells** contribute to the development of skeletal and connective tissues in the face and skull. **Trunk neural crest cells** that migrate away from the neural tube to ventral locations, form sensory neurons of the dorsal root ganglia, nerves of the autonomic ganglia, and Schwann cells that insulate nerve fibers, while trunk neural crest cells that migrate laterally away from the neural tube differentiate into pigment cells of the skin. Changes in mesodermal cells rapidly form the skeleton, skeletal musculature, connective tissue, and two layers of cells, the outer layer associated with the inner body wall and the inner layer associated with the outer lining of the gut tube. These two layers of cells form the body cavity (coelom) in between them.
- **Details**: Understand how a cell's fate can become determined. Know how the neural tube is formed in mammals. Know the role of neural crest cells in vertebrate development. Know the germ layer derivation of the major tissue types in animals.

53.5 Organizers determine the dorsal-ventral axis in vertebrates.

- **Overview**: **Spemann and Mangold** found that cells that give rise to the notochord located at the dorsal lip of the blastopore in amphibians could give rise to a second notochord when transplanted in the belly region of another amphibian embryo. They concluded that these cells must release diffusible signaling molecules (**morphogens**) that convey positional information to other cells, and thus act as **organizers**. The Spemann organizer is formed by the movement of maternally encoded dorsal determinants to cells that form the **Nieuwkoop center**. Cells in the Nieuwkoop center release a signaling molecule that causes the cells above them to become the organizer. Wnt signaling molecules in *Xenopus* are maternally encoded dorsal determinants. Molecules synthesized by the Spemann organizer actually inhibit ventral development, rather than activate dorsal development. The organizer secretes molecules that bind to **BMP4** and antagonize its action, which is required to induce ventral mesodermal cell fates. Cells farthest from the organizer differentiate into ventral mesoderm structures due to fewer inhibitors of BMP4 function. In chicks, cells of **Henson's node** function similarly to the cells in the Spemann organizer. **Shh** produced by the notochord specifies ventral cell fate. **Primary inductions** are due to interactions between the three primary germ layers, while **secondary inductions** occur between tissues whose developmental pathway has already been specified.
- **Details**: Know how the Spemann organizer is formed, and how these cells stimulate development of dorsal structures. Understand how inhibitors secreted by the organizer affect dorsal-ventral axis formation. Understand why organizers are believed to be present in all vertebrates. Know how Spemann showed that secondary induction is involved in lens formation in the vertebrate eye.

53.6 Human embryonic development takes place in three trimesters.

- **Overview**: Human embryonic development is divided into three **trimesters**. During the **first trimester**, the zygote undergoes rapid cell division and differentiation. Gastrulation takes place during the second week following fertilization, and the **placenta** is formed. This provides the embryo with nourishment, and allows gas exchange. Neurulation takes place during the third week after fertilization, and organogenesis occurs in the fourth week, when the eyes form, the heart develops, and arm and leg buds form. By the ninth week, all of the major organs of the body are established in their proper locations. During the third month, the nervous system develops. During the **second trimester**, bones enlarge and prebirth growth begins. During the **third trimester**, growth continues and organs mature. Many new neurons and nerve tracts in the brain are formed during this time, which continues after birth. Prostaglandins initiate uterine contractions that stimulate the release of **oxytocin** from the posterior pituitary gland of the mother. Positive feedback leads to an increase in contractions resulting in the birth of the baby. The development of **mammary alveoli** occurs during pregnancy. **Prolactin** secretion by the mother's anterior pituitary gland after birth stimulates mammary alveoli to produce milk. After birth, the baby undergoes **allometric growth** in which different parts grow at different rates, but the brain, cerebral skull, and jaw grow at the same rate. The first two years of life are particularly important for the development of intellectual potential.

- **Details**: Know the structure of the placenta and the functions that it provides to the developing embryo. Know the events in human embryological development that occur during the first, second, and third trimesters. Understand how hormones inhibit milk production before birth, but stimulate it after birth.

CHALLENGING YOUR UNDERSTANDING—Part I

1. Explain why early cleavage patterns differ in different organisms. Describe the result of holoblastic cleavage and meroblastic cleavage. Give an example of organisms that undergo each pattern of cleavage. Describe how the cleavage pattern in amphibians differs from other organisms that under holoblastic cleavage.

2. Complete the following flowchart to indicate the formation and the fate of neural crest cells found during vertebrate development.

neural groove ⟶ neural tube ⟶ neural crest cells ⟨

Neuration (closing of neural groove)

a. _____ _____

b. _____ _____

c. _____ _____

Type of neural crest cell   Tissue produced

CHALLENGING YOUR UNDERSTANDING—Part II

1. Name the structures described in the following flowchart which shows the progression of vertebrate embryo development.

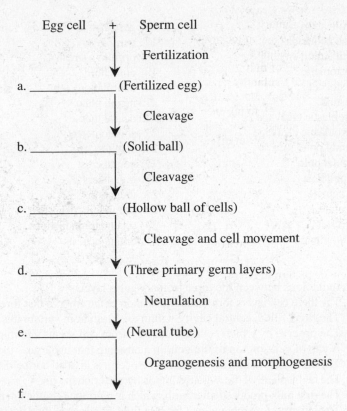

Egg cell + Sperm cell

Fertilization

a. _____ (Fertilized egg)

Cleavage

b. _____ (Solid ball)

Cleavage

c. _____ (Hollow ball of cells)

Cleavage and cell movement

d. _____ (Three primary germ layers)

Neurulation

e. _____ (Neural tube)

Organogenesis and morphogenesis

f. _____

2. Describe the similarities and the differences between gastrulation in birds and mammals.

KEY TERMS

Match the numbered term with the definition that fits it best. Put the corresponding number in front of the appropriate definition.

1. fertilization	16. gastrulation	31. archenteron
2. zona pellucida	17. germ layers	32. blastopore
3. fertilization envelope	18. primitive streak	33. cell determination
4. blastomere	19. notochord	34. extraembryonic membranes
5. blastocoel	20. neurulation	35. amnion
6. blastula	21. neural plate	36. chorion
7. holoblastic cleavage	22. neural tube	37. yolk sac
8. meroblastic cleavage	23. somitomeres	38. allantois
9. animal pole	24. somites	39. trimesters
10. vegetal pole	25. neural crest	40. lactation
11. trophoblast	26. organizers	41. colostrum
12. invaginate	27. induction	42. allometric growth
13. involute	28. primary inductions	43. blastodisc
14. ingression	29. secondary inductions	
15. delamination	30. organogenesis	

a. _____ Inductions between the three primary germ layers.

b. _____ The three cell layers formed at gastrulation of the embryo that foreshadow the future organization of tissues.

c. _____ The fluid-filled, central cavity within the blastula in vertebrates.

d. _____ The process by which cells break away from cell sheets and migrate as individual cells.

e. _____ A cap of cells on top of the yolk in a bird egg that undergoes cleavage and gives rise to the embryo.

f. _____ The blocks of tissue into which the mesoderm is divided during differentiation of the vertebrate embryo.

g. _____ The hemisphere of the zygote comprising cells rich in yolk.

h. _____ The first milk produced after birth, which is nutritious and rich in maternal antibodies.

i. _____ The innermost membrane that forms a fluid-filled sac around the embryo in reptiles, birds, and mammals.

j. _____ A hollow structure formed from cells of the vegetal plate invaginating; represents the future digestive cavity.

k. _____ A process in early embryonic development where a dorsal band of ectoderm thickens, rolling into the neural tube.

l. _____ A furrow of cells ingressed into the blastocoel cavity in the embryos of reptiles, birds, and mammals.

m. _____ An outpouching of the gut in an amniotic egg that functions in respiration and excretion in birds and reptiles.

n. _____ A cluster of cells that release diffusible signaling molecules that convey positional information to other cells.

o. _____ The process by which a cell sheet dents inward.

p. _____ A pattern of cleavage characteristic in eggs with little yolk, where cell divisions occur throughout the entire egg.

q. _____ A pattern of growth in which different components grow at different rates.

r. _____ In sea urchins, a hardened, elevated vitelline envelope through which additional sperm cannot penetrate.

s. _____ In vertebrate embryos, the outer ectodermal layer of cells surrounding the blastocoel and ICM in the blastocyst.

t. _____ A process by which a cell's fate becomes fixed.

u. _____ A structure formed from thickening of the ectoderm above the notochord in vertebrates.

v. _____ In organisms with asymmetrical yolk distribution, the hemisphere of the blastula with cells poor in yolk.

w. _____ A series of rounded regions formed by sheets of mesoderm on the sides of the notochord separating.

x. _____ The formation of organs in their proper locations as a result of interactions within and between germ layers.

y. _____ Three periods of time that characterize embryonic development from fertilization to birth in humans.

z. _____ The process by which one sheet of cells splits into two sheets.

aa. _____ The opening that connects the archenteron cavity of a gastrula stage embryo with the outside in vertebrates.

bb. _____ The pattern of cleavage where cell divisions occur only in the blastodisc, due to a large amount of yolk.

cc. _____ The process by which sheets of smaller cells roll inward from the surface of the blastula.

dd. _____ An outer protective coat that encases a mammalian egg, and can be degraded by acrosomal enzymes.

ee. _____ In vertebrates, an early embryonic stage consisting of a hollow, fluid-filled ball of cells one layer thick.

ff. _____ The developmental process that converts the blastula into an embryo with three embryonic germ layers.

gg. _____ A structure formed by closing the neural groove, which will become the brain and spinal cord in vertebrates.

hh. _____ The outer membrane of the double membrane that surrounds the embryo of reptiles, birds, and mammals.

ii. _____ Inductions between tissues that have already been specified to develop along a particular developmental pathway.

jj. _____ In chordate embryos, a dorsal rod of cartilage that runs the length of the body forming the primitive axial skeleton.

kk. _____ The fusion of two haploid gamete nuclei to form a diploid zygote nucleus.

ll. _____ Milk production in mammals occurring in the alveoli of the mammary glands when stimulated by prolactin.

mm. _____ Each individual cell in the tightly packed mass of cells formed by cleavage in an embryo.

nn. _____ A strip of cells that develops just before the neural groove closes over to form the neural tube in vertebrates.

oo. _____ Membranes formed from embryonic cells that are located outside of the body of the embryo.

pp. _____ The membrane that surrounds the yolk of an egg and connects the yolk to the embryo via blood vessels.

qq. _____ The process by which a cell or group of cells instructs neighboring cells to adopt a particular fate.

LEARNING BY EXPERIENCE

1. Match the following tissues and organs with the germ layer from which they are derived. Each germ layer may be used as an answer more than once.

_____ a. heart   i.   endoderm
_____ b. skin   ii.   ectoderm
_____ c. lungs   iii.   mesoderm
_____ d. central nervous system
_____ e. digestive tract
_____ f. muscles

2. Label the following parts on the figure depicting gastrulation in frogs below: archenteron, blastocoel, ectoderm, endoderm, mesoderm, yolk.

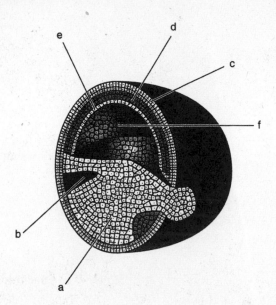

3. Label the following parts on the figure depicting mammalian gastrulation below: ectoderm, endoderm, and mesoderm, primitive streak.

EXERCISING YOUR KNOWLEDGE

Briefly answer each of the following questions in the space provided.

1. What impact does sperm penetration have on a vertebrate egg?

2. Why is the amount of yolk present in an egg cell a significant factor in development?

3. How are organizers and morphogens involved in induction?

4. What happens during gastrulation that makes it such an important stage in development?

5. The prefix *meso-* means "middle." Why is "mesoderm" an appropriate name?

6. At what point in development does the first event unique to vertebrates occur? What is that event, and why is it important?

7. Why is it not surprising that epinephrine and norepinephrine are very similar chemically and functionally even though epinephrine is a hormone and norepinephrine is a neurotransmitter?

8. Why is it more correct to say that the Spemann organizer inhibits ventral development, rather than activating dorsal development?

9. Why should a woman be very careful about what she eats, drinks, or is exposed to during the first trimester of her pregnancy?

10. Why do newborn chimpanzees and newborn humans look so much more similar to each other than the adults do?

Circle the letter of the one best answer in each of the following questions.

11. When does a human egg cell complete its second meiotic division?
    a. just before ovulation
    b. just before sperm penetration
    c. after sperm penetration
    d. after cleavage has begun
    e. after implantation in the uterus

12. Which of the following is NOT an effect of fusion of the sperm and egg membranes during fertilization?
    a. movement of the egg cytoplasm
    b. an increase in the levels of free intracellular Ca^{2+} ions in the egg
    c. an increase in protein synthesis and metabolic activity in the egg
    d. initiation of a block to polyspermy
    e. none of the above

13. Where does the gray crescent form?
    a. on the head of the sperm cell
    b. on the side of the egg cell opposite where the sperm penetrated
    c. on the part of the egg cell where the sperm penetrated
    d. in the middle of the yolk plug
    e. between the endoderm and ectoderm

14. Cleavage is characterized by
    a. rapid cell division.
    b. rapid growth in the size of the embryo.
    c. each cell having the same components as its neighbors.
    d. all of these.
    e. none of these.

15. In meroblastic cleavage, cleavage occurs
    a. only in the placodes.
    b. only in the yolk.
    c. only at the vegetal pole.
    d. only in the blastodisc.
    e. throughout the whole egg.

16. The vertebrate notochord is located _____ the neural tube.
    a. above
    b. beside
    c. within
    d. below
    e. in front of

17. What type of animal forms a trophoblast during its early development?
    a. mammal
    b. amphibian
    c. bird
    d. reptile
    e. fish

18. During what stage of development do the primary germ layers appear?
    a. cleavage
    b. blastulation
    c. fertilization
    d. neurulation
    e. gastrulation

19. The gut or digestive tract of a vertebrate arises from the
    a. vegetal pole.
    b. primitive streak.
    c. archenteron.
    d. blastocoel.
    e. somites.

20. In mammals, the embryo develops from a group of cells called the
    a. trophoblast.
    b. blastodisc.
    c. neural crest.
    d. inner cell mass.
    e. yolk plug.

21. What type of tissue gives rise to the notochord?
    a. ectoderm
    b. mesoderm
    c. endoderm
    d. all of these

22. Cells that migrate from somites form the
    a. respiratory system.
    b. digestive system.
    c. skeletal muscles.
    d. reproductive system.
    e. smooth muscles.

23. The trophoblast gives rise to the
    a. yolk sac.
    b. amnion.
    c. allantois.
    d. chorion.
    e. egg shell.

24. The first truly vertebrate phase of development is marked by the formation of the
    a. archenteron.
    b. primitive streak.
    c. coccyx.
    d. notochord.
    e. neural crest.

25. The primary way that cells communicate with and influence each other during the development of organs is by
    a. involution.
    b. invagination.
    c. induction.
    d. magic.

26. Cells in the Nieuwkoop center do which of the following?
    a. secrete molecules that inhibit ventral development
    b. release signaling molecules that specify cells in the dorsal marginal zone to become the organizer
    c. assemble a microtubule array enabling the egg's plasma membrane and underlying cortical cytoplasm to rotate
    d. give rise to the notochord
    e. move away from the organizer site to stimulate development of different organs

27. Which extraembryonic membrane functions as the lung of a bird embryo by carrying out gas exchange through the egg shell?
    a. amnion
    b. chorion
    c. yolk sac
    d. allantois
    e. all of these

28. When does neurulation occur during human development?
    a. first week
    b. second week
    c. third week
    d. fourth week
    e. second month

29. Which of the following is NOT a function of the placenta in development of the human embryo?
    a. the detoxification of certain molecules that pass into embryonic circulation
    b. the secretion of hormones
    c. the prevention of the passage of alcohol and antibiotics from the mother's bloodstream into the embryo
    d. providing nourishment for the embryo
    e. allowing the exchange of gases between the mother and the embryo

30. Which of the following events happens right before, during, or soon after birth?
    a. Prostaglandins cause the uterus to contract.
    b. Uterine contractions during labor are regulated by a negative feedback loop.
    c. Oxytocin stimulates the mammary glands to produce milk.
    d. Colostrum causes the afterbirth to be expelled.
    e. All of these happen.

ASSESSING YOUR KNOWLEDGE

Answers to the questions in this section test your ability to synthesize information gained from the chapter and to solve challenging problems on an exam or in everyday life.

Challenging Your Understanding—Part I, Answers

1. Different organisms have different amounts of nutritive yolk in their eggs. This characteristic has the largest effect on the cleavage pattern in an egg. Organisms with eggs that have little or no yolk undergo holoblastic cleavage that results in the formation of a symmetrical blastula, composed of a single layer of cells of approximately equal size surrounding a blastocoel. The eggs of echinoderms, mollusks, annelids, mammals, and nematodes undergo holoblastic cleavage. Meroblastic cleavage in eggs from organisms that have large amounts of yolk is restricted to the blastodisc so the resulting embryo has a thin cap on top of a mass of yolk. The eggs of reptiles, birds, and some fishes undergo meroblastic cleavage. Amphibian eggs contain more yolk in the vegetal than in the animal hemisphere. Therefore, cleavage furrows are displaced toward the animal pole. As a result, holoblastic cleavage results in an asymmetrical blastula with larger, yolk-filled cells at the vegetal pole, and smaller, more numerous cells with less yolk at the animal pole, and a displaced blastocoel.

2. a. Cranial neural crest cells: skeletal and connective tissue of skull/face
b. Ventral trunk neural crest cells: sensory neurons, Schwann cells, adrenal medulla
c. Lateral trunk neural crest cells: melanocytes of the skin

Challenging Your Understanding—Part II, Answers

1. a. zygote; b. morula; c. blastula; d. gastrula; e. neurula; f. embryo

2. In both birds and mammals, the embryo develops from a flattened collection of cells. The blastoderm in birds, which is pressed against a mass of yolk, or the inner cell mass in mammals, which are missing the yolk, form the embryo. Gastrulation in birds and mammals progresses the same even though mammals lack the yolk of the egg. In both, a primitive streak is formed, which gives rise to three primary germ layers: the ectoderm, mesoderm, and endoderm. Mammalian embryos, like bird embryos, form a yolk sac from extraembryonic cells that migrate away from the lower layer of the blastoderm and line the blastocoel cavity. Unlike mammals, the yolk sac in birds nourishes the embryo.

Key Terms—Answers

a. 28, b. 17, c. 5, d. 14, e. 43, f. 24, g. 10, h. 41, i. 35, j. 31, k. 20, l. 18, m. 38, n. 26, o. 12, p. 7, q. 42, r. 3, s. 11, t. 33, u. 21, v. 9, w. 23, x. 30, y. 39, z. 15, aa. 32, bb. 8, cc. 13, dd. 2, ee. 6, ff. 16, gg. 22, hh. 36, ii. 29, jj. 19, kk. 1, ll. 40, mm. 4, nn. 25, oo. 34, pp. 37, qq. 27.

Learning by Experience—Answers

1.	a. iii
	b. ii
	c. i
	d. ii
	e. i
	f. iii
2.	a. yolk
	b. blastocoel
	c. ectoderm
	d. mesoderm
	e. endoderm
	f. archenteron
3.	Compare to figure 53.14d (page 1097) of your textbook.

Exercising Your Knowledge—Answers

As you check your answers, put a mark in the review (Rvw.) column for the answers you missed. If you didn't miss any, congratulations—you have mastered the chapter! If you missed some, review the section (Sect.) in the text where this concept is discussed. In order to develop an efficient review strategy, it is important that you understand what types of questions you missed. The questions with asterisks test more for understanding of the **concepts**, whereas the others test more for **detail**. *See the preface for learning strategies for concepts and for detail.*

	Sect.	Rvw.
*1. Sperm penetration stimulates the egg nucleus to finish its second meiotic division, causes movement of the cytoplasm that sets the stage for later developmental patterns, and causes an increase in protein synthesis and metabolic activity in the egg.	53.1	
*2. Yolk-rich cells divide more slowly than cells without much yolk. The amount of yolk determines whether cleavage will be holoblastic and whether the resulting blastula will be symmetrical or asymmetrical. It also impacts the mechanics of gastrulation and how cells move.	53.2	

*3. Organizers produce signaling molecules called morphogens, the gradient of which helps migrating cells determine their position.	53.5
*4. The three primary germ layers (ectoderm, mesoderm, endoderm) form. All other tissues in the vertebrate body are derived from them. The basic architecture of the embryo is initiated during gastrulation.	53.3
*5. Mesoderm forms between the ectoderm and the endoderm in the gastrula. It is in the middle between the other two layers.	53.3
*6. Formation of the neural crest occurs during neurulation. Only vertebrates form a neural crest. Neural crest cells migrate throughout the body of the developing embryo and give rise to numerous structures, including sensory organs and parts of the nervous system and gill arches. These structures allowed vertebrates to become faster moving and more active than their primitive chordate ancestors.	53.4
*7. Epinephrine is produced by the adrenal medulla, and norepinephrine is produced by neurons of the sympathetic division of the autonomic nervous system. The adrenal medulla and sympathetic neurons have the same developmental origins—both being derived from neural crest cells.	53.4
*8. The organizer secretes a host of BMP4 inhibitory molecules that prevent BMP4 from binding to its receptor. BMP4 binding induces a more ventral mesodermal fate. The concentration of BMP4 inhibitory molecules is highest closest to the organizer and there is a gradient of inhibitory molecules declining in the dorsal to ventral direction. BMP4 function is least inhibited in the cells farthest away from the organizer, promoting ventral development. BMP4 is still present in cells close to the organizer, but its activity is impaired by the inhibitors the cells in the organizer secrete. If these inhibitors were not present, BMP4 could promote ventralization of the dorsal side as well because the organizer does not secrete dorsal promoting factors. For this reason, it is most correct to say that the organizer inhibits ventral development, rather than promoting dorsal development.	53.5

*9. The first trimester of the pregnancy is the most crucial for proper development of the embryo. This is when blastulation, gastrulation, neurulation, organogenesis, and morphogenesis all occur. Any substance the woman ingests, inhales, or absorbs through her skin has the potential of affecting the developing embryo if the substance is taken up by the mother's circulatory system and then diffuses into the embryo's blood in the placenta. Many substances (for example, alcohol, cigarette smoke, and some prescription drugs) are known to interfere with proper development. Unfortunately, the woman may not even know she is pregnant during the first few months and may not take proper precautions.	53.6
*10. Chimps and humans have basically the same head proportions at birth, but postnatal development is different in the two species. In humans, the brain and cerebral part of the skull as well as the jaw continue to grow postnatally so the basic proportions of the adult head are similar to proportions in the newborn. Chimps, however, have allometric growth – not all parts grow at the same rate. In chimps, the brain and cerebral skull hardly grow at all postnatally, but the jaw grows a lot, totally changing the proportions of the head.	53.6
*11. c	53.1
*12. e	53.1
*13. b	53.1
*14. a	53.2
*15. d	53.2
16. d	53.4
17. a	53.2
18. e	53.3
19. c	53.3
20. d	53.3
21. b	53.4
22. c	53.4
23. d	53.3
24. e	53.4
25. c	53.4
*26. b	53.4
27. d	53.3
28. c	53.6
*29. c	53.6
*30. a	53.6

CHAPTER 54 BEHAVIORAL BIOLOGY

MASTERING KEY CONCEPTS

Of all the living organisms on earth, only multicellular animals show complex behavioral responses to external stimuli. Both nature (instinct) and nurture (learning) are important in determining *how* an animal behaves, and proximate and ultimate causes explain *why* an animal behaves the way it does. Communication through behavior helps animals find mates, reproduce, care for young, locate food, and avoid predators. The behavior of any animal is crucial in determining the success of that animal and is as much of an evolutionary adaptation as are the morphology and physiology. Behavior is selected for or against, and behavior evolves. Different environmental conditions select for different types of behavior, such as mating systems, parental care, group living, foraging behavior, and territoriality.

54.1 Many behavioral patterns are innate.

- **Overview**: **Behavior** is the response to stimuli in the environment. An organism's behavior consists of two components: the **proximate cause** (how a behavior occurs) and the **ultimate cause** (why a behavior evolved). Both **instinct** and **experience** determine behavior. **Innate behaviors** are instinctive. They are triggered by a **sign stimulus** that is detected by an **innate releasing mechanism** that results in a **fixed action pattern** by the organism. These behaviors are likely due to a genetically controlled response. Sign stimuli do not have to be specific and **supernormal stimuli** can trigger the same fixed action pattern as normal stimuli.
- **Details**: Understand the two components of behavior. Understand the innate egg-rolling response in geese in terms of the sign stimulus, innate releasing mechanism, and fixed action pattern. Recognize why innate behaviors are likely to be genetically controlled.

54.2 Behavioral genetics involves components of behavior that are hereditary.

- **Overview**: Behavioral differences among individuals are often the result of genetic differences, which can be passed from one generation to the next. Mutations in single genes in *Drosophila* and mice can cause behavioral abnormalities. For example, female mice with both alleles of *fosB* inactivated, inspect their young, but then ignore them. This is in sharp contrast to mice with the *fosB* alleles present that inspect their young and then care for them. Differences in the number of vasopressin and oxytocin receptors in the brains of prairie voles compared to the number of receptors in the brains of montane voles explains why prairie voles exhibit pair-bonding behavior, while montane voles do not.

- **Details**: Understand the evidence that suggests that the ability to learn and other behaviors are genetically determined. Know the examples in *Drosophila*, mice, and the prairie and montane voles that show that single gene mutations can change behaviors.

54.3 Learning influences behavior.

- **Overview**: Animals can alter their behavior as a result of **learning** by experience. **Habituation** is a form of **nonassociative learning** resulting in a decreased response to a repeated stimulus that has neither positive nor negative consequences (the ability to ignore a stimulus). **Associative learning** either **classical conditioning** or **operant conditioning** causes a modification in behavior due to an association between two stimuli, or between a stimulus and a response, respectively. Classical conditioning (Pavlovian conditioning) causes an animal to form an association between two different stimuli due to the consistency of their paired presentation. Operant conditioning causes an animal to associate its behavioral response with a reward or a punishment. It is now clear that instinct guides learning by determining what an animal can learn and the associations that it can make.
- **Details**: Understand the differences between habituation and associative learning, and between classical and operant conditioning. Understand how instinct affects learning.

54.4 Genetic and learned components interact during development to shape behavior.

- **Overview**: Behavior has both genetic and learned components. **Filial imprinting** is the social attachment that is formed between parents and offspring. This imprinting occurs at a critical time in development. **Konrad Lorenz** demonstrated that geese will follow the first object that they see after hatching. Studies have also indicated that a constant "mother figure" is required for normal growth and psychological development, and that there is a biological need for parent-offspring interactions, social interactions, and physical touch early in life. Evidence suggests that organisms have a genetic template that guides them in what they learn.
- **Details**: Know the examples that demonstrate the importance of parent-offspring interactions and physical contact. Understand the evidence that suggests that organisms may have a genetic template that guides them in what they learn.

54.5 Some animals may also be capable of cognitive behavior.

- **Overview**: A number of examples suggest that animals display cognitive behavior or conscious thinking, not just instinctive behaviors or simple programmed learning.

- **Details**: Know the examples suggesting that animals can think and process information.

54.6 Orientation and migratory behaviors exhibited by some animals are goal-oriented movements.

- **Overview**: Animals orient themselves by tracking stimuli in the environment. Some animals become more or less active when stimulus intensity increases (**kineses**), but don't move toward or away form the stimulus (**taxis**). Migrations are long-range, two-way movements. Experiments on migrating birds indicate that inexperienced birds migrate by **orientation**, whereas birds that have migrated previously, continue to do so, but by **navigation**, using the Sun, stars, and the Earth's magnetic field as guides.
- **Details**: Understand how migratory animals orient themselves. Know the differences between the migratory behaviors of inexperienced birds compared to older birds.

54.7 Animal communication plays a critical role in social interactions and reproduction.

- **Overview**: **Communication**—including visual, auditory, tactile, and chemical signals—plays a key role in behaviors, such as social interactions and reproduction. Successful reproduction in some species depends on a **stimulus-response chain** where the behavior of one individual leads to a certain behavior by another individual. Many signals, such as **pheromones** or acoustic signals, are species specific leading to the enforcement of reproductive isolation. Communication facilitates social groups. **Von Frisch** demonstrated that honeybees use a waggle dance to direct other bees to a food source. Animals can use language to communicate the presence of predators. Similarities in human languages reflect the way our brains handle abstract information. Levels of specificity in communication vary. Signals can be sent to members of the same species, several species, other animals, or many groups of other animals.
- **Details**: Know how signals between animals can affect reproductive behavior and social interactions. Understand how honeybees direct each other to food sources and the basis of human language.

54.8 Behavioral ecology is the study of how natural selection shapes behavior.

- **Overview**: **Niko Tinbergen** is one of the founders of **behavioral ecology**, the study of how natural selection shapes behavior, or how behavior may increase survival and reproduction. This field of biology is concerned with two basic questions: is behavior adaptive, and how does a behavior increase reproductive success or

survival? Natural selection favors organisms that practice energy-efficient foraging behaviors, and can avoid predators and find mates. Natural selection also favors **territoriality** when the benefits of exclusive use either for food or for access to females, outweigh the costs in defending the area.
- **Details**: Know the basis of behavioral ecology. Understand how natural selection affects feeding, reproductive, and territorial behaviors.

54.9 Reproductive strategies and sexual selection are behaviors aimed at maximizing reproductive success.

- **Overview**: An animal's **reproductive strategy** is concerned with decisions regarding how many mates to have and how much energy to devote to raising their offspring in order to maximize reproductive success. In many species, males and females have different reproductive strategies. The individual that puts more into the **parental investment** typically spends more time evaluating a mate's quality and deciding whether or not to mate (**mate choice**), while the other individual is less selective. This is due to the fact that one parent typically expends more energy producing and rearing the offspring than the other parent. **Sexual selection** is a form of natural selection that favors traits that make an individual better at competing for mates or more attractive to potential mates. **Mating systems**, or the number of individuals an organism mates with, have evolved to maximize reproductive fitness. These systems are strongly influenced by ecology and are constrained by the needs of offspring. DNA fingerprinting can be used by behavioral ecologists to determine the reproductive success of individual mates. Using this technology, researchers have found that **extra-pair copulations** in birds are much more prevalent than was once expected.
- **Details**: Understand how the reproductive strategies of males and females differ and why. Understand the differences between **intrasexual** and **intersexual selection**. Know what is meant by the direct and indirect benefits of mate choice. Understand the evolutionary advantage of extra-pair copulations to males and females.

54.10 Altruistic behaviors seem to benefit other individuals more than the actor.

- **Overview**: **Altruism** is the performance of an action by one individual that benefits another individual, imposing a cost on the actor. How this could be favored by natural selection is difficult to understand because natural selection acts on individuals, but group selection is rare. Altruism might not actually be that costly to the performer in the long run because these actions may be reciprocated later (**reciprocal altruism**), or may increase the propagation of alleles in relatives (**kin selection**). Kin selection can also lead to complex social systems such as that found in bees, wasps, and ants (**eusocial system**), where there is a reproductive division of labor and cooperative care of the brood with more than one generation living together.

- **Details**: Understand the possible explanations for why organisms may participate in altruism. Know why kin selection may be beneficial to organisms and examples of this type of selection. Understand how kin selection influences the eusocial system exhibited by bees.

- **Overview**: A **society** is a group of organisms of the same species that are organized in a cooperative manner. Individuals in some species live in groups due to kin selection, benefits that result from social living, such as protection from predators, or increased feeding success. Insect colonies, common to honeybees and leaf-cutter ants, are composed of **castes** consisting of individuals that differ in size, morphology, and jobs. Vertebrate social groups are usually less rigidly organized and less cohesive, and display more conflict and aggression among their members due to competition for food and mates.

- **Details**: Understand why some species live in groups. Know the organization of the social systems of insects and vertebrates.

54.11 Organisms benefit from living in social groups.

CHALLENGING YOUR UNDERSTANDING—Part I

1. Below is a graph showing a population of rats and the total number of errors that they made negotiating a maze in 14 trials. In this graph, circle the rats that should be mated to establish a population of "maze-bright" rats, and put a square around the rats in the parental generation that should be mated to establish a population of "maze-dull" rats.

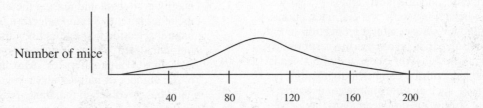

2. Draw a graphical representation of what offspring in the first, second, fifth, and seventh generations will look like in terms of navigating the maze if the rats circled or squared above are used as the parental generation and the "maze-bright" rats are mated only to each other, while the "maze-dull" rats are also mated only to each other. In each generation, put a circle and a square around the group of rats that are mated to establish offspring in the subsequent generations that can navigate the maze even more quickly or more slowly than their parents.

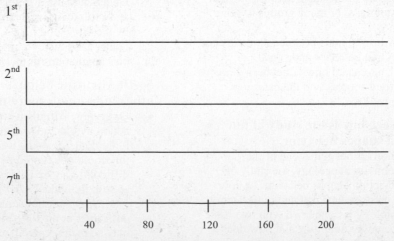

Total number of errors in negotiating the maze (14 trials)

3. Using the rats from the seventh generation above as the new parental generation, draw what will happen in each of the subsequent generations listed if the rats from both populations are randomly mated.

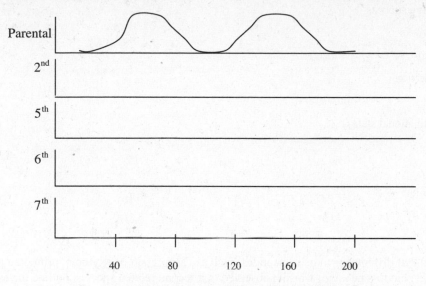

Total number of errors in negotiating the maze (14 trials)

4. What do the results in question 2 demonstrate about the ability of the rats to learn the maze?

5. Describe an experiment that could be done to determine if the genes that control this behavior are specific for this maze or not.

6. What type of results would suggest that the genes are specific to learning this maze?

7. What type of results would suggest that the genes that control maze learning may act less specifically?

8. If the genes seem to act nonspecifically, what could be an alternate explanation for the function of the genes in these mice that affect their abilities to do the maze?

CHALLENGING YOUR UNDERSTANDING—Part II

1. Classify each of the following as an ultimate (U) or a proximate (P) cause of behavior.

a. _____ Reproductive success

b. _____ Nerve networks

c. _____ Morphology

d. _____ Natural selection

e. _____ Muscles

f. _____ Drive (Motivational state)

g. _____ Survival

h. _____ Hormones

i. _____ Adaptive value

j. _____ Physiology

2. If you suspected that differences in neuropeptides, such as vasopressin or oxytocin, promoted pair-bonding in a particular species, but this behavior was not observed in a second related species, outline the experiments that you could do to determine why this is true.

3. Match the following examples of behaviors exhibited by animals on the left with the terms that most accurately describe them on the right.

_____ a. Birds follow their mother within a few
                hours after hatching.

_____ b. Young birds ignore falling leaves.

_____ c. Vampire bats share blood with other bats
                who have shared with them.

_____ d. A dog smells meat and hears a ringing bell
                at the same time several times, and begins
                salivating. The dog then salivates every
                time it hears a bell.

_____ e. A chimp in a room with boxes and bananas
                hanging from the ceiling stacks the boxes
                to reach the bananas.

_____ f. A bird gives an alarm call when it spies a predator.

_____ g. A dog lies down and then gets a treat.

_____ h. A fostered bird attempts to mate with members of the
                species that raised it.

1. Altruism
2. Filial imprinting
3. Sexual imprinting
4. Cognitive behavior
5. Operant conditioning
6. Habituation
7. Reciprocal altruism
8. Classical conditioning

KEY TERMS

Match the numbered term with the definition that fits it best. Put the corresponding number in front of the appropriate definition.

1. behavior
2. sign stimulus
3. innate releasing mechanism
4. fixed action potential
5. supernormal stimuli
6. learning
7. nonassociative learning
8. habituation
9. associative learning
10. classical conditioning
11. operant conditioning
12. imprinting
13. sexual imprinting
14. filial imprinting
15. genetic template
16. cognitive behavior
17. taxis
18. kineses

19. migrations
20. orientation
21. navigation
22. pheromones
23. level of specificity
24. stimulus-response chain
25. survival value
26. behavioral ecology
27. adaptive significance
28. optimal foraging theory
29. territoriality
30. reproductive strategy
31. mate choice
32. parental investment
33. sexual selection
34. intrasexual selection
35. intersexual selection
36. sexual dimorphism

37. sperm competition
38. handicap hypothesis
39. sensory exploitation
40. altricial
41. precocial
42. extra-pair copulations
43. altruism
44. reciprocal altruism
45. kin selection
46. Hamilton's rule
47. eusocial
48. society
49. castes

a. _____ A sequence in which the behavior of one individual in turn releases a behavior by another individual.
b. _____ The evolution in males of an attractive signal that exploits preexisting biases of females to promote mate choice.
c. _____ A response by which animals become more or less active when stimulus intensity increases.
d. _____ A model that predicts that altruistic acts are favored when organisms are related due to greater genetic payoff.
e. _____ A set of behaviors that have evolved in organisms to maximize reproductive success.
f. _____ A process in which an individual learns to direct its sexual behavior toward members of its own species.
g. _____ Chemical messengers used for communication between individuals of the same species.
h. _____ The paired presentation of two different stimuli that causes an animal to form an association between them.
i. _____ A motor program initiated by a neuronal response that is triggered by a sign stimulus.
j. _____ The ability to process information and respond in a manner that is suggestive of thinking.
k. _____ The benefit in an animal's behavior that allows it to stay alive or to keep its offspring alive.
l. _____ A description of offspring requiring little parental care.
m. _____ A process by which animals alter their behavior as a result of previous experiences.
n. _____ The contribution that each sex makes in producing and rearing offspring.
o. _____ A decrease in response to a repeated stimulus that has no positive or negative consequences.
p. _____ The idea that natural selection favors individuals whose foraging behavior is as energetically efficient as possible.
q. _____ Groups of individuals that differ in size and morphology and perform different tasks.
r. _____ Differences between the traits of two sexes, such as size or structures like horns, antlers, or large teeth.
s. _____ The process by which an animal learns to associate its behavioral response with a reward or punishment.
t. _____ The performance of an action that benefits another individual at a cost to the actor.
u. _____ A behavior where an individual defends a portion of its home range and uses it and its resources exclusively.
v. _____ The neural instructions that are generated by a sign stimulus leading to a fixed action pattern.
w. _____ Sexual selection involving interactions between members of one sex; the power to conquer others in battle.
x. _____ A group of organisms of the same species that are organized in a cooperative manner.
y. _____ The idea that females prefer mates with traits that are detrimental to survival because they are believed to be genetically superior.
z. _____ The process by which animals position themselves by tracking stimuli in the environment.
aa. _____ The study of how natural selection shapes behavior.
bb. _____ A sign stimulus that is similar to a normal stimulus an organism encounters, but much larger.
cc. _____ A process where animals form social attachments to other animals or develops preferences as it matures.
dd. _____ Movement toward or away from a stimulus.
ee. _____ Sexual selection involving interactions mate choice; the power to charm.
ff. _____ Fertilization of a hatchling by a male other than the territory owner.

gg. ____ Learning that doesn't require an animal to connect two stimuli, or to connect a stimulus and a response.

hh. ____ Selection that favors altruism directed toward relatives.

ii. ____ The way an animal responds to stimuli in its environment.

jj. ____ Offspring that require prolonged and extensive care.

kk. ____ Long-range, two-way movements.

ll. ____ A phenomenon in which the sperm of two males compete with each other for fertilization of an egg.

mm. ____ A behavior in which one sex evaluates the quality of the other sex and then decides whether or not to mate.

nn. ____ The ability to set or adjust a bearing and then follow it.

oo. ____ An innate program that guides what an organism can learn.

pp. ____ How behavior may increase survival and reproduction.

qq. ____ A particular factor that triggers an innate releasing mechanism to initiate a specific motor program.

rr. ____ A change in behavior involving an association between two stimuli or between a stimulus and a response.

ss. ____ A characteristic of a signal from an organism that determines who can receive it based on its intended function.

tt. ____ A system in which there is a reproductive division of labor, cooperative care of a brood and generational overlap.

uu. ____ Social attachments formed between parents and offspring.

vv. ____ The mutual exchanges of altruistic acts that benefit both participants.

ww. ____ The competition for mating opportunities.

LEARNING BY EXPERIENCE

1. Choose an animal and think about some of its behavior. Give two examples of a proximate explanation of its behavior and two examples of an ultimate explanation.

2. Stage a debate or write an essay on whether animals are capable of cognitive thinking. Is there some way to scientifically test this?

3. This is figure 54.25 from the text, showing the mussel diet of shore crabs. Why do you think the crabs don't gain more energy from eating the largest-sized mussels?

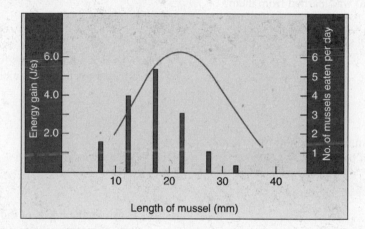

4. Complete the following chart by providing the appropriate mating system term for each definition.

Term	Definition
a. _____	One male mates with several females.
b. _____	One male mates with one female.
c. _____	One female mates with several males.

5. Fill in the following chart by listing the proportion of alleles likely to be shared by (the same in) different types of relatives. Choices = all, ½, ¼, ⅛, none.

Relationship	Proportion of shared alleles
parent – child	a.
full siblings	b.
half siblings	c.
full cousins	d.
aunt or uncle – niece or nephew	e.
stepparent – stepchild	f.

EXERCISING YOUR KNOWLEDGE

Briefly answer each of the following questions in the space provided.

1. Which is more important in determining an animal's behavior, proximate causes or ultimate causes?

2. Why were the experiments with maze-running in rats significant? What was learned from them?

3. Why is habituation an important and advantageous type of behavior?

4. Proud pet owners often boast that their dogs can learn anything. Is this true—can animals learn anything and everything?

5. Why is it advantageous for different species to have elaborate and distinct courtship behaviors? What is the disadvantage?

6. Why don't animals always forage in a way that maximizes their caloric intake?

7. Under what conditions should an animal be territorial?

8. Why is it advantageous for male Mormon crickets to choose heavier females as mates?

9. How can the needs of the offspring influence the type of mating system displayed by a species?

10. What other reasons besides kin selection might favor group living? What disadvantages can you think of for group living?

Circle the letter of the one best answer in each of the following questions.

11. A goose retrieving a stray egg and rolling it back into its nest is an example of
    a. instinctive behavior.
    b. operant conditioning.
    c. associative behavior.
    d. navigation.
    e. cognitive behavior.

12. Which of the following is a question about the ultimate causation of a behavior?
    a. What muscles are involved when a hummingbird hovers over a flower?
    b. When is the critical period for imprinting in a young goat?
    c. Which hormones must be present at what levels to make a female lizard receptive to male courtship?
    d. All of these are examples of ultimate causation questions.
    e. None of these is an example of an ultimate causation question.

13. Studies have shown that pigeons can learn to associate danger with _____, but not with _____.
    a. colors; smell
    b. smell; sounds
    c. taste; sounds
    d. sounds; colors
    e. colors; taste

14. Which of the following involves trial-and-error learning?
    a. habituation
    b. classical conditioning
    c. imprinting
    d. operant conditioning
    e. taxis

15. A sensitive phase or critical period is associated with what type of behavior?
    a. cognitive
    b. nonassociative
    c. imprinting
    d. orientation
    e. classical conditioning

16. How is the distance to a food source communicated by a dancing bee?
    a. by the tempo or degree of vigor of the dance
    b. by the direction it waggles its abdomen
    c. by how far it moves during the straight portion of the dance
    d. by which direction it turns after the straight portion of the dance
    e. none of these; bees cannot communicate distance information, only direction.

17. Which of the following did Harry Harlow find that an orphaned rhesus monkey became most attached to?
    a. a wire frame
    b. the first object it saw after birth
    c. a wire frame covered with a cloth
    d. the first object that provided it with food
    e. a wire frame that provided food

18. Which of the following does NOT seem to be required for normal growth and psychological development according to studies in primates and humans?
    a. tactile stimulation
    b. social contact
    c. physical contact between parent and offspring
    d. a constant "mother figure"
    e. none of the above

19. Which of the following does NOT suggest that animals may have cognitive capabilities?
    a. A chimpanzee pulling leaves off a tree branch to probe a termite nest
    b. A mouse crouching over its young and retrieving them if they move away
    c. A bird removing a foil cap from a nonhomogenized bottle of milk
    d. A raven retrieving a piece of meat hanging from a string
    e. A sea otter cracking a clam against a rock to break it open

20. Which of the following statements about orientation and migratory behavior in animals is true?
    a. Celestial cues indicate the general direction in which migration should occur, while magnetic cues indicate the specific path.
    b. Inexperienced birds fly by orientation, while experienced birds learn true navigation.
    c. Established ranges where some species migrate to can change, but the migratory pattern seems to remain the same.
    d. Some organisms engage in goal-oriented movements by tracking environmental stimuli.
    e. All of the above.

21. Optimal foraging theory predicts that animals feed in such a way as to
    a. maximize net energy intake.
    b. minimize net energy intake.
    c. maximize risk of predation.
    d. spend as much time as possible feeding.
    e. eat only one type of food.

22. All human languages are a reflection of the way our brains handle abstract information, which is
    a. a genetically determine characteristic.
    b. an instinctive behavior.
    c. a habitual response.
    d. a conditioned response.
    e. a result of imprinting.

23. It is adaptive for parent gulls to remove the eggshells after their chicks hatch because removing them decreases the likelihood of
    a. the chicks being injured by the sharp edges.
    b. bad odors.
    c. fungal growth that can make the chicks sick.
    d. predators spotting the nest.
    e. a mineral imbalance in their diet.

24. Which of the following statements about territoriality is true?
    a. Territoriality is always beneficial to an animal.
    b. Territories frequently overlap in time or space.
    c. Territories rarely contain any resources.
    d. All of these are true.
    e. None of these are true.

25. Which of the following is known to influence foraging behavior?
    a. age of the individual
    b. risk of predation
    c. conflicting activities
    d. all of these
    e. none of these

26. Which sex should show mate choice?
    a. always males
    b. always females
    c. the sex with the higher parental investment
    d. the sex with the lower parental investment
    e. neither sex

27. Which of the following is associated with monogamy?
    a. altricial young
    b. sexual dimorphism
    c. two males mating with one female
    d. all of these
    e. none of these

28. Which mating system is most common in mammals?
    a. monogamy
    b. polygyny
    c. polyandry
    d. They are all equally common.

29. When a predator approaches, which of the following Belding's ground squirrels is most likely to give an alarm call?
    a. a female with no kin nearby
    b. a female with kin nearby
    c. a male with no kin nearby
    d. a male with kin nearby
    e. They are all equally likely to call.

30. In the haplodiploidy sex determination of bees, males
    a. are sterile.
    b. can be either diploid or haploid.
    c. are diploid.
    d. are haploid.
    e. do not exist.

ASSESSING YOUR KNOWLEDGE

Answers to the questions in this section test your ability to synthesize information gained from the chapter and to solve challenging problems on an exam or in everyday life.

Challenging Your Understanding—Part I, Answers

1.

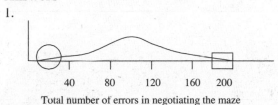

Total number of errors in negotiating the maze

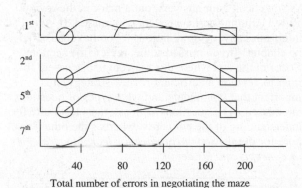

Total number of errors in negotiating the maze

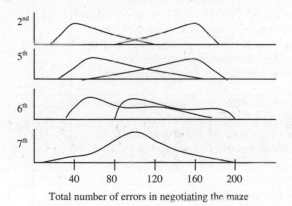

Total number of errors in negotiating the maze

4. The results in question 2 indicate that the ability to learn the maze must, at least in part, be genetic because the ability to do the maze either fast or slow is passed on from one generation to the next.

5. To determine if the genes that control the ability to learn the maze are specific or not, you could take the rats in both populations from the seventh generation and test them in other behavioral tasks, such as timing how long it takes for them to run a

completely different maze, or to run a race, or to find a hidden treat.

6. If the genes that cause the rats to move more quickly, or more slowly through the maze are specific to that maze, you would expect to see no difference between the two populations of rats when performing other behavioral tasks such as running a different maze, running a race, or finding a hidden treat.

7. If the two populations of rats, the fast and the slow, performed similarly on average in the other behavioral tasks as they did on the original maze so that the fast and the slow populations were distinguishable in every task, it would suggest that the genes controlling "maze learning" may in fact affect some physical characteristic of the rats, or generally improve the mental capacity of the rats that can do the maze quickly. This gene or genes would then generally affect their overall ability to perform a variety of tasks.

8. Although not immediately phenotypically apparent, the "maze-dull" rats or the "maze-bright" rats may have some type of genetically controlled difference that either physically affects the ability of the rats to do the maze or affects their mental capacity in general. For example, the "maze-dull" rats may have slightly shorter limbs, have a defect in their olfactory or visual senses, have shorter nails or fatter bodies, a general mental defect, or another defect that ultimately makes them not only do the maze more slowly, but also do other behaviors more slowly. Likewise, the "maze-bright" rats may have a beneficial difference that is genetically based that makes them superior not only in doing the maze, but also in performing a variety of behavioral tasks.

Challenging Your Understanding—Part II. Answers

1. a. ultimate, b. proximate, c. proximate, d. ultimate, e. proximate, f. proximate, g. ultimate, h. proximate, i. ultimate, j. proximate.

2. First, you would compare how the two species act before and after mating and when injected with a range of different concentrations of vasopressin or oxytocin in the absence of mating. These experiments should identify whether vasopressin or oxytocin is responsible for the pair-bonding behavior. Second, you would attempt to identify the receptor

for the neuropeptide responsible for the behavior and determine if receptor number or sensitivity differs in one species compared to the other. This could be done by injecting a range of different concentrations of vasopressin or oxytocin in the two species in question. If one gives the desired response at a lower concentration of one of the hormones than the other species, it suggests that that species may have more receptors, or more sensitive receptors, than the other species. If the second species does not give the desired response at any concentration, it suggests that the receptor may not be present in the second species, or may be unable to bind to the neuropeptide. It could be confirmed that this receptor and its neuropeptide are indeed involved in giving the pair-bonding response by using the gene coding for the receptor to make a transgenic mouse expressing this gene. These transgenic mice, along with control mice, would then be injected with the neuropeptide specific for the receptor and it would be determined if the mice exhibit pair-bonding behaviors. If they do and the control mice still do not, it would conclusively show that this receptor was responsible for the behavior in the one species.

3. a. 2, b. 6, c. 7, d. 8, e. 4, f. 1, g. 5, h. 3.

Key Terms—Answers

a. 24, b. 39, c. 18, d. 46, e. 30, f. 13, g. 22, h. 10, i. 4, j. 16, k. 25, l. 41, m. 6, n. 32, o. 8, p. 28, q. 49, r. 36, s. 11, t. 43, u. 29, v. 3, w. 34, x. 48, y. 38, z. 20, aa. 26, bb. 5, cc. 12, dd. 17, ee. 35, ff. 42, gg. 7, hh. 45, ii. 1, jj. 40, kk. 19, ll. 37, mm. 31, nn. 21, oo. 15, pp. 27, qq. 2, rr. 9, ss. 23, tt. 47, uu. 14, vv. 44, ww. 33.

Learning by Experience—Answers

1. For whatever animal and behaviors you picked, the proximate explanation should address an immediate cause of the behavior, such as hormones, the way the nervous and muscular systems work, etc. The ultimate explanations should address how the behavior increases the likelihood of the animal surviving and reproducing (for example, more likely to find food, get a mate, etc.).
2. Anecdotal evidence and some experimental evidence support the hypothesis that humans are not the only animals capable of cognitive behavior or reasoning and conscious thought (for example, ability to solve problems, giving false information). But it is very difficult to test conclusively since we have no way to

"get inside the animal's head" and know what it is or isn't thinking.
3. The larger the mussel, the greater the processing cost. It is harder and takes more energy to break open the shell. Large mussels may also be rarer, and therefore it takes more energy to search for them.

4.   a. polygyny
      b. monogamy
      c. polyandry

5.   a. ½
      b. ½
      c. ¼
      d. ⅛
      e. ¼
      f. none

Exercising Your Knowledge—Answers

As you check your answers, put a mark in the review (Rvw.) column for the answers you missed. If you didn't miss any, congratulations—you have mastered the chapter! If you missed some, review the section (Sect.) in the text where this concept is discussed. In order to develop an efficient review strategy, it is important that you understand what types of questions you missed. The questions with asterisks test more for understanding of the **concepts**, whereas the others test more for **detail**. *See the preface for learning strategies for concepts and for detail.*

	Sect.	Rvw.
*1. Neither is more important than the other. They are just two different ways of looking at the situation—the immediate explanation of how the behavior occurs versus the evolutionary explanation of why the behavior occurs. Proximate and ultimate explanations are interrelated – natural selection acts on the morphology and physiology that provide the proximate mechanisms for behavior. Without one, there could not be the other.	54.1	
*2. By selecting for maze-bright and maze-dull rats over several generations, Tryon was able to show that there was a genetic component to the behavior (for example, it was heritable) and that the genes were specific for that particular type of behavior.	54.2	
*3. An incredible number of stimuli constantly surround and bombard animals. Habituation allows an animal to filter out and ignore those that are not immediately relevant to its well-being so that it can focus on those that are. It prevents sensory overload.	54.3	
*4. No; animals have limits to what they can learn based on their genetic templates. These templates influence what type of behaviors can be learned, in what context, and when. The templates are relevant to the ecology and lifestyle of the animal.	54.4	

*5. Distinctive courtship behaviors are advantageous because animals avoid wasting time and energy on courtship and mating that may lead to hybridization and may not produce viable young. They are disadvantageous because the elaborate courtship itself requires energy expenditure on the behavior and/or the development of the morphology used in the display. The display may also make the performer more noticeable to predators as well as potential mates. The fact that elaborate courtship behavior exists implies that the reproductive benefits outweigh the other costs in those cases.	54.7
*6. There are constraints, such as trying to avoid predation or injury – feeding is often risky business. Or the animal may be trying to do something else of importance too, such as finding, attracting, and/or keeping, a mate.	54.8
*7. When the benefits of territoriality outweigh the costs; the resource being defended is valuable, but not too rare and not too common; the costs of defending it are not too high.	54.8
*8. Heavier females produce more eggs than lighter females, thus they produce more offspring. By choosing heavier females as mates, males will have more offspring. Male Mormon crickets should be choosy because they have a very large parental investment in the form of a large, protein-rich spermatophore.	54.9
*9. If the young are altricial and need care from both parents in order to survive, monogamy is favored. If the young are more precocial and require care from only one parent, polygyny or polyandry is favored.	54.9

*10. There may be greater protection from predation in a group or increased feeding success (learning the location of food from group members, being able to handle larger prey). Disadvantages include increased competition with group members, easier spread of diseases and parasites, or easier for predators to find a large group than a solo individual.	54.10
11. a	54.1
*12. e	54.1
13. d	54.3
14. d	54.3
15. c	54.4
16. a	54.7
17. c	54.4
*18. e	54.4
*19. b	54.5
*20. e	54.6
*21. a	54.8
*22. a	54.7
23. d	54.8
*24. e	54.8
25. d	54.8
*26. c	54.9
27. a	54.9
28. b	54.9
29. b	54.10
30. d	54.10

CHAPTER 55 POPULATION ECOLOGY

MASTERING KEY CONCEPTS

Ecology is the study of the relationships among organisms and their environments. Populations—all the individuals of a particular species living in a particular area--are not static. The size, growth, and distribution of a population are influenced by interactions within the population, with other populations, and with environmental factors. Our population, the human population, has grown exponentially in the last three hundred years until it now stands at over 6 billion with built-in potential for further growth. The Earth's carrying capacity for people is not known.

55.1 Organisms must cope with a varied environment.

- **Overview**: Temperature, water, sunlight, and soil determine where different organisms can live. Some organisms use physiological, morphological, and behavioral mechanisms to maintain internal homeostasis, and others conform to their environments. Natural selection for individuals adapted to their environments leads to evolutionary change.
- **Details**: Know the environmental factors that regulate where an organism can live. Understand the mechanisms that organisms employ to respond to environmental changes.

55.2 Populations are groups of individuals of the same species that live in the same place.

- **Overview**: Three characteristics of populations are important: the area throughout which a population occurs (range), the spacing between the individuals of the population in that area, and the changes in a population's size over time. The range of a population is determined by factors such as temperature, humidity, food availability, and the presence of predators, competitors, or parasites. Balance between these factors determines if an environment is suitable for a particular population of organisms. Population ranges change over time due to changes in the environment or the ability of organisms to circumvent inhospitable habitats to colonize suitable, previously unoccupied areas. Humans have allowed some organisms to expand their ranges, and have served as agents aiding in the dispersal of many species, often at the expense of native species. Seeds have evolved a number of dispersal mechanisms allowing the establishment of new populations. Individuals in a population are distributed **randomly**, **uniformly**, or **clumped** in one area. These patterns of distribution are dependent upon interactions between individuals in the population and competition for resources. **Metapopulations** are networks of distinct populations that interact with one another by exchanging individuals. The degree to which these populations interact depends on the amount of dispersal. Metapopulations prevent long-term extinction, and they allow species to occupy larger areas. In **source-sink metapopulations**, dispersers are continually sent out from the populations in better areas to populations in poorer areas, thus maintaining the sink populations.

- **Details**: Know the factors that affect a population's range. Know the circumstances under which individuals in a population will be distributed randomly, uniformly, or clumped. Understand how metapopulations affect the range of a population and why metapopulations are advantageous.

55.3 Population dynamics depend critically upon age distribution.

- **Overview**: Changes in population size are affected by the population's **sex ratio**, **generation time**, and **age structure**. A large number of females in a population, a short generation time, and a large number of young individuals promote population growth. **Life tables** can be used to assess how populations in nature are changing. Every age group in a population has a characteristic birthrate (**fecundity**) and **mortality** rate, and each population has a characteristic **survivorship curve** that relates the age of the members of a given population to their percent survival. Humans have a type I curve in which mortality rates rise steeply with age; hydra have a type II curve in which individuals are equally likely to die at any age; and oysters have a type III curve in which survival and mortality rates are inversely related.

- **Details**: Understand how a population's sex ration, generation time, and age structure affect its growth. Understand the information that a life table and a survivorship curve provide.

55.4 Life histories often reflect trade-offs between reproduction and survival.

- **Overview**: How long an individual lives and how many young it produces each year are two factors that affect the number of surviving offspring in the next generation. Organisms allocate their resources to reproducing now, or to surviving and reproducing in the future. In general, individuals should produce as many offspring as possible when the costs are low, and expend energy to enhance growth and survival when the costs of reproduction are high. Energy devoted to increasing an organism's reproductive success early in life, or energy devoted to current reproductive efforts cannot be used for growth and reduce an organism's future reproductive potential (**cost of reproduction**). Therefore, it may be beneficial for an organism to devote its energy to growth early in life and delay reproduction because it increases the organism's chance for future reproductive success. A balance must be reached between the size of each offspring and the number of offspring produced, and between reproductive efforts and survival of the organism that is reproducing to allow future reproduction.

- **Details**: Know the two factors that contribute to the number of surviving offspring in the next generation. Understand how reproductive success can be maximized when the costs are low or high. Understand why balances must be reached between energy expended for growth or reproduction, reproductive efforts and survival, and the size and number of offspring produced.

55.5 Population growth is limited by the environment.

- **Overview**: A population will increase in size if the birthrate is greater than the death rate, and the number of individuals moving into an area is greater than the number of individuals moving out of an area. The **biotic potential** is the rate at which a population will increase if no limits are put on it. When resources are not limiting, a population will grow exponentially. No matter how rapidly populations grow, they eventually reach the **carrying capacity**, the maximum number of individuals an environment can support. Due to fewer resources, population growth tends to slow as the carrying capacity is approached. **Logistic growth** tends to return a population to the same size because populations always tend to move toward the carrying capacity.
- **Details**: Understand how population growth is limited, and what would happen if it were not limited. Understand the relationship between population growth rate and population size.

55.6 Density-dependent and density-independent factors regulate population sizes.

- **Overview**: Some factors that affect population size are dependent on the size of the population (**density-dependent**), and others are not (**density-independent**). Density-dependent effects, such as a decline in reproductive rates, an increase in mortality rates due to a competition for resources, an increase in predators, or an increase in toxic waste production, regulate population size by negative feedback. Behavioral changes, such as fighting, less breeding, or stress among the members of a population, and increased rates of emigration also negatively regulate the population size. Growth rates can increase with population size

(**Allee effect**) due to large groups deterring predators, or providing stimulation for breeding activities. Factors that are unrelated to the size of the population but limit growth rate of a population are density-independent factors. These factors include weather extremes, volcanic eruptions, and certain natural catastrophes. Populations influenced by these factors will have erratic growth patterns. Many populations exhibit regular cycles in size due to a combination of factors, such as food and predators and their interactions. Populations that are **K-selected** are adapted to thrive when a population is at, or near, its carrying capacity, whereas **r-selected** populations favor individuals that can produce the highest number of offspring.

- **Details**: Understand the difference between density-dependent and density-independent factors that control population size. Understand the factors that affect population cycles. Understand how resource availability affects life history adaptations.

55.7 The human population has grown explosively in the last three centuries.

- **Overview**: The human population grew slowly during its early history, but increased rapidly following the Industrial Revolution, and has continued to grow. Over the last three hundred years, the birthrate has not changed, but there has been a significant decrease in the death rate. The current human population is 6.5 billion people. The population is increasing most rapidly in developing countries in Africa, Asia, and Latin America. **Population pyramids** can be used to predict demographic trends in births and deaths. In general, stable populations are rectangle shaped, while growing populations are triangle shaped, and decreasing populations have the shape of an inverted triangle. The growth in the human population has put the world's ecosystem under extreme stress, and the death rates in some areas of the world are already increasing due to malnutrition and AIDS. The world population growth rate is now declining in great part due to worldwide family planning efforts. Population size and **per capita consumption** of resources must be limited in order for the Earth to be able to maintain resources and sustain future populations, which will be even larger than they are today.
- **Details**: Understand why the human population has grown so rapidly over the last three hundred years. Know how population pyramids can be used to predict demographic trends in births and deaths. Understand why future growth is uncertain and the measures that must be taken to limit population size and per capita consumption.

CHALLENGING YOUR UNDERSTANDING

1. Fill in the following letters with the types of vegetation that grow at the indicated elevations.

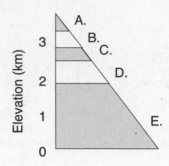

2. Draw a straight line that represents the relationship between (A) organism size and the length of generation and (B) age of first reproduction and life span.

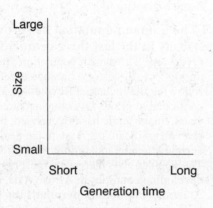

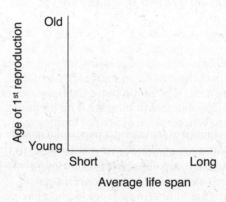

3. The line drawn below represents the number of prey present in an area over a period of 30 years. Draw a second line that represents the number of predators that you would expect to see in that same area during those same years.

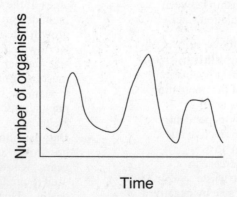

KEY TERMS

Match the numbered term with the definition that fits it best. Put the corresponding number in front of the appropriate definition.

1. populations
2. demography
3. sex ratio
4. metapopulations
5. source-sink metapopulations
6. generation time
7. cohort
8. fecundity
9. mortality rate
10. age structure

11. life table
12. survivorship
13. life history
14. cost of reproduction
15. semelparity
16. iteroparity
17. biotic potential
18. carrying capacity
19. sigmoidal growth curve
20. density-dependent effects

21. density-independent effects
22. Allee effect
23. K-selected
24. r-selected
25. biosphere
26. population pyramid
27. ecological footprint

a. _____ The rate at which a population of a given species will increase when no limits are placed upon it.
b. _____ An outline of the fate of a cohort from birth until death, showing the number of offspring, and deaths each year.
c. _____ A graphical means of assessing the rate at which a population can be expectd to grow in the future.
d. _____ The phenomenon by which growth rates can actually increase with population size in some instances.
e. _____ The number of offspring produced in a standard time; the birthrate.
f. _____ Groups of individuals that occur together at one place and time.
g. _____ The relative number of individuals in each cohort of a population that has a critical effect on its growth rate.
h. _____ Selection in populations that favors individuals with the highest reproductive rates.
i. _____ The reduction in future reproductive potential resulting from current reproductive efforts.
j. _____ The average interval between the birth of an individual and the birth of its offspring.
k. _____ Factors that affect population growth rates as the size of the population increases.
l. _____ The maximum number of individuals that the environment can support.
m. _____ The world's interacting community of living things.
n. _____ The number of females in a population relative to the number of males.
o. _____ A practice in which an organism puts all of its reproductive resources into a single large event and then dies.
p. _____ Selection in populations that favors individuals that can compete effectively and utilize resources efficiently.
q. _____ The percentage of an original population that lives to a given age.
r. _____ A group of individuals of the same age.
s. _____ The amount of productive land required to support an individual at a particular standard of living throughout life.
t. _____ A network of distinct populations that interact with one another by exchanging individuals.
u. _____ A growth curve characteristic of populations whose growth rate slows upon nearing the carrying capacity.
v. _____ The number of individuals that die in a standard time; the death rate.
w. _____ Factors that are not related to the size of the population itself that limit population growth rates.
x. _____ The complete life cycle of an organism.
y. _____ The quantitative study of populations.
z. _____ A population network in areas where some habitats are suitable for long-term maintenance but others are not.
aa. _____ A practice in which organisms produce offspring several times over many seasons.

LEARNING BY EXPERIENCE

1. Shown below are the dispersion patterns of three different species of wildflowers. Each dot represents the location of a single plant, and the box represents the area where the wildflowers were studied. Name the type of dispersion pattern exhibited by each species.

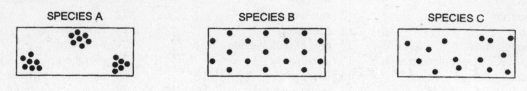

SPECIES A   SPECIES B   SPECIES C

2. Draw an example of an exponential growth curve and a sigmoid growth curve on the blank graphs below. Be sure to label the axes on both graphs. On the sigmoid curve, indicate where the carrying capacity (*K*) is.

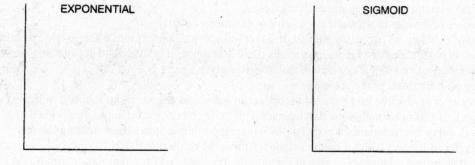

EXPONENTIAL   SIGMOID

3. Draw and label a type I survivorship curve, a type II curve, and a type III curve on the following graph.

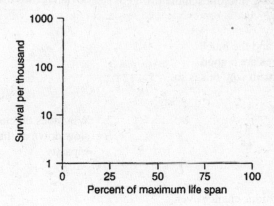

4. Do carrying capacities change or are they constant attributes?

EXERCISING YOUR KNOWLEDGE

Briefly answer each of the following questions in the space provided.

1. The long ears of jackrabbits and the much shorter ears of snowshoe hares are a good example of Allen's rule. Explain why this is so.

2. Why do the ranges of populations change over time? What role do humans play in this?

3. Why are metapopulations important in conservation biology efforts?

4. How do the sex ratio, generation time, and age structure affect a population's potential for growth?

5. Why are organisms faced with trade-offs between reproduction and survival?

6. Under what conditions is semelparity more advantageous than iteroparity?

7. Why does the population growth rate usually slow down as the population approaches carrying capacity?

8. Giant land tortoises weighing up to 150 kg live on a large tropical atoll in the western Indian Ocean. The population is quite large, with more than 150,000 individuals. The tortoises graze during the early morning and late afternoon, but spend midday resting in any available shade. If they do not get out of the hot, tropical, noonday sun, they overheat and die. Trees and bushes are scarce in many parts of the atoll, so shade is often scarce too. Are the sun and the shade density-dependent or density-independent factors for the tortoises?

9. Do you think endangered species are more likely to be r-selected or K-selected? Why?

10. Industrialized countries and developing countries are sometimes referred to as the "haves" and the "have nots," respectively. Explain what is meant by this and how population growth factors in.

Circle the letter of the one best answer in each of the following questions.

11. Which of the following statements is true about how organisms cope with environmental conditions?
    a. Some frogs secrete a waxy substance to prevent loss of water through their skin.
    b. Some insects add glycerol to their blood in the winter to act like antifreeze and prevent freezing.
    c. Humans can produce more red blood cells in response to high altitudes and decreased oxygen availability.
    d. All of these are true.
    e. None of these are true.

12. Which dispersion pattern is least common in nature?
    a. uniformly spaced
    b. randomly spaced
    c. clumped
    d. All are equally common.
    e. None of these are found in nature.

13. Cattle egrets and starlings are both examples of species that
    a. have been able to quickly and greatly expand their range once they reach a new area.
    b. are endangered because of a very limited range.
    c. have exceeded their carrying capacity.
    d. have high costs of reproduction.
    e. are source-sink metapopulations to each other.

14. Metapopulations
    a. belong to different species.
    b. occur in the exact same area.
    c. exchange individuals.
    d. never change size.
    e. always go extinct.

15. Which of the following has undergone the largest elevation shift due to climate changes since the glacial period 15,000 years ago in the mountains of southwestern North America?
    a. alpine tundra
    b. spruce-fir forests
    c. mixed conifer forests
    d. woodlands
    e. grasslands, chaparral, and desert scrub

16. Short generation times are usually correlated with
    a. metapopulations.
    b. a sex ratio biased in favor of males.
    c. a sex ratio biased in favor of females.
    d. short life spans.
    e. long life spans.

17. The vast majority of acorns produced by an oak tree never germinate or die during their first year of growth. If they survive past the first year, however, they are likely to live the maximum life span. This is an example of what type of survivorship curve?
    a. type I
    b. type II
    c. type III
    d. can't tell from the information provided

18. In a life table, a cohort refers to
    a. a group of individuals of the same age.
    b. a specific rate of mortality.
    c. a specific rate of fecundity.
    d. a group of individuals that does not reproduce.
    e. an estimated probability of going extinct.

19. What type of survivorship curve do humans have?
    a. type I
    b. type II
    c. type III
    d. none of the above; humans don't have survivorship curves.

20. Which of the following is NOT included in a life table?
    a. The number of offspring produced each year.
    b. The percentage of an original population that survives to a given age.
    c. The average interval between the birth of an individual and the birth of its offspring.
    d. The number of individuals that die each year.
    e. The age of the cohort.

21. Which of the following reproductive and life history patterns would you expect a species to have in response to a very high cost of reproduction?
    a. large clutch sizes
    b. large-sized eggs or offspring
    c. frequent reproduction
    d. all of these
    e. none of these

22. Which of the following is NOT a trade-off that is necessary for the reproductive success of an organism?
    a. age at the time of the first reproduction and life span
    b. reproductive efforts and growth
    c. the number of offspring and the size of each
    d. age at the time of the first reproduction and the number of mates
    e. the number of reproductive events and how long an organism lives

23. In the formula for biotic potential ($dN/dt = r_iN$), what does N stand for?
    a. the carrying capacity
    b. change in time
    c. the number of individuals in the population
    d. the age distribution of the population
    e. the intrinsic rate of natural increase of the population

24. The r-selected species tend to have
    a. few offspring.
    b. little parental care.
    c. sigmoid growth curves.
    d. all of these.
    e. none of these.

25. Which of the following is likely true of populations far below the carrying capacity?
    a. Only a few large offspring are produced per reproductive event.
    b. Populations are r-selected.
    c. Selection favors individuals that utilize resources efficiently.
    d. The costs of reproduction are high.
    e. Resources are limited.

26. A recent review of hundreds of long-term studies of various species of animals found that population cycles occurred in nearly _____ of them.
    a. none
    b. 5%
    c. 30%
    d. 65%
    e. all

27. Which of the following is a K-selected species?
    a. coconut palm
    b. dandelion
    c. aphids
    d. mice
    e. none of these

28. What is the size of the human population today?
    a. 10.2 billion
    b. 6.5 billion
    c. 2.7 billion
    d. 1.1 billion
    e. 30.6 million

29. What type of population would be associated with a population pyramid that had an extremely broad base?
    a. a population with more males than females
    b. a population with more old individuals than young individuals
    c. a stable population
    d. an expanding population
    e. a declining population

30. Which of the following statements about the human global population is true?
    a. It is currently growing at the rate of about 1.3% per year.
    b. Approximately 150 people are born every minute, the majority of them in developing countries.
    c. About 19% of the world's population lives in industrialized countries.
    d. About 80% of all energy consumption occurs in the industrialized countries.
    e. All of these are true.

ASSESSING YOUR KNOWLEDGE

Answers to the questions in this section test your ability to synthesize information gained from the chapter and to solve challenging problems on an exam or in everyday life.

Challenging Your Understanding—Answers

1. A. Alpine tundra; B. Spruce-fir forests; C. Mixed conifer forests; D. Woodlands; E. Grassland/desert scrub.

2.

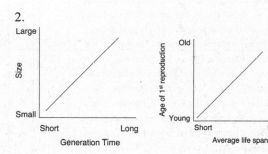

3.

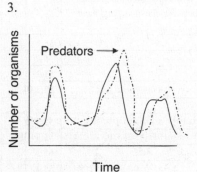

Key Terms—Answers

a. 17, b. 11, c. 26, d. 22, e. 8, f. 1, g. 10, h. 24, i. 14, j. 6, k. 20, l. 18, m. 25, n. 3, o. 15, p. 23, q. 12, r. 7, s. 27, t. 4, u. 19, v. 9, w. 21, x. 13, y. 2, z. 5, aa. 16.

Learning by Experience—Answers

1.	Species A = clumped
	Species B = uniformly spaced
	Species C = randomly spaced
2.	

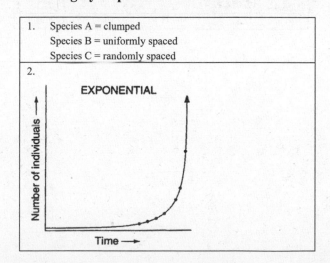

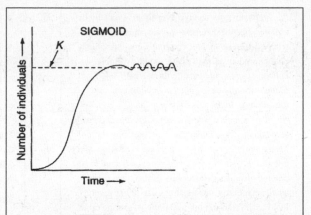

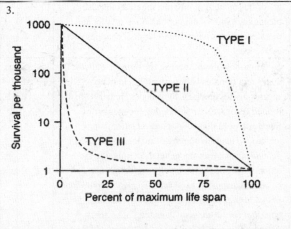

4. Every environment has a carrying capacity for each population that occurs there, so in that sense carrying capacity is a constant attribute. However, the actual carrying capacity (the number of individuals the environment can support) definitely changes over time. Climatic changes (short- and long-term, such as droughts or ice ages), catastrophes (for example, hurricanes or fires), and human impacts (for example, development or pollution) can all influence how many individuals the environment can support. Carrying capacity is unique for each population in any given environment under the current prevailing conditions.

Exercising Your Knowledge—Answers

As you check your answers, put a mark in the review (Rvw.) column for the answers you missed. If you didn't miss any, congratulations—you have mastered the chapter! If you missed some, review the section (Sect.) in the text where this concept is discussed. In order to develop an efficient review strategy, it is important that you understand what types of questions you missed. The questions with asterisks test more for understanding of the **concepts**, whereas the others test more for **detail**. *See the preface for learning strategies for concepts and for detail.*

	Sect.	Rvw.
*1. Jackrabbits live in hot desert climates, and snowshoe hares live in very cold climates. According to Allen's rule, mammals from cold climates have shorter ears and limbs; this decreases surface area and thus decreases heat loss.	55.1	

*2. Environments change over time, favorably or unfavorably for different species, thus changing where different species can live. New, previously unoccupied areas may also become available. Humans play a role by intentionally or unintentionally changing the environment and introducing organisms to new areas.	55.2	
*3. Natural habitats are increasingly fragmented these days, dividing species into metapopulations. Metapopulations can help prevent extinction, since not all members of the species are restricted to just one location if a disaster hits. If there are source-sink metapopulations, sources can help prevent local extinction of sink populations. On the other hand, fragmentation into metapopulations also means each individual population is smaller and therefore more vulnerable to random changes and extinction.	55.2	
*4. In monogamous species, the number of both males and females is important, but in many species, males compete for females (females are a limited resource). So increasing the number of females would mean more reproduction, while increasing just the number of males would not. In general, the shorter the generation time, the more quickly the population can grow, though that can be counterbalanced by short life spans. Populations with a high proportion of young have a built-in potential for future growth as the young reach reproductive age. Populations with more old than young cohorts may decline in size.	55.3	
*5. Resources are limited, and there is not an infinite supply of accessible energy. Because of this finite energy budget, energy spent on producing young is energy that can not be spent on growth or escaping predators, and vice versa.	55.4	
*6. Semelparity can be advantageous for short-lived species, when the chances of surviving to the next reproductive season are low, or when the cost of reproducing is extremely high.	55.4	
*7. As the population approaches carrying capacity, resources become more limiting; there are fewer resources per individual since the resources are being shared among more individuals. This can lead to increased competition, stress, injury, disease, death, emigration, predation, buildup of wastes, or decreased reproduction--all of which can cause population growth to slow.	55.5	

*8. The sun is density independent since the size of the tortoise population does not influence the brightness or heat of the sun or whether there is any cloud cover. The availability of shade, however, is density-dependent. The more tortoises there are in an area, the harder it is for all of them to find shade; there is a limit to how many tortoises can pile under the few available trees and bushes.	55.6	
*9. Endangered species are more likely to be K-selected. Their delayed age at first reproduction, long generation time, and small clutch size make them more vulnerable to extinction than r-selected species with their early age at first reproduction, short generation times, and large clutch sizes.	55.6	
*10. Industrialized countries have much higher per capita annual income, much higher capital wealth, greater energy usage, and greater scientific expertise in residence. Developing countries, on the other hand, have the greatest number of people and will experience the vast majority of future population growth. In other words, the countries that can least afford it will experience the greatest growth, and the gaps between the haves and have nots will get bigger.	55.7	
11. d	55.1	
*12. b	55.2	
13. a	55.2	
14. c	55.2	
15. e	55.2	
*16. d	55.3	
*17. c	55.3	
18. a	55.3	
19. a	55.3	
20. c	55.3	
*21. e	55.4	
*22. d	55.4	
23. c	55.5	
24. b	55.6	
25. b	55.6	
26. c	55.6	
27. a	55.6	
28. b	55.7	
*29. d	55.7	
30. e	55.7	

CHAPTER 56 COMMUNITY ECOLOGY

MASTERING KEY CONCEPTS

A community is defined by the different populations that coexist in a given area. The populations of a community interact in complex ways, from predator-prey interactions and parasitism, to mutually beneficial relationships. Over evolutionary time, many populations have adapted and adjusted to each other. This coevolution has led to remarkable chemical, morphological, and behavioral defenses, countering predatory strategies, mimicry, and symbiotic relationships.

56.1 Biological communities are composed of species that occur together.

- **Overview**: A **community** consists of all of the species that occur in a particular location; subsets of species within this community are called **assemblages**. Communities are characterized by their constituent species, or by properties such as species richness or primary productivity. Communities can be viewed as an aggregation of individual species (**individualistic concept**) that respond independently of each other to changing environmental conditions, or as an integrated unit (**holistic concept**) in which species change in a synchronous pattern. In nature, there are examples of both types of communities. Interactions among the members of a community, such as predation or mutualism, affect the success of populations and the patterns of natural selection within the community that lead to evolutionary change.
- **Details**: Understand the definition of a community and the different ways a community can be viewed. Understand how the predictions made about the integrity of communities across space and time differ in the individualistic view compared to the holistic view. Know examples of each.

56.2 Interactions among competing species shape ecological niches.

- **Overview**: An organism's **niche** defines its lifestyle, where it lives, what it eats, how it mates, and the role that it plays. Interactions between different species can positively or negatively impact an organism's niche. These include **interspecific competition** for the same limiting resource, **interference competition** to defend access to resources, or **exploitative competition**, in which the same resource is consumed by more than one species. All of these can prevent a species from occupying its entire or **fundamental niche**, and can instead force it to occupy only its **realized niche,** which can be considerably smaller. The presence of a competing species, the absence of another species, or the presence of a predator can all

limit the size of an organism's realized niche. In studies using different species of *Paramecium*, **G. F. Gause** found that no two species with the same niche could coexist indefinitely when resources are limiting, but if the realized niches of the two species did not significantly overlap, then both species could survive. **Robert MacArthur** found that some species subdivide a niche to avoid competition with one another (**resource partitioning**). Natural selection can also cause initially similar species to diverge in their resource use. Character displacement is favored among sympatric species to reduce competition for the same resources. Competition between two species is difficult to detect because another environmental factor may have an opposite effect on two opposing species as well. Experimental field studies where the two species occur alone or together can determine whether the presence of one has a negative impact on the other.
- **Details**: Understand the realized and fundamental niches of *C. stellatus* and *S. balanoides* and what occurs in the absence of one of these competing species. Understand Gause's **principle of competitive exclusion** and the experiments that led to this principle. Understand how interspecific competition between two species can be detected and how this can affect population sizes, behavior, and individual growth rates. Know the limitations of experimental studies and how results could be misinterpreted.

56.3 Predation has ecological and evolutionary effects.

- **Overview**: Predators can have large effects on prey populations. Likewise, the elimination of prey can greatly affect the population of predators. Predation can place strong selective pressure on a population of prey to develop characteristics that will decrease its probability of capture, but counter adaptations in predator populations can lead to coevolution of a predator with its prey. Plants and animals have evolved mechanisms, such as morphological adaptations and chemical defenses, to defend themselves from herbivores or predators, respectively. Some poisonous animals use warning coloration to indicate that they are poisonous to their predators, while others use cryptic coloration to camouflage themselves from their predators. **Henry Bates** made the observation that many palatable butterflies and moths mimic the coloration of other brightly colored, distasteful species (**Batesian mimicry**). **Fritz Muller** noticed that several unrelated, protected species resemble each other gaining an advantage because predators will learn to avoid them more quickly (**Mullerian mimicry**).

- **Details**: Understand how prey and predator populations affect each other. Recognize the defenses that plants use to protect themselves against herbivores and how certain organisms have evolved to overcome these defenses. Know the defense mechanisms that different animals use to protect themselves from other species. Understand the difference between Batesian mimicry and Mullerian mimicry.

56.4 Species within a community interact in many ways.

- **Overview**: Many species living together in one community have changed or adjusted to each other through evolutionary time. Two or more organisms often participate in **symbiotic relationships** with each other and many of these organisms have coevolved with each other. Symbiotic relationships can involve **commensalism**, **mutualism**, or **parasitism**. Commensalism involves relationships that benefit only one species, while the other species is neither helped nor harmed. Mutualism benefits both species involved, and parasitism benefits one species, while the other is harmed. Parasites can feed off the exterior surface of an organism (**ectoparasites**), or can live within their bodies (**endoparasites**). Parasites can require multiple hosts to complete their life cycle, and can alter the behavior of one host to promote its transmission to the next host. Interactions among species can be complex. Predators can have more than one type of prey, and they can eliminate competitors of other species. Parasites can affect organisms differently and can thus also influence interactions among sympatric species. The presence of one species can also have an indirect effect on another species by way of its interactions with a third species. All of these factors combined can make the interactions among the members of a community quite complex.
- **Details**: Understand the three types of symbiotic relationships. Know examples of each in terms of which organisms participate, who benefits, and how. Understand how parasites can alter the behavior of their hosts. Recognize how multiple effects, such as symbiotic relationships, competition, and predation, can lead to complex

interactions among the members of a community.

56.5 Ecological succession may increase the species richness of communities.

- **Overview**: The species composition of a community changes over time from simple to complex by the process of **succession**, even when the climate changes very little. **Primary succession** occurs on bare, lifeless substrates, while **secondary succession** occurs where an existing community has been disturbed, but organisms have been left behind. Succession occurs because the organisms living there change the habitat. This occurs by three basic mechanisms: **tolerance**, **facilitation**, and **inhibition**. Early succession is characterized by organisms tolerant of harsh conditions that can change the environment in such a way so as to facilitate the growth of less tolerant species. As these species grow, the habitat changes, inhibiting growth of the original species. Succession typically leads to an increase in the number of species, but it can also lead to a decline in species richness if superior competitors force out other species. Succession occurs in both plant and animal communities. Communities are constantly changing due to climate changes, species invasions, and local or widespread **disturbances,** which can interfere with succession. Moderate amounts of disturbance can lead to higher levels of species richness, then little or greater amounts of disturbance (**intermediate disturbance hypothesis**). This could be due to the fact that moderate disturbances allow a full range of species at all stages of succession, or these disturbances may prevent communities from reaching the final stages of succession.
- **Details**: Understand how primary and secondary succession occur, and why. Understand how different changes can affect species richness. Know how plant and animal succession occurred after the volcanic eruption on the Krakatau islands in 1883. Understand how disturbances affect succession and why moderate levels of succession may allow for the greatest amount of species richness.

CHALLENGING YOUR UNDERSTANDING

1. Graphs A and B show the beak depth (size) of two species of finches that evolved on separate islands from a common ancestor. In graphs C and D, draw the beak sizes that you might find for the same two finches if they had evolved while inhabiting the same island.

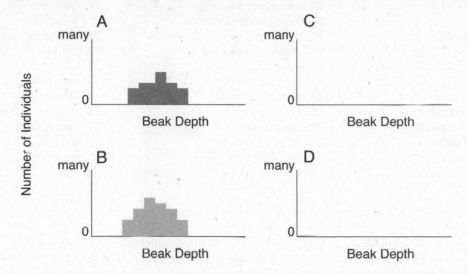

2. Consider two species of mice that occupy the same ecological niche. Draw hypothetical graphs representing the expected survival of one of the species if it were isolated in an enclosure or if it were placed in an enclosure with the second species if the following types of coexistence occur.

   A. Competitive exclusion   B. Resource partitioning

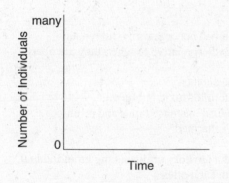

C. If you observed the data graphed in part A, what alternative explanations (other than competitive exclusion) could have produced those results?

3. Draw a flowchart that demonstrates the typical primary succession that occurs on a moraine left by a glacier in northern climates by filling in the boxes with organisms in the appropriate order. Below each box, indicate what change this organism brings to the ecosystem.

A.	→	B.	→	C.	→	D.

E. _____   F. _____   G. _____   H. _____

_____   _____   _____   _____

KEY TERMS

Match the numbered term with the definition that fits it best. Put the corresponding number in front of the appropriate definition.

1. community
2. assemblage
3. individualistic concept
4. holistic concept
5. ecotones
6. niche
7. interspecific competition
8. interference competition
9. exploitative competition
10. fundamental niche
11. realized niche
12. competitive exclusion

13. resource partitioning
14. character displacement
15. predation
16. secondary chemical compounds
17. Batesian mimicry
18. Mullerian mimicry
19. symbiosis
20. ectoparasites
21. endoparasites
22. parasitoids
23. keystone species

24. indirect effects
25. succession
26. secondary succession
27. primary succession
28. oligotrophic
29. eutrophic
30. equilibrium
31. nonequilibrium
32. commensalism
33. mutualism
34. parasitism

a. ____ The process by which communities change from simple to complex.
b. ____ The role played by a particular species in its environment.
c. ____ The subdivision of a niche by different species to avoid direct competition with one another.
d. ____ A situation in which several unrelated but protected animal species come to resemble one another.
e. ____ Poor in nutrients.
f. ____ Species whose effects on the composition of communities are greater than expected based on their abundance.
g. ____ A symbiotic relationship between organisms in which both species benefit.
h. ____ The actual set of environmental conditions in which a species can establish a stable population.
i. ____ The viewing of communities as integrated units whose species function as part of a greater whole.
j. ____ When two species attempt to use the same resource and there is not enough to satisfy both.
k. ____ Communities that are constantly changing as a result of climatic changes, species invasions, and disturbances.
l. ____ Insects that lay eggs on living hosts.
m. ____ When two species consume the same resources.
n. ____ Changes that occur in areas where an existing community has been disturbed but organisms still remain.
o. ____ Differences in morphology exhibited by species when they occur together, relative to when they are apart.
p. ____ Rich in nutrients.
q. ____ All of the species that occur in a particular location and interact with one another.
r. ____ A survival strategy in which a palatable organism resembles a distasteful or toxic organism.
s. ____ The entire niche that a species is capable of using, based on its physiological tolerance limits and resource needs.
t. ____ A symbiotic relationship in which one species benefits but the other is harmed.
u. ____ Parasites that live within the body of their hosts.
v. ____ Physical interactions over access to resources, like fighting to defend a territory or displacing an individual.
w. ____ A subset of species within a community that are likely to interact with each other.
x. ____ When the presence of one species affects a second species by way of interactions with a third species.
y. ____ A stable condition in a community that resists change and returns quickly to its original state if disturbed.
z. ____ When two or more kinds of organisms interact in often elaborate and more-or-less permanent relationships.
aa. ____ Changes that occur on bare, lifeless substrates, such as rocks, where organisms gradually move into an area.
bb. ____ A relationship where one species benefits while the other is neither hurt nor helped by the interaction.
cc. ____ The idea that a community is nothing more than an aggregation of species that happen to occur together.
dd. ____ The consuming of one organism by another.
ee. ____ Parasites that feed on the exterior surface of an organism.
ff. ____ Chemicals produced by plants that are either toxic to most herbivores or disturb their metabolism greatly.
gg. ____ Places where the environment changes abruptly.
hh. ____ The idea that if two species compete for a limited resource, the species that uses the resource more efficiently will eliminate the other locally.

LEARNING BY EXPERIENCE

1. Match each of the following organisms with the type of defense it uses to deter predation. Answers may be used more than once.

    _____ a. cactus
    _____ b. poison ivy
    _____ c. inchworm caterpillar
    _____ d. milkweed
    _____ e. monarch butterfly

    i.   morphological defense
    ii. secondary compounds
    iii. warning coloration
    iv. cryptic coloration

2. Complete the following chart on Batesian and Mullerian mimicry by indicating the palatability of the model and the mimic (poisonous or edible) in each system.

	Palatability	
Mimicry system	Model	Mimic
Batesian	a.	b.
Mullerian	c.	d.

3. The following diagram represents the distribution of individuals of two different plant species (Species x and Species o) in a particular environment. Is competitive exclusion occurring between these two species?

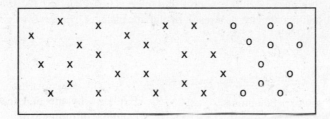

557

EXERCISING YOUR KNOWLEDGE

Briefly answer each of the following questions in the space provided.

1. Why are ecotones important in understanding communities?

2. Distinguish between a fundamental niche and a realized niche for a species. Why aren't realized niches identical to fundamental niches?

3. Persistent competition between two species is rare in natural communities. What usually happens instead?

4. What characteristics would you expect animals with warning coloration to have? What characteristics would you expect cryptically colored animals to have?

5. Cabbage butterfly caterpillars can feed on mustard plants, and monarch butterfly caterpillars can feed on milkweed plants. Why are these considered evolutionary "breakthroughs"? What are the implications for such breakthroughs in terms of natural selection and competition?

6. For Batesian mimicry systems to work, what two traits must the predators have?

7. What would you predict should be the relative abundance of the models and the mimics if a Batesian mimicry system is to be effective? Explain.

8. Of the three forms of symbiosis (commensalism, mutualism, and parasitism), which is the hardest to document?

9. Explain why ants and acacias are a good example of mutualism.

10. What role does disturbance play in succession and species richness?

Circle the letter of the one best answer in each of the following questions.

11. Which of the following is true as determined by J. H. Connell in his studies on two competing species of barnacles?
    a. *S. balanoides* is physiologically adapted to live in warmer waters, and *C. stellatus* is not.
    b. The realized niche of *S. balanoides* is the same as its fundamental niche.
    c. In the absence of *C. stellatus*, *S. balanoides* is unable to occupy rocks that remain underwater at low tide.
    d. The fundamental niche of *C. stellatus* consists only of rocks that remain underwater at low tide.
    e. In the absence of *S. balanoides*, the realized niche of *C. stellatus* consists only of rocks that are exposed at low tide.

12. Character displacement is associated with
    a. sympatric species.
    b. allopatric species.
    c. keystone species.
    d. primary succession.
    e. secondary succession.

13. The realized niche of a species tends to be
    a. the same size as the fundamental niche.
    b. smaller than the fundamental niche.
    c. larger than the fundamental niche.
    d. less important than the fundamental niche.
    e. harder to document than the fundamental niche.

14. Who formulated the principle of competitive exclusion?
    a. Connell
    b. Darwin
    c. MacArthur
    d. Gause
    e. Park

15. Under what conditions would you expect competitive exclusion to occur between two species?
    a. when the niches of the two species overlap significantly
    b. when resources are limiting
    c. both of these
    d. none of these

16. Resource partitioning
    a. increases interspecific competition.
    b. decreases interspecific competition.
    c. has never been documented in the wild.
    d. results in organisms with very similar traits.
    e. only occurs when resources are unlimited.

17. Which of the following helps a prey species avoid being detected by a predator?
    a. Mullerian mimicry
    b. secondary chemical compounds
    c. aposematic coloration
    d. cryptic coloration
    e. Batesian mimicry

18. Which of the following is an example of a plant morphological defense against herbivores?
    a. Beltian bodies
    b. mustard oils
    c. epiphytes
    d. "honeydew"
    e. silica

19. Why are monarch butterflies toxic?
    a. They produce their own secondary compounds.
    b. They incorporate mustard oils from the plants they eat as caterpillars.
    c. They incorporate cardiac glycosides from the plants they eat as caterpillars.
    d. Monarchs are not toxic—they only look that way.

20. A number of nonrelated, different kinds of stinging wasps have black-and-yellow striped abdomens and similar behavior. This is an example of
    a. Mullerian mimicry.
    b. Batesian mimicry.
    c. cryptic coloration.
    d. commensalisms.
    e. parasitism.

21. A predator can
    a. limit the size of its prey population.
    b. drive its prey population to extinction.
    c. reduce competition among prey species.
    d. do all of these.
    e. do none of these.

22. Which of the following is *not* an example of symbiosis?
    a. lichens
    b. mycorrhizae
    c. sympatric Caribbean *Anolis* lizard species
    d. clown fishes and sea anemones
    e. brood parasites and their host

23. Generally, do ectoparasites or endoparasites tend to have more extreme specializations?
    a. ectoparasites
    b. endoparasites
    c. They tend to be equally specialized.
    d. Neither usually has extreme specializations.

24. Which of the following statements about symbiotic relationships is true?
    a. In a parasitic relationship, both organisms are harmed.
    b. Symbiotic organisms have usually undergone little or no coevolution.
    c. A relationship that appears commensalistic may in fact be mutualistic but is never parasitic.
    d. All of these are true.
    e. None of these are true.

25. Rodents have an indirect positive effect on ant population size because of which of the following?
    a. Rodents dig up small seeds, but do not eat them.
    b. Excrement from rodents makes the soil more suitable for plants with small seeds.
    c. Ants require excrement from rodents as a source of nutrients.
    d. Rodents eat large seeds, leading to an increase in the number of plants with small seeds.
    e. Ants require rodents to remove the hardened outer covering of seeds before they can be ingested.

26. Beavers and alligators are keystone species because they
    a. are physically large.
    b. are such efficient predators.
    c. significantly physically modify their environments.
    d. have such strong symbiotic relationships.
    e. None of these are correct; beaver and alligators are not keystone species.

27. Which of the following is NOT a benefit that acacia obtain from the stinging ants that inhabit their thorns?
    a. Ants cut away encroaching branches from other plants.
    b. Ants decay within the acacias providing them with a rich source of carbon.
    c. Ants protect acacias from other herbivores.
    d. Organic materials brought in by the ants and their excretions provide the acacias with nitrogen.
    e. None of the above.

28. Removing a major predator from a community tends to cause _____ in species diversity in the community.
    a. a decrease
    b. an increase
    c. no change
    d. wild fluctuation

29. Which of the following is a factor that could account for the fact that communities with moderate amounts of disturbance will have higher levels of species richness?
    a. Species of all stages of succession will be present.
    b. The community will continually be in the earliest stages of succession.
    c. Dominant predators will always exist, but intermediate predators will not.
    d. Species that survive these disturbances become more competitive, promoting species richness.
    e. All of the above.

30. Which of the following statements about succession is true?
    a. Oligotrophic lakes contain more nutrients than do eutrophic lakes.
    b. Communities always eventually reach a climax stage that does not change.
    c. Early successional stages are usually associated with K-selected species.
    d. Over the course of succession, the types of species present change, but the number of species present tends to stay the same.
    e. Succession occurs because species alter the habitat and resources available.

ASSESSING YOUR KNOWLEDGE

Answers to the questions in this section test your ability to synthesize information gained from the chapter and to solve challenging problems on an exam or in everyday life.

Challenging Your Understanding—Answers

1.

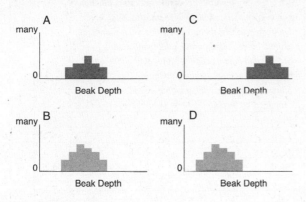

2

A.

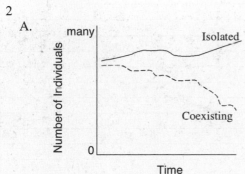

B.

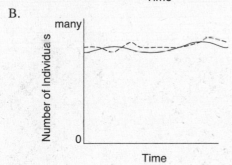

C. The removed species may prey on the other. Alternatively, the removed species may normally attract predators or parasites to the area that harm the other species.

3. A. lichens; B. mosses; C. alders; D. spruce; E. lower soil pH and break down rock; F. build-up of organic matter and nutrients; G. fixation of nitrogen through bacterial symbiotic relationship; H. dense forestation.

Key Terms—Answers

a. 25, b. 6, c. 13, d. 18, e. 28, f. 23, g. 33, h. 11, i. 4, j. 7, k. 31, l. 22, m. 9, n. 26, o. 14, p. 29, q. 1, r. 17, s. 10, t. 34, u. 21, v. 8, w. 2, x. 24, y. 30, z. 19, aa. 27, bb. 32, cc. 3, dd. 15, ee. 20, ff. 16, gg. 5, hh. 12.

Learning by Experience—Answers

1.	a. i
	b. ii
	c. iv
	d. ii
	e. ii and iii
2.	a. poisonous
	b. edible
	c. poisonous
	d. poisonous
3. Competitive exclusion might explain the nonoverlapping distribution of the two species, but other factors might be at work too, such as habitat differences and physiological constraints. More information is needed, and could be gotten by detailed observations and experimental studies involving removing one species and seeing if the other expands its range, and then repeating the experiment removing the other species.	

Exercising Your Knowledge—Answers

As you check your answers, put a mark in the review (Rvw.) column for the answers you missed. If you didn't miss any, congratulations—you have mastered the chapter! If you missed some, review the section (Sect.) in the text where this concept is discussed. In order to develop an efficient review strategy, it is important that you understand what types of questions you missed. The questions with asterisks test more for understanding of the **concepts**, whereas the others test more for **detail**. *See the preface for learning strategies for concepts and for detail.*

	Sect.	Rvw.
*1. Ecotones are places where environmental conditions change abruptly. Species composition also frequently changes abruptly and synchronously at ecotones. In other places, species tend to vary independently.	56.1	
*2. An organism's niche is the sum of all it does, where it lives, what it eats, how it behaves, and the role it plays in its environment. The fundamental niche is the niche a species is theoretically capable of having, based on its traits and requirements; the realized niche is the niche it actually has. The realized niche may be restricted compared to the fundamental niche because of the presence of other species (for example, predators or competitors) or the absence of other species (for example, prey or required symbiotic partners).	56.2	
*3. Usually one species drives the other to local extinction, or natural selection acts to reduce the competition through character displacement and resource partitioning.	56.2	

*4. Animals that are toxic or have some other strong defense system, such as poisonous stingers or bites, should be aposematically colored to warn potential predators to leave them alone. Animals that are palatable and have no strong defense mechanisms should be cryptically colored to avoid being seen and eaten by their predators.	56.3	
*5. The ability of those caterpillars to feed on those particular plants required the evolution of the ability to break down or tolerate the toxic secondary chemical compounds produced by the mustard plants and milkweeds. Earlier in evolutionary time, the plants evolved the ability to produce the secondary compounds, which was a breakthrough for them and would be strongly selected for since it protected them from herbivory. The ability to feed on the mustard and milkweed would also be strongly selected for since it allowed the butterflies to have access to a new source of food and one for which there was very little competition since other herbivores could not handle the toxic secondary compounds.	56.3	
*6. Predators must use visual cues to detect their prey so they can see the coloration pattern. They also must be capable of learning to avoid the particular color pattern, or it must be an instinctive response.	56.3	
*7. The models (the truly unpalatable) should outnumber the mimics (the actually palatable). This way, a naive predator is more likely to get the right message the first time it eats an organism with the warning coloration. If the mimics are more common than the models, the predator is likely to be able to eat them without repercussion and thus not learn to avoid that color pattern.	56.3	
*8. Commensalism; it is hard to know if the relationship is truly neutral for the other species. Further detailed study might reveal that the second species actually benefits from the relationship or is harmed by it, thus making the symbiosis mutualism or parasitism, respectively, rather than commensalism.	56.4	

*9. Both ants and acacias benefit from the relationship. The acacia's protein-rich Beltian bodies are the primary food source for the ants, and the plants also supply the ants with nectar and a place to live. The ants protect the acacia from herbivores and from other plants that try to overgrow it.	56.4	
*10. Disturbances, whether caused by nature or humans, can interrupt succession and reset the area to an earlier successional stage. Intermediate levels of disturbance can result in higher levels of species richness by providing a mosaic of different successional stages, each with its own complement of particular species, or by preventing the community from reaching a climax stage dominated by a relatively few species.	56.5	
11. b	56.2	
*12. a	56.2	
13. b	56.2	
14. d	56.2	
*15. c	56.2	
16. b	56.2	
17. d	56.3	
18. e	56.3	
19. c	56.3	
20. a	56.3	
*21. d	56.3	
22. c	56.4	
23. b	56.4	
*24. e	56.4	
25. d	56.4	
26. c	56.4	
27. b	56.4	
28. a	56.5	
29. a	56.5	
*30. e	56.5	

CHAPTER 57 DYNAMICS OF ECOSYSTEMS

MASTERING KEY CONCEPTS

In order to live, all organisms on Earth need to obtain nutrients, water, and energy. The minerals and other chemicals that make up nutrients, as well as water, are continually cycled from the nonliving environment to living organisms and back to the environment. Energy, on the other hand, flows through ecosystems, is not recycled, and is lost along the way, primarily in the form of heat. The diversity and numbers of organisms in an ecosystem are influenced by physical aspects of the environment; they, in turn, influence the cycling of chemicals and the transfer of energy within the ecosystem, as well as the stability of the system.

57.1 Chemicals cycle within ecosystems.

- **Overview**: An **ecosystem** consists of all of the organisms that live in a particular place and their nonliving environment. The atomic constituents of matter that make up all living things are continuously moving from the nonliving environment into living organisms and back to the environment in **biogeochemical cycles**. **Carbon**, the major constituent in organic molecules, is fixed by photosynthetic organisms that take in CO_2 from the atmosphere. Energy is obtained by both the photosynthetic organisms themselves and by the animals that ingest them by breaking down these organic compounds to produce CO_2 by aerobic cellular respiration. Decaying organisms also produce CO_2 and methanogens produce methane, which is oxidized to CO_2 in the atmosphere. **Water** is synthesized by aerobic cellular respiration and chemically split during photosynthesis. Water in oceans or in rivers on Earth circulates from the Earth's surface back to the atmosphere by evaporation. Water in the form of precipitation circulates from the atmosphere to the Earth's surface or into plants, and then back to the atmosphere by evaporation. **Nitrogen**, a key component of proteins and nucleic acids, is fixed by prokaryotes that can convert N_2 gas into ammonia or nitrate making it accessible to plants and algae. Other prokaryotes can convert the nitrogen in nitrate into nitrogen gas by **denitrification**. Human use of fertilizers that contain fixed forms of nitrogen are drastically changing the nitrogen cycle. **Phosphorus** is an element required in nucleic acids, membrane phospholipids, and other essential compounds (ATP). Phosphorus in free inorganic PO_4^{-3}, which is found in the water and soil, can be used directly by plants and algae to synthesize phosphorus-containing compounds, which can then be used by animals to make their own phosphorus-containing compounds.

- **Details**: Know how carbon, water, nitrogen, and phosphorus move through biogeochemical cycles. Understand how human activities are altering these cycles. Know how the phosphorus cycle differs from the nitrogen cycle.

57.2 Energy flows through ecosystems.

- **Overview**: **Energy**, unlike matter, is not recycled. It makes a one-way pass through an ecosystem and is then converted to heat and radiated back into space. Energy frequently changes forms and organisms can only use certain forms of energy. Use of light energy or chemical bond energy always gives off heat, which cannot be converted to any other form of energy, and organisms cannot use heat. Only about 1% of the solar energy is captured by plants and used for photosynthesis, the remainder is absorbed as heat. Organisms are arranged as **producers** or **consumers** in different **trophic levels**, with autotrophs acting as the **primary producers**. **Autotrophs** are eaten by **herbivores** who are eaten by **primary carnivores** who are eaten by **secondary carnivores** in a **food chain**. Chemical bond energy decreases as energy is passed from one trophic level to the next due to the production of feces, loss of energy as heat by cellular respiration, or death. This limits the length of a trophic chain, and the number of individual top carnivores that can be supported. More energy is available from eating primary producers, rather than animals because the amount of energy in each trophic level always forms a pyramid shape going from lower to higher trophic levels.

- **Details**: Understand the forms of energy, those that are useful to living organisms, and the flow of energy through an ecosystem. Understand how human activities are affecting energy flow. Understand why chemical bond energy decreases as it is passed from one trophic level to the next, and what this means for an ecosystem.

57.3 Interactions occur among different trophic levels.

- **Overview**: Species at any trophic level can have effects on other trophic levels, either flowing up through a trophic chain (**bottom-up effect**) or flowing down through the trophic chain (**top-down effect**) because food chains of different organisms are linked. Bottom-up effects are caused by changes in primary productivity; top-down effects are caused by changes in higher trophic levels affecting lower ones, such as the addition or the removal of predators.

- **Details**: Understand how bottom-up or top-down effects can lead to changes in ecosystems, and how humans can impact other organisms by top-down effects.

57.4 Biodiversity promotes ecosystem stability.

- **Overview**: Experiments done by **David Tilman** have demonstrated that plant **species richness** is related to community stability. He found that plots with more species of plants display less year-to-year variation in biomass, are less affected by drought, and are more resistant to invasion by new species. Species richness also correlated with greater nitrogen uptake and total amount of biomass produced. Controlled laboratory studies also support these conclusions, but not all ecologists agree because some argue that the results could be due to the fact that one species is particularly productive itself. Species richness is affected by primary productivity, habitat heterogeneity, and climatic factors. Intermediate productivity, spatially heterogeneous environments, and stable climates support species richness. There is a steady incline in species richness from the Arctic to the tropics (**species diversity cline**). There are many hypotheses about why this is true, but the absolute cause is not certain.

- **Details**: Understand the field and laboratory studies that suggest that species richness promotes stability, and why some disagree with this conclusion. Know what factors influence species richness and what characteristics of these factors promote species richness. Know the hypotheses suggested to explain why there is greater species richness in the tropics.

57.5 Species richness on islands is a dynamic equilibrium between colonization and extinction.

- **Overview**: The number of species on an island is determined by the rates of colonization and extinction, which in turn are influenced by the size of the island and its distance from the mainland and other islands. Equilibrium is reached when the colonization rate and the extinction rate are equal. Smaller islands have fewer species because they have higher rates of extinction than large islands. Islands closer to the mainland or another island have more species than islands far from the mainland because they have higher rates of colonization.

- **Details**: Understand MacArthur and Wilson's **species-area relationship** and the equilibrium model proposed for extinction and colonization of islands. Understand how size and distance from the mainland affect species richness.

CHALLENGING YOUR UNDERSTANDING

1. Draw arrows between the following ecosystem components that depict the direction of movement of energy in the ecosystem.

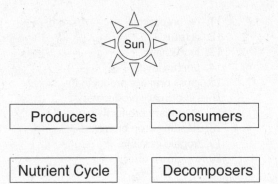

2. Draw a straight line that represents the relationship between biodiversity (number of species) and the stability (average amount of biomass) in an ecosystem.

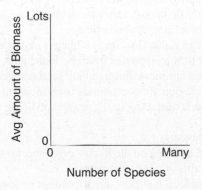

3. Why is the chemical bond energy available to one trophic level less than 30% of the energy available to the trophic level preceding them?

4. Place the following ecosystems in order from most productive to least productive based first on productivity per unit area (A) and based second on total yearly worldwide production (B): savanna; algal beds and reefs; desert and semidesert; open ocean; temperate evergreen forest; temperate deciduous forest; tropical rain forest; tundra and alpine; temperate grasslands; wetlands.

Most productive ──▶ Least productive

A.

B.

C. Why is the relative worldwide productivity of some of these ecosystems dramatically different from their relative productivity per unit area?

KEY TERMS

Match the numbered term with the definition that fits it best. Put the corresponding number in front of the appropriate definition.

1. biogeochemical cycles	11. decomposers	21. bottom-up effect
2. aquifers	12. detritus	22. species diversity cline
3. nitrogen fixation	13. food chain	23. species area relationship
4. nitrification	14. trophic levels	24. species turnover
5. limiting nutrient	15. gross primary productivity	25. photoautotrophs
6. primary producers	16. net primary productivity	26. chemoautotrophs
7. consumers	17. secondary productivity	27. heterotrophs
8. herbivores	18. standing crop biomass	28. detritivores
9. primary carnivores	19. trophic cascade	
10. secondary carnivores	20. top-down effect	

a. _____ Organisms that synthesize organic compounds from inorganic precursors using light energy.

b. _____ The raw rate at which the primary producers synthesize new organic matter.

c. _____ Organisms that feed on primary carnivores.

d. _____ The synthesis of nitrogen-containing compounds from N_2.

e. _____ All heterotrophs that feed directly on the primary producers.

f. _____ The amount of organic matter present at a particular time.

g. _____ Effects exerted at a lower trophic level that flow up to influence higher trophic levels.

h. _____ A sequence of species describing how food passes from one to the next.

i. _____ The movement of atoms of various chemicals through biological and geological processes in ecosystems.

j. _____ Organisms that can not synthesize organic compounds from inorganic precursors.

k. _____ The rate of synthesis of new organic matter minus the respiration of the primary producers.

l. _____ The oxidation of NH_3 to form NO_3^-.

m. _____ All heterotrophs that feed on herbivores.

n. _____ The effect of geographic area and isolation on the likelihood of species extinction and colonization.

o. _____ Organisms that feed on the remains of dead organisms.

p. _____ Effects exerted at an upper trophic level that flow down to influence lower trophic levels.

q. _____ The element in shortest supply in an ecosystem relative to the needs for it by the plants and algae.

r. _____ Microbes and other minute organisms that live on and break up dead organic matter.

s. _____ Permeable, underground layers of rock, sand, and gravel that are often saturated with water.

t. _____ The steady incline in species richness from the Arctic to the Tropics.

u. _____ The productivity of a heterotroph trophic level.

v. _____ Dead organic matter.

w. _____ All of the autotrophs in an ecosystem making up the first trophic level.

x. _____ The process by which effects at an upper trophic level flow down to influence two or more lower levels.

y. _____ The process by which some species perish and new species arrive.

z. _____ The limited number of feeding levels recognized by ecologists.

aa. _____ All of the heterotrophs in an ecosystem that make up all of the trophic levels except the first.

bb. _____ Organisms that synthesize organic compounds using energy obtained by inorganic oxidation reactions.

LEARNING BY EXPERIENCE

1. In biogeochemical cycles, chemicals are found in living organisms and in nonliving reservoirs in the environment such as the atmosphere, aquifers, and rocks. List which of those reservoirs is significant for each of the following chemicals:

    water

    carbon

    nitrogen

    phosphorus

2. The Hubbard Brook Experimental Forest in New Hampshire has taught us a lot about how chemicals cycle in and through ecosystems. Diagram what happened to each of the following chemicals after clear-cutting of part of the forest. Use an upward-pointing arrow if there was a greater loss of the chemical from the ecosystem, use a downward-pointing arrow if there was a greater accumulation (less loss) of the chemical in the ecosystem, and use a horizontal line if there was no net change in the amount of the chemical leaving the ecosystem.

    water

    calcium

    phosphorus

    nitrogen

3. Use the following terms to construct a properly labeled pyramid that illustrates the structure of a typical ecosystem. Note: Every level in the pyramid should have at least three terms in it, and one term is used more than once.

    autotrophs
    carnivores
    herbivores
    heterotrophs
    primary consumers
    primary producers
    secondary consumers
    trophic level 1
    trophic level 2
    trophic level 3

4. Look at figure 57.22b in your textbook (p. 1208) and answer the following questions:

What two terms describe the type of island that has the greatest species richness?

What two terms describe the type of island that has the lowest species richness?

Two different types of islands are shown to have the same species richness. What two terms describe each of them?

EXERCISING YOUR KNOWLEDGE

Briefly answer each of the following questions in the space provided.

1. The first two sentences of the chapter say, "The Earth is a relatively closed system with respect to chemicals. It is an open system in terms of energy, however." Explain what this means.

2. Why is the term "biogeochemical cycles" a good way to describe the way materials move in an ecosystem?

3. List one major way that human activity disrupts each of the following cycles: water, carbon, phosphorus.

4. What long-term problems are we facing with regard to groundwater?

5. To which trophic level do decomposers belong?

6. There are bumper stickers that say, "Have you hugged a tree today?" Why is this a biologically appropriate question?

7. Why do most ecosystems usually have only three or four trophic levels?

8. Why is all the chemical energy available in one trophic level not incorporated into biomass at the next trophic level?

9. It has been said that eating meat is a luxury many of the world's people cannot afford. From a *biological* perspective, and considering what you know about energy flow through an ecosystem, does this statement make sense?

10. Describe the relationships between animal species richness, plant species richness, and spatial heterogeneity.

Circle the letter of the one best answer in each of the following questions.

11. Which of the following statements about the nitrogen and phosphorus cycles is NOT true?
    a. Phosphorus does not cycle through the atmosphere, while nitrogen does.
    b. Nitrogen in urine released by mammals into the soil has to be converted into a usable form by microbes.
    c. Weathering of rocks releases phosphates but not nitrogen-containing compounds into terrestrial environments.
    d. Phosphorus exists in a single oxidation state, while nitrogen exists in several different chemical forms.
    e. Decomposition of animal and plant tissues releases usable phosphates and nitrogen-containing compounds that plants and algae can use.

12. In terrestrial ecosystems, the vast majority of moisture in the air gets there from
    a. transpiration by plants.
    b. photosynthesis by plants.
    c. exhalation by animals.
    d. sweating by animals.
    e. evaporation from swimming pools.

13. The single greatest reservoir for freshwater in the United States is
    a. glaciers.
    b. springs.
    c. rivers and streams.
    d. lakes and ponds.
    e. groundwater.

14. Which of the following reservoirs contains the most carbon on a global basis?
    a. the atmosphere
    b. the oceans
    c. fossil fuels
    d. They all contain equally large amounts.
    e. None of them contain carbon.

15. The limiting nutrient in two-thirds of the oceans and in many terrestrial ecosystems is which of the following?
    a. carbon
    b. oxygen
    c. nitrogen
    d. phosphorus
    e. iron

16. Approximately what percentage of the Earth's atmosphere is made up of nitrogen gas?
    a. 0%
    b. 0.03%
    c. 10%
    d. 52%
    e. 78%

17. Which of the following statements about the carbon cycle is NOT true?
    a. Animals build their own tissue by using carbon atoms from the organic compounds that they eat.
    b. Aerobic cellular respiration by plants and animals, and decaying organisms account for all of the atmospheric CO_2.
    c. Photosynthetic organisms take in atmospheric CO_2 to synthesize organic compounds.
    d. Methane that enters the atmosphere is oxidized abiotically to CO_2.
    e. Dissolved CO_2 and HCO_3^- ions in aquatic ecosystems can both be used for photosynthesis.

18. What has happened to the amount of carbon dioxide in the atmosphere in the last one hundred years?
    a. It has increased.
    b. It has decreased.
    c. It has stayed the same.
    d. It has fluctuated wildly.
    e. We have no way of knowing.

19. Green plants capture approximately what percentage of the solar energy striking their leaves?
    a. 0.03%
    b. 1%
    c. 10%
    d. 40%
    e. 62%

20. For human populations, the most energy is available from eating which of the following?
    a. herbivores
    b. secondary carnivores
    c. primary carnivores
    d. plants
    e. detritivores

21. Bacteria play many biological roles, including
    a. decomposers.
    b. photosynthesizers.
    c. nitrogen fixers.
    d. all of these.
    e. none of these.

22. Which of the following conclusions was made about the plots at the Cedar Creek Natural History area?
    a. Plots with more species showed more year-to-year variation.
    b. More biomass was produced on plots with a greater number of species.
    c. Species-rich plots allow new species to become established more easily.
    d. The more species a plot has, the more nitrogen is produced in the soil.
    e. More than one of the above is correct.

23. Which of the following is NOT a true statement about the flow of energy in ecosystems?
    a. Energy frequently changes form.
    b. Light and chemical-bond energy are ultimately completely converted to heat.
    c. Energy in the form of heat is used by organisms to stay alive.
    d. Energy is never recycled.
    e. Energy converted to heat is radiated back into space.

24. Which of the following terrestrial ecosystems is the most productive?
    a. cultivated land
    b. temperate grasslands
    c. wetlands
    d. tropical seasonal forest
    e. temperate evergreen forest

25. With approximately _____ of the energy available in one trophic level getting incorporated, on average, as biomass in the next trophic level, energy transfer between trophic levels can be characterized as _____.
    a. 1%, inefficient
    b. 10%, inefficient
    c. 30%, inefficient
    d. 60%, efficient
    e. 80%, efficient

26. Which of the following ecological pyramids can never be inverted in a natural ecosystem?
    a. pyramid of numbers
    b. pyramid of biomass
    c. pyramid of energy
    d. All can be inverted.
    e. None can be inverted.

27. Secondary consumers having an indirect impact on producers are an example of a(n)
    a. species turnover.
    b. species diversity cline.
    c. species-area relationship.
    d. bottom-up effect.
    e. trophic cascade.

28. In general, ecosystems that are rich in species tend to
    a. cover extensive areas.
    b. be located only in the tropics.
    c. be endangered.
    d. accumulate biomass at an accelerating rate.
    e. be able to resist disturbances.

29. Which of the following statements is true?
    a. There are more species in the tropics than in temperate latitudes, but scientists are not sure why.
    b. There are more species in the tropics than in temperate latitudes, and scientists have proven why.
    c. There are more species in temperate latitudes than in the tropics, but scientists are not sure why.
    d. There are more species in temperate latitudes than in the tropics, and scientists have proven why.

30. Who proposed the equilibrium model of island biogeography?
    a. Herbert Bormann and Gene Likens
    b. Lamont Cole
    c. Aldo Leopold
    d. Robert MacArthur and Edward O. Wilson
    e. David Tilman

ASSESSING YOUR KNOWLEDGE

Answers to the questions in this section test your ability to synthesize information gained from the chapter and to solve challenging problems on an exam or in everyday life.

Challenging Your Understanding—Answers

1.

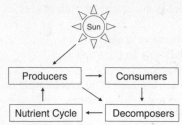

2.

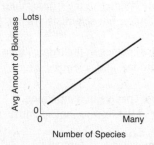

3. Most of the energy is given off as heat from cellular respiration, disposed of as feces, or lost to death, rather than consumption.

4. A. algal beds and reefs→tropical rain forests→wetlands→temperate evergreen forest→temperate deciduous forest→savanna→temperate grassland→tundra and alpine→open ocean→desert and semidesert.

B. open ocean→tropical rain forests→savanna→temperate deciduous forest→ temperate evergreen forest→temperate grassland→wetlands→ algal beds and reefs→desert and semidesert → tundra and alpine.

C. The difference occurs because some very productive ecosystems are not very abundant on Earth while other not very productive ecosystems, such as the open ocean, cover a very large area of the Earth.

Key Terms—Answers

a. 25, b. 15, c. 10, d. 3, e. 8, f. 18, g. 21, h. 13, i. 1, j. 27, k. 16, l. 4, m. 9, n. 23, o. 28, p. 20, q. 5, r. 11, s. 2, t. 22, u. 17, v. 12, w. 6, x. 19, y. 24, z. 14, aa. 7, bb. 26.

Learning by Experience—Answers

1.	water: atmosphere, aquifers carbon: atmosphere nitrogen: atmosphere phosphorus: rocks
2.	water: ↑ calcium: ↑ phosphorus: — nitrogen: ↑

3. Bottom level = trophic level 1, autotrophs, primary producers; middle level = trophic level 2, heterotrophs, herbivores, primary consumers; top level = trophic level 3, heterotrophs, carnivores, secondary consumers.

4. greatest species richness = large, near mainland; lowest species richness = small, far from mainland; same species richness = small, near mainland and large, far from mainland

Exercising Your Knowledge—Answers

As you check your answers, put a mark in the review (Rvw.) column for the answers you missed. If you didn't miss any, congratulations—you have mastered the chapter! If you missed some, review the section (Sect.) in the text where this concept is discussed. In order to develop an efficient review strategy, it is important that you understand what types of questions you missed. The questions with asterisks test more for understanding of the **concepts**, whereas the others test more for **detail**. *See the preface for learning strategies for concepts and for detail.*

	Sect.	Rvw.
*1. Chemicals on the Earth are constantly recycled between and among living organisms and the abiotic environment, and there is very little input or loss extraterrestrially (from outside the Earth's ecosystem). With energy, on the other hand, there is constant extraterrestrial input and loss.	57.1 57.2	
*2. Materials (**chemicals**) move back and forth (**cycle**) between living organisms (**bio = life**) and the nonliving environment (**geo = Earth**), thus the term **biogeochemical cycles**.	57.1	
*3. The water cycle is disrupted by deforestation, which eliminates the return of moisture to the air through transpiration. The carbon cycle is disrupted by burning fossil fuels and thus adding huge amounts of carbon (in the form of carbon dioxide) into the atmosphere. The phosphorus cycle is disrupted by heavy use of fertilizers.	57.1	
*4. Aquifers are becoming polluted and depleted. In many areas, we are removing water from aquifers faster than the aquifers can recharge or refill. As pollutants seep into groundwater, aquifers are virtually impossible to clean up.	57.1	

*5. Decomposers belong to different trophic levels depending on what they are feeding on. They are never producers (trophic level 1), but they might be primary, secondary, or tertiary consumers (trophic levels 2, 3, or 4, respectively) if they are breaking down plants, herbivores, or carnivores, respectively.	57.2	
*6. Besides giving us many commercially valuable products, trees – like all plants – are primary producers that convert solar energy to chemical energy. Without these autotrophs, there would be no heterotrophs such as ourselves. It is the autotrophs that produce the oxygen and the glucose on which we depend.	57.2	
*7. Energy transfers are inefficient. On average, only about 10% of the energy available at one trophic level gets converted into biomass at the next trophic level. After three or four transfers, there's not enough energy left to support another trophic level.	57.2	
*8. Usually, not all of the biomass available at one trophic level is consumed by the next trophic level. Of the biomass that is consumed, some is indigestible, and the energy is not captured. Of the digestible material, some energy is lost in the form of heat, produced by metabolic processes, and some energy is used for other processes (e.g., locomotion, organ functioning, and reproduction) rather than for adding biomass.	57.2	
*9. There is a biological basis to the high cost of meat. The fewer the number of steps in a food chain, the more efficient it is, since energy is lost at every step. Much more energy is available to humans by eating plants directly than by first passing them through a cow. Being a carnivore is expensive energetically and therefore expensive economically.	57.2	

*10. In general, animal species richness is a reflection of the richness of plant species, and plant species richness reflects the amount of spatial heterogeneity in an ecosystem. The more variable the habitat, the greater the diversity of plant species and thus the greater the diversity of animal species.	57.4	
*11. e	57.1	
12. a	57.1	
13. e	57.1	
14. c	57.1	
*15. c	57.1	
16. e	57.1	
*17. b	57.1	
*18. a	57.1	
19. b	57.2	
*20. d	57.2	
*21. d	57.2	
22. b	57.4	
*23. c	57.2	
24. c	57.2	
25. b	57.2	
26. c	57.2	
27. e	57.3	
*28. e	57.4	
*29. a	57.4	
30. d	57.5	

CHAPTER 58 THE BIOSPHERE

MASTERING KEY CONCEPTS

The organisms that live on the Earth are not scattered about the surface of the planet in a random pattern. Distribution patterns are determined by the environmental conditions in different parts of the world and by the ability of organisms to adapt to and survive in those conditions. A diversity of climatic conditions results in a diversity of terrestrial and aquatic ecosystems. No matter where they are, however, all ecosystems are affected by human activities.

58.1 Climate shapes the character of ecosystems.

- **Overview**: The shape of the Earth and the tilt of its axis cause different amounts of solar radiation to reach different parts of the Earth and cause seasonal variations. Global circulation patterns in the atmosphere are also caused by the uneven heating of the Earth and the Earth's rotation. Air flows toward the equator in both hemispheres at the surface, rises at the equator, and flows away from the equator at high altitudes. This air then circulates back to the surface of the Earth at 30° of latitude. During the course of these movements, the moisture content of the air changes. This change is responsible for creating rain at latitudes near the equator, and deserts at latitudes near 30°. Winds move in curved paths across the surface of the Earth due to the Earth's rotation (**Coriolis effect**). In the northern hemisphere, winds curve to the right of their direction of motion, but in the southern hemisphere, they curve to the left. Winds at the surface of the Earth affect ocean currents. Currents in the Atlantic and Pacific Oceans move in **gyres**, or giant closed curves, between land masses. Regional and local effects of solar radiation, air and water circulation, and elevation all play major roles in determining climate. Mountains can produce **rain shadows** where one side of the mountains is considerably drier than the other side. Seasonally shifting winds (**monsoons**) affect rainfall patterns, while increases in **elevation** cause decreases in temperature.
- **Details**: Know the two factors that affect global patterns of life on Earth. Understand how the Earth's shape and tilt on its axis affects climate and seasonal variations in different parts of the world. Understand the global patterns of atmospheric circulation and the Coriolis effect. Know the direction of current flow in the oceans at different latitudes.

58.2 Biomes are widespread terrestrial ecosystems.

- **Overview**: **Biomes** are major types of ecosystems on land largely defined by their climatic conditions. Temperature and moisture in particular help to define biomes because they

directly correlate with the primary productivity of a region. Seasonal variations, soil structure, and mineral composition are other factors that influence biomes. **Tropical rain forests** are the richest ecosystems on land because they have both high temperatures and high levels of precipitation. **Savannas** are transitional ecosystems between rain forests and deserts where rainfall is often seasonal, but temperatures are high. **Deserts** have extreme temperatures and unpredictable rainfall. **Temperate grasslands** and **temperate deciduous forests** have warm summers but cool winters. **Temperate evergreen forests** occur along coastlines with temperate climates. The **taiga** is characterized by winters that are extremely cold with limited precipitation in the summer. North of the taiga is the **tundra** where little rain or snow falls, and tree growth is limited.
- **Details**: Know the eight principal biomes and their characteristic temperatures and precipitation patterns. Recognize how these two factors correlate with primary productivity in different biomes.

58.3 Freshwater ecosystems are defined by depth and oxygen availability.

- **Overview**: Only 2% of the Earth's surface is covered by freshwater where primary production occurs by algae floating on the water, or growing on the bottom of the water, or by rooted plants. Freshwater communities are determined by the concentration of dissolved oxygen, which is added by photosynthesis and by atmospheric aeration, and is removed by heterotrophs and decaying microbes. The amount of sunlight reaching photosynthetic organisms in lakes and ponds decreases with increasing depth. Only some of the upper waters, the **photic zone**, receive enough sunlight for **phytoplankton** to undergo photosynthesis and produce oxygen near the surface. **Thermal stratification** determines how much oxygen moves from the surface to the deeper waters. The shallow and deeper waters are mixed during the **spring** and **fall overturns**. **Oligotrophic** waters have little algal material and are high in dissolved oxygen, and **eutrophic** waters have a large amount of algal nutrients and growth. Therefore, light does not penetrate eutrophic waters as well, and they tend to be low in dissolved oxygen concentration.
- **Details**: Know the different lake zones and how productive they are. Understand the annual cycle of thermal stratification in a temperate-zone lake. Know how oxygen is added and removed from bodies of freshwater and the effect that this has on aquatic life. Understand the relationship between the density of algae and oxygen availability.

58.4 Marine habitats are also defined by depth, which determines the temperature of the water and how much light is available.

- **Overview**: Seventy-one percent of the Earth's surface is covered by oceans. Oceans are so vast that they include many different types of ecosystems, including **open oceans**, **continental self ecosystems**, **upwelling regions**, and **deep sea**. Photosynthesis in the oceans occurs between the surface and 200 m, the depth at which solar illumination is close to zero. Nutrients in the photic zone are low because they have been largely lost to the deep sea. Therefore, primary productivity in large parts of the ocean is also low (oligotrophic ocean). In contrast, continental shelf ecosystems, near the coastlines, including **estuaries**, coral reefs, and banks, are productive because the **neritic waters** that flow over them are rich in nitrate and other nutrients. Here the water is shallow relative to the waters in the open oceans. Upwelling regions have the highest primary productivity per unit area in the world's oceans because deep water, rich in nitrate and other nutrients, is constantly being drawn to the surface by local forces in these areas. The deep sea is cold, dark, and seasonless, but many species of animals live there feeding on 1% of the primary production from the surface. **Hydrothermal vent communities** are also located in the deep sea, living on local primary production by **sulfur-oxidizing bacteria**.
- **Details**: Know the four major types of ocean ecosystems, and the characteristics of each in terms of depth, location, and productivity. Know the cause of **El Niño**.

58.5 Human activities are leading to pollution and resource depletion placing stress on the biosphere.

- **Overview**: Pollution, consumption, and the introduction of nonnative species of plants and animals by humans threaten our freshwater supplies. Deforestation due to cutting or burning of trees by individuals or by corporations threatens terrestrial habitats, resulting in extreme losses of biodiversity, increased desertification, loss of soil nutrients coupled with nutrient accumulation in waters downstream, and disruption of the water cycle. The effects of **acid rain** and loss of topsoil also threaten terrestrial ecosystems. Oceans are being overfished, coastal ecosystems are deteriorating, and ocean pollution is on the rise. **Ozone depletion** caused by chlorofluorocarbons (CFCs) released into the atmosphere is a worldwide problem that is increasing the UV radiation that reaches the Earth and is leading to increased risks of UV-B damage.
- **Details**: Know the different forms of pollution, why they are occurring, and the measures being taken to prevent them. Know the human threats to terrestrial ecosystems. Understand how the ozone layer is being depleted, and why depletion is particularly significant over Antarctica. Know the effects of depletion, and what is being done now to stop it.

58.6 Human activities are also responsible for global warming.

- **Overview**: Concentrations of gases in our atmosphere, particularly CO_2, keep the temperature on Earth 25°C higher, than it would be if they were absent. Burning of coal and petroleum by humans is increasing the atmospheric CO_2 concentration, leading to an increase in the temperature of the Earth's surface (**global warming**). CO_2 is a **greenhouse gas** that affects global temperature because it absorbs long wavelengths of electromagnetic radiant energy, retarding the rate at which energy of long wavelengths travels away from the Earth. Methane and nitrous oxide are other greenhouse gases that may increase with global warming, or increased use of fertilizers, energy consumption, or industrial use. Global warming will lead to an increase in sea levels, an increase in extreme severe weather events, a shift in rainfall patterns, an expansion of the range of tropical diseases such as malaria and dengue fever, and other adverse effects on human health, and have positive and negative effects on agriculture.
- **Details**: Know the cause of global warming, the evidence that confirms that it is occurring, and the effects on ecosystems. Know how global warming will affect humans.

CHALLENGING YOUR UNDERSTANDING

1. Name the five major biomes that are depicted across the following elevations in part a. Then indicate where the same five biomes are commonly found at different latitudes on Earth by shading, coloring, or labeling the depiction of the Earth in part b.

   a. Elevation-derived changes in biomes

   b. Latitude-derived changes in biomes

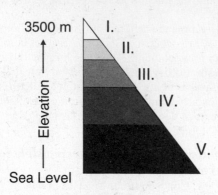

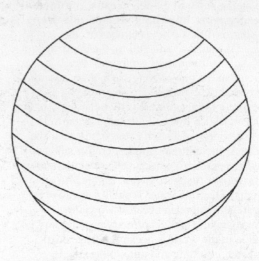

2. Classify each of the following biomes as one of the following conditions: cold and dry; hot and dry; warm and semidry; warm and moist; warm and wet; hot and wet.

   a. desert _____

   b. tundra _____

   c. savanna _____

   d. tropical rainforest _____

   e. temperate grassland _____

   f. temperate deciduous forest _____

   g. temperate evergreen forest _____

3. Draw lines that depict the relationship between productivity and precipitation (a) and productivity and temperature (b).

   a.

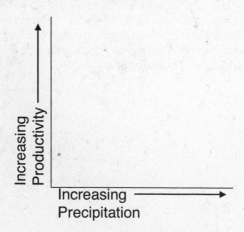

   b.

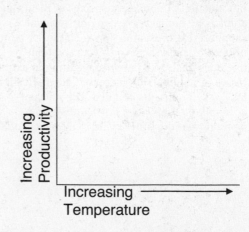

KEY TERMS

Match the numbered term with the definition that fits it best. Put the corresponding number in front of the appropriate definition.

1. Coriolis effect
2. rain shadow
3. microclimate
4. monsoons
5. biomes
6. tropical rain forest
7. savannas
8. deserts
9. prairies
10. temperate deciduous forests

11. taiga
12. tundra
13. permafrost
14. neritic zone
15. pelagic zone
16. benthic zone
17. thermal stratification
18. thermocline
19. plankton
20. intertidal region

21. estuaries
22. photic zone
23. diffuse pollution
24. point-source pollution
25. ozone hole
26. acid precipitation
27. greenhouse effect
28. global warming

a. _____ The water column in the open ocean.
b. _____ Temperate regions located halfway between the equator and the poles, covering the interior of North America.
c. _____ Seasonally shifting winds in the regions of the Indian Ocean and western tropical Pacific Ocean.
d. _____ Treated effluents or contaminated water that comes from an identifiable location, such as a factory.
e. _____ A transitional layer between the warm and the cold layers of a lake formed during the summer.
f. _____ A place along a coastline that is partially surrounded by land in which freshwater mixes with ocean water.
g. _____ The region where the tides rise and fall along the shoreline of marine ecosystems.
h. _____ The accumulation of infrared radiation due to CO_2 retarding the rate at which energy travels away from the Earth.
i. _____ An effect produced when one side of a mountain is considerably drier than the other side.
j. _____ An open, windswept, boggy landscape that is extremely cold; located in a band at latitudes above the taiga.
k. _____ Excessive run-off of nitrates and phosphates that enter freshwaters at countless locations.
l. _____ Major types of ecosystems on land that have characteristic appearances defined by regional climatic conditions.
m. _____ The bottom of marine ecosystems.
n. _____ Waters near the surface that receive enough light for phytoplankton to exhibit a positive net primary productivity.
o. _____ Soil ice that persists through all seasons usually existing within a meter of the ground surface.
p. _____ An increase in the average temperature of the Earth's surface due to changes in atmospheric composition.
q. _____ Dry regions where rain and vegetation are sparse and the temperatures are extreme.
r. _____ Highly localized sets of climatic conditions that vary significantly on small spatial scales.
s. _____ When water warmed by the Sun floats on top of colder, denser water in lakes and ponds.
t. _____ Free-floating, microscopic, aquatic organisms.
u. _____ Sulfuric acid produced as a result of burning coal that is picked up by falling rain or snow.
v. _____ A great band of northern forest dominated by coniferous trees with severely long, cold winters.
w. _____ The curvature of the paths of the winds due to the Earth's rotation.
x. _____ Tropical or subtropical grasslands with widely spaced trees or shrubs where rainfall is highly seasonal.
y. _____ The shallow waters over continental shelves that tend to have concentrations of nitrate and other nutrients.
z. _____ Regions with warm summers, cold winters, and plentiful rains located in the eastern United States and Canada.
aa. _____ An area of depletion in the stratospheric layer of the Earth's atmosphere that filters out UV radiation.
bb. _____ The richest ecosystems on land that have high temperatures, high precipitation, and very high biodiversity.

LEARNING BY EXPERIENCE

1. Using different colors for each, color the taiga, the tropical rain forest, and the desert biomes on this map of the world.

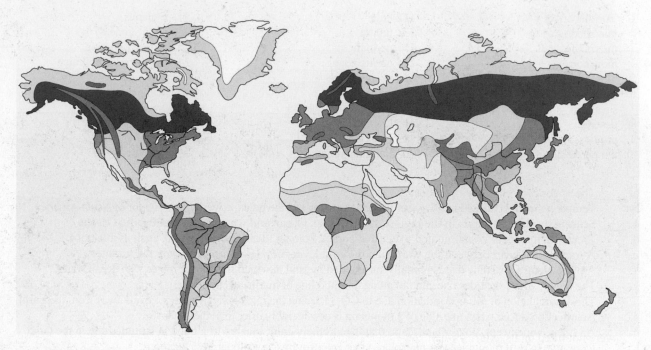

2. Place the following states into groups according to the average acidity of their rain fall: Nebraska, Indiana, Ohio, Wisconsin, New York, Pennsylvania, Oregon, Arizona, California, Florida, Idaho, Maryland, Mississippi.

<u>Most acidic</u>   <u>Mildly acidic</u>   <u>Least acidic</u>

3. Place the following world regions into categories according to how many degrees above average their 2005 temperature was: Western Europe, India, Western United States, Eastern United States, middle of the Pacific Ocean, Northern Asia, Western Australia, Alaska.

<u>Largest increase (>0.8°)</u>   <u>Medium increase (0.2°-0.8°)</u>   <u>Smallest increase (<0.2°)</u>

4. Are wetlands worth preserving, or can the land be put to better use? [*Write an essay to answer this question, or stage a debate or discussion with a classmate.*]

EXERCISING YOUR KNOWLEDGE

Briefly answer each of the following questions in the space provided.

1. What does air temperature have to do with precipitation patterns?

2. What might happen to the world's biomes if atmospheric circulation stopped?

3. What would happen climatically if the Earth were not tilted on its axis?

4. In general, do grasses or trees require more water?

5. How would you describe diversity in tropical rain forests with regard to the number of species and the number of individuals in each species?

6. Why are temperate deciduous forests found in such geographically separated places as eastern North America and eastern Asia?

7. Do aquatic or terrestrial ecosystems tend to be more limited by the availability of water, light, and nutrients?

8. What are the consequences of increased concentrations of carbon dioxide in the atmosphere?

9. Why does acid precipitation kill organisms?

10. The United States banned the production of chlorofluorocarbons (CFCs) in 1995, and worldwide agreements were signed to phase out production by 2000. However, the ozone layer continues to be depleted. Why?

Circle the letter of the one best answer in each of the following questions.

11. The tropics are warmer than temperate regions because
    a. there are fewer clouds in the tropics.
    b. the tropics receive more solar energy per unit area because of an almost perpendicular angle of incidence of sunlight.
    c. tropical soils are chemically easier to heat than are temperate soils.
    d. the rotation of the Earth spins the atmosphere in such a way that the heat gets trapped near the equator.
    e. it rains a lot in the tropics, and it tends to be warmer in wet areas than in dry areas.

12. At about 30° north and south latitude, air is _____ and there is _____ precipitation.
    a. rising and cooling, little
    b. rising and warming, much
    c. descending and warming, little
    d. descending and warming, much
    e. descending and cooling, little

13. Rain shadow areas with little precipitation occur on the _____ side of mountain ranges.
    a. leeward
    b. windward
    c. low
    d. high

14. Which of the following climatic patterns is mismatched with its geographical region?
    a. Mediterranean climate – western sides of continents
    b. cold temperatures – high latitudes or high elevations
    c. some major deserts – interiors of large continents
    d. doldrums – near the equator
    e. monsoons – southern Africa

15. What two environmental parameters are best at defining biome distribution?
    a. temperature and soil type
    b. cloud cover and wind speed
    c. temperature and precipitation
    d. precipitation and soil type
    e. precipitation and wind speed

16. Which biome is transitional between tropical rain forest and desert?
    a. temperate grassland
    b. savanna
    c. taiga
    d. temperate deciduous forest
    e. tundra

17. Permafrost is associated with
    a. tundra.
    b. temperate evergreen forests.
    c. taiga.
    d. all of these.
    e. none of these.

18. Which biome is considered the richest ecosystem on Earth in terms of species diversity?
    a. savanna
    b. temperate deciduous forest
    c. temperate evergreen forest
    d. tropical rain forest
    e. temperate grassland

19. How much rain do deserts receive in a typical year?
    a. none, ever
    b. less than 25 cm
    c. 25 – 75 cm
    d. 75 – 140 cm
    e. 140 – 450 cm
    f. more than 450 cm

20. Which of the following is *not* characteristic of temperate grasslands?
    a. perennial grasses with deep roots
    b. herds of grazing mammals such as bison and pronghorns
    c. transitional between temperate deciduous forests and taiga
    d. fertile soil
    e. also called prairies

21. Gyres in the northern hemisphere move
    a. clockwise.
    b. counterclockwise.
    c. north to south.
    d. east to west.
    e. totally randomly.

22. In the southern hemisphere, which edge of continents tends to be warmer because of oceanic circulation patterns?
    a. northern
    b. southern
    c. eastern
    d. western
    e. There's no pattern.

23. What happens during an El Niño event?
    a. Easterly trade winds fail in the southern Pacific.
    b. Warm water shifts eastward in the southern Pacific.
    c. Major changes in temperature and precipitation patterns occur in many places around the world.
    d. Commercial fisheries in the eastern Pacific are devastated.
    e. All of these are correct.

24. Photosynthetic oceanic plankton
    a. are found only in the neritic zone.
    b. are found only in the benthic zone.
    c. are frequently bioluminescent.
    d. survive on geothermal energy at great depths.
    e. are responsible for about 40% of all the photosynthesis that occurs on the planet.

25. Which of the following is NOT a threat to fresh water habitats?
    a. destruction of salt marshes
    b. introduction of nonnative species
    c. eutrophication
    d. extraction of water
    e. stirring up bottom sediments

26. Which of the following ecosystems has the highest productivity?
    a. open ocean
    b. fast-moving streams
    c. oligotrophic lakes
    d. eutrophic lakes
    e. They are all extremely productive.

27. Which of the following is NOT an effect of deforestation?
    a. loss of soil nutrients
    b. increased desertification
    c. depletion of the ozone layer
    d. loss of habitat
    e. disruption of the water cycle

28. At the current rate of loss, it is estimated that all of the world's tropical rain forests will be gone in about
    a. 5 years.
    b. 15 years.
    c. 30 years.
    d. 50 years.
    e. 100 years.

29. Lakes and forests in North America and Europe are dying because of acid precipitation caused by atmospheric pollution from
    a. chlorofluorocarbons.
    b. chlorinated hydrocarbons.
    c. the ozone hole.
    d. the clear-cutting of tropical forests.
    e. the industrial burning of fossil fuels.

30. Which of the following is NOT an effect of global warming?
    a. Sea levels are increasing due to the melting of glaciers and the increase in ocean temperatures.
    b. The fish populations in the oceans are being depleted.
    c. An increase in the number and the severity of weather events, such as hurricanes, drought, and storms.
    d. Mass "bleaching" of corals.
    e. Migratory birds are arriving earlier at their summer breeding grounds.

ASSESSING YOUR KNOWLEDGE

Answers to the questions in this section test your ability to synthesize information gained from the chapter and to solve challenging problems on an exam or in everyday life.

Challenging Your Understanding—Answers

1. a. I. polar ice; II. tundra; III. taiga;
IV. temperate forest; V. tropical rain forest.
b.

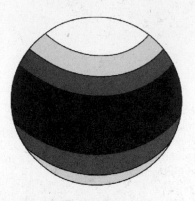

2. a. desert; hot and dry
b. tundra; cold and dry
c. savanna; hot and semidry
d. tropical rainforest; hot and wet
e. temperate grassland; warm and semidry
f. temperate deciduous forest; warm and moist
g. temperate evergreen forest; warm and wet

3. .
a.

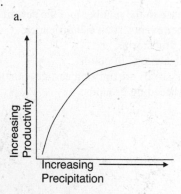

b.

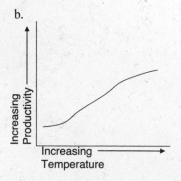

Key Terms—Answers

a. 15, b. 9, c. 4, d. 24, e. 18, f. 21, g. 20, h. 27, i. 2, j. 12, k. 23, l. 5, m. 16, n. 22, o. 13, p. 28, q. 8, r. 3, s. 17, t. 19, u. 26, v. 11, w. 1, x. 7, y. 14, z. 10, aa. 25, bb. 6.

Learning by Experience—Answers

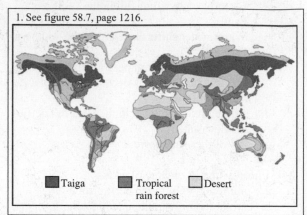

1. See figure 58.7, page 1216.

■ Taiga   ■ Tropical   □ Desert
rain forest

2. Most acidic: Indiana, Ohio, New York, Pennsylvania, Maryland.
Mildly acidic: Wisconsin, Florida, Mississippi, Arizona.
Least acidic: Nebraska, Oregon, California, Idaho.

3. Largest increase: Western Europe, Western United States, Northern Asia, Alaska.
Medium increase: India, Eastern United States, Western Australia.
Smallest increase: Middle of the Pacific Ocean.

4. Wetlands are well worth saving. They are extremely productive ecosystems, are home to many species, and play key ecological roles as water storage basins that moderate floods and droughts.

Exercising Your Knowledge—Answers

As you check your answers, put a mark in the review (Rvw.) column for the answers you missed. If you didn't miss any, congratulations—you have mastered the chapter! If you missed some, review the section (Sect.) in the text where this concept is discussed. In order to develop an efficient review strategy, it is important that you understand what types of questions you missed. The questions with asterisks test more for understanding of the **concepts**, whereas the others test more for **detail**. *See the preface for learning strategies for concepts and for detail.*

	Sect.	Rvw.
*1. The warmer the air temperature, the more moisture it can hold. As air becomes cooler, it cannot hold as much moisture, so precipitation occurs. As air warms, it can hold more moisture, so there is little precipitation.	58.1	

*2. There would be drastic changes in ocean circulation and climate and therefore in the distribution and existence of biomes. Regional temperature and precipitation patterns would change greatly.	58.2	
*3. There would be no seasonal differences in temperature (for example, no winter versus summer) for any given spot on the globe.	58.1	
*4. Trees require more water; that's why forest biomes are only found in the areas of the world that have more precipitation.	58.2	
*5. Tropical rain forests are characterized by a high number of species but relatively few individuals in each species.	58.2	
*6. Temperate deciduous forests are found in such disparate geographic areas because these areas have similar climates.	58.2	
*7. In general, aquatic ecosystems face no shortage of water, but light and nutrients can be limiting.	58.3 58.4	
*8. Increased concentrations of CO_2 lead to increased global temperature, potential for rising sea levels, and changes in precipitation and temperature patterns, all of which affect natural ecosystems and agriculture.	58.6	
*9. Increased acidity of soils and water can have direct chemical effects, as well as weakening organisms and making them more susceptible to diseases, predators, and parasites. If pH changes, enzyme function can be inhibited or stopped completely, and enzymes are necessary to catalyze all the biochemical reactions that take place in organisms.	58.5	
*10. It takes a long time for chlorofluorocarbons (CFCs) to work their way into the stratosphere.	58.5	

*11. b	58.1	
*12. c	58.1	
13. a	58.1	
14. e	58.2	
*15. c	58.2	
16. b	58.2	
17. a	58.2	
18. d	58.2	
19. b	58.2	
20. c	58.2	
21. a	58.1	
22. c	58.1	
*23. e	58.4	
24. e	58.4	
*25. a	58.5	
26. d	58.3	
*27. c	58.5	
28. c	58.5	
29. e	58.5	
*30. b	58.6	

CHAPTER 59 CONSERVATION BIOLOGY

MASTERING KEY CONCEPTS

Around the world, species are going extinct at an accelerating rate, primarily due to the activities of humans, and at great cost ecologically and economically. In the new discipline of conservation biology, scientists are studying which species are most vulnerable and why, and are designing conservation and recovery plans in an effort to stem the losses. There have been, and will continue to be, both successes and failures in these complex, imperative efforts.

59.1 The new science of conservation biology is focused on conserving biodiversity.

- **Overview**: Extinction of many species in different parts of the world has been associated with the arrival of humans, who have hunted larger animals and birds, and have burned and cleared forested land. Since the year 1600, 2.1% of known species of mammals and 1.3% of known species of birds have become extinct, and these numbers are on the rise in recent years. The majority of historic extinctions have occurred on islands where many of the species have evolved without predation, and where human invasion has introduced competitors and diseases. Today, extinctions occur primarily on continents. Although mass extinctions have occurred in the past, this extinction event is different because it is being caused by a single species and is eliminating a vast amount of biodiversity that may not be able to rebound as it has in the past due to loss of habitats and resources. **Endemic** species are found naturally in only one geographic location and many are extremely vulnerable to extinction. **Hotspots** are regions in the world with a high number of endemic species and biodiversity. There have been 25 hotspots identified that make up only 1.4% of the surface of the Earth. The human population is growing at a rate exceeding the global average in 19 of these hotspots, causing high rates of habitat destruction.
- **Details**: Understand why the mass extinction event that is currently occurring is different form the mass extinctions of the past, and why biodiversity may not rebound this time. Know the locations of biodiversity hotspots in the world. Understand how population growth is threatening these hotspots.

59.2 There is value in biodiversity that extends beyond pure economic gain.

- **Overview**: Biodiverse species have direct economic value as sources of food, medicine, clothing, shelter, and biomass. They also have indirect economic value because they are essential to the stability and productivity of ecosystems. Protection of biodiverse species is an ethical issue because many believe that every species has value even if it does not provide economic value to humans. It is our responsibility to protect life around us, rather than destroying it. In the end, we will benefit by being able to enjoy the aesthetic value that other species provide.
- **Details**: Know the direct and indirect economic values of biodiversity. Understand the importance of maintaining ecosystems rather than destroying them. Know the economic trade-offs involved. Understand why it is our responsibility to protect biodiversity.

59.3 A variety of causes, independent or connected, are responsible for extinctions.

- **Overview**: Overexploitation was historically the major cause of extinction, but today it is habitat loss, followed by the introduction of nonnative species that compete with, or prey on native species. Other contributing factors include overexploitation, loss of genetic diversity, disruption of ecosystem interactions, pollution, and catastrophic disturbances. These factors and the interactions among them can lead to the extinction of a species. Declines in the amphibian populations around the world indicate that the global environment is deteriorating in a number of different ways. Destruction, pollution, disruption, and habitat fragmentation are four factors that contribute to habitat loss. Hunting or harvesting of species by humans for their own economic gain also significantly contributes to extinction. **Colonization** brings together species that have no history of interaction with each other. This can lead to competition and predation, which can lead to extinction of native species. This naturally rare process has been made much more common by humans. Nonnative species cause huge economic problems, can eliminate native species, and transform entire ecosystems. Loss of a **keystone species** can have dramatic effects on other species, and can disrupt an entire ecosystem. Small populations are particularly vulnerable to extinction because they are not equipped to withstand catastrophic events, and have little genetic variability.
- **Details**: Know the factors that contribute to species extinction. Understand why declines in the number of amphibians are worrisome. Know the factors that contribute to habitat loss. Know the effects of habitat fragmentation and how it correlates with extinction rates. Know what species are exploited by humans and why they are of economic interest. Understand the ways in which colonization occurs, how humans have

influenced this naturally rare process, and the effects on humans and on native ecosystems. Know how loss of a keystone species can affect an ecosystem. Understand why small populations are particularly vulnerable to extinction.

59.4 Successful recovery efforts need to be multidimensional.

- **Overview**: **Conservation biology** is concerned with preserving populations of species that are in danger of becoming extinct. This is only possible if there are species left to preserve, if not, restoration is necessary. If all of the species in an area have been wiped out, but the habitat is still intact, pristine restoration in which all of the original species are identified and reintroduced may restore the ecosystem. If one species in particular has destroyed a habitat, the habitat can be restored by removing the introduced species. If chemical pollution has destroyed a habitat, it can be restored by cleaning it up and rehabilitating it. Species, such as the peregrine falcon and the California condor, have been reestablished by **captive breeding programs**. Release of two complete gray wolf packs into Yellowstone National Park has restored the ecosystem to a balanced state by reducing deer and elk populations.

- **Details**: Know approaches that can be taken to restore habitats that have been destroyed. Understand how specific species can be reestablished and how ecosystems can be restored following loss of a particular species. Understand why this reestablishment of a species or restoration of an ecosystem is important.

59.5 Biodiversity can be preserved by conserving ecosystems.

- **Overview**: Some species require large habitats in order to survive. These species in particular are in danger when their habitats are fragmented. By preserving lands in national parks and reserves as pristine areas where no human disturbance of the ecosystem is allowed, as well as areas surrounding protected areas where some minimal human disturbance is allowed, and corridors of dispersal, conservationists hope to increase population sizes. Efforts are also now being focused on preserving ecosystems, rather than just preserving individual species.

- **Details**: Know what efforts are being made to counter the problem of habitat fragmentation.

CHALLENGING YOUR UNDERSTANDING—Part I

1. Fill in the blanks to indicate how human activities are leading to a loss of biodiversity, why we should care, and the measures that we can take to put an end to this dangerous trend.

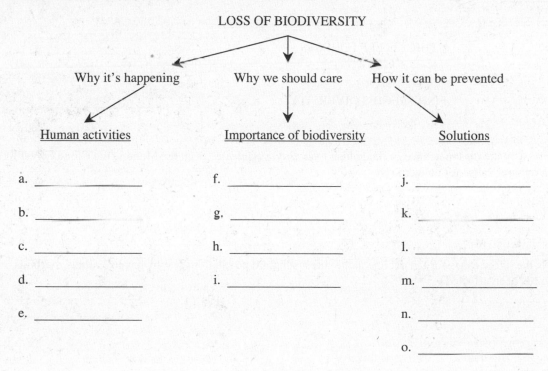

LOSS OF BIODIVERSITY

Why it's happening Why we should care How it can be prevented

Human activities Importance of biodiversity Solutions

a. _____ f. _____ j. _____

b. _____ g. _____ k. _____

c. _____ h. _____ l. _____

d. _____ i. _____ m. _____

e. _____ n. _____

  o. _____

CHALLENGING YOUR UNDERSTANDING—Part II

1. Fill in the blanks to indicate how each of the populations of organisms listed was affected by the overharvesting of whales by commercial whalers (increase or decrease in size). To the side, indicate why this effect likely occurred. (Note: The first one is done for you as an example.)

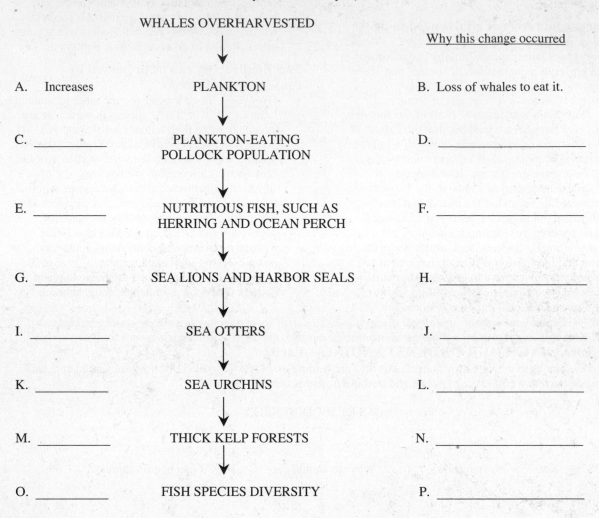

WHALES OVERHARVESTED

Why this change occurred

A. Increases   PLANKTON   B. Loss of whales to eat it.

C. _____   PLANKTON-EATING
POLLOCK POPULATION   D. _____

E. _____   NUTRITIOUS FISH, SUCH AS
HERRING AND OCEAN PERCH   F. _____

G. _____   SEA LIONS AND HARBOR SEALS   H. _____

I. _____   SEA OTTERS   J. _____

K. _____   SEA URCHINS   L. _____

M. _____   THICK KELP FORESTS   N. _____

O. _____   FISH SPECIES DIVERSITY   P. _____

2. Describe why the disappearance of the golden toad, *Bufo periglenes*, from the Monteverde Cloud Forest Reserve is such a major cause for concern.

3. What is the likely cause for the decline in the forest songbird populations? Why haven't robins, starlings, or blackbirds been affected?

KEY TERMS

Match the numbered term with the definition that fits it best. Put the corresponding number in front of the appropriate definition.

1. endemic
2. hotspots
3. edge effects

4. colonization
5. keystone species
6. habitat fragmentation

a. _____ The relative proportion of the habitat that occurs on the boundary increases as a habitat shrinks in size.
b. _____ A species that exerts a greater influence on the structure and functioning of an ecosystem than would be expected.
c. _____ A species found naturally in only one geographic area and no place else.
d. _____ The carving of populations living in a habitat into a series of smaller, unconnected population patches.
e. _____ Areas that have high endemism that are disappearing at a rapid rate.
f. _____ A natural process by which a species expands it geographic range, bringing together species with no history of interaction.

LEARNING BY EXPERIENCE

1. Consider the following scenario: You are the leader of a tropical country that is very poor, has a fast-growing human population, and is rapidly losing its forests for three main reasons – harvesting to sell the lumber to other countries, clearing land to graze cattle to export beef, and clearing by subsistence-level farmers (who are the majority of your citizens). You are under pressure from international conservation organizations to stop or at least decrease the loss of the tropical forests and all their resident species. What do you do? What do you think your Minister of the Environment, Minister of Economics, and Minister of Human Welfare will advise you to do? [*Write out your answer or stage a discussion/debate with some of your classmates – each could play a different role and represent a different viewpoint. Remember, these are complex issues and there are no easy answers.*]

2. Although restoring a severely degraded ecosystem to pristine conditions is an admirable goal, it is virtually impossible to do. List the reasons why this is so.

3. List four ways in which humans adversely affect natural habitats.

4. List the values of biodiversity— direct, indirect, or otherwise.
Direct:

Indirect:

Other:

EXERCISING YOUR KNOWLEDGE

Briefly answer each of the following questions in the space provided.

1. Major extinction events have occurred in the past, and species diversity has recovered each time. Why are many scientists worried that diversity may not be able to come back this time?

2. Species have both direct and indirect economic value to us. What is the primary difference between these two value categories?

3. What is the link between humans and hotspots?

4. Why are introduced species potentially so harmful?

5. Why does the loss of genetic diversity make a species more vulnerable to extinction?

6. Describe the ways in which habitats destroyed by the removal of all species, by a single introduced species, or by pollution can be restored.

7. Describe the effects of loss and reintroduction of the gray wolves into Yellowstone National Park.

8. Explain what is meant by an "extinction vortex."

9. Why is it important to protect the keystone species in an ecosystem?

10. Explain how conservation biologists are trying to combat habitat fragmentation.

Circle the letter of the one best answer in each of the following questions.

11. Over the last several centuries, the rate of species extinction has been
    a. increasing.
    b. decreasing.
    c. holding steady.
    d. fluctuating wildly.
    e. not measurable.

12. The majority of extinctions in recent times have occurred
    a. in Africa.
    b. in South America.
    c. on the northern continents.
    d. on islands.
    e. in the oceans.

13. Which state has the greatest number of endemic species?
    a. Florida
    b. Texas
    c. Alaska
    d. New York
    e. California

14. When talking about biodiversity, the term "hotspots" refers to areas that have a lot of
    a. pollution.
    b. global warming.
    c. poaching.
    d. endemic species.
    e. endangered species.

15. Approximately what percentage of prescription and nonprescription drugs on the market today contain active ingredients extracted from plants and animals?
    a. 20%
    b. 40%
    c. 60%
    d. 75%
    e. 80%

16. Which of the following is an example of a trophic cascade?
    a. loss of sea otters in Alaska
    b. loss of the golden toad in Costa Rica
    c. loss of songbirds in North America
    d. all of these
    e. none of these

17. Use the following scenario to answer questions 17–19. Tropical forests in South America are being clear-cut, but patches of the original forest are being left in various sizes, surrounded by clear-cut areas. Scientists are monitoring three such patches: A is 10,000 acres in size, B is 1000 acres, and C is 100 acres. In which of the patches would you expect to see the greatest decrease in both the size of populations (number of individuals) and the number of species present?
    a. A
    b. B
    c. C
    d. Losses should be equal in all three.
    e. No losses should occur in any of them.

18. Species living in patch B are likely to be impacted in a negative way by
    a. habitat fragmentation.
    b. the edge effect.
    c. increased exposure to parasites and predators.
    d. all of these.
    e. none of these.

19. Which patch is likely to experience the greatest edge effect?
    a. A
    b. B
    c. C
    d. They should all experience an equal edge effect.
    e. None of them should experience an edge effect.

20. The single greatest factor threatening species today and causing their extinction is
    a. loss of genetic variability.
    b. loss of habitat.
    c. introduced species.
    d. overexploitation.
    e. ecodisruption.

21. Historically, the single greatest cause of species extinction has been
    a. loss of genetic variability.
    b. loss of habitat.
    c. introduced species.
    d. overexploitation.
    e. ecodisruption.

22. Which type of habitat tends to be the most vulnerable to pollution?
    a. mountains
    b. forests
    c. prairies
    d. deserts
    e. aquatic

23. Which of the following is an example of a species that was threatened with extinction because of overexploitation by humans?
    a. golden toad
    b. peregrine falcon
    c. Lake Victoria cichlids
    d. right whales
    e. all of these

24. Eutrophication is linked to the death and extinction of
    a. songbirds.
    b. passenger pigeons.
    c. humpback whales.
    d. prairie chickens.
    e. Lake Victoria cichlids.

25. In what year did the International Whaling Commission institute a worldwide moratorium on the commercial killing of whales?
    a. 1935
    b. 1946
    c. 1952
    d. 1974
    e. 1986

26. All of the following endangered species have been bred successfully in captivity for reintroduction into the wild *except* the
    a. passenger pigeon.
    b. California condor.
    c. peregrine falcon.
    d. All have been bred successfully in captivity.
    e. None have been bred successfully in captivity.

27. Which of the following would *not* be a good recovery plan for an endangered species?
    a. Move all the remaining individuals into a totally different but protected natural area.
    b. Try to maintain and increase genetic diversity.
    c. Try to preserve or restore the organism's habitat.
    d. Pass legislation to protect the species.
    e. Begin a captive-breeding program.

28. Which of the following is the most effective means of preventing extinctions?
    a. Transplanting individuals from genetically diverse populations into an area
    b. Captive-breeding programs
    c. Passing legislation to protect all endangered species
    d. Preserving ecosystems and monitoring species before they are threatened
    e. Establishing more protected areas

29. How long did African bees ("killer bees") stay confined to the local area in Brazil where they were first introduced?
    a. 1 week
    b. 1 season
    c. 1 year
    d. 3 years
    e. 15 years

30. More and more conservation efforts today are focusing on saving
    a. microscopic organisms.
    b. charismatic megafauna.
    c. plants.
    d. intact ecosystems.

ASSESSING YOUR KNOWLEDGE

Answers to the questions in this section test your ability to synthesize information gained from the chapter and to solve challenging problems on an exam or in everyday life.

Challenging Your Understanding—Part I, Answers

1. a-e. Overexploitation
         Introduced species
         Habitat loss
         Ecological disruption
         Small population size leading to loss of genetic variation

   f-i. Interdependence of organisms
         Ecosystem function and stability
         Economic value of species
         Quality of life value of species

   j-o. Regulate exploitation
         Establish protected areas
         Restore degraded habitats
         Breed in captivity
         Breed for increased genetic diversity
         Reintroduce species into former habitat

Challenging Your Understanding—Part II, Answers

1. C. Increase in plankton-eating pollock population.
   D. More plankton available to eat.
   E. Decrease in nutritious fish, such as herring and ocean perch.
   F. Competition with the pollock.
   G. Decrease in sea lions and harbor seals.
   H. Less nutritious pollocks could not sustain them.
   I. Decrease in sea otter populations.
   J. Killer whales eat new prey due to decline in sea lions and harbor seals.
   K. Increase in sea urchin populations.
   L. No sea otters to eat them.
   M. Decrease in the thickness of the kelp forests.
   N. Large sea urchin populations feed on kelp.
   O. Decrease in fish species diversity.
   P. Kelp beds can no longer support them.

2. The disappearance of the golden toad, *Bufo periglenes*, from the Monteverde Cloud Forest Reserve is a major cause of concern because this species disappeared from a well-protected ecosystem, with no obvious threats of pollution, introduction of nonnative species, overexploitation, or any other factors. In fact, scientists and conservationists knew about this population and were monitoring it. This severely questions whether we will be able to preserve global biological diversity. The decline is also of major concern because amphibians essentially measure the state of the environment. This is because they have moist skin that allows chemicals in the air to pass into their bodies and they produce larva in aquatic habitats. If amphibians are dying out in what appears to be pristine environments where they are not challenged by any outside competition introduced by humans, or otherwise, it says that the environment itself must be in pretty bad shape. Finally, the decline is of concern because the cause of it is unknown. If the cause were known, efforts could be made to stop the decline, but different species are declining for different reasons, implying that the environment is deteriorating in many different ways.

3. The forest songbird populations are likely declining due to habitat fragmentation and loss. Breeding habitats in the summer nesting grounds in the United States and Canada have been fragmented, while many of these species of birds are adapted to living and raising their young in large contiguous wooded areas. The winter habitat of these birds in Central and South America is also deteriorating. Birds that spend the winter in good habitats have a better chance of successfully migrating to their breeding grounds in the summer. Birds that spend the winter in substandard scrubs leave their winter homes and arrive at their summer homes later, thereby producing fewer young. These declines in reproduction result in population declines. Robins, starlings, and blackbirds have not been affected because they prosper around humans and are year-long residents.

Key Terms—Answers

a. 3, b. 5, c. 1, d. 6, e. 2, f. 4.

Learning by Experience—Answers

1. There is no single right or wrong answer, and no easy answers. A leader would have to consider multiple factors (for example, habitat protection, economic development, quality of life for people, cost of plans) and should try to obtain sustainable use of forests that will generate revenue, training/education for farmers, and international financial support.
2. Restoration efforts can never get back to the exact same environmental conditions and the exact same species assemblages. Ecosystems are too complex. The restoration will have a different starting point and will experience different influences and interactions over time than would have occurred in the original ecosystem.
3. Destruction, pollution, disruption, habitat fragmentation.
4. Direct: Biodiversity provides sources of food, medicine, clothing, biomass, and shelter. Indirect: Biodiversity maintains the chemical quality of natural water, buffers ecosystems against extreme weather catastrophes such as drought and storms, preserves soils and prevents loss of minerals and nutrients, moderates local and regional climate, absorbs pollution, promotes the breakdown of organic wastes and cycling of minerals, promotes stability and productivity of ecosystems. Other: Biodiversity has ethical and aesthetic value.

Exercising Your Knowledge—Answers

As you check your answers, put a mark in the review (Rvw.) column for the answers you missed. If you didn't miss any, congratulations—you have mastered the chapter! If you missed some, review the section (Sect.) in the text where this concept is discussed. In order to develop an efficient review strategy, it is important that you understand what types of questions you missed. The questions with asterisks test more for understanding of the **concepts**, whereas the others test more for **detail**. *See the preface for learning strategies for concepts and for detail.*

	Sect.	Rvw.
*1. Species recovery in the past has taken millions of years. Also, humans are overexploiting resources and destroying habitats, so there will not be much available for new species.	59.1	
*2. With direct economic value, the benefit is obtained by directly using or consuming the species. With indirect, the benefit is obtained because of what the species do in their normal functioning rather than by how we consume them.	59.2	
*3. Human activities threaten the biodiversity in hotspots, and hotspots tend to have large and increasing human populations.	59.1	
*4. Introduced species may not have any predators or parasites to help limit their population size in the new habitat. They have to eat, and native species will not have had the opportunity to evolve any defenses against these particular herbivores or predators, so introduced species may be able to outcompete the native species for limited resources.	59.3	
*5. Loss of genetic diversity decreases the likelihood that at least some individuals will be adapted to future changes in the environment. Inbred individuals tend to be less fit.	59.3	
*6. Habitats destroyed by the removal of all species can be restored by the identification of all of the plant and animal species that lived there, followed by their reintroduction, although the exact ratio of the numbers of organisms relative to each other will likely never be achieved. Habitats destroyed by a single species can be restored by the quick removal of that species from the habitat. Habitats damaged by chemical pollutants can be restored by cleaning up the pollution and rehabilitating the area.	59.4	

	Sect.	Rvw.
*7. Loss of the gray wolves in Yellowstone National Park put the ecosystem out of balance because the populations of deer and elk increased dramatically, damaging vegetation. Reintroduction of the gray wolves has made the elk congregate in larger herds again and avoid areas near the rivers where they are vulnerable to the wolves. This has allowed riverside trees to increase, providing food for the beavers, allowing them to build dams and create ponds. The reintroduction of the wolves has also led to an increase in some species of birds.	59.4	
*8. An extinction vortex refers to the spiraling, negative impacts that interact to drive a species to extinction. As a population decreases in size, it loses genetic variation and becomes more vulnerable to demographic catastrophe, both of which make it more vulnerable to extinction.	59.3	
*9. Keystone species must be protected because they are crucial to the structure and functioning of the whole ecosystem and all of its species.	59.3	
*10. Conservation biologists are trying to combat habitat fragmentation by not only preserving as much land as possible in state parks and reserves, but also by conserving corridors of dispersal between protected areas suitable for migration, and by conserving areas surrounding protected areas where some nondestructive harvesting of resources can take place. By using these areas, the total area available to species in these regions is increased. Since isolated patches of species are more vulnerable to extinction than large areas of species, conservationists hope that these additional areas, although not fully protected, will provide suitable habitats for many species.	59.5	
11. a	59.1	
12. d	59.1	
13. e	59.1	
14. d	59.1	
15. b	59.2	
16. a	59.3	
*17. c	59.3	
*18. d	59.3	
*19. c	59.3	
20. b	59.3	
21. d	59.3	
22. e	59.3	
23. d	59.3	
24. e	59.3	
25. e	59.3	
26. a	59.4	
*27. a	59.4	
*28. d	59.4	
29. b	59.4	
*30. d	59.5	